D0944094

Introduction to Special Relativity

INTERNATIONAL SERIES IN PURE AND APPLIED PHYSICS
Leonard I. Schiff, Consulting Editor

Adler, Bazin, and Schiffer Introduction to General Relativity
Allis and Herlin Thermodynamics and Statistical Mechanics
Becker Introduction to Theoretical Mechanics
Bjorken and Drell Relativistic Quantum Mechanics
Bjorken and Drell Relativistic Quantum Fields
Chodorow and Susskind Fundamentals of Microwave Electronics
Clark Applied X-rays
Collin Field Theory of Guided Waves
Evans The Atomic Nucleus
Feynman and Hibbs Quantum Mechanics and Path Integrals
Ginzton Microwave Measurements
Gurney Introduction to Statistical Mechanics
Hall Introduction to Electron Microscopy
Hardy and Perrin The Principles of Optics
Harnwell Electricity and Electromagnetism
Harnwell and Livingood Experimental Atomic Physics
Henley and Thirring Elementary Quantum Field Theory
Houston Principles of Mathematical Physics
Jammer The Conceptual Development of Quantum Mechanics
Kennard Kinetic Theory of Gases
Leighton Principles of Modern Physics
Lindsay Mechanical Radiation
Livingston and Blewett Particle Accelerators
Middleton An Introduction to Statistical Communication Theory
Morse Vibration and Sound
Morse and Feshbach Methods of Theoretical Physics
Morse and Ingard Theoretical Acoustics
Muskat Physical Principles of Oil Production
Newton Scattering Theory of Waves and Particles
Present Kinetic Theory of Gases
Read Dislocations in Crystals
Richtmyer, Kennard, and Lauritsen Introduction to Modern Physics
Schiff Quantum Mechanics
Schwartz Introduction to Special Relativity
Seitz The Modern Theory of Solids
Slater Introduction to Chemical Physics
Slater Quantum Theory of Atomic Structure, Vol. I
Slater Quantum Theory of Atomic Structure, Vol. II
Slater Quantum Theory of Matter
Slater Electronic Structure of Molecules: Quantum Theory of Molecules and Solids, Vol. 1
Slater Symmetry and Energy Bands in Crystals: Quantum Theory of Molecules and Solids, Vol. 2
Slater Insulators, Semiconductors, and Metals: Quantum Theory of Molecules and Solids, Vol. 3
Slater and Frank Electromagnetism
Slater and Frank Introduction to Theoretical Physics
Slater and Frank Mechanics
Smythe Static and Dynamic Electricity
Stratton Electromagnetic Theory
Tinkham Group Theory and Quantum Mechanics
Townes and Schawlow Microwave Spectroscopy
Wang Solid-State Electronics
White Introduction to Atomic Spectra

The late F. K. Richtmyer was Consulting Editor of the series from its inception in 1929 to his death in 1939. Lee A. DuBridge was Consulting Editor from 1939 to 1946; and G. P. Harnwell from 1947 to 1954.

Introduction to Special Relativity

Herman M. Schwartz
Professor of Physics
University of Arkansas

McGraw-Hill Book Company
New York St. Louis
San Francisco
Toronto London
Sydney

Introduction to Special Relativity

Library of Congress Catalog Card Number 67-19152

55765

1234567890 MPMM 7432106987

Preface

This book was written with the following objectives in mind: to present the principal ideas and methods of the special theory of relativity, to give some indication of the place of this theory in current fundamental research, and to pave the way for the study of the general theory of relativity. In attempting to come reasonably close to meeting the first objective in a book whose primary motivation is didactic, it seemed best to concentrate on a selected number of topics rather than to aim at any comprehensiveness of coverage. Moreover, the choice of topics has been partly influenced by the other two objectives.

Einstein's general theory of relativity, which after half a century of intensive investigation still presents many challenging questions, is an outgrowth of the special theory. Although this outgrowth has been of a radical nature, in part bursting the framework of the special theory, a thorough appreciation of the principles and central results of the latter theory is a prerequisite to an understanding of the general theory. In order to enhance the usefulness of the book in this capacity, a fairly extensive discussion of general tensor analysis in flat spaces is included in Chap. 5. With this formalism it is then possible to express the relativistic equations of continuous media and fields, and in particular of the electromagnetic field, in a form that can be retained in the general theory of relativity (Chaps. 6 and 7). It is also possible, when discussing special relativistic theories of gravitation (Appendix 7B), to include a very brief sketch of the elements of the general theory of relativity for purposes of comparison.

Although the special theory of relativity can be considered by and large a closed subject—with its simpler elements in recent years widely incorporated in texts on mechanics, electrodynamics, and modern physics—it is not only in connection with general relativity that a more intensive study of the special theory is of interest at the present time. This theory enters significantly in one of the most challenging of current scientific fields, the field of elementary particle physics. A partial indication of this fact is contained in Chap. 8. Because of prerequisites that cannot be assumed for this text, as well as owing to the enormous complexity of the subject, the most interesting phases relating to the place of special relativity in particle physics could not be included, but the topics that are included—such as those connected with relativistic wave equations (Secs. 8-2 and 8-3) and the representations of the homogeneous and inhomogeneous Lorentz groups (Appendixes 8B and 8C)—can provide some idea of this place, as well as aid in the specialized study of a number of significant theoretical developments in particle physics.

It is with the latter purpose in mind that Appendix 8A, which contains a cursory introduction to group representations, includes also a very brief indication of the Cartan-Weyl theory together with fairly extensive references to the literature on this subject. The relativistic extension of the empirically conceived dynamical symmetries pertaining to particle interactions (such as SU_6) is among the immediate intriguing questions in the present exploratory stage of elementary particle theory. This topic could have been included in the discussion of Chap. 8 were it not for its still uncertain state, as well as for the desirability of keeping down the size of an already rather lengthy chapter. The general theme of this chapter is the interplay of the relativistic and quantum-mechanical principles, and Sec. 8-1 contains a very brief historical introduction to this topic centering on, and ending with, Dirac's relativistic wave equation. Again, the exciting more recent phases of this history fall outside the scope of this text, but helpful references to the literature are included.

The field of ultrahot plasma, which is still in its early stages of development, is another new area of possible application of special-relativistic methods. Parts of Chaps. 6 and 7, dealing with continuous media, that can have a bearing on the macroscopic treatments in that subject, are therefore considered in somewhat greater detail than would have been otherwise indicated.

As stated, this book is intended primarily to serve as a text. In keeping with this purpose the material is accordingly, on the whole, arranged in order of increasing difficulty. It could thus be used as an undergraduate text for a short course on the subject by excluding all of Chap. 8, and parts of Chaps. 3 to 7, at the discretion of the instructor. The omitted topics can then serve as reference material in later studies. When used as a more advanced text, suitable in general for graduate instruction, the essential prerequisites are represented by the standard subject matter contained, for instance, in the texts of Panofsky and Phillips on electrodynamics, Goldstein on mechanics, and Schiff on quantum mechanics. The last-named subject is required only in connection with Chap. 8. The first seven chapters are self-contained and constitute an adequate unit for a one-semester course.

Because a complete course in special relativity is as yet not generally a standard item in the graduate or advanced undergraduate curriculum, and the more advanced parts of the subject must therefore be learned outside the classroom, it seemed particularly desirable to include problems with each chapter. These problems in many instances supplement and extend the discussion in the text and form an integral part of the chapter. Many problems contain solution hints, enclosed in brackets, that can be resorted to if needed. In addition, answers to a few selected problems are given at the end of the book. There is one category of problems that has been kept at a minimum; namely, those dealing with practical applications and manipulation of formulas, not because such problems are deemed unimportant—far from it—but rather with the expectation that they could be profitably and easily supplemented by the individual instructor, or by the reader who is his own instructor.

The subject of relativity concerns physicists primarily. Yet, possibly owing to the highly mathematical character of the general theory of relativity or to its particular aesthetic appeal, that subject has long attracted the interest of mathematicians as well. A book on the special theory of relativity can therefore be expected to find readers whose chief interest is in mathematics. An attempt has consequently been made to keep mathematical lapses at a minimum. On the other hand, for the benefit of the reader of limited algebraic background, brief introductions to a few needed algebraic topics are presented in mathematical appendixes. These are not intended as a substitute for firsthand study of the topics, but only as a convenient stopgap.

The mathematical notation chosen in this book constitutes in some instances a compromise between aptness and expediency—not however, it is hoped, at the expense of clarity. Moreover, no special attempt has been made to keep the notation uniform throughout the book. For instance, different symbols are used to designate matrices. A point can indeed be made for the pedagogical desirability of not insisting too much on complete uniformity in notation, there being little of it in the literature on the subject. However, the reader will find a helpful listing of a number of unusual terms and symbols under the headings *Terminology* and *Notation* in the Subject Index.

A bibliography is given at the end of the book. This bibliography is far from exhaustive; the richness of the literature on relativity is such that the only practical and sensible thing to do in a book of this character is to limit oneself to a selected list. The basis of choice of the included books to which reference is made in the text by means of bracketed numbers, is explained in the bibliographic section. A few other standard books on the subject are also included in the bibliography, and references are made in the text to books on related subjects and to original papers of either current or historic interest. Again, in keeping with the character of the book, such references are kept at a minimum, but in important cases sources of more complete references are included.

Grateful acknowledgments are due the reviewers of this book for helpful suggestions, the University of Arkansas for financial support of all clerical assistance in connection with the preparation of the typescript, and the patient young women who were involved in that demanding task. Above all, I am indebted to my wife and sons who bore with good grace the inconveniences that the writing of this book entailed for them, and who never failed to support me with their encouragement and assistance.

Herman M. Schwartz

Contents

Chapter 3 Einstein's Special Theory of Relativity and its Basic Kinematic Results 37

Chapter 4 Relativistic Mechanics 89

Chapter 5 Tensor Analysis in Flat Spaces 131

Chapter 6 Relativistic Mechanics of Continuous Media 171

Chapter 7 The Electromagnetic Field 221

Introduction to Special Relativity

1

Basic Ideas of Newtonian Mechanics and Galilei-newtonian Relativity

In this introductory chapter it is our aim chiefly to call attention to basic concepts that underlie classical mechanics, and hence also its relativistic extensions. To this end we sketch out one possible method of analysis of these concepts. The blueprint for any such analysis is of course to be found in Newton's *Principia*, when properly interpreted. In one form or another it has occupied students of mechanics from Bishop Berkeley in Newton's day to Ernst Mach and many others in our own.

A critical examination of the premises and central definitions in the newtonian formulation of mechanics is complicated by the elusive interdependence of the kinematic and dynamic elements at the base of this theory. Tempting as it is for purposes of analysis, the notions of space and time, of force and mass, cannot be pigeonholed into perfectly separate conceptual compartments. Although an extensive analysis of these questions belongs more to the field of the philosophy of physics than of physics proper, it cannot be entirely avoided in any critical study of the new relativistic ideas.

The physical ideas connected with the notions of space and time have held a central place in the development of the special and general theories of relativity. Of the modern contributions to clarification of these ideas, those of Henri Poincaré have been among the most eloquent and thought provoking.‡ Einstein's own thinking on this subject has followed along kindred lines.§ The present descriptive discussion relating to the space and time concepts as they arise in classical mechanics is based largely on the ideas of these two men.

On the strictly mathematical side, an important tool for the analysis of spatial properties is provided by the theory of groups, and particularly by the theory of groups of transformations. Although we shall make use here of little more than a few elementary definitions and results of this theory, these enter significantly in our discussion, and they are therefore reviewed briefly in Appendix 1A.¶

The analysis of the fundamental ideas of newtonian dynamics as outlined in this chapter follows more closely the original approach developed in the *Principia* than is the case in most modern works dealing critically with the subject.‡‡ For reasons stated in the text, it is here found preferable to retain the idea of newtonian force as an independent physical concept, rather than treating it following Mach,§§ as little more than a name for the product *mass times acceleration*.

1-1 PHYSICAL SPACE; NEWTON'S ABSOLUTE SPACE; EUCLIDEAN GEOMETRY

Our first concern is with the definition or specification of physical space, that is, the space of kinematics. A possible starting point is the realization that quantitative geometric relations can be developed initially only with the aid of rigid bodies. The notion of a perfectly rigid body is of course only an abstraction. It is a far-reaching extrapolation from daily experience and observation pertaining to manifold permanence properties of solids, and in the last analysis it must be introduced as a primitive physical postulate. Measurement of *length* and changes of *position* can then be constructively specified in terms of a set of rigid bodies, including a *unit measuring rod*, in a manner that is generally known. The relations governing the results of such measurements, properly extrapolated to allow for the approximate

‡ See especially the pertinent discussion in his books, "Science and Hypothesis," and "The Value of Science," Dover Publications, Inc., New York.

§ See, e.g., Physics and Reality, *J. Franklin Inst.*, **221**: 349 (1936), sec. 2; and [3], pp. 1–9. (Numbers in brackets refer to the bibliography at the end of this book.)

¶ Further discussion concerning continuous groups of transformations, and references, are contained in Appendix 3A, and in Chaps. 5 and 8.

‡‡ See, e.g., R. B. Lindsay and H. Margenau, "Foundations of Physics," chap. 3, Dover Publications, Inc., New York.

§§ E. Mach, "The Science of Mechanics," The Open Court Publishing Company, La Salle, Ill., 1942. Also, G. Kirchhoff, "Vorlesungen über Mechanik," B. G. Teubner, Leipzig, 1876.

nature of the measuring process, constitute the *physical geometry* at the base of kinematics.

How should we interpret the transition from empirical geometry to space proper? No one answer can be singled out and expert opinions differ. Is "space" merely a symbol for the totality of all the interconnected geometric relations of which physical objects are capable, or is it some sort of entity independent of the physical objects? Does a body move "in space," or does its motion in a sense generate its own space? If we limit ourselves to kinematics, there is no unique answer, except in so far as one is guided mainly by intellectual taste. It is only when kinematics is imbedded in a general theory of dynamics that a choice of the concept to be attached to the word "space" as a physical term becomes possible on the basis of suitably chosen epistemological criteria.

Newton's "absolute space" can be interpreted in this vein, the designation "absolute" being taken in one and only one sense, namely, as denoting insensibility to any outside influence. This is in fact the only sense which enters, not in Newton's wording, but in his physical theoretical use of the idea. Absolute space as it is used in the *Principia* serves only as a hypothetical spatial reference frame with respect to which the laws of motion of all physical objects can be formulated consistently with the principle of inertia; whereas it itself is in no way affected by such objects. This reference frame may be imagined as a substance that is found *everywhere* and fills *everything*, but is possessed of no material property whatever save that connected with spatial relationship and implying, in particular, its universal *immobility*.‡ This mental image, moreover, may seem to arise from our deep-seated intuition of space. We shall leave it an open question whether this is indeed the case, and whether for that matter, this mental image is completely meaningful. That its statement involves us in a vicious circle in what concerns the definition of space, is all too evident.

An alternative pictorialization equivalent in its effect to Newton's hypothesis involves the assumption of a remote unobservable object that serves as the embodiment of the newtonian frame of reference—the "body alpha" of Carl Neumann.§ What mental comfort there is to be derived from such an object—of which, as Poincaré shrewdly put it, all we are ever destined to know is its name—is another question.

It is the unobservability of Newton's absolute space that makes it scientifically unpalatable. It has a specific function to perform in Newton's structure of mechanics, the function for which it has been invented; but it admits of no other contact with physical phenomena, and that as a matter of principle. If the neutrino were destined by its very nature never to

‡ The ether of Lorentz's electrodynamic theory has much in common with such a hypothetical universal substance. (See Chap. 2.)

§ Carl Neumann, "Die Principien der Galilei-Newtonschen Theorie," Leipzig, 1870.

perform any other function except the one for which it was originally invented by Pauli, it would provide an example of a similar 'unobservable.'

Returning to our original question as to the specification of physical space, it would appear logically safest in the light of the foregoing discussion, to limit ourselves to the purely *relational* or *ordering* aspects of this concept; or, in other words, to start with our geometry as the primary theoretical idea. Since the geometry of our experience is euclidean, this is symbolized by the statement that the 'space' of our experience is euclidean. But in what sense is the geometry of our experience euclidean? And if we refer this geometry to a three-dimensional continuum of *points*, do we not end up with a 'space' that is mathematically, and therefore also theoretically, in no way distinguishable from Newton's three-dimensional euclidean absolute space?

A full discussion of the last question would fall outside the scope of the present merely suggestive outline. We shall only point out the following. If we consider a space generated by all the possible 'virtual' motions of some test body T relative to a given reference body R in the sense that this process can be taken as wholly independent of the particular body T, it cannot be asserted in general that there must also be independence of the body R. Thus, even if the associated mathematical continuum has precisely the same structure as that which corresponds to Newton's space, the physical situations represented are nevertheless in general not identical. One of the important conclusions of Einstein's special theory is in fact—roughly speaking—the dependence of such an "R space" on the state of motion of R. (The sense in which this assertion is to be taken will be understood from the discussion in Chap. 3.)

The first question must also be dealt with summarily. We cannot enter here into a logical inquiry concerning the methods of determining an empirical geometry and of delimiting its function and its scope. The writings of Poincaré referred to earlier can serve as an excellent starting point for anyone interested in pursuing such an inquiry.‡ For our immediate purpose the following remarks must suffice.

It is a firmly established fact of experience that all accurate measurements of distances and of angles on a laboratory or locally astronomical scale always yield results that can be consistently represented within the scheme of Euclid's geometry, when proper account is taken of the instrumental errors of measurement and of all pertinent environmental factors. We need not stop here to discuss the nature of these environmental factors, except for recalling the observation made two paragraphs earlier.

This observation belongs historically to the special theory of relativity, but with the wisdom of hindsight it can be seen to have a logical place in the present discussion. When we speak of environmental influences upon

‡ A suggestive and lucid elementary introduction to this subject is also contained in Emile Borel, "Space and Time," Dover Publications, Inc., New York.

spatial measurements, we normally think of effects such as temperature, pressure, fields of force. We do not as a rule include the state of motion relative to the measuring device of the object that is being measured, because ordinary large-scale measurements involve either no relative motion or only motions of moderate relative velocity. But there is certainly no logical reason whatever, a priori, to exclude from such consideration the overall state of motion of the measured body any more than it would be to disregard its internal thermodynamic state. Therefore, if we recall what we have earlier called briefly an "R space," it can be concluded that in its definition the virtual motion of the generating body T must be assumed to proceed sufficiently slowly. In all strictness, T would in fact have to symbolize the potential collection of all bodies that are always at rest relative to R. One might say in a sense that something of *absolute space* has here entered by the back door. However, this something is not independent of physical bodies, but is on the contrary, so to speak, attached to one particular body, namely, R, or, more precisely, to every body that is permanently at rest relative to R.

Our last remark relates to the extrapolations to the infinitely small and to the infinitely large, which are involved in our adopting euclidean space as the exact mathematical model of kinematic space. As long as subatomic phenomena are left out of consideration, the former extrapolation need not concern us; but as a matter of fact, the unrestricted validity of euclidean geometry in the microscopic domain is still at the core of all present theory. The extrapolation in the cosmic domain, on the other hand, falls within the scope of our present considerations. Both the newtonian idea of space as well as the related idea of space-time of the special theory of relativity imply unlimited extension, as is apparent from the content of the galilei-newtonian law of inertia.‡

The foregoing discussion has given us an indication of the sense in which three-dimensional euclidean space can be taken as a strict *mathematical model* of what we have called "physical" or "kinematic" space. It is permissible to take the view—not indeed the prevailing view in the past—that the role of this model in physical theory differs little from the role of other mathematical representations of groups of aspects of physical phenomena. It is with this view in mind that we now turn to a brief examination of the structure of mathematical euclidean space.

1-2 MATHEMATICAL EUCLIDEAN SPACE; THE GROUP OF DISPLACEMENTS; RELATIVITY OF POSITION

By euclidean space of three dimensions in its strict mathematical sense, we understand a three-dimensional, totally unbounded, connected, continuous

‡ This law remains essentially unchanged in the special theory of relativity—as is shown in Chap. 3. On the other hand, with the far-reaching generalization of the principle of inertia effected by the general theory, other modes of spatial behavior on the cosmic scale also become possible.

aggregate of points endowed with a *euclidean* metric. By a *metric* one understands in general the association with every pair of points P_1, P_2 of the space of a *distance function* $D(P_1,P_2)$. The metric is "euclidean" when the theorem of Pythagoras involving the distance function is satisfied throughout the space. It is then, in particular, positive definite. [A positive definite metric involves in general a distance function $D(P_1,P_2)$ that is symmetric, positive definite, and satisfies the triangle inequality: $D(P_1,P_2) = D(P_2,P_1)$; $D(P_1,P_2) > 0$ $(P_1 \neq P_2)$, $D(P,P) = 0$; and $D(P_1,P_2) \leq D(P_1,P_3) + D(P_3,P_2)$. In the generalization represented by the Minkowski metric, to be discussed in Chap. 3, only the first condition is satisfied.] Although it is possible to encompass all the characteristic space properties in a synthetic treatment, it is simpler and, from our applicational point of view, more useful, to apply the analytic method of coordinates in conjunction with elementary considerations involving groups of coordinate transformations.

The central idea of the analytic method of characterizing a space, which we shall employ, involves the singling out of a family of coordinate systems having a distinctive association with the space. In our case this family $\mathfrak{F}$ is determined by the following two conditions:

1. Each member S_x of $\mathfrak{F}$ represents a one-to-one mapping of the points P of our space on the real-number triplets (x_1,x_2,x_3).
2. The distance function $D(P_1,P_2)$ has in S_x the representation

$$D(P_1,P_2) = +\sqrt{\sum_{i=1}^{3} (x_i^{(1)} - x_i^{(2)})^2} \tag{1-1}$$

In the terminology of Appendix 1A, condition (2) states that D is a form invariant relative to the family $\mathfrak{F}$, and, as will be presently indicated, the properties of the coordinate systems of this family can be readily determined from this relationship.‡

All the basic geometric relations associated with our space can be established step by step, starting with the above formulation. They can be based on the metric and orientational properties of *straight lines.*

The straight-line segment connecting two given points is uniquely determined by the requirement that its length be smaller than that of any other curve connecting these points. Because the idea of an extremal line, or *geodesic*, will be of significance to us in later connections, we shall consider its present exemplification in some detail.

Let us rewrite Eq. (1-1) in the more familiar form

$$\Delta s^2 = \sum_{i=1}^{3} \Delta x_i^2 \tag{1-2}$$

‡ The idea of characterizing a geometry in terms of an associated group of transformations was first developed in a general way by the mathematician Felix Klein in his celebrated *Erlanger Program* of 1872 [see *Math. Ann.*, **43:** 63 (1893)].

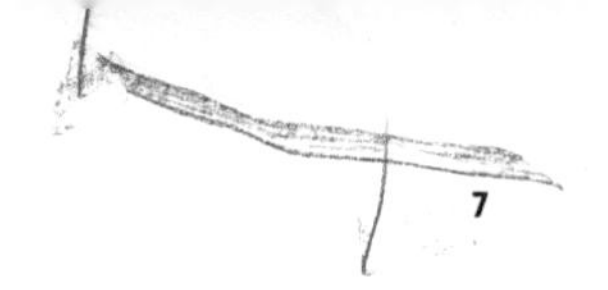

Corresponding to an arbitrarily close mutual approach of the points P_1, P_2, this distance expression assumes the differential form

$$ds^2 = \sum_{i=1}^{3} dx_i^2 \tag{1-3}$$

Consider the parametric representation

$$\begin{aligned} x_i &= x_i(u), \qquad 0 \leq u \leq 1 \\ x_i(0) &= x_i^{(0)} \\ x_i(1) &= x_i^{(1)} \qquad i = 1, 2, 3 \end{aligned} \tag{1-4}$$

of a curve connecting two given points P_0, P_1 having in S_x the coordinates $x_i^{(0)}$ and $x_i^{(1)}$ respectively. A necessary condition for the length of this curve to be a minimum, when compared with the family of other curves connecting these two points, is the vanishing of the *first variation* of the length integral. In view of Eqs. (1-3) and (1-4) this condition can be written

$$0 = \delta \int_{P_0}^{P_1} ds = \delta \int_0^1 \sqrt{\sum_{i=1}^{3} (x_i')^2}\, du \equiv \delta \int_0^1 L\, du, \qquad x' \equiv \frac{dx}{du} \tag{1-5}$$

The *Euler equations* of this simple variational problem are

$$0 = \frac{d}{du}\frac{\partial L}{\partial x_i'} = \sum_{j=1}^{3} \frac{\partial^2 L}{\partial x_i'\, \partial x_j'} x_j'', \qquad i = 1, 2, 3 \tag{1-6}$$

They have the family of general solutions

$$x_i = a_i u + b_i, \qquad i = 1, 2, 3 \tag{1-7}$$

provided we impose on the parameter u the condition

$$\sum_{i=1}^{3} x_i' x_i' = \text{constant along the extremal} \tag{1-5a}$$

(See Prob. 1-2.) The boundary conditions given in Eq. (1-4) fix the values of the six constants a_i, b_i for our particular solution, the extremal between the points P_0, P_1. It is moreover easy to show that this extremal is necessarily minimal.

The above discussion is easily extended to provide a proof that all straight lines can be represented by the parametric equations (1-7). In particular, it follows that the *coordinate lines* of S_x are *straight* lines. In order to establish their relative orientation we require an expression for the *angle* between two coplanar straight lines. We need not enter here into a complete discussion of the derivation of this expression from our premises. The following indication should suffice for our present purpose.

By the foregoing result it is seen that a straight line is completely determined by any two of its points, and that the differences Δx_i of the coordinates of these points have ratios that depend only on the line itself and not on the particular choice of the point pair. These ratios serve, therefore, to specify a property of the line that can be shown to represent what we intuitively understand by its *direction* in space. It can also be shown that if we are given two straight lines with the direction ratios $\Delta x_1 : \Delta x_2 : \Delta x_3$ and $\Delta y_1 : \Delta y_2 : \Delta y_3$, respectively, then the expression

$$\cos\theta = \frac{\sum_{i=1}^{3} \Delta x_i \, \Delta y_i}{\sqrt{\Sigma \, \Delta x_i^2} \sqrt{\Sigma \, \Delta y_i^2}} \tag{1-8}$$

(which depends of course only on the ratios) defines a quantity θ whose properties correspond fully to those we are accustomed to associate with the "angle" between two directions (see Prob. 1-3). In particular, the straight lines of direction ratios (Δx_i) and (Δy_i) are mutually *orthogonal* when

$$\sum_{i=1}^{3} \Delta x_i \, \Delta y_i = 0 \tag{1-9}$$

By applying the condition (1-9), it is at once established that the systems of our family $\mathfrak{F}$ are, in addition to being rectilinear, also orthogonal in the sense employed in analytic geometry. They are thus what are known as "rectangular cartesian," or simply "cartesian" systems. Moreover, the fundamental metric relationship (1-2) is now seen to be an expression of the all-important theorem of Pythagoras. (For the general case when the sides of the right triangle have arbitrary orientations, see Prob. 1-3.)

Although no explicit mention has been made of condition (1) in the above discussion, it has of course been used significantly throughout, beginning in fact with Eq. (1-1). It includes the analytic formulation of the *three-dimensionality* of physical space.‡

In addition to representing specific properties of physical space, our mathematical formulation reflects also the relationship existing between our common idea of space and the complex of changes of position of rigid bodies from which it is largely derived. These changes of position, or

‡ Conditions (1) and (2) taken together are seen to imply not only the reciprocal single-valuedness of the mapping of the points of our space onto the number triplets, but also the bicontinuity of this mapping—continuity being defined by the process of limits in terms of the corresponding distance function D and the expression to the right of Eq. (1-1), which can be considered as the metric of three-dimensional euclidean number space E_3. The topological properties of our space, and in particular its continuity and dimensionality properties, are therefore identical with those of the number space E_3. The statement concerning dimensionality is not entirely obvious intuitively. The implied topological invariance (that is, invariance under one-to-one and bicontinuous transformations, the so-called "homeomorphic" transformations) has been proved only in 1911 (in a famous paper by the mathematician L. E. J. Brouwer).

rigid body displacements, can be represented in our mathematical model by the totality of transitions from one cartesian coordinate system to another, i.e., by the *group* of coordinate transformations generated by our invariant D (see Appendix 1A).‡

The analytical structure of the group of displacements can be deduced from the condition of invariance of the differential expression (1-3). If S_x and $S_{x'}$ are two arbitrary cartesian systems, then

$$dx'_i\, dx'_i = dx_i\, dx_i \tag{1-10}$$

[*Note:* We have omitted the symbol Σ, thus adopting the convenient *summation convention*, introduced by Einstein, according to which summation is automatically performed over repeated indices, the summation range being understood from the context if not otherwise indicated.] Let the transformation (1A-2) between S_x and $S_{x'}$ have the explicit form

$$x'_i = f_i(x_1, x_2, x_3), \qquad i = 1, 2, 3$$

By Eq. (1-10),

$$\left(\frac{\partial f_i}{\partial x_k}\frac{\partial f_i}{\partial x_r} - \delta_{kr}\right) dx_k\, dx_r = 0$$

where the *Kronecker delta*, δ_{kr}, is defined in Eq. (1A-4). Since this is an identity in the dx_i, it follows that§

$$\frac{\partial f_i}{\partial x_k}\frac{\partial f_i}{\partial x_r} = \delta_{kr} \tag{1-11}$$

Differentiating these equations with respect to x_s and subtracting the resulting set of equations Σ_{krs} from the same set with the indices k, r, s interchanged cyclically (i.e., from the set Σ_{rsk}) we obtain a set that, when added to Σ_{ksr}, yields the equations

$$\frac{\partial^2 f_i}{\partial x_k\, \partial x_r}\frac{\partial f_i}{\partial x_s} = 0$$

Since the functional determinant of the f_i with respect to the x_i cannot vanish (remembering that a coordinate transformation represents a one-to-one mapping), it follows that all $\partial^2 f_i/\partial x_k\, \partial x_r$ are zero and the functions f_i are linear.¶ Thus,

$$x'_i = A_{ij}x_j + b_i$$

‡ Recall in this connection the double interpretation of the transformation equations as representing changes in coordinate frames or changes in position of rigid bodies relative to a fixed frame.

§ Henceforth we also omit explicit indication of the ranges of free indices whenever that is understood from the context.

¶ It is worth noting that it is also possible to derive this result by a more directly geometric method that makes use of the properties of the coordinate lines of cartesian systems we obtained earlier (see Prob. 1-4).

Or, in the still more succinct matrix notation,

$$x' = Ax + b \tag{1-12}$$

where $A \equiv \|A_{ij}\|$, and x', x, and b represent here one-column *matrices*. Conditions (1-11) can now be written

$$\tilde{A}A = I; \qquad \tilde{A}_{ij} \equiv A_{ji}, \qquad I_{ij} = \delta_{ij} \tag{1-13}$$

The group of displacements comprises the subgroup of *rotations* represented by Eq. (1-12) with vanishing b, and with the matrices A satisfying in addition to Eq. (1-13) also the condition

$$\det A > 0 \tag{1-14}$$

and the subgroup of *translations* corresponding to vanishing A. The former subgroup is also called the (three-dimensional) "orthogonal group"; or, more precisely, the "proper orthogonal group"—the orthogonal group being given by Eq. (1-13) without condition (1-14). The orthogonal subgroup mirrors the *isotropy* of space—the kinematic equivalence of all directions. In the same way the group of translations is related to the *homogeneity* of space—the kinematic equivalence of any two of its points. We can speak here in an obvious sense of a relativity of position.

1-3 PHYSICAL TIME; NEWTON'S ABSOLUTE TIME; ABSOLUTE SIMULTANEITY

Our intuition of a temporal ordering among happenings is perhaps even more deep-rooted than our intuition of spatial ordering. This does not make the problem of a quantitative specification of the corresponding synthetic conceptual construct, time, any the easier. As pointed out by Poincaré, neither the continuity nor the one-dimensionality of the manifold of *instants* (i.e., time points) can be taken as intuitively given. We fare scarcely better with the notion of temporal congruence. When Newton tells us in his first Scholium of the *Principia* that "absolute, true, and mathematical time . . . flows equably . . . ," we can overlook, as we have done in the case of his absolute space, the wording and its extraphysical connotations, but what possible a priori sense can one attach to the words "flows equably"? It is only what Newton calls "relative, apparent, and common time," which is "a measure of duration by the means of motion," that can be utilized, when properly formulated, as a basic element of physical theory.

When one examines the possibilities for such a formulation, it can be appreciated why Newton refers to *motion* as the means by which a practical procedure for time measurement is set up. In order to be at all able to specify what one is to understand by *equal intervals of time*, it is necessary to resort to some suitable lastingly identifiable repetitive process. We require, in other words, a temporal analog of the rigid rod. Just as the latter is a conceptual idealization of successively more suitable practical quasi-rigid rods, so also the former can only be an idealization of successively more suitable cyclical processes. In Newton's time—as, from a certain point of view, also in our own—such clocks can be practically realized only by appropriate oscillatory or rotational motion, such as is represented, for example, by the swings of a carefully prepared and carefully maintained pendulum clock or by the rotation of the earth.

The rotation-clock is particularly suited to represent the properties of the time manifold that is associated with it. This manifold is, by the very operation of such a clock, parametrized by the angle of rotation as measured from a fixed base line with a specified sense of rotation. The mathematical model of the time manifold has, therefore, the structure of the continuum of real numbers, or, also, of an unbounded, spatial straight line.

We spoke of the time manifold *associated* with a given clock. In all strictness this qualification must be introduced to begin with. If it can then be assumed that it is always possible, at least in principle, to synchronize the readings of any two clocks whatever their locations and states of motion, and that the corresponding unique time variable is the one that enters into the mechanical equations of motion, one is led to a *universal time,* which can serve as a sensible interpretation of Newton's "absolute time."

Both assumptions, though, are far from being either obvious or necessary. The second assumption is of course tied up with the entire theoretical system of mechanics. Similarly, the practical regulation of a 'clock' such as the rotating earth, for example, must already involve a considerable portion of theoretical mechanics. This interdependence is in itself not logically inadmissible. The interconnectedness of all the basic concepts of kinematics and dynamics is a complication it does not seem possible to avoid. Thus on a pragmatic basis the assumption in question concerning our universal time variable is in itself not objectionable. But it must be recognized as an assumption, whose utility can be judged only by the overall success of the general theory that incorporates this variable.

The first assumption, namely, that clock synchronization always makes sense as a matter of principle, that is to say, that it makes sense to speak of *absolute simultaneity,* is one that apparently has been taken for granted without much questioning by most men until Einstein's searching analysis of the notion of simultaneity. In order to better bring out the observational implications of this assumption, we shall replace it by another assumption of which it can be taken as a consequence, as follows:

I *There exist 'signals' of infinite velocity.*

This assumption is in fact satisfied if one grants the validity of action at a distance such as newtonian gravitational action. On the contrary, if we reject assumption I then such action becomes also inadmissible. Neither can the idea of a universal time be accepted then without essentially additional considerations.

1-4 THE METRIC OF TIME AND THE GALILEI–NEWTONIAN PRINCIPLE OF INERTIA

When one examines the principles of dynamics as formulated by Newton, with a view to ascertaining possible prescriptions which can be set up with their aid for defining a workable time metric, it is found that already Newton's first law can serve for that purpose. A particle that is moving in accordance with that law constitutes an ideal clock, the distances which it traverses as measured from a given point of its path serving as its time readings. Practically, it is obviously a very poor clock. Purely theoretically it is a convenient one, because there is a minimum of general mechanical theory directly involved in its formulation.

Newton's first law ("every body continues in its state of rest, or of uniform motion in a right line, unless it is compelled to change that state by forces impressed upon it"‡) can be restated for our purpose as follows, in terms of the distinguished, or *absolute*, space discussed in Sec. 1-1, which we shall denote by S_{abs}:

II *Relative to* S_{abs} *there exists a universal time parameter* T *such that every material particle far enough removed from all outside influence (i.e., from the influence of all other physical systems; or, more precisely, in the extrapolated asymptotic limit of complete removal of all such influence) moves with uniform rectilinear motion; i.e., in such a way that its cartesian coordinates* X_i *relative to* S_{abs} *satisfy the differential equation*§

$$\frac{d^2X_i}{dt^2} = 0 \tag{1-15}$$

The sense in which the term "universal" is here being used has been indicated in the discussion connected with postulate I. A 'material particle' is a familiar enough abstraction of great flexibility on which we need not elaborate. Only the meaning to be attached to the phrase "outside influence" requires elucidation. From the point of view here taken this is not too easy a task. If we had started with the assumption that the time T is already known and that consequently the validity of equations such as Eq. (1-15) for a given particle could be ascertained, at least in principle, this

‡ See F. Cajori's edition of Newton's "Principia" (University of California Press, Berkeley, Calif., 1934) for a revised translation and illuminating notes.

§ The proposed use of a 'freely' moving particle as a theoretical 'clock' for the measurement of the variable T that enters in postulate II may appear to involve us in circular reasoning. However, it should be noted that postulate II leads to the significant implication that *all* such clocks are fully equivalent.

validity could be used for the *definition* of nonexistence of outside influence—or of "impressed forces" in Newton's phraseology. As it is, we must assume instead that in each particular case it is possible to ascertain, at least in principle, the approximate state of 'isolation' of our particle, and that the state of perfect isolation is the corresponding conceptual asymptotic limit. This corresponds essentially to the method followed by Galileo in arriving at the principle of inertia by inductive reasoning.

As to the manner in which it is possible to define constructively the notion of a practically isolated physical system, i.e., the absence with sufficient approximation of all interaction between this system and the rest of the physical universe, this must be considered in connection with Newton's second law. As a consequence, also our theoretical construct T involves this second law. But as we have already noted before, it is in any case necessary to recognize that the entire scheme of mechanics is in some measure involved in any definition of physical time.

1-5 NEWTON'S SECOND AND THIRD LAWS; DEFINITIONS OF FORCE AND OF INERTIAL MASS

The question of the most convenient interpretation of Newton's second law is even as yet far from being a matter of universal agreement. In keeping with our interpretation of the first law, we shall follow Newton in adopting the notion of *force* as one of our primary physical quantities. On a large-scale laboratory level it is indeed possible to give an operational quantitative specification of forces by means of suitable dynamometric measurements. The Cavendish and the Coulomb torsion-balance experiments are well-known examples of this method. The fact that the interpretation of such measurements involves implicitly the ensemble of mechanical principles need in itself disturb us no more than the similar complications encountered in the analysis of the notions of physical space and of physical time. It is, rather, owing to the severe limitations in the range of application of such measuring devices that the notion of force of newtonian theory can be adequately introduced only in the context of a suitable mathematical model.

We begin with the general assumption that all the mechanical systems under consideration can be taken to consist of permanently identifiable material particles whose motion relative to S_{abs} is determined for all time by the mutual influences between the particles, that is to say, by their mutual interactions. We shall call systems that satisfy this *and the following assumptions* "newtonian systems." They in fact comprise largely all systems contemplated by Newton and his immediate followers.

Our second general assumption is in part a corollary of the principle of inertia II. According to II if, at a given time T, the acceleration vector $d^2\mathbf{X}/dT^2 \neq 0$, $\mathbf{X}$ being the position vector of a given particle relative to a frame fixed in S_{abs}, we can conclude that this particle is, at the time T, interacting with other particles. We therefore write in general

$$\frac{d^2\mathbf{X}}{dT^2} = \mathbf{\Phi} \tag{1-16}$$

and assume that the vector $\mathbf{\Phi}$, which we shall call "interaction function," can be chosen in all cases as a vector function of kinematic and structural specifications of the given particle and of all the particles that influence its motion, in such a way that Eq. (1-16) is identically satisfied for all the T under consideration. In other words, the differential equation (1-15), descriptive of the motion of an *isolated* particle, is generalized in Eq. (1-16) to a representation of the motion of an *interacting* particle. But this generalization must be completed on the practical as well as on the logical side.

It is obvious that a differential system of the form (1-16), in which the necessary kinematic specifications of all the particles with which the given one is interacting must be independently assigned for all T under consideration, is of little practical value. It is necessary to adjoin to Eq. (1-16) similar equations for each of the other particles involved in the interaction: if we denote the original particle by M_1 and the others by M_2, M_3, . . . , then we must replace Eq. (1-16) by the differential system

$$\frac{d^2\mathbf{X}_i}{dT^2} = \mathbf{\Phi}_i, \qquad i = 1, 2, 3, \ldots \tag{1-17}$$

A further sharpening of our general dynamical assumption is obtained by imposing on the $\mathbf{\Phi}_i$ the natural restriction that they involve no higher derivaties of the $\mathbf{X}$ than the first. Since, moreover, we are supposing that both sides of Eq. (1-17) are taken at the same universal time T, i.e., that we are dealing with *action at a distance*, it follows that when

$$\mathbf{X}_i \text{ and } \frac{d\mathbf{X}_i}{dT} \text{ are assigned for } T = T_0 \tag{1-18}$$

then the motion of all the particles of our system is completely determined for all T both greater and smaller than T_0 for which the $\mathbf{\Phi}_i$ are specified.‡

In considering the differential equations (1-17) together with the initial conditions (1-18) as representing a *complete* description of the motion of a newtonian system, we are involved in two tacit interrelated assumptions. We suppose that our system is *isolated;* and in utilizing the universal time T, we are committed, as discussed in Sec. 1-4, to a priori knowledge of how to recognize the nonexistence of interaction. This logical difficulty is

‡ This form of "determinism," as thus represented in our mathematical model, constitutes a most remarkable induction from observation and experience, with which the names of Galileo Galilei and Isaac Newton are mainly associated. Until the advent of quantum mechanics there was no occasion to doubt its universal validity, with proper adaptation in the case of classical fields.

resolved (in the context of the mechanics of newtonian systems) by assuming, in conformity with empirical evidence, that the interaction function $\mathbf{\Phi}$ relative to a given particle drops practically to zero when the distances from this particle to all the particles with which it is interacting increase sufficiently. In this way, physical isolation is practically insured by sufficient spatial isolation.‡

We arrive at Newton's second and third laws by considering isolated binary newtonian systems (M_1,M_2) with the associated interaction functions $\mathbf{\Phi}_{12}$ and $\mathbf{\Phi}_{21}$. It can be concluded from all direct as well as indirect empirical evidence (the direct evidence historically coming chiefly from experiments with colliding, practically rigid, elastic balls) that it is always possible to determine positive numbers m_{12},m_{21} associated with M_1 and M_2 so that

$$m_{12}\mathbf{\Phi}_{12} + m_{21}\mathbf{\Phi}_{21} = 0 \tag{1-19}$$

and that, furthermore, if we consider a given particle M_1, and all possible binary newtonian systems (M_1,M_i) $(i = 2, 3, \ldots)$, then all the associated m_{1i} are identical—so that we can write simply, m_1. Upon suitable normalization, i.e., choice of a *unit*, there is thus associated with every particle a unique positive structural parameter, its *mass*, or more precisely, its *inertial mass.*§ It follows that if we write

$$m_1\mathbf{\Phi}_{12} = \mathbf{F}_{12}, \qquad m_2\mathbf{\Phi}_{21} = \mathbf{F}_{21}$$

then Eqs. (1-17) and (1-19) yield the relations

$$m_1\frac{d^2\mathbf{X}_1}{dT^2} = \mathbf{F}_{12}, \qquad m_2\frac{d^2\mathbf{X}_2}{dT^2} = \mathbf{F}_{21} \tag{1-20}$$

and

$$\mathbf{F}_{12} + \mathbf{F}_{21} = 0 \tag{1-21}$$

which are recognized as the expressions of Newton's second and third laws for binary systems. The newtonian 'forces' $\mathbf{F}_{12}$ and $\mathbf{F}_{21} = -\mathbf{F}_{12}$ are seen to

‡ But, of course, though infinite spatial separation is a sufficient condition, it is not in general a necessary condition for physical isolation. Thus to take an extreme example, if we consider the idealized system whose particles consist of perfectly rigid elastically colliding spheres, then the associated $\mathbf{\Phi}$ are nonvanishing only when two particles touch. It must also be borne in mind that what we are presently discussing in general is an idealized mathematical model whose correspondence to phenomena is never more than approximate. This can be expected, of course, to be true to a larger or smaller degree of all physical theory.

§ Historically, it was not of course in this manner that the notion of mass was arrived at. It was rather the proportionality of the mass of a body to its weight that provided a ready means of measuring masses at a given geographic locality. At the same time, this very proportionality made it easy to confuse the two concepts of mass and of weight, and one of the great merits of Newton's work was the clear explicit distinction between them which it expounds.

constitute two reciprocal aspects of the mutual state of interaction between M_1 and M_2.‡

We have still to extend the equations of motion (1-20) to arbitrary newtonian systems. A priori, there need be no complete dependence of $\mathbf{F}_{1,23\cdots}$ (i.e., of the force on M_1 in the presence of $M_2, M_3, \ldots$) on the binary forces $\mathbf{F}_{12}, \mathbf{F}_{13}, \ldots$, nor need it be simple if it exists. It is a fortunate empirical fact that for newtonian systems—that is to say, for practically all nonmicroscopic particle systems—the following very simple relationship does in fact hold:

$$\mathbf{F}_{1,23\cdots} = \mathbf{F}_{12} + \mathbf{F}_{13} + \cdots \tag{1-22}$$

This is an expression of the *principle of superposition* with whose aid the desired extension is immediately effected.

1-6 GALILEI–NEWTONIAN RELATIVITY

The formulation of the principles of newtonian mechanics outlined in the preceding sections is based in the first instance on the notion of absolute space. More precisely, all that is required is a reference frame fixed in S_{abs}. The choice of origin or of the direction of axes is immaterial. This represents, as we have seen, a positional relativity associated with the homogeneity and isotropy of space and reproduced by the kinematic group of rigid displacements.§ The equations of motion of the newtonian theory lead to a significant enlargement of the associated relativity group.

These equations of motion have the following general form, consistently with Eqs. (1-20) and (1-22),

$$m_s \frac{d^2\mathbf{X}_s}{dT^2} = \mathbf{F}_s\left(\mathbf{X}_1, \mathbf{X}_2, \ldots ; \frac{d\mathbf{X}_1}{dT}, \frac{d\mathbf{X}_2}{dT}, \ldots\right) \tag{1-23}$$

$$s = 1, 2, \ldots ; \text{no summation}$$

The crucial point to note is that by our assumed positional relativity it can be concluded that the dependence of the $\mathbf{F}_s$ on the particle positions must involve effectively only the *relative* position vectors $\mathbf{X}_1 - \mathbf{X}_2$, etc. A similar conclusion can also be arrived at regarding the particle velocities. (These are in any case not involved in ordinary newtonian forces.) Consequently

‡ At this point it may appear from our mode of introducing these forces that, in effect, we have followed Mach in defining force as "mass times acceleration." But we must remember that in the present formulation, the interaction function is *not defined by* Eq. (1-16), but has an independent operational existence. This, as we have seen, is methodologically preferable in the formulation here outlined.

§ We employ the term "positional relativity" in an extended sense to include also the equivalence of directions. It is also referred to as "geometric" or "spatial" relativity (or "symmetry").

Eqs. (1-23) are *form invariant* under the transformations

$$x_i = X_i + A_i T, \qquad t = T \tag{1-24}$$
$$A_i \text{ constants}$$

which represent the transition from our reference frame fixed in S_{abs} to frames having uniform rectilinear motion relative to S_{abs} (the axes remaining parallel). It follows that this invariance obtains likewise with respect to the transformations

$$(x;t) \to (x';t'): \quad x'_i = x_i + a_i t, \qquad t' = t \tag{1-25}$$
$$a_i \text{ constants}$$

where the space-time coordinate systems $(x;t)$ and $(x';t')$ are given by Eq. (1-24), and for obvious reasons are known as *inertial systems*. Every inertial system is thus completely equivalent to S_{abs} as far as the formulation of the laws of newtonian mechanics is concerned. In this sense S_{abs} loses its privileged status and is replaced by the family of all inertial systems. The relativity implicit in this arbitrariness in the coordinate frames is referred to as *galilei-newtonian relativity.*‡

These considerations point to the requirement that the family of transformations (1-25) form a group. This is indeed readily verified. This group of coordinate transformations is known as the *galilean group.*

In arriving at the above conclusions we made the tacit assumption that the parameters that enter in the equations of motion (1-23) remain unchanged under the transformations (1-24) and, in particular, that this is true of the inertial parameters m_s. For later reference we state the latter assumption explicitly:

III *The inertial mass of a body is an absolute invariant of motion of the body; in particular, it does not depend on its velocity relative to* S_{abs}.

APPENDIX 1A TRANSFORMATION GROUPS AND FORM INVARIANTS

Before we review what is meant by a group of transformations, let us recall the definition of a mathematical group in general. Such a group is a mathematical system consisting of a set $\mathcal{G} = \{A, B, \ldots\}$ (this set being finite, denumerably infinite, or continuously infinite) and a binary rule of composi-

‡ In the *Principia* this idea is expressed, in Corollary V to the Laws of Motion, in the following words: "The motions of bodies included in a given space are the same among themselves, whether that space is at rest, or moves uniformly forwards in a right line without any circular motion."

tion defined over $\mathcal{G}$, call it $\circ$, which satisfies the following conditions:‡

1. $A \circ B$ is a unique element of $\mathcal{G}$ whenever A and B are in $\mathcal{G}$.
2. $(A \circ B) \circ (C) = A \circ (B \circ C)$.
3. $\mathcal{G}$ contains an element I, the *unit* or *identity*, such that $I \circ A = A \circ I = A$ for every A in $\mathcal{G}$.
4. With every element A, $\mathcal{G}$ contains an element A^{-1}, the *inverse* of A, such that $A^{-1} \circ A = A \circ A^{-1} = I$.

A *group of transformations* is obtained, e.g., when $\mathcal{G}$ consists of a given family $\{A, B, \ldots\}$ of one-to-one mappings of some set $\mathcal{R} = \{\alpha, \beta, \ldots\}$ onto itself, with $B \circ A$ representing the mapping that results from the successive application of A followed by B. In fact, if $A(\alpha) = \alpha'$, and $B(\alpha') = \alpha''$, then $C = B \circ A$ is defined by the relation

$$(B \circ A)(\alpha) = B(A(\alpha)) = B(\alpha') = \alpha'' = C(\alpha) \tag{1A-1}$$

The condition (1) is immediately verified. It is easy to check rule (2); while rule (3) is satisfied by taking for I the identity transformation, i.e., the transformation that maps every element of $\mathcal{R}$ into itself. Since we have assumed that our transformations are *one-to-one*, that is to say, every $A(\alpha)$ has only one value, α', and every value α' is obtained from only one α(or, in other words, that the mapping is single valued in both directions), it follows that if we take the operation A^{-1} inverse to A [defined by $\alpha = A^{-1}(\alpha')$], this operation is in $\mathcal{G}$ and can be identified with the inverse of rule (4).

We arrive finally at the notion of a group of *coordinate transformations* when we identify $\mathcal{R}$ with the set $\{x(P)\}$, where P stands for a representative point in a given space or spatial region and x symbolizes a set of coordinates that specifies this point in a unique manner. It should be noted that in the present case two distinct interpretations of $\mathcal{G}$ are possible. A transformation

$$x \rightarrow x' = A(x) \tag{1A-2}$$

can be taken to represent a change of coordinates, $x(P) \rightarrow x'(P)$. In this interpretation, the elements of $\mathcal{R}$ are strictly the x, while the P serve merely to number the elements (in a *continuous* way, of course, in general). We can also look upon Eq. (1A-2) as representing a *mapping of the points P*. In this interpretation, we suppose the coordinate system fixed, and understand by $x'(P)$ the coordinates in this system of the point P' into which P (whose coordinates are x) is transformed by Eq. (1A-2). It is the first interpretation that will be usually assumed in this book.

The special case of *linear transformations* presents particular interest.

‡ We are not concerned with the complete logical independence of the conditions.

A linear transformation (1A-2) is represented by a set of linear equations‡

$$x'_i = \sum_{j=1}^{n} A_{ij}x_j, \qquad i = 1, 2, \ldots, n \tag{1A-3}$$

It is then also completely specified by the matrix $\|A_{ij}\| \equiv \mathfrak{A}$. By applying the rule of multiplication of matrices, it is seen that if the matrices $\mathfrak{A}$ and $\mathfrak{B}$ are associated with the transformations A and B, respectively, then the matrix $\mathfrak{B} \cdot \mathfrak{A}$ is associated with the transformation $B \circ A$ as defined in Eq. (1A-1). The unit matrix

$$\mathfrak{I} \equiv \|\delta_{ij}\|, \qquad \delta_{ij} = \begin{matrix} 1 & i = j \\ 0 & i \neq j \end{matrix} \tag{1A-4}$$

is obviously associated with the identity transformation. Hence it follows that the inverse transformation A^{-1} must be associated uniquely with the reciprocal matrix $\mathfrak{A}^{-1}$. This conclusion is also checked directly by solving Eqs. (1A-3) for the x in terms of the x', the nonsingularity of the matrix $\mathfrak{A}$ (i.e., the nonvanishing of its determinant) being insured by our assumption of the unique reversibility of the associated transformation.

We have thus established that the set of our matrices $\mathfrak{A}, \mathfrak{B}, \ldots$ together with matrix multiplication as the rule of composition, forms a group. Moreover, this group is in no way distinguishable from the group of transformations $\{A, B, \ldots\}$ as far as *abstract group structure* is concerned. Such a relationship is obviously a significant one. It is known as *isomorphism.*§

We require one further mathematical concept—that of a *form invariant.* This is defined relative to a family of coordinate transformations $\mathfrak{F}$ associated with a given space. A function of one or more points $f(P_1, P_2, \ldots)$ defined over the space is a form invariant relative to the family $\mathfrak{F}$ when its analytic expression takes the same form in every system of $\mathfrak{F}$. This relationship between f and $\mathfrak{F}$ can be reversed. Instead of assigning the family $\mathfrak{F}$ we can assign the point function f and look for the family $\mathfrak{F}_f$ of coordinate systems relative to which f is a form invariant. Now, it is easily verified that the set of all the transformations associated with any given family of coordinate systems forms a group. The group associated with the family $\mathfrak{F}_f$ is thus a group of coordinate transformations *generated* by the given form invariant f. The group of displacements of ordinary space, including reflections, is generated by the form invariant (1-1).

‡ Strictly speaking, Eqs. (1A-3) are linear and homogeneous, and the corresponding transformations should therefore be termed "linear *homogeneous*," but this qualifying adjective is generally omitted.

§ A group $\mathcal{G} \equiv \{\alpha, \beta, \ldots ; \circ\}$ is *isomorphic* with a group $\mathcal{G}' \equiv \{\alpha', \beta', \ldots ; \circ'\}$ when (1) to every element of $\mathcal{G}$ there corresponds a unique element of $\mathcal{G}'$ so that to $\alpha \circ \beta$ there corresponds the element $\alpha' \circ' \beta'$, and (2) when the correspondence between $\mathcal{G}$ and $\mathcal{G}'$ is one to one; it is *homomorphic,* when one stipulates condition (1) but not condition (2). The terms "simply isomorphic" and "isomorphic," respectively, are also used for these concepts in the older mathematical literature.

Problems

1-1 (*a*) Is the idea of 'motion' involved implicitly in the discussion of physical space outlined in this chapter? Explain. (*b*) What significant connection is there between our assumption I of the existence of infinitely fast signals and the positing of ideal rigid bodies? (*c*) In what respect is the clock represented by the earth rotating about its axis similar to the 'inertial clock' referred to in Sec. 1-4?

1-2 (*a*) Prove that Eqs. (1-7) represent the general solution of the differential system (1-6) under the condition (1-5*a*). Obtain the general solution when this condition is not satisfied. Show that the solutions of the variational problem (1-5) always yield a *minimum* of the length integral. (*b*) Consider the similar general problem when in place of Eq. (1-3) we deal with the differential metric form

$$ds^2 = g_{ab}\, dx_a\, dx_b \qquad \begin{array}{l} g_{ab} = g_{ba} \text{ constants} \\ \text{summation over } a,\ b = 1, 2, \ldots, n \end{array} \tag{i}$$

it being assumed that this quadratic form is *positive definite*, i.e., that expression (i) is never negative and is zero only for vanishing dx_a. What can you say about the coordinates x_a? In proving the minimal property of the geodesics, introduce the simplifying assumption that $g_{ab} = 0$ when $a \neq b$ (i.e., that the coordinate system is orthogonal). (c) When it is also assumed that the g_{ab} are not constants but are functions of $x_1, \ldots, x_n$, show that the equations of the geodesics have the form:

$$\frac{\partial F}{\partial x_a} - \frac{dz_a}{du} + \frac{z_a}{2F}\frac{dF}{du} = 0 \tag{ii}$$

where

$$F \equiv g_{ab}x'_a x'_b \qquad x'_a \equiv \frac{dx_a}{du} \qquad z_a \equiv \frac{\partial F}{\partial x'_a} \tag{iii}$$

Show also that when the parameter u is chosen so that

$$\frac{dF}{du} = 0 \text{ along the extremals} \tag{iv}$$

[see condition (1-5*a*)], and when Eqs. (ii) are expanded, they assume the form

$$g_{ab}x''_b + [bc,a]x'_b x'_c = 0 \tag{v}$$

where‡

$$[bc,a] = \frac{1}{2}\left(\frac{\partial g_{ba}}{\partial x_c} + \frac{\partial g_{ca}}{\partial x_b} - \frac{\partial g_{bc}}{\partial x_a}\right) \tag{vi}$$

‡ The symbols (vi) and other related symbols permitting further simplification of Eqs. (v) are studied in Sec. 5-5 as part of the general subject of tensor analysis. The topic of geodesics is of interest in the special theory of relativity, and it is also of central importance in the general theory of relativity.

Show finally that condition (iv) and Eqs. (ii) are consistent. (*d*) Referring to the discussion in Sec. 1-2, and using the present results, verify that a euclidean metric (in other words, a euclidean geometry) is already implied by the differential relation (1-3).

1-3 (*a*) Show that the absolute value of the expression to the right of Eq. (1-8) is always ≤ 1. By considering the analytic relations in terms of cartesian coordinates that hold for triangles in a euclidean plane, establish the trigonometric equation (1-8), as well as the analytic expression of the theorem of Pythagoras for arbitrary right triangles. [Recall the Cauchy inequality that follows from the identity $\sum a_i^2 \sum b_i^2 - \left(\sum a_i b_i\right)^2 = \sum\sum_{i<j} (a_i b_j - a_j b_i)^2$.]
(*b*) Check the validity in the case of our metric (1-2) of the 'triangle inequality' defined in Sec. 1-2.

1-4 By utilizing the properties of the coordinate lines of cartesian systems obtained in Sec. 1-2, deduce the result (1-12), i.e., the linearity of the transformations connecting such coordinate systems. (It will help to determine first the shape of the coordinate surfaces of cartesian systems.)

1-5 (*a*) Prove directly that the family of matrices satisfying Eq. (1-13) forms a group and that the matrices that satisfy, in addition, the relation (1-14) form a subgroup of this group. Justify condition (1-14) in the case of displacements. What is the geometric meaning of the orthogonal transformations for which this condition does not hold? Do they form a group? (*b*) Find the form of the matrices (or order 4) that result from combining the orthogonal transformations with the transformations (1-25) and compare with the matrices of the Lorentz transformations (2-6).

1-6 (*a*) Consider the available methods for measuring lengths on the laboratory, on the atomic, and on the astronomic scales, and examine the physical principles and assumptions that can be seen to be involved directly or indirectly in these measurements. What are the optimum percentage accuracies in the measurement of spatial intervals presently obtainable? Are any or all of the measuring setups in question based on the assumption that the spatial metric is euclidean? (*b*) Consider the similar question for the measurement of time. Here the main interest lies in the establishing of reproducible and relatively durable standards of optimum accuracy. Compare the methods of calibration and the accuracy obtainable by astronomical means and with the aid of quartz crystal as well as atomic-molecular and nuclear resonance techniques. [On the topic of measurement of time the following are a few references (which the reader will want to bring up to date, as well as supplement with articles dealing with the measurement of length): G. M. Clemence, Astronomical Time, *Rev. Mod. Phys.*, **29**: 2 (1957); C. H. Townes, Recent Developments in Measurement of Time, *Nuovo Cimento*, **5**: Suppl., 222 (1957); F. G. Merril, Frequency and Time Standards, *I. R. E. Trans. Instr.*, **1–9**: 117 (1960).]

1-7 A straight line in euclidean space can be obtained by displacing a line element parallel to itself. What deduction concerning Newton's first law can one make from this fact by arguments involving the principle of sufficient reason?

1-8 Newton's corollary I to his Laws of Motion reads: "A body acted on by two forces simultaneously, will describe the diagonal of a parallelogram in the same time as it would describe the sides by those forces separately." What is the connection of this corollary to assumption (1-22)? What dynamical and what kinematic relations are involved in this assumption?

1-9 (*a*) In Galileo's system of mechanics the earth played essentially the role of an inertial frame; in Newton's system that role was taken over by the collection of 'fixed' stars; we now know that these stars generally form part of our galaxy, and that the telescopically accessible universe consists of a vast multitude of galaxies all in apparent continual dispersal from each other. Discuss the practical legitimacy of Galileo's and Newton's reference frames, and the choice of a suitable inertial frame for the description of galactic motion. (*b*) It has sometimes been suggested that one might define S_{abs} in terms of the center of mass of the universe. Do you find such a definition more acceptable than that provided by Neumann's body alpha? Does such a definition involve us in any circular reasoning?

1-10 Newton's celebrated 'rotating bucket experiment' (F. Cajori, *op. cit.*, pp. 10–11) consisted in observing that the surface of the water in a rotating bucket was little changed at the beginning of the bucket's rotation when the water had the largest acceleration relative to the bucket, while the greatest peripheral rise of the water was reached when it attained its greatest acceleration and had consequently become stationary relative to the bucket. He concluded that this result provided a demonstration of the *absoluteness of acceleration*, reasoning that the experiment showed that it was not the relative but the absolute acceleration that had visible effects on the water. Do you agree with Mach that in view of the relatively insignificant mass of the bucket there is little scope to Newton's argument? What do you consider nevertheless to be a significant conclusion that can be drawn from this experiment? What constructive implication can you see in Mach's critique? {"Mach's principle," so named by Einstein [*Ann. Physik*, **55**: 241 (1918)], states that the inertia of bodies is determined by interaction with the rest of the matter of the universe. It has been a subject of active discussion, largely in connection with the general theory of relativity.}

2
Historical Preliminaries

The historical development of a fundamental physical theory does not frequently correspond to the simplest and logically most satisfactory way of presenting it. But a proper recognition of this development can contribute to a fuller appreciation of the theory. This is certainly true of the history of the special theory of relativity, with its decades of a most elusive search in the annals of physics, the search for some trace of an ether wind confidently expected on all sides; and with its culmination in a resolution of this quest by the essential discarding of the object of the search and the adopting instead of startlingly novel ideas concerning time and space. A complete and properly balanced account of the various stages of this development would fill many pages.‡ Only a brief outline of these stages is presented in this second

‡ The literature on this subject is not ample. The most complete reference is perhaps E. T. Whittaker, "A History of the Theories of Aether and Electricity," vols. 1 and 2, Harper & Brothers, New York, 1960. This is a very readable and scholarly treatise, and an excellent source of information in what concerns the experimental and theoretical work that led to the investigations of Larmor, Lorentz, Poincaré, and Einstein (as presented in the first volume), but the discussion of the origin of the theory of special relativity as we understand it at present (which is contained in the second volume) involves a totally strange interpretation of its literature. Other references will be given in the following sections, but it would appear that a definitive and concise history of special relativity is yet to be written.

introductory chapter, which aims mainly to serve as an introduction to the appropriate literature. Some of the relevant theoretical developments are alluded to in the problems.

2-1 ELECTRODYNAMICS OF MOVING MEDIA AND THE LUMINIFEROUS ETHER

Although it is at present possible to develop the special theory of relativity on a very broad scientific base, historically it arose as an outgrowth of the attempts in the last quarter of the nineteenth century and in the first years of this century to extend Maxwell's theory so as to embrace electrodynamic phenomena taking place in moving media. This task turned out to be a most baffling one. In large measure this was doubtless due to the circumstance that the physicists of that day were imbued with a strong belief in the possibility of expressing all of physics in terms of the conceptual scheme of newtonian mechanics—a belief which, narrow as it may appear to us at present, is entirely understandable when we bear in mind that by the second half of the last century the successes of the newtonian theory appeared to be indeed of universal scope, encompassing not only the various branches of terrestrial and celestial mechanics, but nearly all other branches of physics as well. In accordance with this view, the equations of the electrodynamic field ought to be either invariant under the galilean group or else serve to determine a *distinguished* frame of reference—call it S_{em}.

An attempt at implementing the first alternative was made by H. Hertz in 1890, as well as by O. Heaviside at about the same time; but the resulting theory was in disagreement with a number of important experiments.‡ The second alternative had, in any case, much wider appeal. It afforded the possibility of taking S_{em} for the frame of reference associated with Newton's absolute space. In addition, with the experimental confirmation by Hertz (1884–1894) of the identity of light and high-frequency electromagnetic waves, as theoretically predicted by Maxwell,§ S_{em} could be identified with the luminiferous ether, which, ever since the days of Descartes, Hooke, and Huygens, had been postulated as the all-pervading material medium in which optical disturbances are propagated.¶

It is of interest to note in this connection that even Newton, although a leading proponent of the corpuscular theory of light, was far from excluding

‡ For details and references, see [5], secs. 2 and 3; and Whittaker, *op. cit.*, vol. 1, pp. 328–331, 403–404. (See Prob. 2-1.)

§ James Clerk Maxwell, "A Treatise on Electricity and Magnetism," vol. 2, chap. 10, Dover Publications, Inc., New York (reprint of 3d ed., Oxford University Press, London, 1904). It may be noted parenthetically that this treatise can be considered in many respects as the Principia of the nineteenth century.

¶ The designation *ether* for this hypothetical medium actually came into use at a later date.

this postulate of a material ether entirely from his considerations, as concerns both optics and gravitation.‡ In fact, until about the middle of the eighteenth century, when the action-at-a-distance approach gained general predominance, the majority of physicists following Leibnitz and Huygens favored some type of contact action, which they imagined to take place through the intermediacy of a universal medium, this medium being capable of sustaining longitudinal vibrations representing light, in analogy to the elastic vibrations associated with sound waves. The luminiferous ether returned to favor in the nineteenth century with the advent of the refined undulatory theories of light of Young and of Fresnel.§ The recognition of the transversality of light vibrations led to the introduction of the perfectly rigid elastic model for the ether, the general theory of elasticity being simultaneously forged out towards the middle of the last century by Navier, Cauchy, Stokes, and others. Especially Stokes sought to find an acceptable explanation for the seemingly contradictory attributes one was forced to assign to the ether: absolute rigidity of its substance and complete penetrability through it of all ponderable bodies. But in general, it seems that the conviction of the necessity of the ether postulate was so overriding, that its paradoxical attributes caused no undue concern.

A particular boost to the prestige of this postulate was provided by Fresnel's successful explanation (1818) of Arago's experiment on the refraction of stellar light in prisms, in terms of the hypothesis of the partial dragging of the ether by moving bodies, the velocity of drag being the fraction $(1 - 1/n^2)$ of the velocity of the body relative to the otherwise absolutely stationary ether (n being the index of refraction of the transparent body when at rest in the ether).¶ This hypothesis was successful not only in explaining the failure to detect any effect of the earth's motion through the ether in Arago's experiment, but also in a number of later related experiments, such as that of Fizeau (1851) on the interference of two light beams sent in opposite directions through water flowing in a tube, which was later verified by more refined experiments by Michelson and

‡ See, e.g., Cajori's edition of Newton's "Principia," pp. 636–637, (University of California Press, Berkeley, Calif., 1934); and Newton's "Opticks," Queries 18–23, 29, Dover Publications, Inc., New York (based on the 4th ed., London, 1730).

§ See Whittaker, *op. cit.*, vol. 1, chaps. 4 and 5.

¶ Fresnel deduced his result from the assumption that the square of the index of refraction is given by the ratio of the density of the ether in the body to that in vacuum: $n^2 = \rho/\rho_0$. On the wave-theory explanation of n this seemed a reasonable assumption; and his deduction based on it is straightforward. According to a later version due to Stokes, we need only invoke the principle of hydrodynamic continuity to conclude that if v is the outside velocity of the ether relative to the body (in a given direction) and $v - \eta v$ is the corresponding velocity inside the body, then $\rho_0 v = \rho(v - \eta v)$, and hence $\eta = 1 - \rho_0/\rho = 1 - 1/n^2$.

Morley (1886) and by Zeeman (1914–1927); and that of Airy (1871) on the aberration of light moving through telescopes filled with water.‡

It was in this kind of ether-dominated scientific climate that the investigators of that period attacked the challenging problems presented by one of the grandest theoretical structures of the nineteenth century, Maxwell's theory of the electromagnetic field. Both Maxwell himself and his immediate followers considered the postulate of a universal material medium subject to the laws of continuum mechanics, and serving as the seat of all electromagnetic actions, as an integral part of the general theory of electrodynamics.§ How else, it was felt, could energy and momentum be propagated in the presence of a field? Consequently it was generally held that it should be possible to detect the motion of the earth relative to the reference frame determined by this universal medium, i.e., relative to S_{em}, by means of suitable electromagnetic experiments performed at different phases of the earth's orbit and with different orientations of some pertinent directions of the apparatus relative to the direction of the motion of the earth. It will be recalled that the average orbital speed of the earth relative to the sun is about 30 km/sec. If we take this value as an estimate of the average speed v of the earth relative to the hypothetical S_{em} during some parts of its journey, the resulting order of magnitude, 10^{-4}, for the ratio v/c is sufficiently large for effects involving v/c (referred to as "first-order effects") to be unambiguously detected not only in optical experiments (such as those referred to earlier), but also in suitably chosen purely electromagnetic experiments. Such experiments were set up with great care by a number of skillful investigators, but all of them led to negative results: not a trace of an effect of the earth's presumed motion through the ether could be found.¶

‡ In the former experiment, if L is the length of the light path in one direction, then for monochromatic radiation of frequency ν, the difference in phase of the two beams is seen to be $L\nu/(c/n - \eta v) - L\nu/(c/n + \eta v) = 2L\eta v\nu n^2/c^2 = 2(n^2 - 1)(L/\lambda)(v/c)$ to first order in v/c. See [6], chap. 1. This contains a very clear exposition of the theory of the optical ether experiments.

§ Maxwell's original development of his theory of the electromagnetic field is presented in his masterly paper, A Dynamical Theory of the Electromagnetic Field, *Royal Soc. Trans.*, pp. 459–512 (1865) (or, "Scientific Papers," vol. I, pp. 526–597, Cambridge University Press, London, 1890). Maxwell's contribution, Ether, in "Encyclopaedia Britannica," 9th ed. vol. 8, pp. 568–572 (1878), contains an interesting sketch of the thinking on this subject by his contemporaries and himself.

¶ In addition to the previously given references, pertinent discussion is also to be found in the first two chapters and in appendix D of J. Larmor, "Aether and Matter," Cambridge University Press, London, 1900; in [7], secs. 1, 2, and 3; and in W. K. H. Panofsky and M. Phillips, "Classical Electricity and Magnetism," 2d ed., chap. 15, Addison-Wesley Publishing Company, Inc., Cambridge, Mass., 1962. A survey of the major experiments that paved the way for the theory of relativity is contained in the paper by J. Laub, Über die experimentellen Grundlagen des Relativitätsprinzips, *Jahrbuch Radioakt. Elektronik*, **7**: 405–463 (1910).

Since there is no longer the need, which existed in the early and largely unfriendly days of the theory of relativity, of justifying it with reference to each and every ether-drift experiment, these experiments now possess mainly historical interest.

It was under the influence of these persistent and futile attempts to identify experimentally the then universally accepted electromagnetic ether, that many of Lorentz's significant contributions to electromagnetic theory were evolved.

2-2 THE RELATIVISTIC EQUATIONS OF LORENTZ AND POINCARÉ

An important impetus to one series of extensive optical and electrodynamic researches of H. A. Lorentz, covering nearly two decades,‡ was his attempt to uphold Fresnel's ideas concerning optical phenomena in moving bodies on the assumption of a perfectly stationary ether, against the alternative ideas of G. G. Stokes (1845), which involved the assumption of the total dragging of the ether by massive bodies. A crucial issue was presented by the theoretical deduction of stellar aberration.§ Lorentz showed that this is possible on Fresnel's assumptions, but that those made by Stokes involved an inner contradiction. It was chiefly to put these rival ideas to a test that Michelson devised his famous interferometer experiment (1881), which was perfected by him and Morley (1887), and is widely known as the "Michelson-Morley experiment." The negative result of this experiment could be interpreted as a confirmation of the theory of Stokes, since obviously no optical experiments performed on the earth can be affected by its motion if it carries with it the optical medium of propagation. Nevertheless, because Lorentz was convinced that the logical weaknesses in Stokes' theory were serious and that all the suggestions for remedying them led to implausible conclusions, he stuck to what he called "Fresnel's ether," and proceeded to introduce additional hypotheses of his own in order to account for Michelson's null result as well as for other related results. These far-reaching theoretical steps will now be sketched out briefly.

It will be recalled that the theory of "electrons" (i.e., of charged 'elementary' particles) as developed by Lorentz, is based on Maxwell's equations for the vacuum electromagnetic field coupled to charge and current densities arising from electron distributions, together with the equation giving the force per unit charge arising from the electromagnetic field. In gaussian

‡ Beginning with De L'influence du mouvement de la terre sur les phénomènes lumineaux, *Verslag K. Akad. Wet. Amsterdam,* **2**: 297 (1886), or "Collected Papers," vol. 4, pp. 153–214, M. Nijhoff, The Hague, 1934–1939, and culminating in his celebrated paper of 1904 (the second paper in [2]).

§ This minute displacement in the apparent position of the stars arising from the motion of the earth, discovered by Bradley (1728), is, as is well known, immediately accounted for on the corpuscular theory of light; but on the wave theory involving a material propagation medium, its explanation can become fairly involved, depending on the hypotheses made concerning the structure of the medium and the states of relative motion of the bodies concerned and portions of this medium. See H. A. Lorentz, "Theory of Electrons," chap. 5, Dover Publications, Inc., New York, 1952 (reprint of 2d ed., Leipzig, 1916); and [6], chap. I.

units these equations are respectively:‡

$$\operatorname{curl} \mathbf{E} = -\frac{1}{c}\dot{\mathbf{B}}, \qquad \operatorname{div} \mathbf{B} = 0 \tag{2-1}$$

$$\operatorname{div} \mathbf{E} = 4\pi\rho, \qquad \operatorname{curl} \mathbf{B} = \frac{1}{c}(\dot{\mathbf{E}} + 4\pi\rho\mathbf{u}) \tag{2-2}$$

$$\mathbf{f} = \mathbf{E} + \left[\frac{\mathbf{u}}{c} \times \mathbf{B}\right] \tag{2-3}$$

These equations were assumed to hold relative to S_{em}. In order to explain the aforementioned experimental results involving effects of first order in v/c, v representing the speed of the moving body relative to S_{em}, while retaining Fresnel's immobile ether, Lorentz was led to search for transformation equations connecting S_{em} and the system S' attached to the moving body, for which Eqs. (2-1) to (2-3) remain form invariant at least to the first order. This first attempt at establishing the "covariance" of the Maxwell-Lorentz theory was only partially successful. At this stage, Lorentz still retained the galilean transformation (1-25) ($a_i = -v_i$, $v_iv_i = v^2$) as far as the spatial coordinates are concerned, but he replaced the formula $t' = t$ of Eq. (1-25) by

$$t' = t - \frac{1}{c^2} v_i x_i \tag{2-4}$$

With the associated law of transformation for the field vectors taken to be of the form

$$\mathbf{E}' = \mathbf{E} + \left[\frac{\mathbf{v}}{c} \times \mathbf{B}\right], \qquad \mathbf{B}' = \mathbf{B} - \left[\frac{\mathbf{v}}{c} \times \mathbf{E}\right] \tag{2-5}$$

Lorentz found that upon neglecting terms of order higher than first in v/c and u/c the transformed field equations in S' assumed the same form as Eqs. (2-1) to (2-3). (See Prob. 2-2.) He could thus account for all the optical "first-order results."§ Moreover, not only was Fresnel's result reestablished in this way, without any added assumption about a partial convection of the ether, but it was even significantly extended to take care of dispersion effects in the transparent media.¶

‡ See Lorentz, *op. cit.*

§ H. A. Lorentz, "Versuch einer Theorie der elektrischen und optischen Erscheinungen in bewegten Körpern," E. J. Brill, Leiden, 1895; reprinted in "Collected Papers," vol. 5, pp. 1–37. Transformation (2-4) is introduced in sec. 31.

¶ The theory of dispersion on the basis of a model of hertzian radiating oscillators was one of the many important topics incorporated in Lorentz's theory. For those bearing especially on the present discussion, see his "Theory of Electrons," secs. 44, 45, and 46, and chap. 5. This book, incidentally, can be recommended as an excellent example of lucid scientific exposition in physics, and although some parts are now chiefly of historical interest, much of it has still high instructional value.

On the other hand, by its very nature, this theory could not cope with the negative results of second order in v/c such as that provided by the Michelson and Morley optical experiment.‡ In order to overcome this difficulty, Lorentz at first introduced one more special hypothesis, one that was independently proposed earlier by FitzGerald, and is therefore known as the FitzGerald or, the FitzGerald-Lorentz contraction hypothesis. According to it, every body moving with the speed v relative to S_{em} has its spatial extension in the direction of motion contracted by the factor $v^2/2c^2$.§ Finally, dissatisfied with the obviously provisional character of this hypothesis,¶ Lorentz generalized further the transformation equations for going from S_{em} to S', with a view to insuring form invariance in the electromagnetic equations *exactly* and not to any specific order.

This generalization consisted in the first place in bringing the kinematic relations connecting S_{em} and S' to their final form (corresponding to the motion of S' relative to S_{em} with velocity v in the positive x direction—see Fig. 2-1):‡‡

$$x' = \gamma(x - \beta ct), \qquad y' = y, \qquad z' = z, \qquad ct' = \gamma(ct - \beta x)$$
$$\gamma \equiv \gamma_v = (1 - \beta^2)^{-1/2}, \qquad \beta = \frac{v}{c} \tag{2-6}$$

‡ This experiment and other related ones are described in the references given earlier in connection with the first-order effects. The Michelson and Morley experiment is of course among the best known in modern physics. (See Prob. 2-3.) Another important electromagnetic experiment, that of Trouton and Noble (1903), is discussed in Chap. 6 in connection with its relativistic explanation.

§ Secs. 89–92 of "Versuch einer Theorie"; reprinted in [2].

¶ Moreover, this hypothesis, when taken *by itself*, appeared to be contradicted by the null results of experiments such as, for example, those of Rayleigh (1902) and of Brace (1904), in which it was attempted to detect the small double-refraction effect that would be expected, on the Lorentz theory, to arise in transparent bodies as a result of their FitzGerald contraction.

‡‡ Lorentz at first included an additional constant common factor, l, in these equations and subsequently established that $l = 1$ by considerations concerning the dynamical equations for an electron. See [2], Paper 2; or, "Theory of Electrons," pp. 196 ff.

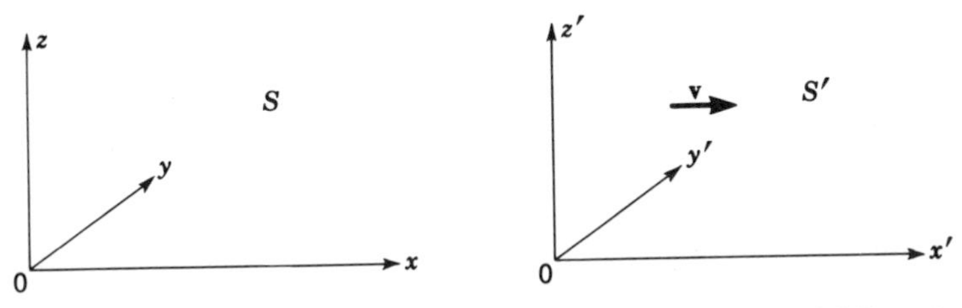

Fig. 2-1 Orientation of axes and relative velocity in the special Lorentz transformations as given in Eq. (2-6) (where, as first introduced in the text, $S \equiv S_{em}$, but generally S represents an arbitrarily given inertial frame).

With these were associated the transformation formulas for the field quantities:

$$\begin{aligned} E'_x &= E_x, & E'_y &= \gamma(E_y - \beta B_z), & E'_z &= \gamma(E_z + \beta B_y) \\ B'_x &= B_x, & B'_y &= \gamma(B_y + \beta E_z), & B'_z &= \gamma(B_z - \beta E_y) \end{aligned} \tag{2-7}$$

Although the transformation formulas that Lorentz put forth for charge density, velocity, and electric force were not consistent with the complete form invariance of all the electrodynamic equations, it was nevertheless possible for him to account for all the crucial optical and electromagnetic experimental results then known with the aid of his revised theory. But aside from the complex and in part problematic reasoning involved in Lorentz's approach, this lack of complete symmetry in his transformation theory was of course a significant flaw that could be expected to show up in future experiments.

This flaw was corrected by Poincaré at about the same time as Einstein was independently and very differently at work on the entire problem. Poincaré supplied the correct expressions for the transformation of ρ, $\rho\mathbf{u}$, and $\mathbf{f}$:‡

$$\rho' = \gamma\rho\left(1 - \beta\frac{u_x}{c}\right), \qquad \rho' u'_x = \gamma\rho(u_x - \beta c), \qquad \rho' u'_y = \rho u_y, \qquad \rho' u'_z = \rho u_z \tag{2-8}$$

$$\begin{aligned} \mathfrak{F}'_x &= \gamma\left(\mathfrak{F}_x - \beta\mathfrak{F}\cdot\frac{\mathbf{u}}{c}\right) \\ \mathfrak{F}'_y &= \mathfrak{F}_y \\ \mathfrak{F}'_z &= \mathfrak{F}_z \end{aligned} \qquad \mathfrak{F} = \text{force per } \textit{unit volume} \tag{2-9}$$

He deduced the transformation for the electric density ρ by finding the proper transformation for an element of volume and by making the reasonable assumption that electric charge is an absolute invariant. The transformation of the velocity vector $\mathbf{u}$ is obtained directly from Eqs. (2-6). In order to derive the last transformation equations, Poincaré assumed the form invariance of the Lorentz force expression (per unit volume). (See Prob. 2-5.)

Poincaré was also the first to note that the class of all "Lorentz transformations" forms a group,§ and to utilize the group property to deduce very

‡ H. Poincaré, *Compt. Rend.*, **140**: 1504 (1905). His ideas on this subject are more fully developed in the first part of his comprehensive paper, Sur la Dynamique de l'Électron, *Rend. Circ. Mat. Palermo*, **21**: 129 (1906).

§ The designation *Lorentz transformation* for Eqs. (2-6) is also due to Poincaré. The fact that transformations similar to these had already been considered earlier in another context by W. Voigt was not then known to Poincaré, any more than to Lorentz or Einstein. (See reference to Voigt in Lorentz's "Theory of Electrons," p. 198, footnote 1; see also Prob. 2-4.) Apparently overlooked, too, was J. Larmor's anticipation of Eqs. (2-6) except for a difference of second order in the time transformation formula. It

simply that $l = 1$. He also came close to anticipating the four-dimensional space-time treatment of H. Minkowski (to be discussed in Chaps. 3 and 5); though, rather surprisingly, he stopped short of fully exploring its possibilities.

The set of Eqs. (2-6) to (2-9) requires only the addition of the reasonable hypothesis, which was in effect contemplated by Lorentz, that not only the electric but also all other forces transform in accordance with Eqs. (2-9) under transformations (2-6), to make it possible analytically to proceed with a deduction of the dynamics of special relativity. If, nevertheless, we refer to the *relativistic equations* of Lorentz and not to the theory of relativity of Lorentz, it is because, as a matter of historical fact, Lorentz did not consider his theory in such light. Far from discerning in it any indication for a relativity in the notions of space and of time, he adhered strictly in all his investigations to the idea of a universal ether, which made it possible to think of an absolutely stationary spatial reference frame, of absolute rest, of absolute motion, and of absolute lengths. The FitzGerald contraction therefore required an explanation in terms of the structure of matter and structure of the electron. As to the time dilatation deducible from the Lorentz transformation, that was to him only in the nature of a mathematical artifice; the time t' of Eqs. (2-6), which he termed "local time," he considered as essentially different from t, his "universal time."‡

The latter idea was apparently universally shared before the appearance of Einstein's paper on the subject—not excluding even Poincaré, who, in some of his writings and in his address entitled "Principles of Mathematical Physics," delivered in 1904 at the St. Louis Congress of Arts and Sciences (published in English translation in the *Monist,* January 1905), appears to have been close to freeing himself of current preconceptions.§ Despite his

---

should be noted, in fact, that the researches of Lorentz in the field under review were paralleled in part by the investigations of Larmor. See especially chaps. 10 and 11 of his "Aether and Matter."

‡ As stated earlier, Whittaker's *History,* although on the whole very competent, presents the history of special relativity, which he terms the "relativity of Lorentz and Poincaré," in a totally strange light. Suffice it here to quote Lorentz himself ("Theory of Electrons," p. 321 ff.—a passage written in 1915): "If I had to write the last chapter now, I should certainly have given a more prominent place to Einstein's theory of relativity (§ 189) by which the theory of electromagnetic phenomena in moving systems gains a simplicity that I had not been able to attain. The chief cause of my failure was my clinging to the idea that the variable t only can be considered as the true time and that my local time t' must be regarded as no more than an auxiliary mathematical quantity." For a clear elementary discussion of Lorentz's position in the history of relativity see D. Bohm, "The Special Theory of Relativity," chaps. 6–10, W. A. Benjamin, Inc., New York, 1965.

§ The penetrating though groping nature of Poincaré's insights in this area is epitomized by these words from his St. Louis address: "Perhaps likewise, we should construct a whole new mechanics, that we only succeed in catching a glimpse of, where inertia increasing with the velocity, the velocity of light would become an impassable limit."

profound philosophical sophistication and breadth of scientific vision, Poincaré never did make the daring leap in the interpretation of the transformation equations, which constitutes Einstein's formulation of the special theory of relativity.

Problems

2-1 The electrodynamic equations of H. Hertz for moving media result from Maxwell's phenomenological electromagnetic equations by the replacement in the latter of the ordinary partial time derivative $\partial/\partial t$ by the 'motional time derivative' D/Dt, defined by the formula [for the flux of a vector field $\mathbf{A}(\mathbf{x},t)$ through a *moving* surface S]

$$\frac{d}{dt}\int_S \mathbf{A}\cdot d\mathbf{S} = \int_S \frac{D\mathbf{A}}{Dt}\cdot d\mathbf{S} \tag{i}$$

(*a*) Show that the Hertz equations are form invariant under the galilean group of transformations, and even more generally under the group of transformations representing *arbitrary* relative rigid motion of the coordinate frames, it being assumed that the field quantities are not affected by motion, and that newtonian kinematics s retained. In particular, show that the Maxwell-Hertz phenomenological field equations (apart from the constitutive equations) have the following form in gaus ian units:

$$\begin{aligned} \operatorname{div}\mathbf{D} &= 4\pi\rho, & \operatorname{div}\mathbf{B} &= 0 \\ \operatorname{curl}\mathbf{E}^* &= -\frac{1}{c}\dot{\mathbf{B}}, & \operatorname{curl}\mathbf{H}^* &= \frac{1}{c}(\dot{\mathbf{D}} + 4\pi\mathbf{j}^*) \end{aligned} \tag{ii}$$

where

$$\begin{aligned} \mathbf{E}^* &= \mathbf{E} + \frac{1}{c}[\mathbf{v}\times\mathbf{B}] \\ \mathbf{H}^* &= \mathbf{H} - \frac{1}{c}[\mathbf{v}\times\mathbf{D}] \\ \mathbf{j}^* &= \mathbf{j} + \rho\mathbf{v} \end{aligned} \tag{iii}$$

and the other symbols have their usual significance, the velocity vector $\mathbf{v}$ referring to the 'moving body' with respect to which the field equations hold. Prove this by referring directly to the integral relation (i) and also by subjecting the differential field equations to the coordinate transformations. [In the latter proof for the general case, it may help to recall the identity

$$(\operatorname{curl}[\mathbf{A}\times\mathbf{v}])_i = v_i \operatorname{div}\mathbf{A} - A_i \operatorname{div}\mathbf{v} + \mathbf{A}\cdot\frac{\partial v_i}{\partial\mathbf{x}} - \mathbf{v}\cdot\frac{\partial A_i}{\partial\mathbf{x}} \tag{iv}$$

and the relation (1-13) satisfied by orthogonal matrices, from which it follows that $\tilde{A}\dot{A} + \dot{\tilde{A}}A = O \equiv$ zero matrix. It is also convenient to employ the Levi-Civita symbols ϵ_{ijk} that are antisymmetric in all the indices and have the value 1 for $i = 1$, $j = 2$, and $k = 3$; and make use in particular of the following identity holding for a proper orthogonal matrix A,‡

$$\epsilon_{ijk}A_{rj}A_{sk} = \epsilon_{prs}A_{pi} \tag{v}$$

For the explicit expression of $D\mathbf{A}/Dt$ see, e.g., Panofsky and Phillips, *op. cit.*, sec. 9-3.] (*b*) Is there any similarity between the theory of Hertz and the optical theory of Stokes involving a totally dragged ether? Is the Michelson-Morley experiment in agreement with the theory of Hertz? What well-known and firmly established experiments disprove this theory? (The optical experiments associated with Fresnel's hypothesis form an important class of such experiments. What is Fresnel's dragging coefficient according to Hertz's theory? See [5], secs. 2 and 3.)

2-2 With the availability of the straight and easy approach to the relativistic transformation theory that was opened up by Einstein, it is not easy to appreciate the difficulties encountered by Lorentz in his attempts to find his way to an invariance theory for his field equations (theory of "corresponding states"—in Lorentz's terminology). The root of the difficulty was of course Lorentz's belief in the universal validity of newtonian kinematics. But it is easily established that it is not possible to retain the galilean transformations intact (as in the case of Hertz's theory) along with Lorentz's assumption of a stationary electromagnetic ether. It is for this reason that Lorentz found it necessary to introduce his "local time." In order to perceive the origin of this idea in the 'first-order' theory, consider the transformations (1-25) ($a_i = -v_i$) with the last equation replaced by

$$t' = t + \beta T(\mathbf{x}), \quad \beta \equiv \frac{v}{c} \tag{i}$$

and let the associated transformations of the field quantities have the form

$$\mathbf{E}' = \mathbf{E} + \beta\mathbf{E}_1, \qquad \mathbf{B}' = \mathbf{B} + \beta\mathbf{B}_1 \tag{ii}$$

Show that to first order (both with respect to v/c as well as u/c) we obtain equations of the form (2-1) to (2-3), provided

$$\text{grad } T = -\frac{\mathbf{v}}{vc}, \qquad \mathbf{E}_1 = \frac{\mathbf{v} \times \mathbf{B}}{v}, \qquad \mathbf{B}_1 = -\frac{\mathbf{v} \times \mathbf{E}}{v}$$

[Identity (iv) recalled in Prob. 2-1 will also be helpful here. Note also that quantities such as ρ and $\mathbf{f}$ are taken to be unchanged under our transformation in agreement with the newtonian viewpoint, and that, of course, $\mathbf{u}' = \mathbf{u} - \mathbf{v}$.]

‡ This is found from the relation, det $A = 1$, or, $\epsilon_{ijk}A_{pi}A_{rj}A_{sk} = \epsilon_{prs}$, with the aid of Eq. (1-13) (these symbols are discussed in Sec. 5-4).

2-3 The Michelson-Morley experiment, performed nearly a century ago [*Am. J. Sci.* **22:** 120–129 (1881); **34:** 333–345 (1887); for further references see, e.g., Panofsky and Phillips, *op. cit.*, p. 277], still repays careful examination. It is an outstanding example of how important consequences can flow from relatively simple theoretical ideas and how a brilliant feat of experimental skill can be associated with a very simple experimental idea. In fact, as the reader will recall, these ideas can be outlined in a few words (see Fig. 2-2).‡ On the premise of the existence of a stationary ether with respect to which the earth moves with the velocity **v**, and assuming that one of the two perpendicular arms of the interferometer (each of effective length L) lies in the direction of **v**, an elementary calculation gives the value $2L(\gamma^2 - \gamma) \approx Lv^2/c^2$ for the difference in the paths of the two beams between their splitting and their recombination—the velocity of light with respect to the ether being taken, of course, as the same in all directions; so that for monochromatic light of wavelength λ, when the interferometer is rotated through a right angle, the interference pattern should shift by $2Lv^2/\lambda c^2$ fringes.

Can you see why Maxwell in his letter to Michelson (1880) suggesting the idea of the experiment, thought the expected effect to be too small for detection? If the experiment were to be repeated today, would present laboratory techniques render the task easier than it was in Michelson's

‡ A very good description of the Michelson-Morley experiment is to be found, e.g., in A. Sommerfeld, "Optics," sec. 14, Academic Press, Inc., New York, 1954 (translated by O. Laporte and P. A. Moldauer).

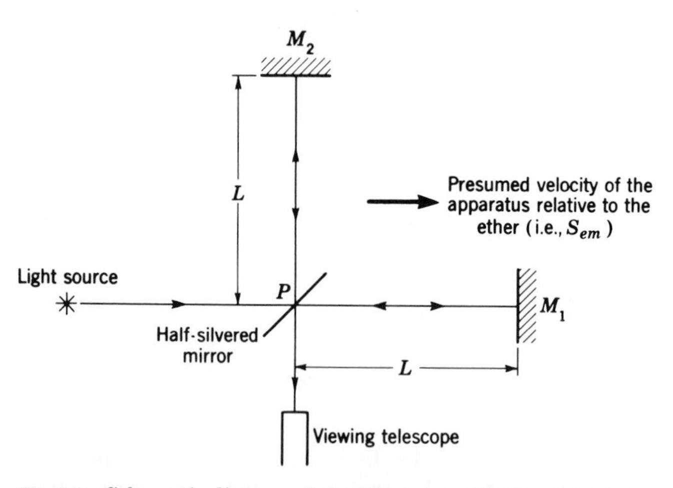

Fig. 2-2 Schematic diagram of the Michelson-Morley experiment. On pre-relativity kinematic considerations, the times of to and fro passage of light between P and M_1 and P and M_2 are respectively $L[(c - v)^{-1} + (c + v)^{-1}] - 2Lc/(c^2 - v^2) = 2L\gamma^2/c$, and $2L\gamma/c$ [the latter following from the equation $(vt)^2 + L^2 = c^2t^2$ for the time t of single passage between P and M_2].

time? (See in this connection recent references given in the footnote on page 40.) Does our expanded astronomical knowledge regarding the velocity of the solar system within our galaxy and of the relative velocities of galactic systems have any relevance to the interpretation of this experiment?

The Michelson-Morley experiment has been repeated with extraterrestrial light sources [R. Tomaschek, *Ann. Physik* **73:** 105 (1924); D. C. Miller, *Proc. Nat. Acad. Sci.* **11:** 311 (1925)], again with negative results. What conclusion can be drawn from these results regarding Ritz's emission theory?‡

2-4 The partial anticipation by W. Voigt (*Göttingen Nachr.*, 1887, pp. 41-51) of the Lorentz transformations is, in addition to its early date and different physical starting point (light treated as an oscillational process in an elastic medium), also noteworthy because the mathematical method is similar to that later employed by Einstein. It involves the requirement of invariance of the wave equation

$$\left(\frac{1}{c^2}\frac{\partial^2}{\partial t^2} - \nabla^2\right)\Psi = 0 \tag{i}$$

(*a*) With this requirement, obtain Voigt's transformations

$$\begin{gathered} x_i' = \lambda x_i + (1 - \lambda)\alpha_i\alpha_j x_j - v\alpha_i t, \qquad t' = t - \frac{v}{c^2}\alpha_i x_i \\ \alpha_i\alpha_i = 1,\ \lambda \equiv \frac{1}{\gamma} = \left(1 - \frac{v^2}{c^2}\right)^{1/2} \end{gathered} \tag{ii}$$

where v has its usual meaning. Start with the assumption, as Voigt did, that the transformations are linear, with $\partial t'/\partial t = 1$; i.e., that they have the form

$$x_i' = a_{ij}x_j - p_i t, \qquad t' = t - q_i x_i \tag{iii}$$

and assuming also that $a_{ij} = a_{ji}$, find (ii) with $\alpha_i = v_i/v$. {The calculation can be carried out conveniently in matrix notation, with the first set of Eqs. (iii), for instance, expressed as $x' = Ax - pt$ [see Eq. (1-12)]. The covariance of Eq. (i) is found to imply the matrix relation (as, by assumption, $\tilde{A} = A$)

$$A^2 = \frac{1}{c^2}p\tilde{p} + \lambda^2 I \tag{iv}$$

‡ According to this theory the velocity of light must be taken relative to the emitting source, and newtonian kinematics (and in particular, the newtonian law of composition of velocities) is assumed to have general validity. For references to this theory of Ritz, see footnote on page 40.

One also finds that $p = v$, where v now stands for the one-column matrix representing $\mathbf{v}$, and that

$$Av = v \tag{v}$$

i.e., that v is an eigenvector of A with eigenvalue 1.} In what respect does Voigt's transformation resemble the first-order theory of Lorentz? (*b*) Consider the linear transformations that differ from Eqs. (iii) only by the coefficient of t in the last equation not being restricted to unity; i.e., with the last equation in (iii) replaced by $t' = \sigma t - \tilde{q}x$. On the assumption that the matrix A is symmetric, show that the differential operator in Eq. (i) is form invariant under these transformations, provided

$$\begin{gathered} a_{ij} = \delta_{ij} + \frac{1}{v^2}(\gamma - 1)v_i v_j \\ p_i = \gamma v_i, \qquad \sigma = \gamma, \qquad q_i = \frac{1}{c^2}\gamma v_i \end{gathered} \tag{vi}$$

(disregarding some arbitrariness in signs). [The deduction can proceed quite similarly to that for the result in (*a*). The eigenvalues of A associated with v are now $\pm\gamma$, with the $+$ sign corresponding to Eq. (vi). An alternative method—based on another form invariant—of deriving the transformation equations defined by Eq. (vi) (which will be later found to constitute a subset of the general Lorentz transformations) is presented at the beginning of Sec. 3-4.]

2-5 Deduce the transformation Eqs. (2-8) and (2-9) along the lines outlined in the accompanying text. In finding the transformations under Eqs. (2-6) of an element of volume of an 'electron' moving with velocity $\mathbf{u}$ with respect to the frame S, Poincaré considers first what he calls "a sphere carried along with the electron," whose equation in S is

$$(\mathbf{x} - \mathbf{u}t)^2 = r^2 \tag{i}$$

and by substituting the S' coordinates according to Eqs. (2-6) and then taking $t' = 0$, he finds for the ratio of the volume of the sphere referred to S' and S respectively, the expression

$$\frac{V'}{V} = \frac{1}{\gamma}\left(1 - \frac{\beta u_x}{c}\right)^{-1} \tag{ii}$$

Verify this result, and examine the operational significance of this derivation. Deduce result (ii) by considering directly the measure of volume in S and in S'. [See Sec. 3-1 and Eq. (i), Prob. 3-3.]

3

Einstein's Special Theory of Relativity and Its Basic Kinematic Results

What came to be known as the special theory of relativity had its initial formulation in Albert Einstein's celebrated paper, *Zur Elektrodynamik bewegter Körper.*‡ As is indicated by its title, this paper is concerned with the questions surveyed in the last chapter. Einstein's resolution of the ether-experiment difficulties is also based on the group of Lorentz transformations. It differs from the earlier work of Lorentz in two respects: the Lorentz transformations are not guessed at, but are derived from two basic postulates; and, what is more significant, a fundamentally new interpretation is given to the physical content of these transformation equations. The essential ideas of this approach are outlined in Sec. 3-1.

Einstein's postulate of the constancy of light velocity is the simplest result that follows from Maxwell's electromagnetic theory and, in conjunction with the postulate of relativity proper, leads to the Lorentz group. This postulate, moreover, is intimately connected with Einstein's prescription for clock synchronization (see Prob. 3-1), a prescription that recommends itself strongly both on logical and pragmatic grounds. In a certain

‡ A. Einstein, *Ann. Physik,* **17**: 891 (1905); paper 3 in [2] is an English translation.

sense, however, it is possible to dispense with the constancy-of-light principle as a separate postulate in the derivation of the Lorentz group: one needs only to draw directly upon the law of inertia, a law that is, of course, in any case significantly involved in any formulation of this group. This approach is developed in Sec. 3-2.

Although in most cases it is possible to limit oneself to the *special* Lorentz transformations, there are applications, such as the Thomas precession (treated in Sec. 3-5) for which this is not possible. The structure of the *general* Lorentz matrices is moreover of independent theoretical interest. This topic is discussed in Sec. 3-4, which includes also a few introductory ideas in the geometry of space-time of STR.‡ It is of some interest to deduce the general Lorentz group directly by the method of Sec. 3-2. This is done in Appendix 3B with the help of the infinitesimal elements of this group. The elementary notions of infinitesimal transformations, which will also be useful to us later in other connections, are discussed in Appendix 3A.

Of the many interesting kinematic applications of STR a few are given in Secs. 3-3 and 3-5, and in the Problems.

3-1 EINSTEIN'S DERIVATION OF THE LORENTZ TRANSFORMATION EQUATIONS; RELATIVITY OF TIME AND SPACE

Einstein's paper of 1905 contained a completely new approach to the problem discussed in Sec. 2-2. Setting entirely aside any considerations of an ether or an associated S_{em}, while at the same time aiming at the maximum possible adherence to the principles of newtonian mechanics, Einstein proposed a drastic modification in the newtonian scheme at just that point where it was dictated neither by experience nor by inner logical consistency, but solely by long-established and deeply ingrained prejudice. In the formulation of the newtonian principles as presented in Chap. 1, this point is reflected in postulate I. In terms of that formulation, Einstein's modification can be expressed as a simple negation of I:

I* *In every inertial system there is a finite upper bound to signal velocities.*

Postulate I*, as will be shown presently, when combined with the other assumptions of the theory, is in fact fully equivalent to Einstein's original formulation as embodied in his celebrated principle of the constancy of light velocity (the second of the two he enunciated):

B *The speed of light in vacuo referred to an inertial system is independent of the velocity of its source.*

Einstein's other basic principle gives explicit expression to the idea of galilei-newtonian relativity, boldly generalized so as to refer to *all* physical

‡ We shall henceforth employ this abbreviation for "the special theory of relativity."

phenomena.‡ The gist of this principle can be stated as follows:

A *All inertial space-time reference systems are completely equivalent for the purpose of the formulation of physical laws.*

In other words, the mathematical expression of such laws has a form that is independent of the particular choice of reference system, provided only that it is inertial.

The definition of the family of inertial systems, which is thus of central importance in Einstein's theory no less than in the newtonian theory, is taken over from the latter theory. This will be here always understood in the sense of its modern formulation, for instance, along the lines sketched out in Chap. 1. Expressed in terms of locally measured space and time intervals essentially as understood in newtonian mechanics, and as indicated in Chap. 1, this definition can be incorporated in a general statement of Newton's first law, such as II of Chap. 1, which we here restate more succinctly as follows:

II* *There exist reference systems $S\{x,t\}$, the inertial systems, relative to which the equation of motion of free particles are of the form*

$$\frac{d^2\mathbf{x}}{dt^2} = 0 \tag{3-1}$$

The meaning of "free," i.e., free from interaction, cannot be defined simply, nor with absolute strictness, as pointed out in Secs. 1-4 and 1-5. A more searching analysis of this question is provided by Einstein's general theory.

The derivation of the kinematic transformation equations of Lorentz, Eq. (2-6), on the basis of postulates A and B, presents little difficulty and is generally known. It will suffice here to outline briefly the principal steps in the deduction. (See also Prob. 2-4.) First, in accordance with these postulates, the velocity of light *in vacuo* referred to any inertial system has the same magnitude c independently of the direction of propagation. In familiar notation this can be expressed by the form invariance of the equation

$$c^2\,\Delta t^2 - \Delta\mathbf{x}\cdot\Delta\mathbf{x} = 0 \tag{3-2}$$

under all Lorentz transformations. It is necessary next to establish the linearity of the transformation equations. This can be done with the aid of postulate II* (see Sec. 3-2). However, the same conclusion can also be drawn directly from the form invariance of Eq. (3-2), and this has been indeed the usual procedure. Combining our two results, and invoking

‡ Gravitational phenomena, however, must be excluded, and this is always tacitly assumed in this book (with the exception of Appendix 7B, where special relativistic treatments of gravitation are discussed).

It should be noted also that in Poincaré's paper quoted in Sec. 2-2 there is already contained the conjecture of a principle such as postulate A.

the homogeneity and isotropy of physical space, it is easily proved that the transformation equations connecting the coordinates (x) and (x') of two inertial frames S and S' (having parallel coordinate axes and relative motion of speed v along the x axis) have the following form:

$$\begin{aligned} ct' &= \lambda(v)\gamma(ct - \beta x) \\ x' &= \lambda(v)\gamma(x - \beta ct) \\ y' &= \lambda(v)y \\ z' &= \lambda(v)z \end{aligned} \tag{3-3}$$

using the notation employed in Eqs. (2-6). Finally, by taking account of the *group* properties of our set of transformations that are implied by the postulate of relativity, A, it follows at once that $\lambda(v) = 1$, and Eqs. (3-3) reduce to Eqs. (2-6). (See Prob. 3-2.)

The immediate end result of Einstein's basic principles, the Lorentz group, is thus completely identical mathematically with the starting point of the theory of Lorentz. The far-reaching difference lies in the physical interpretation of the formulas. By isolating postulate B our attention is focused sharply on significant structure in the complex of space and time measurements additional to that contained in the classical theory, which is revealed by, or at least is fully consistent with, the aggregate of optical and electrodynamic experiments designed to detect the hypothetical S_{em}.‡

‡ In addition to the experiments that preceded the work of Lorentz and of Einstein, referred to in Chap. 2, many more were performed subsequently, some of them being merely improved or modified versions of the older experiments, such as, for instance, the Fizeau-type experiments of Zeeman (1914–1927); while others embodied new ideas. (See the relevant references given in Chap. 2.) Of the latter, especially interesting are the experiments of Ives and Stilwell (1938, 1941) on the so-called transverse Doppler effect (discussed in Sec. 3-3) and of Kennedy and Thorndike (1932), which is a modification of the Michelson-Morley experiment consisting in taking the arms of the interferometer as unequal in length as possible. For a discussion of the significance of these experiments, see H. P. Robertson, *Rev. Mod. Phys.*, **21**: 378 (1949). Very interesting are also recent pertinent measurements utilizing masers [see, e.g., T. S. Jaseja, A. Javan, J. Murray, and C. H. Townes, *Phys. Rev.*, **133**: A1221 (1964)], or the Mössbauer effect in Fe^{57} [see, e.g., H. Frauenfelder, "The Mössbauer Effect," W. A. Benjamin, Inc., New York, 1962; G. K. Wertheim, "Mössbauer Effect," Academic Press, Inc., New York, 1964; D. C. Champeney, G. R. Isaak, and A. M. Khan, *Phys. Letters (Netherlands)*, **7**: 241 (1963); K. C. Turner and H. A. Hill, *Phys. Rev.*, **134**: B252 (1964)]. But it is scarcely necessary to discuss here these and related experiments, great as their interest certainly is, when one considers that the foundations of STR are at present quite firmly established by the experimental agreement of its many kinematic and dynamic implications in high-energy physics. For this reason, too, one can dispense with a discussion of the so-called "emission theories" of light, which aimed to eliminate postulate B while retaining postulate A, and of which the ablest proponent was W. Ritz; the more so, as these theories are in disagreement with a number of well-established experiments. The Ritz theory is discussed, e.g., in [7], sec. 3, and in W. K. H. Panofsky and M. Phillips, "Classical Electricity and Magnetism," 2d ed., sec. 15-5 Addison-Wesley Publishing Company, Inc., Cambridge, Mass., 1962.

This new element of space-time structure is reflected in the first place in the form invariance of the equation of light propagation (3-2), which is manifestly incompatible with the older kinematics. It finds its complete expression in the Lorentz transformations when these are looked upon, following Einstein, as giving the connection between the coordinates of a space-time point as *measured* in two inertial reference frames S and S' in terms of *identical* rods and clocks.

The most startling consequence of this view, as far as our deeply rooted kinematic elements of intuition are concerned, is of course the banishment of objective physical significance from intervals of length and of time taken separately. In accordance with the central role played by the family of inertial systems, the criterion of "objective" or "absolute" physical significance in the present context is of course *invariance* under the group of transformations connecting these systems. In the new theory this is the Lorentz group and, considering the special transformations (2-6), one deduces at once the familiar expression

$$\begin{aligned} \Delta x &= \frac{1}{\gamma}\,\Delta x' \\ \Delta y &= \Delta y' \qquad (\Delta t = 0) \\ \Delta z &= \Delta z' \end{aligned} \tag{3-4}$$

where $\Delta\mathbf{x}$ is the spatial interval as measured in S between two space-time points associated with two points fixed in S'. The condition, $\Delta t = 0$, is clearly necessary for the required measurement. Similarly one finds that

$$\Delta t = \gamma\,\Delta t' \qquad (\Delta\mathbf{x}' = 0) \tag{3-5}$$

where now one requires $\Delta\mathbf{x}'$ to be zero, inasmuch as a clock involves some regular cyclic process that is *localized*. For a graphic representation of these relations, due to Minkowski, see Fig. 3-1.

The results (3-4), representing the *FitzGerald contraction*, and (3-5), giving the *time dilatation* of a moving clock, are not in any sense fictitious, but from the present point of view they have as much physical content as, say, the notions of length and of duration themselves when employed in a *fixed* inertial system.

In this connection it must be clearly understood that a physical quantity—such as duration, for example, which does not have objective significance as judged by Lorentz invariance—can have nevertheless, strict physical significance *relative* to a given inertial system, where its measurement is unambiguously defined. It is of course essentially this fact that is described by the term "relativity." Most physical quantities we measure in the laboratory are in fact *relative* to the inertial frame associated with the laboratory; whereas, in general, quantities which are invariant under the Lorentz group (in a sense that will be made more precise in the following

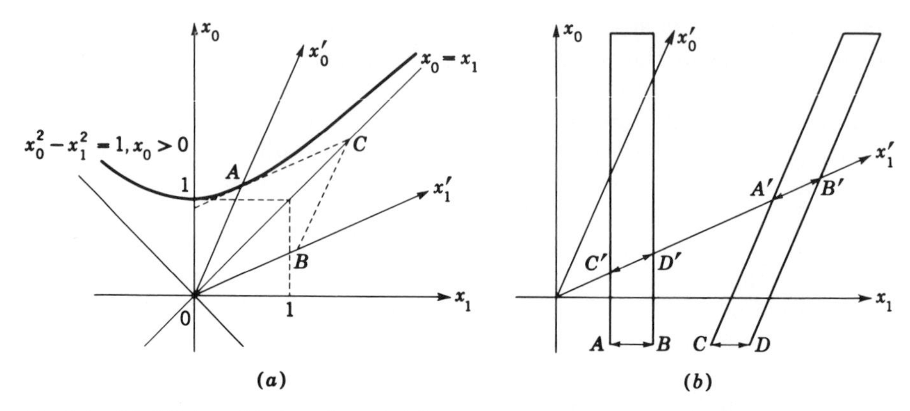

Fig. 3-1 (*a*) Minkowski plot of special Lorentz transformations, with indication of the construction of the unit measures OA and OB along the axes of the primed coordinate system. AC is tangent to the unit hyperbola at A, and the quadrilateral $OACB$ is a parallelogram. (*b*) A representation of relativistic contraction of lengths. $ABC'D'$ and $CDA'B'$ represent the world diagrams (with suppression of two spatial dimensions) of two identical bodies at rest in the two respective coordinate frames; $\overline{AB} = \overline{A'B'}$ and $\overline{CD}/\overline{AB} = \overline{C'D'}/\overline{A'B'} = 1/\gamma_v$, where v is the relative velocity of the two frames, as can be proved from the geometry of diagram (*a*). See Minkowski's paper in [2], and Sommerfeld's note (2), p. 93. [These results follow also directly upon noting that if α is the slope of OB, then that of OA is $1/\alpha$, and $\alpha = v/c$, whence $x_0' = K(x_0 - \alpha x_1)$, $x_1' = K(\alpha x_0 - x_1)$, $K^2(1 - \alpha^2) = 1$, $K = \gamma_v$.]

chapters) can be taken as *absolute*. In particular, the *space-time* manifold itself can be thought of as partaking of the absoluteness belonging to physical space in Newton's theory. This point of view was first clearly expressed by H. Minkowski. (See Sec. 3-4.)

Two further observations concerning the relations (3-4) and (3-5) should be made at this point. In the first place, it is clear that in order that the statements expressed by these equations have strict physical content, it is necessary that there be given, at least in principle, a complete and consistent prescription for the synchronization of clocks everywhere in S and in S'. As noted earlier, the utilization of the method of light signaling recommends itself on purely conceptual as well as on theoretically practical considerations.‡ Secondly, on the purely practical side, it is to be noted that since

$$\gamma - 1 = \tfrac{1}{2}\beta^2 + O(\beta^4)$$

it follows that in the case of relative velocities v such that $(v/c)^2$ is negligibly

‡ This method is outlined in Einstein's first paper on STR. The reader who wishes to study these questions more fully may wish to consult among others, M. Schlick, "Space and Time in Contemporary Physics," Oxford University Press, London, 1920, and H. Reichenbach, "The Philosophy of Space and Time," Dover Publications, Inc., New York, 1957.

small, newtonian metric relations are practically valid. It is indeed owing to the fact that normally the relative velocities of all but atomic objects belong to this category that it takes such an effort of the imagination to perceive the complete naturalness of the kinematic implications of Einstein's conceptual analysis of the Lorentz group.

3-2 AN ALTERNATIVE DERIVATION OF THE LORENTZ TRANSFORMATIONS; COMPOSITION OF VELOCITIES

Although, as we have seen, there are cogent reasons for deriving the Lorentz transformations on the basis of the property of light propagation as given in Einstein's postulate B, the employment of such properties is not essential for this derivation. This is related to the fact that the special theory of relativity, notwithstanding its intimate historical connection with the theory of electromagnetism, has in fact much wider scope transcending this connection. The postulate I*, which was introduced as a logical experiment-dictated extension of the classical theory, accords with the greater generality thus implied in the foundations of relativistic kinematics. The maximum signal velocity asserted in that postulate has no specific reference to light propagation. Indeed, as we know at present, this maximum velocity characterizes the free-space motion not only of *photons* but also of other "elementary particles," such as neutrinos, whose rest mass is zero.

In order to see in a general way that in the establishment of the Lorentz transformations it is indeed possible to replace postulate B by postulate I* (the validity of postulate A being of course assumed) we need only observe that under the contrary assumption, it would follow that we could distinguish between inertial systems according to the differing values of the maximum signal velocities associated with them, contrary to the implications of postulate A. Moreover, the common maximum signal velocity c must be *finite*, since otherwise we would come back to the classical case.

It is not difficult to supply a direct proof of the conclusion just outlined; namely, that on the assumption of postulate A alone, but taken in its widest possible sense—of permitting no general physical process that can serve to distinguish in any way between two inertial systems—it can be concluded that all inertial systems have the same maximum signal-velocity magnitude, whose finiteness characterizes the new kinematics. A closely related theorem was in fact proved for the first time by Frank and Rothe.‡ They deduced the Lorentz transformation equations starting with the following assumptions:

1 The family of coordinate transformations forms a linear homogeneous group.

‡ P. Frank and H. Rothe, *Ann. Physik,* **34**: 825 (1911). Brief discussion and further references will be found in [7], sec. 4.

2 The contraction of lengths (that is, of lengths at rest in one inertial system and observed in another system that is moving uniformly relative to the first) is a function only of the magnitude of the relative velocity of the two systems.

Many variants have since been published, including, no doubt, a few rediscoveries, of which, in fact, the following is one.

It is not difficult to convince oneself that for our purpose it suffices to consider the case of one spatial dimension. We must remember that except for postulate I, the structure of classical kinematics is being retained. In particular, it is possible to appeal to the properties of isotropy and homogeneity of the space-time continuum, which are manifested by the *group of rigid displacements* forming a *subgroup* of our group of coordinate transformations in space-time. One can therefore choose the orientation of the spatial axes of the two systems so that the relative motion is along the common x direction, while the other axes are respectively parallel to each other. (See relevant discussion in Sec. 3-4.) By considerations of symmetry it is then readily ascertained that, except for a possible shift in origin, the coordinates y and z remain unchanged.‡

The Frank-Rothe assumption (1) can be established along the lines indicated in Sec. 3-1. By postulate A one can conclude that the transformations must form a group; the *linearity* of the transformation equations can be deduced from the requirement, following from postulate II*, that these equations should transform straight lines of space-time into such lines (see Prob. 3-6); and the homogeneity of the equations follows by a proper choice of the space-time origins in our systems S and S'.

Thus, we can start with the equations

$$x' = Ax + Bt, \qquad t' = Cx + Dt \tag{3-6}$$

The inverse transformation is then given by the equations

$$x = \frac{1}{\Delta}(Dx' - Bt') \qquad \Delta = \begin{vmatrix} A & B \\ C & D \end{vmatrix} \qquad t = \frac{1}{\Delta}(-Cx' + At') \tag{3-7}$$

From the requirement, which can be seen to be dictated by postulate A, that the velocity of S relative to S' as measured in S' should be the negative of

‡ See the corresponding discussion in Einstein's first paper in [2], pp. 46–48. Similar reasoning was also used by Poincaré, who employed the group notions directly.

the velocity of S' relative to S as measured in S, it follows that

$$\left.\frac{dx}{dt}\right|_{x'=0} = v = -\frac{B}{A}, \qquad \left.\frac{dx'}{dt'}\right|_{x=0} = -v = \frac{B}{D} \tag{3-8}$$

Hence

$$A = D \tag{3-9}$$

Again, by postulate A, it can be concluded that the contraction of lengths in S' as found in S must be the same as the corresponding contraction in S as measured in S', with a similar result holding for dilatation of time intervals:

$$\begin{aligned} \left.\frac{dx'}{dx}\right|_{dt=0} &= A = \left.\frac{dx}{dx'}\right|_{dt'=0} = \frac{D}{\Delta} \\ \left.\frac{dt'}{dt}\right|_{dx'=0} &= \frac{\Delta}{A} = \left.\frac{dt}{dt'}\right|_{dx=0} = \frac{1}{D} \end{aligned} \tag{3-10}$$

From either one of these relations and Eq. (3-9) it then follows that

$$\Delta = 1 \tag{3-11}$$

We now apply the group rule (1) of Appendix 1A. Suppose that the system S'' moves with velocity v_1 in the positive x direction relative to S' as measured in S', and that V is the velocity of S'' relative to S as measured in S. By virtue of the results (3-8) and (3-9), the group property can be written as follows in terms of the matrices of the three transformations $S \to S'$, $S' \to S''$ and $S \to S''$:

$$A(v_1)\begin{bmatrix} 1 & -v_1 \\ \Gamma(v_1) & 1 \end{bmatrix} A(v)\begin{bmatrix} 1 & -v \\ \Gamma(v) & 1 \end{bmatrix} = A(V)\begin{bmatrix} 1 & -V \\ \Gamma(V) & 1 \end{bmatrix}$$

$$\Gamma(v) \equiv \frac{C(v)}{A(v)} \tag{3-12}$$

Multiplying out the first two matrices, we find

$$A(v_1)A(v)(1 - v_1\Gamma(v)) = A(v_1)A(v)(1 - v\Gamma(v_1)) = A(V) \tag{3-13a}$$

$$A(v_1)A(v)(v + v_1) = A(V)V \tag{3-13b}$$

From Eq. (3-13a) it follows that

$$\Gamma(v) = \alpha v, \qquad \alpha \text{ independent of } v \tag{3-14}$$

It is seen at once that the value zero of α leads to classical kinematics. To see the significance of this constant when $\alpha \neq 0$, let us determine V as a function of v and v_1. This is accomplished at once by dividing Eqs. (3-13), obtaining

$$V = \frac{v + v_1}{1 - \alpha v v_1} \tag{3-15}$$

It is seen that α has the dimensions of the reciprocal square of a velocity. Calling the magnitude of this velocity c, and observing that a positive α is incompatible with the physical significance of the quantities v, v_1, and V, and with postulate A,‡ it follows that

$$\alpha = -c^{-2} \tag{3-16}$$

Combining Eqs. (3-6) to (3-9), (3-11), (3-12), (3-14), and (3-16), one finds $A^2(1 - v^2/c^2) = 1$, i.e., $A^2 = \gamma^2$; by our tacit assumption that *inversions* of the space and time axes are excluded, it then follows that $A = \gamma \equiv |\gamma|$, and we obtain the Lorentz transformation equations (2-6). At the same time Eqs. (3-15) and (3-16) yield the relativistic law of *composition of velocities* for unidirectional motion [which is, of course, also immediately derivable directly from Eqs. (2-6)]. When $\alpha = 0$, one obtains the corresponding newtonian results, as one should.

3-3 APPLICATIONS OF RELATIVISTIC KINEMATICS; EXPERIMENTAL CHECKS OF TIME DILATATION

Before the advent of high-energy physics, the principal domain of application of relativistic kinematics was in optics. It provided a remarkably simple explanation of Fresnel's formula relating to Fizeau's experiment and involving his drag coefficient;§ more importantly, it led to a significant extension of the formulas for the Doppler effect and for the aberration of light.

The Fresnel first-order formula for Fizeau's experiment can be obtained with the aid of the law of composition of velocities, Eq. (3-15). It suffices to identify S' with a reference frame attached to the flowing liquid, which has the velocity v relative to the 'stationary' system S; while the place of S'' is now taken by a reference frame riding with the light ray whose velocity relative to the flowing medium, and hence relative to S', is $v_1 = c/n$, n being the index of refraction of this medium. One then finds at once the following expression for the velocity V of the light ray relative to S:

$$V = \frac{v + v_1}{1 + vv_1/c^2} = \frac{v + c/n}{1 + v/nc} = \left(\frac{c}{n} + v\right)\left(1 - \frac{v}{nc}\right) + \cdots$$
$$= \frac{c}{n} + v\left(1 - \frac{1}{n^2}\right) + \cdots$$

It is seen that the first two terms of the expansion reproduce Fresnel's formula.

‡ If we had $\alpha = 1/c^2$, all speeds would have to be less than c, as otherwise we could have v and v_1 positive and yet V negative. But then, since Eq. (3-15) can also be looked upon as the transformation equation connecting the velocities V and v_1 of the same motion referred to the systems S and S' respectively, there would ensue a dissymmetry with respect to the actual speed limitations in S and S'.

§ See discussion on page 25.

In order to obtain the relativistic formula for the *Doppler effect,* one can proceed as follows. Suppose that a source of monochromatic radiation is located at the origin O' of an inertial frame S' that is moving with velocity $\mathbf{v}$ relative to the inertial frame S, and that ν is the frequency of the radiation as measured in S, say at the origin O of S. The Doppler formula gives the connection between ν and the frequency ν' of the radiation as measured in S'. To obtain this formula, it is helpful to note that the light waves may be considered as playing here a double role: they act as signals transmitting a message from O' to O, and they furnish a 'clock' through their periodicity. For our present purpose, we may separate the last function and think of an arbitrary ideal clock ticking off the period $\tau' = 1/\nu'$ at O' in S'. If we let τ represent the time interval as measured in S between the times of arrival at O of light signals sent out from O' at the limits of the time interval τ', then obviously

$$\tau = \frac{1}{\nu} \tag{3-17}$$

In order to find how τ' is related to τ, denote by $T(t)$ the time of arrival at O of a light signal sent out from O' at the time t, and by $R(t)$ the distance between O and O' at the time t, *all quantities as measured in* S. Then, $T(t) = t + R(t)/c$, and $\delta T = (1 + dR/c\,dt)\,\delta t$, i.e.,

$$\delta T = (1 - \boldsymbol{\beta} \cdot \mathbf{n})\,\delta t \qquad \begin{aligned} \mathbf{n} &\equiv \mathbf{n}(t) \equiv \frac{\mathbf{R}(t)}{R(t)} \\ \boldsymbol{\beta} &\equiv \frac{\mathbf{v}}{c} \end{aligned} \tag{3-18}$$

the vector $\mathbf{R}$ pointing from O' to O (see Fig. 3-2). By our construction it is clear that when $\delta t = \gamma\tau'$ [the measure of the interval τ' in S, according to Eq. (3-5)], then $\delta T = \tau$, and Eqs. (3-17) and (3-18) thus yield the desired

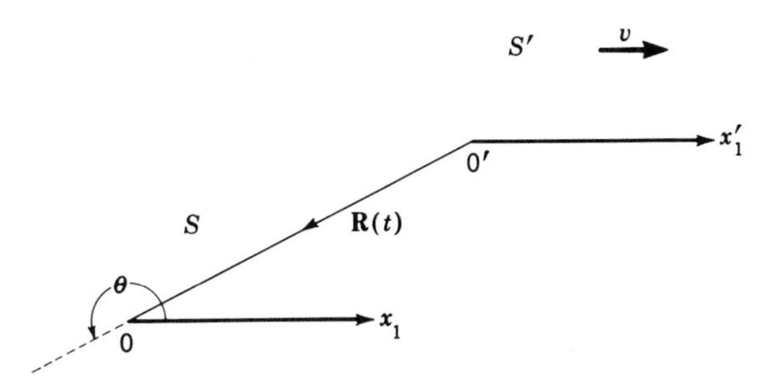

Fig. 3-2 The spatial configuration in S at time t of the light ray $O'O$, in the derivation of the Doppler-effect formula (3-19).

result:

$$\nu = \frac{\nu'}{\gamma(1 - \boldsymbol{\beta} \cdot \mathbf{n})} \tag{3-19}$$

Our method of deriving this relativistic formula makes it clear that it is a direct extension of the classical formula of the Doppler effect (on the assumption that the observer is stationary in S_{em}) obtained by applying the relativistic change of time scale and taking account of the *relative* meaning of **n**.

It is instructive to note that the relativistic optical-aberration formula can be deduced from Eq. (3-19). For this purpose we need only retrace the argument which led to Eq. (3-19)—but now carried out entirely *from the point of view of S′* instead of S—and obtain (with obvious notation, and since $\mathbf{v}' = -\mathbf{v}$)‡

$$\nu' = \frac{\nu}{\gamma(1 + \boldsymbol{\beta} \cdot \mathbf{n}')} \tag{3-20}$$

This leads by Eq. (3-19) to the relation

$$(1 - \boldsymbol{\beta} \cdot \mathbf{n})(1 + \boldsymbol{\beta} \cdot \mathbf{n}') = 1 - \beta^2$$

from which, with $\boldsymbol{\beta} \cdot \mathbf{n} = \beta \cos \theta$ and $\boldsymbol{\beta} \cdot \mathbf{n}' = \beta \cos \theta'$, it follows that

$$\cos \theta = \frac{\cos \theta' + \beta}{\beta \cos \theta' + 1} \tag{3-21}$$

Since θ and θ' are the respective inclination angles of the light ray (in its direction of propagation) in S and S', it is seen that Eq. (3-21) represents indeed the relativistic extension of the classical astronomical aberration formula. (See Fig. 3-3.)

‡ Taking the spatial coordinate axes in S' 'parallel' to the corresponding axes in S. See relevant discussion in Sec. 3-4.

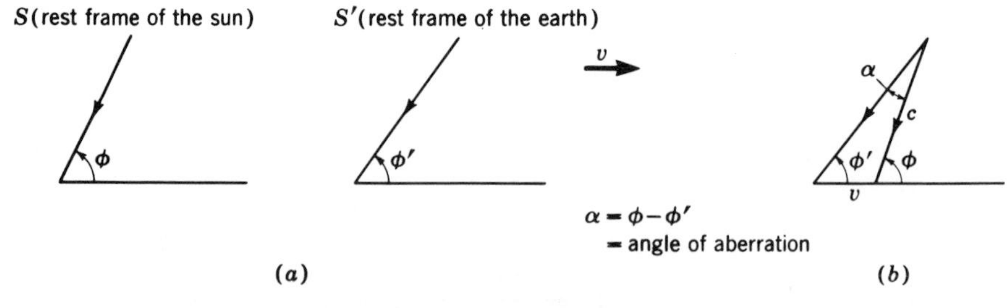

Fig. 3-3 Stellar aberration according to (*a*) STR, and (*b*) newtonian physics. Drawings are schematic. In (*a*), $\phi = \theta - \pi$ (θ as in Fig. 3-1), and hence by (3-21) [or also by (3-22) with $u = u' = c$], $\cot \phi' = \gamma(\cos \phi + \beta)/\sin \phi$. In (*b*), using the diagram, we find $\cot \phi' = (\cos \phi + \beta)/\sin \phi$, and hence to first order in the "aberration constant" β, $\alpha \approx \tan \alpha = \ldots = \beta \sin \phi/(1 + \beta \cos \phi) \approx \beta \sin \phi$.

This result can be deduced more directly from the transformation equations for velocity, which follow straightway from Eqs. (2-6), namely (writing only the first two components)

$$u_x' = \frac{u_x - v}{1 - vu_x/c^2}, \qquad u_y' = \frac{u_y}{\gamma(1 - vu_x/c^2)} \tag{3-22}$$

where $u_x = dx/dt$, etc. The aberration formula is obtained immediately by applying these equations to the velocity vector of a *photon* moving from O' to O.

Both of the above results can also be derived very simply on the basis of the Lorentz form invariance of the phase function

$$2\pi\nu\left(t - \frac{1}{c}\mathbf{n}\cdot\mathbf{x}\right) \tag{3-23}$$

of a plane wave. This was indeed the method initially used by Einstein. However, his proof of the invariance of Eq. (3-23) involves the transformation equations (2-7) of the electromagnetic field vectors.‡

The relativistic correction to the classical aberration formula is inappreciable in astronomical applications, for which β^2 is of the order of 10^{-8}. On the other hand, in the case of the Doppler effect the relativistic correction is just within the range of a laboratory check.

A striking instance of Eq. (3-19) arises for strictly transverse viewing, when $\mathbf{v}\cdot\mathbf{n} = 0$, so that there is no frequency change classically, whereas the relativistic "transverse Doppler effect" is seen to involve the relative frequency shift of magnitude $\beta^2/2$ to second order. This result is, however, at present largely academic. In order not to be masked by the accompanying *first-order* radial effect, a meaningful measurement of this shift would require a precision in the measurement of direction, which by Eq. (3-19) is seen to correspond to the requirement $|\Delta\theta| \ll \beta$, a requirement difficult of practical realization.§ On the other hand, if one considers the mean value of the frequencies ν corresponding to lines of sight that are parallel and antiparallel to $\mathbf{v}$, call it $\bar{\nu}$, one finds

$$\frac{\bar{\nu} - \nu'}{\nu'} = \gamma - 1 \approx \tfrac{1}{2}\beta^2 \tag{3-24}$$

whereas on the classical theory, one finds for this quantity the value $\beta^2/(1 - \beta^2) \approx \beta^2$. With sufficiently refined measuring techniques it is possible

‡ See [2], paper 3, pp. 55–56. For a proof of the invariance of Eq. (3-23) on purely kinematic considerations relating to wave motion, see [6], secs. 3 and 23. The Doppler-effect and aberration-of-light formulas are also considered in Probs. 3-8 and 4-17.

§ However, see W. Künding, *Phys. Rev.*, **129**: 2371 (1963), and the reference given there to earlier measurements utilizing the shift of the Mössbauer absorption line of Fe^{57} when the absorber is set rotating about a fixed Co^{57} source. See Prob. 3-10.

to discriminate between these two values. This was accomplished by Ives and Stilwell with hydrogen canal rays, Eq. (3-24) being verified for the Hβ line and for a range of accelerating voltages up to 42,280 volts.‡

The Ives-Stilwell experiment has particular interest as representing the first essentially direct verification of the time-dilatation formula (3-5). Another check of this formula is provided by the lifetimes of fast-moving mesons. It was first obtained inferentially in connection with high-energy cosmic-ray muons.§ It had been found, at first indirectly and eventually by delayed-coincidence counter measurements, that these particles decay with a lifetime of about 2 μsec.¶ At the same time, evidence was accumulating that these particles observed at sea level must be coming from the outer layers of the atomsphere. This ruled out decidedly a muon lifetime independent of velocity (which would allow it a maximum travel distance of only some 600 m), but was fully consistent with the lengthening of the lifetime in accordance with the relativistic time dilatation.‡‡

This confrontation of relativistic theory and cosmic-ray phenomena was thus not intended as a check of the time dilatation formula (3-5), but on the contrary, this formula (in conjunction with the relativistic kinetic-energy relation) served to introduce consistency in the explanation of those phenomena. A direct check of Eq. (3-5) as applied to decay times was first obtained in measurements of the lifetime of cyclotron-produced charged pions.§§ In this case, too, the experiment was not designed for the purpose of checking Eq. (3-5), but that relation, rather, was utilized in the method of determining the *proper* lifetime¶¶ from the measurements. However, since this lifetime had been also measured directly by means of fast coincidence circuits,‡‡‡ the result constitutes a proof (good to about 10 percent) of the validity of Eq. (3-5) as applied to charged-pion decay.

The significance of these results concerning Eq. (3-5) does not lie so much in their forming a direct check of a basic implication of STR, as in their demonstrating that both a radiating atom and a decaying elementary particle can serve as a fundamental 'clock' possessed of an *invariable* proper period.

‡ H. E. Ives and G. R. Stilwell, *J. Opt. Soc. Am.*, **28**: 215 (1938); **31**: 369 (1941). Other similar measurements: G. Otting, *Physik. Z.*, **40**: 681 (1939); H. I. Mandelberg and L. Witten, *J. Opt. Soc. Am.*, **52**: 529 (1962).

§ What are now called muons (or, formerly, μ-mesons), were in those days—before the discovery of the π-mesons—known simply as mesons, or also frequently as "mesotrons."

¶ B. Rossi and N. Nereson, *Phys. Rev.*, **62**: 417 (1942); **64**: 199 (1943). For other references and general discussion see for instance, A. M. Thorndike, "Mesons," chap. 5, sec. 1 and 2, McGraw-Hill Book Co., Inc., New York, 1952.

‡‡ See for instance B. Rossi and D. B. Hall, *Phys. Rev.*, **59**: 223 (1941).

§§ R. Durbin, H. H. Loar, and W. W. Havens, Jr., *Phys. Rev.*, **88**: 179 (1952).

¶¶ The lifetime relative to an inertial system in which the decaying particle is at rest.

‡‡‡ M. Jacobson, A. Schulz, and J. Steinberger, *Phys. Rev.*, **81**: 894 (1951); C. Wiegand, *Phys. Rev.*, **83**: 1085 (1951).

3-4 THE GENERAL LORENTZ TRANSFORMATIONS AND MINKOWSKI GEOMETRY

The Lorentz transformation of the form of Eq. (2-6) connecting two inertial frames S and S' in relative motion is *special* in the following respect: a common spatial coordinate axis of S and S' is in the direction of their relative velocity. In this case it makes sense to speak of the *parallelism* between corresponding spatial coordinate axes in S and S',‡ notwithstanding the relative nature of simultaneity. But this relativity introduces the question of what one is to understand by parallelism in the case of straight lines inclined to such coordinate axes. A useful convention is to consider the line l in S as parallel to the line l' in S' (S and S' being connected by a special Lorentz transformation) when l' is inclined to the spatial axes of S' as measured in S' in the same way as l is inclined to the corresponding axes of S as measured in S, irrespective of the times of observation in S and in S'. Since this notion of parallelism is not generally synonymous with the usual one, we shall refer to it as "quasi-parallelism."

An extension of the family of transformations (2-6), which naturally presents itself, consists in permitting the relative velocity of S and S' to have any inclination to the coordinate axes of the two frames, while retaining the condition of their mutual quasi-parallelism. The form of the resulting transformations can be obtained directly by utilizing the fundamental properties of a Lorentz transformation represented by the relativistic contraction of lengths and dilatation of time. (See, e.g., [7], footnote on page 10.) It can also be obtained by the following algebraic method, which admits of ready extension to the general case.

In the development of this method it is convenient to introduce notation distinguishing the matrices associated with four-dimensional and three-dimensional space. As a temporary convention, we choose Latin upper- and lowercase letters respectively for this purpose. The set of space-time coordinates, $x_0 = ct, x_1, x_2, x_3,$ will thus be represented by the 1-column 4-rowed matrix $X = \begin{bmatrix} x_0 \\ x \end{bmatrix}$, where x is a 1-column matrix with elements x_1, x_2, x_3. (Except where it is obvious from the context, ordinary numbers will be represented in this discussion by Greek letters.) Our problem is to find the general expression of a transformation, $X \to X' = TX$, connecting two inertial systems S, S', whose spatial axes are mutually quasi-parallel. Suppose that $X \to X^* = RX$ represents a rotation of the spatial axes in S (while t remains unchanged) bringing the x_1 axis in the direction of the velocity $\mathbf{v}$ of S' (i.e., of the spatial origin of S') relative to S; so that

$$R = \begin{bmatrix} 1 & \tilde{n} \\ n & r \end{bmatrix}, \qquad n = \begin{bmatrix} 0 \\ 0 \\ 0 \end{bmatrix}, \qquad r_{1i} = \frac{\beta_i}{\beta}, \ \beta^2 = \beta_i\beta_i \equiv \left(\frac{v}{c}\right)^2 \tag{3-25}$$

‡ Until Chap. 5, it is always tacitly assumed that all spatial coordinate frames are *rectangular*. It is also always assumed that the *standards* of length and of time are identical in all coordinate systems under consideration.

From the definition of quasi-parallelism it follows that the same matrix R is associated with a precisely similar rotation of the axes in S'. Consequently, if L is the matrix of the special Lorentz transformation (2-6) with $v = |\mathbf{v}|$, then $RX' = L(RX)$, or, $X' = R^{-1}LRX$; in other words:

$$T = R^{-1}LR \tag{3-26}$$

By Eq. (3-25), and since, $r\tilde{r} = i$, the unit 3-rowed matrix, [see Eq. (1-13)], one finds that $R^{-1} = \begin{bmatrix} 1 & \tilde{n} \\ n & \tilde{r} \end{bmatrix}$; and by Eq. (2-6)

$$L = \begin{bmatrix} \gamma & \tilde{b} \\ b & g \end{bmatrix}, \qquad b = -\beta\gamma \begin{bmatrix} 1 \\ 0 \\ 0 \end{bmatrix}, \qquad g = i + (\gamma - 1)e, \qquad e = \begin{bmatrix} 1 & 0 & 0 \\ 0 & 0 & 0 \\ 0 & 0 & 0 \end{bmatrix} \tag{3-27}$$

The product (3-26) representing T is therefore $\begin{bmatrix} \gamma & \tilde{b}r \\ \tilde{r}b & \tilde{r}gr \end{bmatrix}$, which, in view of the last sets of equations in Eqs. (3-25) and (3-27), reduces to

$$T = \begin{bmatrix} \gamma & -\gamma\tilde{w} \\ -\gamma w & i + \dfrac{\gamma - 1}{\beta^2} w\tilde{w} \end{bmatrix}, \qquad w = \begin{bmatrix} \beta_1 \\ \beta_2 \\ \beta_3 \end{bmatrix} \tag{3-28}$$

The corresponding transformation equations written out in full are

$$\begin{aligned} x_0' &= \gamma(x_0 - \beta_j x_j) \\ x_i' &= -\gamma\beta_i x_0 + \left(\delta_{ij} + \frac{\gamma - 1}{\beta^2}\beta_i\beta_j\right) x_j \end{aligned} \tag{3-29}$$

or, in vector notation,

$$\begin{aligned} x_0' &= \gamma(x_0 - \boldsymbol{\beta} \cdot \mathbf{x}) \\ \mathbf{x}' &= \mathbf{x} - \left(\gamma x_0 - \frac{\gamma - 1}{\beta^2}\boldsymbol{\beta} \cdot \mathbf{x}\right)\boldsymbol{\beta} \end{aligned} \tag{3-29a}$$

It is easily verified that, unlike the family of transformations (2-6) (with v as the varying parameter), the transformations (3-29) (with the β_i as parameters) do not form a group. This of course reflects the fact that the relationship of quasi-parallelism does not in general obey the law of transitivity. One can expect, on the other hand, that a group will be obtained if we proceed along the lines of reasoning employed in the derivation of Eqs. (3-29), but allow the R transformations in S and in S' to be arbitrary corresponding to an arbitrary 'relative rotation' of the S and S' spatial axes. Expressed in terms of our present notation, the corresponding general transformation matrix is a product similar to (3-26) with the factor R^{-1} replaced by $(R')^{-1}$, where

$$R' = \begin{bmatrix} 1 & \tilde{n} \\ n & r' \end{bmatrix}$$

$$r'_{1i} = \frac{-\beta'_i}{\beta'} \tag{3-30}$$

$$\mathbf{v}' = \text{velocity of } S \text{ relative to } S' \text{ as measured in } S'$$

a rotation in S' that brings the x'_i axis in the direction of the velocity of S' relative to S, *as measured in* S'. By Eqs. (3-25) and (3-27) this product is [anticipating the result (3-42), to be proved presently]

$$\begin{bmatrix} \gamma & -\gamma\tilde{w} \\ \gamma w' & s - \dfrac{(\gamma - 1)}{\beta^2} w'\tilde{w} \end{bmatrix} \qquad \begin{aligned} s &= \tilde{r}'r \\ w' &= \begin{bmatrix} \beta'_1 \\ \beta'_2 \\ \beta'_3 \end{bmatrix} \end{aligned} \tag{3-31}$$

When one compares the 3×3 submatrices in Eqs. (3-31) and (3-28), noting the definitions of the 1-column matrices w and w', it is evident that the orthogonal matrix s must be connected with the deviation from quasi-parallelism of the spatial axes in S and S', that is to say, it must be connected with the 'relative orientation' of their spatial frames. Specifically, by Eqs. (3-25) and (3-30) [and (3-42)],

$$sw = \tilde{r}' \begin{bmatrix} \beta \\ 0 \\ 0 \end{bmatrix} = -w' \tag{3-32}$$

The matrix s is thus indeed associated with a 'rotation' of w into the similar vector $-w'$.

The nature of the matrices (3-31) is apparent from our present construction. But in order to prove in a direct manner that the family of these matrices forms a group and to identify this group fully, it is best to employ the method used in Sec. 1-2 in connection with the group of rigid displacements. To this end we note that by reasoning similar to that employed in the deduction of the form invariance of Eq. (3-2) and in the derivation of the special Lorentz transformations therefrom, it can be concluded that not only Eq. (3-2) but its left-hand side expression as well must be a *form invariant* under the Lorentz group. It follows that the transformations of this group must be *linear*. The proof of the linearity of the transformation equations representing displacements outlined in Sec. 1-2 is applicable here with minor modification. At the same time one obtains also conditions on the transformation matrices similar to Eq. (1-13). If one prefers, this repetitious derivation can be obviated by the very simple device, first introduced by

Poincaré, of replacing the time variable t by

$$x_4 = ix_0 = ict, \qquad i = \sqrt{-1} \tag{3-33}$$

when our form invariant assumes the form

$$\Delta s^2 = -\Delta x_\alpha \, \Delta x_\alpha, \qquad \text{summation over } \alpha = 1, 2, 3, 4 \tag{3-34}$$

The conclusion concerning linearity and the matrix properties (1-13) can then be taken over directly from our older results, because, as is easily verified, these are affected neither by the number nor by the reality of the coordinates. Thus, if we represent by A the matrix of a typical Lorentz transformation and by x and b the 1-column matrices with the respective elements x_1, x_2, x_3, x_4, and b_1, b_2, b_3, b_4, then this transformation is given by Eq. (1-12), and A satisfies the matrix relation (1-13).‡

It is now clear that the *complete* Lorentz group of transformations (1-12) (the "inhomogeneous Lorentz group," or "Poincaré group") corresponds to the group of displacements in ordinary space (including reflections), and the "homogeneous Lorentz group" (or, simply, "Lorentz group") is the analog of the group of rotations and reflections. It can be anticipated that the matrices (3-31) represent the space-time generalization of the subgroup of pure rotations—without reflections. This we now proceed to prove after returning to the real variable x_0.

Referring to Eq. (3-33), it is seen that the aforementioned space-time transformation matrix A and the matrix T of the associated *real* transformation

$$x'_\mu = T_{\mu\nu} x_\nu \qquad \begin{array}{c} \mu, \nu = 0, 1, 2, 3 \\ x_0 = ct \end{array} \tag{3-35}$$

are connected by the equations§

$$T_{00} = A_{44}, \qquad T_{0k} = -iA_{4k}, \qquad T_{k0} = iA_{k4}, \qquad T_{kr} = A_{kr} \tag{3-36}$$

The relations (1-13), i.e.,

$$A_{\alpha\beta} A_{\alpha\gamma} = A_{\beta\alpha} A_{\gamma\alpha} = \delta_{\beta\gamma} \tag{3-37}$$

assume therefore the following form in terms of the real matrix elements $T_{\mu\nu}$:

$$T_{0\mu} T_{0j} - T_{i\mu} T_{ij} = T_{\mu 0} T_{j0} - T_{\mu i} T_{ji} = -\delta_{\mu j} \tag{3-38}$$

$$(T_{00})^2 - T_{i0} T_{i0} = (T_{00})^2 - T_{0i} T_{0i} = 1 \tag{3-39}$$

‡ Note that we are here (as also in the future) changing our notation when convenience dictates it and there is no chance for misunderstanding.

§ Let us recall that in addition to the summation convention concerning repeated indices we are also employing the *free indices* convention. Thus, in Eqs. (3-36) are comprised all equations obtained by setting $k = 1, 2, 3$ and $r = 1, 2, 3$, while Eq. (3-37) contains the set of equations corresponding to $\beta = 1, 2, 3, 4$ and $\gamma = 1, 2, 3, 4$ (each equation involving moreover a summation over $\alpha = 1, 2, 3, 4$).

From Eqs. (3-35) and the equations of the inverse transformation [given by Eqs. (3-37) and (3-36)], one finds that the velocity vectors **v**, **v**′ defined earlier are given respectively [in agreement with Eqs. (3-28) and (3-31)] by the equations

$$\frac{v_i}{c} \equiv \beta_i = -\frac{T_{0i}}{T_{00}}, \qquad \frac{v'_i}{c} \equiv \beta'_i = \frac{T_{i0}}{T_{00}} \tag{3-40}$$

Hence, by Eq. (3-39):

$$T_{00} = \pm(1 - \beta_i\beta_i)^{-1/2} \equiv \pm\gamma \tag{3-41}$$

and

$$\beta'_i\beta'_i = \beta_i\beta_i = \beta^2 \tag{3-42}$$

For ease of comparison with the matrix (3-31), let us revert to the previous matrix notation, writing now

$$T = \begin{bmatrix} \alpha & \tilde{f} \\ g & a \end{bmatrix} \tag{3-43}$$

First we note that by Eqs. (3-40) and (3-41) there is agreement between the quantities α, f, g in Eq. (3-43) and the corresponding quantities in (3-31), provided we take the *positive* sign in Eq. (3-41), i.e., provided

$$T_{00} = \gamma \equiv |(1 - \beta^2)^{-1/2}| \tag{3-41a}$$

In order to discover how the submatrix a is related to the corresponding submatrix in Eq. (3-31), we make use of one set of Eqs. (3-38),‡ which, in the notation of Eq. (3-43) can be written (remembering that we are letting i represent the 3-rowed identity matrix)

$$af - \alpha g = 0, \qquad a\tilde{a} - g\tilde{g} = i \tag{3-38a}$$

These equations imply that

$$a\left(i - \frac{1}{\alpha^2} f\tilde{f}\right)\tilde{a} = i \tag{3-44}$$

It follows that the matrix

$$q = a(i - \lambda f\tilde{f}) \tag{3-44a}$$

will be *orthogonal* ($q\tilde{q} = i$) if λ can be chosen so that $(i - \lambda f\tilde{f})^2 = i - (1/\alpha^2)f\tilde{f}$. Since by Eqs. (3-40) and (3-42), $\tilde{f}f = \alpha^2\beta^2$, this relation will be satisfied provided $\alpha^4\beta^2\lambda^2 - 2\alpha^2\lambda + 1 = 0$, i.e., provided

$$\lambda = \frac{1}{\alpha^2\beta^2}(1 \pm \sqrt{1 - \beta^2}) \tag{3-44b}$$

Similarly we find that $(i - \lambda f\tilde{f})^{-1} = i + \sigma f\tilde{f}$, and hence by Eq. (3-44a)

$$a = q(i + \sigma f\tilde{f}) \tag{3-45}$$

‡ The complimentary set of equations would lead to the same result and by precisely similar steps.

provided

$$\sigma = \frac{\lambda}{1 - \alpha^2\beta^2\lambda} = \frac{-1 \mp \gamma}{\alpha^2\beta^2} \tag{3-46}$$

By Eqs. (3-44a), (3-44b), and (3-38a), it follows then that

$$qf = af(1 - \lambda\alpha^2\beta^2) = \mp \frac{\alpha}{\gamma} g \tag{3-47}$$

and hence, by Eqs. (3-45) and (3-46), that

$$a = q + \frac{\gamma \pm 1}{\alpha\gamma\beta^2} g\tilde{f} \tag{3-48}$$

We can now make the desired comparison with Eq. (3-31). We have already seen that one must make the choice (3-41a) for $\alpha = T_{00}$. Consequently, applying Eqs. (3-40) and (3-42) to (3-48), it can be concluded that q should be identified with the rotation matrix s, and that the lower sign must be taken in Eq. (3-48). This choice of sign is confirmed by a comparison of Eqs. (3-47) and (3-32), in view of Eq. (3-41a). It remains to determine the kinematic significance of the choice of signs in Eqs. (3-41) and (3-46).

In order to bring out the physical significance of the ambiguous sign in Eq. (3-41) it will be helpful to return to Eq. (3-34) and examine some aspects of the structure of space-time determined by this form invariant. Because of its independent interest, we shall consider this topic at some length at this point before returning to our immediate question.

In analogy to the three-dimensional euclidean case of ordinary space, as discussed in Sec. 1-2, one can think of Eq. (3-34) as defining the *metric* of space-time in terms of the coordinates x_α, and one can introduce a corresponding geometric terminology. For instance, perpendicularity of directions is defined by a relation analogous to Eq. (1-9). It should be noted, though, that the usefulness of this analogy is limited: the nonreality of x_4 introduces a significant difference. Space-time is far from being merely a species of euclidean space of four dimensions, and the designation "quasi-euclidean" sometimes applied to its geometry, though entirely logical, is perhaps best avoided in the present context.

On the purely mathematical side, the difference arising from the relation (3-33) is in ready evidence. For instance, the basic theorem concerning *geodesics* which was proved in Sec. 1-2 is unchanged as far as concerns the 'straightness' of the lines, but now in the case of those curves of space-time along which there is defined a real-valued 'length' the extremal in question is not minimal but on the contrary it is *maximal*.‡ One can enumerate other instances, but they are all related to the basic circumstance that the locus of points 'equidistant' from a given point, which is a "hypersphere"

‡ This is connected with the fact that the metric is not positive definite. See Prob. 3-13.

(a three-dimensional spherical 'surface') in four-dimensional euclidean space, consists in space-time of two associated hyper-hyperboloids, as illustrated in part in Fig. 3-1*a* (with the suppression of two spatial dimensions).

The physical properties of space-time, which are of course our chief concern, reflect these mathematical differences. Added to this is the fundamental difference in the physical dimensions of the x_i ($i = 1, 2, 3$) and of t, connected with the dimensional character of the basic universal constant c. In the light of these observations, one must attribute a degree of poetic license to the following celebrated words of Hermann Minkowski: "Henceforth space by itself, and time by itself, are doomed to fade away into mere shadows, and only a kind of union of the two will preserve an independent reality."‡ At the same time, the interconnectedness between space and time measurements—which, as we have noted in Chap. 1, already exists to an appreciable extent in newtonian kinematics—is indeed more pronounced in the kinematics of STR owing to the very existence of the constant c that makes possible the transition from the quantity t to the quantity $x_0 = ct$. Moreover, the introduction of a four-dimensional formalism patterned after familiar and intuitively vivid ideas from geometry and vector analysis, has many heuristic advantages, as we shall have repeated occasion to recognize. This was first effectively shown by Minkowski,§ in whose honor consequently the quasi-euclidean space-time geometry is now generally known as "Minkowski geometry." We shall similarly refer to the metric given by Eq. (3-34), or, in the physical coordinates, by

$$\Delta s^2 = c^2\,\Delta t^2 - \Delta x_i\,\Delta x_i \qquad (3\text{-}34a)$$

as the "Minkowski metric," and to the corresponding space as "Minkowski space," which we shall denote by $\mathfrak{M}$. It is hardly necessary to add that "space," in this connection, is not intended to imply anything more than a continuum that is the seat of a geometry; or, equivalently, that possesses a 'structure' determined by a metric in a manner similar to that outlined in Sec. 1-2 in the case of euclidean space (except for differences arising from the indefiniteness of the metric).

From one point of view Minkowski's declaration concerning the *union* of space and time can be taken at its face value. If his word *reality* is taken to refer only to absolute quantities, those covariant with respect to the group of Lorentz transformations, then there is indeed a substantial degree of mixing of space and time. However, as noted earlier, and as is of course only too evident, the relative quantities must claim their share of attention—the lion's share, in fact, from the practical point of view. These quantities are in a sense the *projections* of corresponding absolute quantities on a particular reference frame, the frame which carries our observers—the physicists who

‡ See translation of the original paper in [2], paper 5, p. 75.

§ See the above reference. Some use of the four-dimensional approach was already made by Poincaré in his 1906 paper.

survey these quantities. Moreover, even from the *absolute* point of view this mixing of space and time is only partial (only "a kind of union," in Minkowski's words). This is exhibited in the pictorial representation shown in Fig. 3-4. The regions marked "past" and "future" on the one hand, and the region marked "present" on the other, are *absolutely separate:* the two sheets of the light hypercone (or, simply "light cone," or "null cone") given by the equation $\Delta s^2 = 0$, remain of course invariant under all Lorentz transformations; and, as obviously, the two regions separated by these sheets are transformed into themselves by all such transformations, these regions being determined by the sign of Δs^2 [as defined in Eq. (3-34*a*)].

We have spoken of the two absolutely separated space-time regions associated with any given "event"‡ E, one interior and the other exterior to the two-sheeted hypercone (the *light cone*) centered at E: a directed segment EE' having a *real* "length" (or, "interval") if the event E' lies in the interior region, and an imaginary interval if it lies in the exterior region. Correspondingly, *vectors* in $\mathfrak{M}$ are classified as "timelike" and "spacelike" respectively, while vectors which correspond to events E' situated on the light cone are called "null vectors"—vectors of zero magnitude. This covariant division of all vectors in $\mathfrak{M}$ into three classes is characteristic of the kinematics of STR. Any event E' inside or on the light cone can be associated in an obvious sense with the motion of a material body or with the propagation of energy, passing through the vertex E—it can be *causally*

‡ That is, *point* of $\mathfrak{M}$; or also, following Minkowski, "world point." Similarly $\mathfrak{M}$ is referred to as the "world" and a curve in $\mathfrak{M}$ is called a "world line."

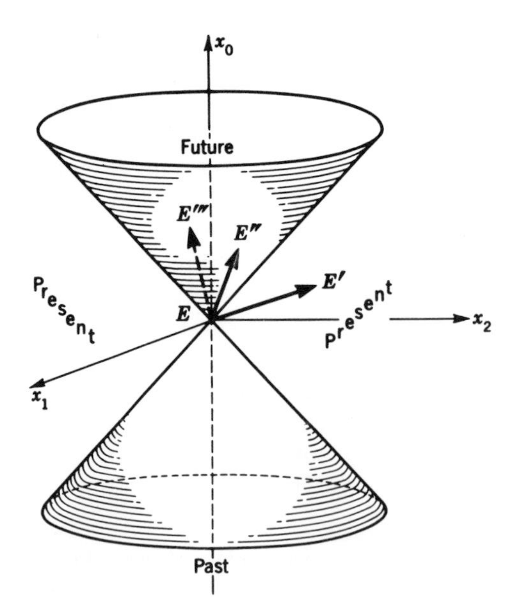

Fig. 3-4 The light cone about event (i.e., space-time point) E, with suppression of one spatial dimension. EE', EE'', EE''' represent spacelike null, and timelike vectors in $\mathfrak{M}$.

connected with E; whereas if E' is outside this cone, such connection is impossible, but instead, it is always possible to select an inertial reference frame (associated with a choice of direction of the x_0 axis lying inside the cone) so that the events E and E' are *contemporaneous*. It is in this extended sense that the space-time region exterior to the light cone can be labeled suggestively as the *present*. In the case of newtonian kinematics ($c = \infty$), this four-dimensional region degenerates into all of three-dimensional ordinary space, each point of which is contemporaneous with E: we have ***absolute simultaneity***.

The division into *past* and *future* as indicated in the diagram, corresponds to the same division along the absolute time axis of classical kinematics by the time point *now*. In the classical theory, this division is invariant with respect to the galilean group: an interchange of past and future can be effected only by a special transformation such as

$$t \rightarrow t' = -t \tag{3-49}$$

In STR, this "time-inversion" transformation is included in the general Lorentz transformations [and this is precisely, as we shall presently show, at the root of the double sign in Eq. (3-41)]. The separation into past and future is therefore a relation which is not covariant with respect to the full Lorentz group. But the Lorentz transformations that do preserve this relation obviously form a subgroup of the complete group. This subgroup is clearly of central importance, since the principle of causality—with which indeed the very ordering of the time manifold is intimately associated—does not lose in STR the role it has in the classical theory.‡

In looking for a proper characterization of this time-direction-preserving subgroup (the "orthochronous Lorentz group"), we note that the positiveness of T_{00} is a necessary condition, since the forward-pointing timelike vector having the components 1, 0, 0, 0 is transformed by Eq. (3-35) into the 4-vector whose time component is T_{00}. This condition is also sufficient. In fact, we have only to apply *Cauchy's inequality*,§ to conclude from the premises $x_i x_i < x_0^2$, $x_0 > 0$, that also $|T_{0i} x_i| < T_{00} x_0$, by virtue of the second equality in Eq. (3-39) and the assumption, $T_{00} > 0$.

This important conclusion can also be deduced very simply from the following elementary result in "$\mathfrak{M}$ geometry":

‡ A sophisticated definition of causality in physics is rather elusive. For a clear-cut definition that reflects the average physicist's intuitive understanding of the concept, see, e.g., H. Reichenbach, *op. cit.*, sec. 21. See also, J. C. Maxwell, "Matter and Motion," sec. 19, Dover Publications, Inc., New York—with replacement of Maxwell's ***absolute time*** and *absolute place* by *space-time*.

§ This inequality for finite sums, it will be recalled, states that $\left(\sum_k a_k b_k\right)^2 \leq \sum_k a_k^2 \sum_k b_k^2$, where the a_k and b_k are real numbers—it follows from the identity given in Prob. 1-3. (The corresponding inequality for integrals, *Schwarz's inequality*, is perhaps better known among physicists.)

1 If a and b are timelike vectors of the same type (i.e., timelike vectors with a_0 and b_0 of the same sign), then their *scalar product* is positive. (The converse is also true, and its proof is immediate.)

The proof of (1) follows from another result of $\mathfrak{M}$ geometry, that has independent interest:

2 If a vector a is timelike, then every vector b which is *orthogonal* to a is necessarily spacelike.

This result follows at once by choosing the x_0 axis in the direction of the vector a. From our condition of orthogonality,

$$(\mathsf{a},\mathsf{b}) \equiv a_0 b_0 - a_i b_i = 0 \tag{3-50}$$

it then follows that $b_0 = 0$ and hence that b is spacelike. Returning to (1), let us consider the vector b as arising by continuous variation from an initial position parallel to the x_0 axis, and without changing its type. Since the initial value of the scalar product (a,b) is positive and since this product is a continuous function of the components, it must remain positive also in its final position, as it cannot vanish according to (2).

The sufficiency of the condition $T_{00} > 0$ in question, can be seen to follow from (1), by noting that by Eq. (3-35), x'_0 can be written in the form of a scalar product (a,x) [see Eq. (3-50)] with $\mathsf{a} = (T_{00}, -T_{01}, -T_{02}, -T_{03})$, and that a is timelike by Eq. (3-39).

In view of Eq. (3-41), it follows that the orthochronous group is characterized by the condition

$$T_{00} \geq 1 \tag{3-51}$$

the equality sign corresponding to a static Lorentz transformation (with the time variable unchanged and the spatial coordinates subjected to an orthogonal transformation). The latter conclusion follows directly from Eqs. (3-39) and (3-38).

The orthochronous group can be reduced further by demanding that the transformations be obtainable by continuous variation from the identity transformation. This excludes *improper* transformations such as the "space-reflection transformation"

$$x'_0 = x_0, \qquad x'_i = -x_i \tag{3-52}$$

The resulting family of transformations is obviously a group. This subgroup of the complete Lorentz group will be denoted by $\mathfrak{L}$, and the term Lorentz group will be taken in the sequel to apply to $\mathfrak{L}$, unless otherwise stated.

Returning to the matrices (3-31), it is now easy to see that the group of transformations that they represent is precisely the group $\mathfrak{L}$. The significance of the signs in Eq. (3-41) has already been established. As to the signs in Eq. (3-46), one can see from Eq. (3-47) their relation to the properness or improperness of our transformation, connected with the properness or improperness of the orthogonal matrix s (i.e., with whether s does or does not represent a pure rotation). When both signs in Eq. (3-41) are allowed and when s is allowed to be improper as well as proper, then the matrices (3-31) yield the full homogeneous Lorentz group.

It is at once deducible from the representation $(R')^{-1}LR$ of the matrix (3-31) [remembering Eq. (3-11)], that the determinant of any matrix representing a transformation in $\mathfrak{L}$ is unity. Generally, it follows from Eqs. (3-37) and (3-36) that the determinant of a general Lorentz matrix is ± 1. This can also be seen directly without the introduction of the imaginary time variable, by noting that the form invariance of the squared interval (3-34*a*) can be expressed in the matrix form

$$\tilde{T}MT = M, \qquad M = \begin{bmatrix} 1 & \tilde{n} \\ n & -i \end{bmatrix} \tag{3-53}$$

The Lorentz matrices of determinant $+1$ evidently form a group, the "proper Lorentz group," of which $\mathfrak{L}$ constitutes a subgroup. Any Lorentz transformation that does not belong to $\mathfrak{L}$ can be obtained by the multiplication of a member of $\mathfrak{L}$ by either the transformation (3-49) (with $x_i' = x_i$) or (3-52), or by their product. Thus from a knowledge of the structure of $\mathfrak{L}$ one can go over easily to that of the complete homogeneous Lorentz group.

After these general considerations, let us return to what is of immediate interest to us—the kinematic significance of the general Lorentz transformations. Though this has already been brought out in the course of our general discussion, the essentials can be seen more simply if we limit ourselves to transformations involving only two spatial dimensions (i.e., leaving one particular spatial coordinate unchanged). These suffice to manifest the sense in which a general transformation in $\mathfrak{L}$ is composed of a special Lorentz transformation and a 'quasi-rotation' of one set of spatial axes relative to the other set of the pair of reference systems connected by the transformation. Moreover, the only application taking us beyond the special Lorentz group we shall presently have occasion to consider (in Sec. 3-5) can be treated adequately with the aid of such transformations.

Referring to our earlier discussion concerning the kinematic significance of the matrix (3-31), it can be seen that it will suffice to consider now only the form the spatial submatrix assumes when one coordinate, say x_3, is unchanged. This submatrix is easily found by specializing Eq. (3-31), and it can also be found directly without difficulty by computing the pertinent product $(R')^{-1}TR$ [which the reader may want to do as a check on the following result, Eq. (3-54)]. If we omit the last row and the last column of our transformation matrix (each having the elements 0, 0, 0, 1), and represent by θ and θ' the angles between $\mathbf{v}$ and the x_1 axis and between $-\mathbf{v}'$ and the

x_1' axis, as measured in S and S' respectively, one finds—denoting $(\theta - \theta')$ by $\Delta\theta$‡—the following explicit result:

$$\begin{bmatrix} T_{11} & T_{12} \\ T_{21} & T_{22} \end{bmatrix} = \begin{bmatrix} \cos\Delta\theta + (\gamma - 1)\cos\theta\cos\theta' & \sin\Delta\theta + (\gamma - 1)\sin\theta\cos\theta' \\ -\sin\Delta\theta + (\gamma - 1)\cos\theta\sin\theta' & \cos\Delta\theta + (\gamma - 1)\sin\theta\sin\theta' \end{bmatrix} \tag{3-54}$$

It is now evident that this submatrix represents indeed, in the classical limit $\gamma \to 1$, the *relative rotation* of the spatial reference frames. It is also seen that the relativistic corrections are of order v^2/c^2, as was to be expected.

We shall conclude the present discussion of the general Lorentz transformations with an examination of the relativistic change in space- and time-interval measures associated with these transformations. Since the rate of a clock that is at rest in a given inertial system cannot possibly be affected by the orientation of the spatial-coordinate axes in that system or in any other inertial system where that rate is being measured, it is obvious that the time-dilatation formula (3-5) must be retained in the general case. This conclusion is verified at once by means of Eqs. (3-35), (3-41a), and the reciprocity relation indicated in the second of the Eqs. (3-10). It also follows directly from the inverse of the transformation (3-35) [immediately deducible from Eqs. (3-37) and (3-36)]:

$$x_0 = T_{00}x_0' - T_{k0}x_k', \qquad x_i = -T_{0i}x_0' + T_{ki}x_k' \tag{3-55}$$

A similar conclusion, which reflects the homogeneity and isotropy properties of ordinary space, can obviously be drawn also regarding spatial intervals. This is likewise readily checked. By Eqs. (3-4), the length Δs in S of a straight line segment $\Delta\mathbf{x}$ resting in S' is related to its length $\Delta s'$ as measured in S' (its *proper* or *rest* length) by the formula

$$\Delta s' = (1 + (\gamma^2 - 1)\cos^2\theta)^{1/2}\,\Delta s \qquad (\Delta t = 0) \tag{3-56}$$

where $\theta =$ angle (in S) between $\Delta\mathbf{x}$ and $\mathbf{v}$. The identical result is easily seen to follow also from Eqs. (3-29), and, clearly, any further relative rotation of coordinate axes cannot in any way affect this result.

With the aid of Eq. (3-56) it is possible to determine the shape of any rigid body at rest in one inertial system as it appears in another such system that is moving relative to it.§

‡ $\Delta\theta$ thus represents, in a sense that is obvious from our earlier discussion, the angle of rotation bringing the x_1 and x_1' axes into the same direction.

§ The word "appears" in this sentence is not to be taken in the sense of visual or photographic manifestation; it is intended to convey only the idea of observation or measurement according to Einstein's prescription, which in any case underlies from an operational point of view the contraction formula (3-56). According to this prescription, the geometric configuration of a body B moving uniformly relative to the inertial system S is specified in S by the position in S of each material point of B *at a fixed instant of S time.* Undoubtedly it is this sense that is intended by Einstein when he discusses change of

3-5 THE CLOCK PARADOX; THOMAS PRECESSION

The two topics treated in this section have the following in common: they involve a consideration of *accelerated* motion relative to inertial frames. This raises the question of the relationship between the readings of *standard* clocks and rods in a given inertial system S and in a system S' which has nonuniform motion relative to S—a question whose general significance in relativistic dynamics is obvious. If one examines this question carefully, one can conclude that it is not possible to obtain the answer as a logical deduction from the postulates of STR so far enunciated. The answer must come either directly from experiment or else by way of an additional postulate. Because of the smallness of relativistic kinematic effects one follows the latter approach, ultimate agreement with observation being in any case a general requirement of all theory. This additional postulate of STR, which is usually made tacitly, can be formulated explicitly as follows.

C *If a space-time reference system S' is attached to a body moving arbitrarily relative to an inertial system S, then at each given instant the connection between the S' and the S measures of an interval as determined in S, is the same as it would be if S' were moving uniformly with the corresponding instantaneous velocity of the body relative to S.*

The important implication of C is that, for example, the rate of an arbitrarily moving standard clock, as compared in an inertial system S with the rate of an identical clock resting in S, is affected by the first derivative but not by the higher derivatives of the position vector of the moving clock relative to S. (See Prob. 3-18.)

When this postulate is accepted, the result of the thought experiment constituting the so-called "clock paradox" follows immediately. The thought experiment (first mentioned in Einstein's pioneer paper—[2], paper 3, p. 49) envisages two identical clocks A, B, with A resting in the inertial system S, and B starting from initial juxtaposition with A and complete synchronism with it and moving away from A in some space-time trajectory that finally brings it back to rest in S near A. If the times of departure and return of B are t_0 and t_1 as measured in S and therefore as

---

shape on p. 48 of [2]. It has been recently pointed out, however, by J. Terrell [*Phys. Rev.*, **116**: 1041 (1959)] that Einstein's remarks appear to have been construed by many writers on relativity as referring to *visual* observation. Clearly, the conditions of such observation differ from those involved in Einstein's prescription and must lead to a different result. For a discussion of this result the reader is referred to Terrell's paper, or to an exposition by V. F. Weisskopf in *Phys. Today* (Sept., 1960). On the other hand, for the possibility of *observing* the relativistic contraction with the aid of a pulsed radar system, see C. W. Sherwin, *Am. J. Phys.*, **29**: 67 (1961).

shown by A, then, according to C and Eq. (3-34a), the corresponding time interval as indicated by B is given by

$$\Delta t' \equiv t_1' - t_0' = \frac{1}{c} \int_{t_0}^{t_1} \sqrt{c^2\, dt^2 - dx_i\, dx_i} = \int_{t_0}^{t_1} \sqrt{1 - \beta_i \beta_i}\, dt \qquad (3\text{-}57)$$

$$c\beta = \text{velocity of } B \text{ in } S$$

Thus, necessarily $\Delta t' < \Delta t$, clock B lags behind clock A. Moreover if the role of the clocks A and B is taken over by the beating hearts of two identical twins, it can be expected (physiological considerations aside) that upon his return twin B will appear younger than twin A to a degree determined by Eq. (3-57) ("twin paradox").

The 'paradoxical' aspect of such thought experiments presents itself only if one mistakenly assumes that there is complete equivalence between the *physical* situations represented by the motion of B relative to A as observed in the A frame and by the motion of A relative to B as observed in the B frame, an assumption that is of course inconsistent with the asymmetrical result of these thought experiments. Actually, this asymmetry corresponds to the overall nonequivalence of the system S and the one riding with B. The latter system S' must be noninertial at least during part of B's journey, and consequently STR cannot tell us what the correlation of the time measurements of S and S' is *from the point of view of* S' during that part of the journey. The theory of general relativity must be invoked in this case. It is perhaps easy to fall into the error of considering the statement C as in some sense reversible. To discern the fallacy in such reasoning one must examine carefully the role of the family of inertial systems in our very definitions of space and time measurements. We have touched on these questions in Chap. 1 and in Sec. 3-1, but we have not stopped to inquire what may be the root of the central significance of the inertial family. This is in fact a question that is still far from being fully understood. In the case of the clock paradox it is clear that the equivalence of systems A and B would be assured by the principle of sufficient reason if no other material system existed in the universe. It is the overall material (and energetic) content of the universe which must be obviously in some way connected with the properties of the inertial systems—a fact to which attention was first called especially in the writings of Mach, and which has therefore come to be known as *Mach's principle* (see Prob. 1-10).

The principle C enters also implicitly in the derivation of the kinematic effect of STR first applied to the orbital motion of a spinning electron in an atom by Thomas‡—the "Thomas precession." To understand this effect, consider a particle whose motion in the inertial system S is described by the equation

$$\mathbf{x} = \mathbf{f}(t) \qquad (3\text{-}58)$$

and suppose that there is associated with the particle a spatial direction $\mathbf{s}$

‡ L. H. Thomas, *Phil. Mag.*, **3**: 1 (1927).

which remains invariable in the following sense. Consider at each instant t of S an inertial frame $S'(t)$ in which the particle is instantaneously at rest at the origin of spatial coordinates—the "comoving system" (or "rest system") of the particle at t. The significance of the family $S'(t)$ follows from postulate C. With the aid of this family we can introduce the notion of quasi-parallelism (discussed in Sec. 3-4) as applied to directed segments 'rigidly' attached to the *spatial* frames $\Sigma(t)$ of the $S'(t)$. The unit vector $\mathbf{s}(t)$ describing such a directed segment in $\Sigma(t)$ is taken to be unchanging in the sense of remaining instantaneously quasi-parallel to itself throughout the motion of the particle; that is to say, for each t under consideration (measured in S), $\mathbf{s}(t)$ and $\mathbf{s}(t + \Delta t)$ are mutually quasi-parallel in the limit $\Delta t \to 0$. From the results discussed in Sec. 3-4 it is clear that as measured in S this 'invariable' direction will in general vary, this variation depending on the motion described by Eq. (3-58). It is this variation relative to a given inertial system that constitutes the Thomas precession. As first applied,‡ the invariable direction $\mathbf{s}$ was that of the spin of an atomic electron treated nonquantally, and the inertial reference system S was that determined by the nucleus of the atom.§

In order to determine the rate of the Thomas precession in S, consider the inertial frames $S'(t)$, $S'(t + \Delta t)$, which we shall denote by S' and S'' respectively. Let T, T', and T'' represent the respective transformations $S \to S'$, $S' \to S''$, and $S \to S''$. We can choose the axes of Σ and Σ' and of Σ' and Σ'' (Σ the spatial frame in S, etc.) to be quasi-parallel, and so that $v_i(t) = df_i/dt = 0$ for $i = 2, 3$, while the velocity $\mathbf{u}'$ relative to S' of the origin of Σ'' is parallel to the $x'_1x'_2$ plane (see Fig. 3-5). Moreover, since we

‡ The original published method differed in detail from that presented here.

§ It is hardly necessary to point out that in speaking of *inertial systems* in practical connections one has always in mind an approximation whose goodness depends on the physical situation under consideration (including the time interval within which it falls).

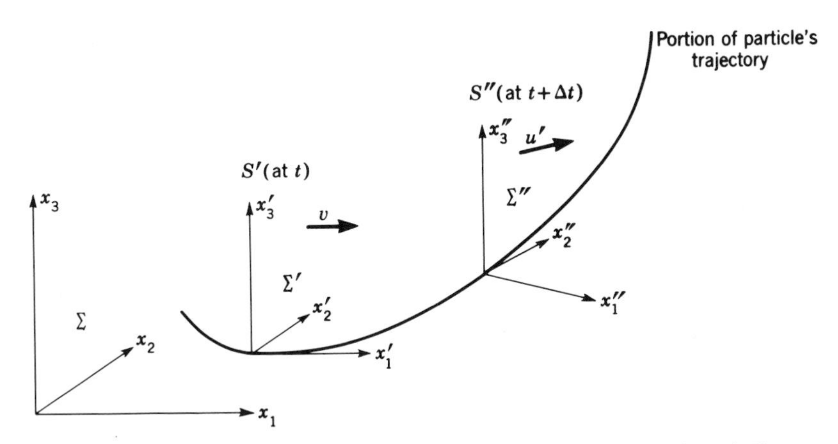

Fig. 3-5 Coordinate frame configurations relating to the discussion of Thomas precession.

are interested here only in the limiting result for $\Delta t \to 0$, it is readily verified that we can treat the u_i' as infinitesimals, the finiteness of the second derivatives of the functions $f_i(t)$ of Eq. (3-58) being of course taken for granted. Consequently, by Eq. (3-29), retaining only terms of the first order in $\beta' \equiv u'/c$, and using the same symbols for the matrices as for the associated transformations,

$$T' = \begin{bmatrix} 1 & -\beta_1' & -\beta_2' \\ -\beta_1' & 1 & 0 \\ -\beta_2' & 0 & 1 \end{bmatrix}$$

where we have omitted the last row and the last column of the matrix. With the same omission one finds therefore, again to first order in β',

$$T'' = T'T = \begin{bmatrix} \gamma(1+\beta\beta_1') & -\gamma(\beta+\beta_1') & -\beta_2' \\ -\gamma(\beta+\beta_1') & \gamma(1+\beta\beta_1') & 0 \\ -\gamma\beta_2' & \gamma\beta\beta_2' & 1 \end{bmatrix} \tag{3-59}$$

and the result we are seeking is obtained with the aid of Eqs. (3-31) and (3-54) as follows.

Comparing the first rows of the matrices (3-59) and (3-31), we find—$\mathbf{u}$ denoting the velocity of Σ'' relative to S—

$$\gamma_u \equiv \Gamma = \gamma(1+\beta\beta_1'), \qquad \Gamma\frac{u_1}{c} = \gamma(\beta+\beta_1'), \qquad \Gamma\frac{u_2}{c} = \beta_2' \tag{3-60}$$

Again, by Eq. (3-54), if $\Delta\theta$ denotes the angle by which the x_1'' axis has turned relative to the x_1 axis (and remembering that the rows are numbered 0, 1, 2): $T_{21}'' - T_{12}'' = -(\Gamma + 1)\sin\Delta\theta$. Hence, by Eqs. (3-59) and (3-60), and noting that both $\Delta\theta$ and β' are infinitesimal with Δt, and that

$$\frac{\gamma^2\beta}{\gamma+1} = \frac{\gamma-1}{\beta}$$

it is readily verified that [using the notation $o(\epsilon)$ to denote an expression $\to 0$ as $\epsilon \to 0$]

$$\Delta\theta = \frac{1-\gamma}{v}u_2 + o(\Delta t)$$

This can also be written (since $v = v_1$)

$$\Delta\theta = \frac{1-\gamma}{v^2}v_1u_2 + o(\Delta t)$$

from which it can be seen, considering the geometric significance of the quantities in Σ, that in coordinate-free form the following relation holds in S:

$$\mathbf{n}\,\Delta\theta = \frac{1-\gamma}{v^2}[\mathbf{v}\times\mathbf{u}] + o(\Delta t)$$

where $\mathbf{n}$ is the unit vector in the direction of the instantaneous axis of precession. Finally, since $\mathbf{v} \times \mathbf{u} = \mathbf{v} \times \Delta\mathbf{v}$, $\Delta\mathbf{v} = \mathbf{u} - \mathbf{v}$, we obtain immediately the following Thomas result as applied to the motion (3-58):‡

$$\mathbf{n}\frac{d\theta}{dt} = \frac{1-\gamma}{v^2}[\mathbf{v} \times \mathbf{a}] = \frac{1}{2c^2}[\mathbf{a} \times \mathbf{v}] + \cdots, \qquad \mathbf{a} = \frac{d\mathbf{v}}{dt} \tag{3-61}$$

APPENDIX 3A CONTINUOUS GROUPS AND INFINITESIMAL TRANSFORMATIONS

The concept of infinitesimal elements of continuous transformation groups is useful both in classical and in quantum physics. We present here a brief introduction to this subject adequate for our immediate purpose.

We need to define first what one understands by a "continuous group." As a matter of fact, all the groups considered in the preceding pages are continuous subgroups of a continuous group—the general Lorentz group.§ For example, it is obvious in what sense one can consider the group of *translations* in $\mathfrak{M}$

$$\mathsf{x} \to \mathsf{x}' = \mathsf{x} + \mathsf{d} \equiv T_{\mathsf{d}}\mathsf{x}, \qquad \mathsf{x} \equiv (x_0,x_1,x_2,x_3) \tag{3A-1}$$

as continuous. There are as many elements T_{d} as there are 4-vectors d, and these are clearly continuous operations: an infinitesimal change in d results in an infinitesimal change in $T_{\mathsf{d}}\mathsf{x}$. Again, the group $\mathcal{R}$ of *rotations* in ordinary space about a fixed point (chosen as the origin of our cartesian coordinates)

$$x_i' = R_{ij}x_j \qquad \begin{matrix} R\tilde{R} = I \\ \det R > 0 \end{matrix} \tag{3A-2}$$

is seen to be continuous in the same sense. As we know, the R_{ij} can be expressed as continuous functions of three independent parameters ranging over a three-dimensional region; the set of Euler angles is a familiar example.

In general, given a family of transformations

$$\begin{aligned} &x' = T_a x: \\ &x_A' = f_A(x_1, \ldots, x_n; a_1, \ldots, a_r) \equiv f_A(x;a) \qquad A = 1, \ldots, n \end{aligned} \tag{3A-3}$$

‡ For the application originally made by Thomas see his paper quoted earlier. For a more recent exposition (containing also a discussion of infinitesimal Lorentz transformation, which can be read in conjunction with the outline in Appendix 3A) see W. H. Furry, *Am. J. Phys.*, **23**: 517 (1955). This contains references to later applications in connection with the spin-orbit coupling in molecules and in nuclei.

§ We have also encountered two *discrete* (and *finite*) subgroups of the Lorentz group. These are of order 2 each, involving respectively the space inversion [given in Eq. (3-52)] and the time inversion [given in Eq. (3-49) together with the equations $x_i' = x_i$]. These two groups, and the group of order 4 formed by their product, are of significance in relativistic quantum mechanics and the theory of elementary particles. (See Chap. 8.)

forming a group, this group is said to be *continuous* when the f_A as functions of the a are continuous over a continuous range of values of the parameters. More specifically, one speaks of an "r-parameter continuous transformation group," or "r-parameter Lie group," when the a-region is r-dimensional (it being assumed that $a_1, \ldots, a_r$ are *real* numbers) and when no equivalent parameters can be found whose domain of definition has smaller dimensionality.‡ Thus, the transformations (3A-1) and (3A-2) form a 4-parameter and a 3-parameter Lie group respectively. The definition of a continuous group involves also differentiability conditions on the f_A as functions of the parameters, and we can in fact assume that these functions are analytic.§ This is obviously true of the groups (3A-1) and (3A-2).

The "infinitesimal elements" of a Lie group are the elements of the group that lie infinitely close to the identity I. Thus, an infinitesimal transformation, I_ϵ, is given by the relation

$$T_{a^0+\epsilon} = I_\epsilon + 0(\epsilon^2), \qquad \epsilon_u \to 0 \qquad \begin{aligned} \epsilon^2 &= \epsilon_u \epsilon_u \\ u &= 1, \ldots, r \end{aligned} \tag{3A-4}$$

where the a_u^0 are the values of the parameters associated with I (which one can in general choose to be 0). More explicitly, one finds by Eq. (3A-3) that

$$I_\epsilon = I + \epsilon_u Q_u \qquad \begin{aligned} Q_u &\equiv f_{Au}(x) \frac{\partial}{\partial x_A} \\ f_{Au}(x) &\equiv \left. \frac{\partial f_A(x;a)}{\partial a_u} \right|_{a=a^0} \end{aligned} \tag{3A-5}$$

Here Q_u is a differential operator $\{(Q_u x)_A \equiv Q_u[x_A]\}$, and, of course, summation is understood for repeated $u = 1, \ldots, r$ and $A = 1, \ldots, n$. It

‡ Such parameter sets are termed "essential." It is to be observed that we are assuming that r is an integer and hence a *finite* number: Lie groups are "*finite* continuous groups." Familiar examples of "*infinite* continuous groups" in classical physics are presented by the canonical transformations of mechanics and the gauge transformations of electrodynamics. The general coordinate transformations of the theory of general relativity constitute another important example.

§ For details, see, e.g., L. Pontrjagin, "Topological Groups," Princeton University Press, Princeton, N.J., 1939. The mathematically minded reader will find in this book an excellent introduction to the mathematically sophisticated questions connected with the subject. Another useful reference in which the many-dimensional differential geometry point of view is in the foreground, is L. P. Eisenhart, "Continuous Groups of Transformations," Princeton University Press, Princeton, N.J., 1933. This book contains extensive references to earlier important publications, and in particular to the pioneer work of Sophus Lie. A concise outline of the elements of Lie's theory is also contained in H. Weyl, "Mathematische Analyse des Raumproblems," appendix 8, Springer-Verlag, Berlin, 1923.

is also easily verified that, to first order in the infinitesimals,

$$I_\epsilon I_{\epsilon'} = I_{\epsilon'} I_\epsilon, \qquad I_\epsilon^{-1} = I_{-\epsilon} \tag{3A-6}$$

The infinitesimal elements of the group of translations are already given by the Eqs. (3A-1) when it is assumed that the d_u are infinitesimal. In the case of the group $\mathfrak{R}$, their deduction is not as immediate, but presents little difficulty. Combining Eqs. (3A-5), (3A-2), and (3A-6), one finds, with the symbols now taken to represent the associated transformation *matrices*, that

$$I_\epsilon = I + S, \quad \tilde{S} = -S, \qquad S_{ij} = \epsilon_k \left.\frac{\partial R_{ij}}{\partial a_k}\right|_0 \tag{3A-7}$$

The infinitesimal skew-symmetric matrix S has precisely three *independent* elements. These can therefore be taken as the parameters for the 'infinitesimal portion' of $\mathfrak{R}$ (whatever the original choice of parameters a_i for the full group $\mathfrak{R}$). Their kinematic meaning can be recognized easily when we rewrite the equations $dx_i = x_i' - x_i = S_{ij}x_j$ with the aid of the *Levi-Civita symbols* ϵ_{ijk} (that have the respective values $+1$, -1, 0 according as the indices i, j, k are an even, odd, or no permutation of 1, 2, 3—they are discussed in Chap. 5). Expressing the three independent elements of S as $\omega_i = \frac{1}{2}\epsilon_{ijk}S_{jk}$ (that is, $\omega_1 = S_{23}$, $\omega_2 = S_{31}$, $\omega_3 = S_{12}$), one finds that

$$dx_i = \epsilon_{ijk}x_j\omega_k \tag{3A-8}$$

since, by virtue of the properties of the ϵ symbols, it follows from the equations defining ω_i, that $S_{ij} = \epsilon_{ijk}\omega_k$. These equations, or, the more familiar vector equation,

$$d\mathbf{x} = \mathbf{x} \times \boldsymbol{\omega} \tag{3A-8a}$$

show that ω_i represents the *infinitesimal* angle of rotation about the x_i axis, and the kinematic significance of the infinitesimal matrix S is thus established. [The fact that $\boldsymbol{\omega}$ is a vector (or more precisely, a pseudovector, or axial vector) follows straightway from results presented in Sec. 5-4.]

The above example can also serve to introduce us to another question of immediate interest to us, that of 'integrating' Eqs. (3A-4), or (3A-5); that is to say, of *generating* the full group (or, in general, a suitable connected part of the group manifold) from its 'infinitesimal part'. This process is, in the case of $\mathfrak{R}$, both analytically simple and intuitively vivid without being as trivially immediate as it is for the group of translations.

What we have to show is that *every* element of $\mathfrak{R}$—for in this case one can in fact generate the complete group—can be obtained by integration of (3A-7). We can make use of an important elementary proposition in the theory of rotations, to the effect that every rotation about a point is equivalent to a rotation around an axis passing through the point.‡ Let the direction of this axis and the associated angle of rotation for a given element of $\mathfrak{R}$ be represented by the direction and magnitude respectively of a vector $\mathbf{\Omega}$, and let the corresponding transformation matrix be denoted by $R_{\mathbf{\Omega}}$. According to Eq. (3A-8*a*), the matrix of the infinitesimal transformation given by Eq. (3A-7) is identical with $R_{\boldsymbol{\omega}}$. Consistently with the *continuity* property of rotation as it presents itself to our spatial intuition, we can therefore expect that

$$R_{\mathbf{\Omega}} = \lim_{\omega \to 0} (R_{\boldsymbol{\omega}})^{\Omega/\omega} \qquad \begin{aligned} \omega &= |\boldsymbol{\omega}| \\ \Omega &= |\mathbf{\Omega}| \end{aligned}$$

when we let $\boldsymbol{\omega}$ remain in the direction of $\mathbf{\Omega}$. We can suppose that Ω/ω is an integer m tending to infinity, so that the iteration process implicit in the above equation is in evidence, as well as the actual limit obtained upon substitution of Eq. (3A-7):§

$$R_{\mathbf{\Omega}} = \lim_{m \to \infty} \left(I + \frac{1}{m}\Omega S_0\right)^m = e^{\Omega S_0}, \qquad (S_0)_{ij} = \epsilon_{ijk}\frac{\omega_k}{\omega} \tag{3A-9}$$

Turning now to group $\mathfrak{L}$, the problem of finding the corresponding infinitesimal matrices presents no difficulty. We can either use the imaginary time variable and proceed precisely as in the case of Eq. (3A-7), or, if we prefer, we can make direct use of Eq. (3-53) and obtain in terms of real coordinates (the quantities now representing *matrices* of order *four*)

$$I_\epsilon = I + MS \qquad \begin{matrix} \tilde{S} = -S \\ S \text{ infinitesimal} \end{matrix} \qquad M = \begin{bmatrix} 1 & & & \\ & -1 & & \\ & & -1 & \\ & & & -1 \end{bmatrix} \tag{3A-10}$$

‡ This is the content of Euler's theorem in kinematics. A geometric proof of this theorem is given, e.g., in E. T. Whittaker, "Analytical Dynamics," p. 2, Dover Publications, Inc., New York, 1944; for an analytic proof see, e.g., H. Goldstein, "Classical Mechanics," sec. 4-6, Addison-Wesley Publishing Company, Inc., Reading, Mass., 1959.

§ Using the relations $S_0{}^2 = S_1$, $(S_1)_{ij} = -\delta_{ij} + n_i n_j$ ($\mathbf{n} = \boldsymbol{\omega}/\omega$), and $S_0{}^3 = -S_0$, Eq. (3A-9) reduces to:

$$R_{\Omega} = I + \sum_{k=0}^{\infty} (-1)^k \frac{1}{(2k+1)!}\Omega^{2k+1}S_0 - \sum_{k=1}^{\infty} (-1)^k \frac{1}{(2k)!}\Omega^{2k}S_1$$
$$= I + (\sin \Omega)S_0 + (1 - \cos \Omega)S_1$$

This yields the known general expression for the rotation:

$$\mathbf{x}' = (\cos \Omega)\mathbf{x} + (1 - \cos \Omega)(\mathbf{n} \cdot \mathbf{x})\mathbf{n} + \sin \Omega(\mathbf{x} \times \mathbf{n})$$

Note also that if, say, the x_3 axis is chosen in the direction of $\mathbf{\Omega}$, and if we suppress the last row and the last column in S_0 and in S_1 (that consist of zeros, corresponding to $dx_3 = 0$), then $S_1 = -I$, and the above formula reduces to the familiar complex variable representation of the rotation (of coordinate axes): $x_1' + ix_2' = e^{-i\Omega}(x_1 + ix_2)$.

Our method of 'integration' of Eq. (3A-7) can clearly be applied also to Eq. (3A-10), with the result:

$$T = e^Q, \qquad MQ \text{ skew-symmetric (and finite)} \qquad (3A\text{-}11)$$

the elements of the matrix MQ being proportional to the corresponding elements of the matrix S in Eq. (3A-10). But is *every* member of $\mathfrak{L}$ representable in the form (3A-11)? If it is, then clearly our integration problem is fully solved. It is not obvious, though, if one can produce a proof that is anywhere as immediate as for the group $\mathfrak{R}$, for we do not have a strict minkowskian analog of Euler's theorem. (However, see Prob. 3-22.) On the other hand, there is available Lie's general theory on the construction of a group from its infinitesimal elements. This theory, though mathematically interesting, is not too simple, and we must content ourselves here with only an indication of the principal steps.‡

This general theory is actually not essential for our immediate purpose. The indication presented in the footnote, page 76, can suffice. (See also footnote §, page 365.)

Our problem is concerned with the determination of the functions f_A of Eq. (3A-3), given a *linearly independent* set of the differential operators (3A-5). The theory must also supply conditions on these operators insuring that the family (3A-3) actually forms an r-parameter group, i.e., insuring the existence of a set of r functions, $h_u(a;b) \equiv h_u(a_1, \ldots, a_r; b_1, \ldots, b_r)$, such that [in the notation of Eq. (3A-3)] one can make the identification

$$T_b T_a = T_{h(a;b)} \qquad (3A\text{-}12)$$

with all the group laws being thereby satisfied.

The first requirement can obviously be met only if one can derive from the infinitesimal transformations (3A-5) an integrable differential system for the f_A. In order to investigate this question, one must have recourse to the theory of systems of total differential equations,

$$\frac{\partial z_A}{\partial y_u} = F_{Au}(z_1, \ldots, z_n; y_1, \ldots, y_r) \equiv F_{Au}(z;y) \qquad \begin{matrix} A = 1, \ldots, n \\ u = 1, \ldots, r \end{matrix} \qquad (3A\text{-}13)$$

for which the basic existence theorem can be stated as follows:§ If the func-

‡ There exist a number of variants to Lie's original method. The mathematically interested reader can consult, e.g., Pontrjagin, *op. cit.*, sec. 56 (and pertinent earlier sections), or Eisenhart, *op. cit.*, chap. 1 (as well as original papers referred to in these books). The approach in Weyl, *op. cit.*, is more direct and intuitively vivid, but the presentation is perhaps somewhat more difficult to follow because of its terse style.

§ For proofs of this theorem, see, e.g., T. Levi-Civita, "The Absolute Differential Calculus," chap. 2, Hafner Publishing Company, Inc., New York; or, H. Weyl, *op. cit.*, pp. 66–68. The necessity of the condition of the theorem is obvious. Note also that in the

tions F_{Au} and their derivatives are continuous in a region $\mathfrak{U}$, then in order that the system have a solution satisfying given initial conditions

$$z_A(\eta_1, \ldots, \eta_r) = \zeta_A, \qquad (\eta;\zeta) \text{ in } \mathfrak{U} \tag{3A-13a}$$

it is necessary and sufficient that

$$\frac{dF_{Au}}{dy_v} - \frac{dF_{Av}}{dy_u} = 0 \text{ identically for } (y;z) \text{ in } \mathfrak{U} \tag{3A-14}$$

where
$$\frac{dF_{Au}}{dy_v} \equiv \frac{dF_{Au}}{dy_v}\bigg|_{z_A = z_A(y)} \equiv \frac{\partial F_{Au}}{\partial y_v} + \frac{\partial F_{Au}}{\partial z_B} F_{Bv} \tag{3A-14a}$$

The solution is then also unique.

In order to find the differential system we are seeking, we consider the transformation $J \equiv T_{a+da}T_{\bar{a}}$, where $T_{\bar{a}} \equiv T_a{}^{-1}$. It is apparent that J is an *infinitesimal* transformation when the da_u are infinitesimal. Explicitly, since $J = T_{h(\bar{a};a+da)}$ [see Eq. (3A-12)], and‡

$$h_u(\bar{a}; a + da) = a_u^0 + g_{uv}(a)\, da_v, \qquad g_{uv}(a) \equiv \frac{\partial h_u(\bar{a};b)}{\partial b_v}\bigg|_{b=a} \tag{3A-15}$$

it follows that $J = T_{a^0+\delta a} = I_{\delta a}$, $\delta a_u = g_{uv}(a)\, da_v$. Hence if $x' = T_a x$, then $dx' = (T_{a+da} - T_a)x = (T_{a+da} - T_a)T_{\bar{a}}x' = (I_{\delta a} - I)x'$, i.e.,

$$dx'_A = f_{Au}(x')g_{uv}(a)\, da_v$$

or,

$$\frac{\partial x'_A}{\partial a_u} = f_{Av}(x')g_{vu}(a) \tag{3A-16}$$

This is the required system, and it is seen to be indeed of the form (3A-13), with the initial conditions (3A-13a) given by

$$x'_A(a^0) = x_A \tag{3A-16a}$$

As to the integrability conditions (3A-14) and (3A-14a), these yield here the identities (dropping now the prime in x', and remembering our summation convention)

$$[g_{wu,v}(a) - g_{wv,u}(a)]f_{Aw}(x) = g_{wu}(a)g_{sv}(a)f_{Aws}(x)$$

---

case $n = r = 3$, with z_A and y_u representing the cartesian components of a vector in ordinary space and the cartesian coordinates in this space; if the F_{Au} are explicitly independent of the z, then the theorem reduces to the known result in vector analysis to the effect that a vector field is irrotational (i.e., expressible as a gradient field) when and only when the curl of the vector vanishes identically. It is in fact possible to generalize the customary proof of this special result so as to obtain the sufficiency proof of the general theorem.

‡ The equations involving differentials are of course written to first order. An essential part of the analysis, which we here omit, is concerned with establishing the existence and the nonvanishing of pertinent first-order terms.

where on the left we have introduced the customary and convenient *comma notation for partial derivatives*, and on the right we have

$$f_{Aws}(x) \equiv f_{As,B}f_{Bw} - f_{Aw,B}f_{Bs} \tag{3A-17}$$

Since (as one can prove from our assumptions—here made mostly tacitly) the matrix $\|g_{uv}(a)\|$ must be nonsingular,‡ we can introduce its inverse§

$$\|h_{uv}(a)\| = \|g_{uv}(a)\|^{-1} \tag{3A-18}$$

and obtain the identities

$$f_{Auv}(x) = h_{ru}(a)h_{sv}(a)[g_{wr,s}(a) - g_{ws,r}(a)]f_{Aw}(x) \tag{3A-19}$$

These being identities in the x and the a, it necessarily follows that the quantities

$$h_{ru}(a)h_{sv}(a)[g_{wr,s}(a) - g_{ws,r}(a)] = c_{wuv} \tag{3A-20}$$

are *constants*. These constants are called "structure constants" of the Lie group, for reasons that will become apparent in what follows.

The identities (3A-19) can be written [by Eqs. (3A-17) and 3A-20)]: $f_{Av,B}f_{Bu} - f_{Au,B}f_{Bv} = c_{wuv}f_{Aw}$; or, more compactly

$$[Q_u,Q_v] = c_{wuv}Q_w, \qquad Q_u \equiv f_{Au}\frac{\partial}{\partial x_A} \tag{3A-21}$$

where the "commutator" operation is defined in the usual way: $[U,V] \equiv UV - VU$. Since (as can be immediately verified, and writing U for Q_u, etc.), $[U,V] = -[V,U]$, $[[U,V], W] + [[V,W], U] + [[W,U], V] = 0$, one finds:

$$c_{wuv} + c_{wvu} = 0, \qquad c_{suv}c_{rsw} + c_{svw}c_{rsu} + c_{swu}c_{rsv} = 0 \tag{3A-22}$$

What we have obtained are in essence necessary conditions to our problem. The burden of the Lie theory is to establish their sufficiency. In other words, it is required to prove that a linearly independent set of differential operators Q_u determines uniquely a finite Lie group for which the Q_u yield the infinitesimal transformations according to (3A-5), provided that the conditions (3A-21) are satisfied, where the constants c_{uvw} obey the relations (3A-22). We present now just the barest outline of such a proof.

Turning to the differential system (3A-16), we observe that to begin with, the functions $g_{vu}(a)$ are not explicitly known, since it is only the functions $f_{Au}(x)$ that are assumed given. We have been however necessarily led to the differential system (3A-20), and it turns out that the relations

‡ In general this will hold only in a suitable vicinity of the identity. In fact, all of this 'integration' theory is, to begin with, in general only *local*. In our case, however, the theory yields all of the finite group, i.e., all of $\mathfrak{L}$.

§ Actually, $h_{uv}(a) = \partial h_u(a;b)/\partial b_v \Big|_{b=a^0}$. The reader may find it instructive to prove this result with the aid of the definition (3A-15).

(3A-22) are precisely the integrability conditions for this system.‡ Using Eq. (3A-18) and the initial conditions $g_{uv}(a^0) = \delta_{uv}$,§ the functions g_{uv} are then completely specified, and consequently so is also the solution

$$x'_A = f_A(a;x) \equiv f_A(x;a)$$

of the system (3A-16). It remains to show that the transformations (3A-3), determined by this solution, form an r-parameter Lie group. This can be done, for instance, by first deriving a system of differential equations for the $h_u(a;b)$ [see Eq. (3A-12)] as functions of the b_u, that is of the same form as Eq. (3A-16), and has Eqs. (3A-20) for its integrability relations, and the equations $h_u(a;a^0) = a_u$ as initial conditions. With the $h_u(a;b)$ thus determined it is then easy to show that the relations (3A-12) are satisfied by the transformations (3A-3) we have constructed, and that the relation $T_a^{-1} = T_{\bar{a}}$ $[h_u(\bar{a};a) = h_u(a;\bar{a}) = a_u^0]$ holds as well.¶ The actual construction of the elements of the Lie group is accomplished most conveniently in terms of its *one-parameter subgroups*, whose usefulness and intuitive significance is manifested, as we have seen, by the theory concerning the rotation group $\mathfrak{R}$. For a discussion of this important topic in the Lie theory the interested reader can consult, e.g., Eisenhart, *op. cit.*, secs. 10 and 11. For our immediate purpose it will suffice to quote the resulting basic theorem ([11.1] in the above reference, which we state here in terms of our notation):

The transformations of an r-parameter Lie group whose 'generators' are Q_u (assumed to form a linearly independent set) consist of the transformations of the one-parameter groups generated by the infinitesimal transformations determined by the operators a_uQ_u (a_u arbitrary real constants), or of products of such transformations.

Returning to our infinitesimal transformations (3A-10)‡‡ it is now clear that if we are to apply Lie's theory, and in particular the above theorem, we have first to establish the integrability relations (3A-21). These relations assume in the case of linear homogeneous transformations [so that

$$f_{Au}(x) = f_{ABu}x_B$$

f_{ABu} *constants*] the *matrix* form:

$$[F_v,F_u] = c_{wuv}F_w, \qquad F_u \equiv \|f_{ABu}\| \tag{3A-23}$$

‡ One applies a corollary to the theorem on total differential equations quoted earlier. See Levi-Civita, *op. cit.*, chap. 3.

§ By Eq. (3A-15), $g_{uv}(a^0) = \partial h_u(a^0;b)/\partial b_v \Big|_{b=a^0} = \partial b_u/\partial b_v = \delta_{uv}$.

¶ See, e.g., Eisenhart, *op. cit.*, sec. 6.

‡‡ Note that in Eq. (3A-10) we have the *matrix* of the transformation.

These commutation relations are easily established for the subgroup $\mathfrak{R}$ of $\mathfrak{L}$.‡ In fact, denoting by U_r the matrices F of Eq. (3A-23) that corresponds to ω/ω in Eq. (3A-8) coinciding with $\mathbf{e}_r$, the unit vectors in the direction of the coordinate axes, one finds§

$$[U_r, U_s] = \epsilon_{srq} U_q \tag{3A-24}$$

and the relations (3A-22) are readily checked for the ϵ symbols.§

The matrices F for $\mathfrak{L}$ can be obtained at this point most simply by introducing the imaginary time variable. By a direct extension of the results for $\mathfrak{R}$, we can then conclude that a complete set of 'generator' matrices F for $\mathfrak{L}$ is given by the six matrices $U_{\alpha\beta}$ ($\alpha,\beta = 1, 2, 3, 4$; $\alpha < \beta$), where $U_{\alpha\beta}$ corresponds to 'rotation' in the $x_\alpha x_\beta$ plane:¶

$$(U_{\alpha\beta})_{\gamma\delta} = \delta_{\alpha\gamma}\delta_{\beta\delta} - \delta_{\alpha\delta}\delta_{\beta\gamma} \tag{3A-25}$$

To simplify the writing and the derivation of the commutation relations, it is convenient to divide the $U_{\alpha\beta}$ into two sets:

$$\begin{aligned} M_1 &= U_{23}, \quad & M_2 &= U_{31}, \quad & M_3 &= U_{12} \\ N_1 &= U_{14}, \quad & N_2 &= U_{24}, \quad & N_3 &= U_{34} \end{aligned} \tag{3A-26}$$

Except for an extra row and column of zeros the M_i are like the U_i, and hence they satisfy the commutation relations (3A-24). By replacing the triplet of axes x_1, x_2, x_3 by all other possible triplets x_α, x_β, x_γ analogous reasoning leads to:

$$\begin{aligned} [N_i, N_j] &= \epsilon_{jik} M_k \\ [N_i, M_j] &= \epsilon_{jik} N_k \end{aligned} \qquad i \neq j \tag{3A-27a}$$

In order to find $[N_i, M_j]$ for $i = j$, let us note that the commutation relations (3A-21) also follow from the easily verifiable fact that when, in the product $TST^{-1}S^{-1}$ of transformations of a Lie group, we substitute infinitesimal transformations, we obtain an infinitesimal transformation (see Prob. 3-19), hence, by Eq. (3A-5), a linear superposition corresponding to Eq. (3A-21). It is obvious that rotations in two perpendicular planes are interchangeable.‡‡

‡ They are of course well known in quantum mechanics. See, e.g., L. I. Schiff, "Quantum Mechanics," 2d ed., pp. 142, 143, McGraw-Hill Book Company, Inc., New York, 1955.

§ From Eq. (3A-8) it follows that $(U_r)_{ij} = \epsilon_{ijr}$, and Eq. (3A-24) is a consequence of the formula, $\epsilon_{ijr}\epsilon_{jks} - \epsilon_{ijs}\epsilon_{jkr} = \epsilon_{srq}\epsilon_{ikq}$. By a shift of indices this formula can be put in the form (3A-22).

¶ Note that $\epsilon_{ijr} = \delta_{si}\delta_{tj} - \delta_{sj}\delta_{ti}$ where r, s, t is a cyclic permutation of 1, 2, 3, so that $(U_r)_{ij} = (U_{st})_{ij}$ are given by expressions of the form (3A-25) in the three-dimensional case.

‡‡ In terms of the real time variable, this interchangeability reflects the readily perceived fact, following from symmetry considerations, that it cannot matter in what order one performs the following two operations: setting a reference system in uniform motion along a given direction, and rotating the coordinate axes around this direction.

The corresponding structure constants must therefore vanish, and hence

$$[N_1,M_1] = [N_2,M_2] = [N_3,M_3] = 0 \tag{3A-27b}$$

It is not difficult to verify that the relations (3A-27) and (3A-24) (for M_i) can be written compactly:

$$[U_{\alpha\beta},U_{\gamma\delta}] = \delta_{\alpha\delta}U_{\beta\gamma} - \delta_{\alpha\gamma}U_{\beta\delta} + \delta_{\beta\gamma}U_{\alpha\delta} - \delta_{\beta\delta}U_{\alpha\gamma} \tag{3A-28}$$

These relations, of course, also follow directly from Eqs. (3A-25).

The integrability conditions (3A-23) and (3A-22) have thus been verified. The associated differential operators therefore generate a 6-parameter group. That this group is precisely the Lorentz group $\mathfrak{L}$ follows by appeal to the theorem referred to earlier, which justifies the building up of the group by first constructing 1-parameter subgroups and multiplying out the resulting transformations.‡

These subgroups can obviously be identified with the groups of rotation about the origin in each of the coordinate planes. For the purely spatial planes these are of course rotations in the ordinary sense of the word, but when the plane contains the time axis we are dealing with an 'imaginary' rotation arising from our use of the imaginary variable $x_4 = ix_0$. This 'rotation' must reduce to a corresponding special Lorentz transformation when the real variable x_0 is reintroduced if the resultant group is indeed to coincide with $\mathfrak{L}$—a conclusion that will now be verified directly.

Our imaginary rotation

$$\begin{aligned} x' &= (\cos\theta)x + (\sin\theta)x_4 \\ x_4' &= -(\sin\theta)x + (\cos\theta)x_4 \end{aligned} \qquad \text{other } x_i \text{ unchanged}$$

(where x stands for x_1, x_2, or x_3) transforms upon the substitution $x_4 = ix_0$, $\theta = i\psi$, into

$$\begin{aligned} x' &= (\cosh\psi)x - (\sinh\psi)x_0 \\ x_0' &= -(\sinh\psi)x + (\cosh\psi)x_0 \end{aligned} \qquad \text{other } x_i \text{ unchanged} \tag{3A-29}$$

These equations reduce to Eq. (2-6) when

$$\tanh\psi = \beta \tag{3A-30}$$

and $\cosh\psi = (1 - \beta^2)^{-1/2}$. As is easily checked, the latter equation is indeed a consequence of Eq. (3A-30).

‡ That *every* transformation of $\mathfrak{L}$ is representable as a product of transformations of $\mathfrak{L}$ each representing a rotation (real or imaginary) within a plane in $\mathfrak{M}$ (and thus each a member of a 1-parameter subgroup), can be established by combining the result on the representation of such a transformation by a product of the form $(R')^{-1}LR$ [as discussed in Sec. 3-4 beginning with the paragraph containing Eq. (3-30)], and the Euler theorem on rotations in ordinary space. We can, in fact, assume that the planes of rotation of the component transformations coincide with coordinate planes, since every spatial rotation can always be written as the product of at most three such rotations.

APPENDIX 3B A GENERAL DERIVATION OF THE GROUP $\mathfrak{L}$

We shall here outline a deduction of the group $\mathfrak{L}$ along the lines discussed in Sec. 3-2, but dealing from the start with all three spatial dimensions.‡ In view of the results developed in Appendix 3A, it suffices to deduce the infinitesimal geneıators of $\mathfrak{L}$; these, as there indicated, determine the full group uniquely.

The proof of the linearity of the transformations of $\mathfrak{L}$ given for the special case discussed in Sec. 3-2 is clearly also applicable in the present general case. We have therefore to derive the quantities f_{ABu} of Eq. (3A-23).

A general infinitesimal transformation connecting two inertial systems S, S' in relative motion can be specified by the components θ_i of the angular displacement vector determining the rotation bringing the spatial frames of S and S' into parallelism, and by their relative velocity components v_i, all these quantities being taken as infinitesimals.§ The *matrix* of such a transformation can therefore be written

$$I + R_i\theta_i + L_iv_i \tag{3B-1}$$

Since the matrices R_i and L_i are independent of the parameters θ_i, v_i, therefore when we set $v_i = 0$ in Eq. (3B-1), the resulting matrix $I + R_i\theta_i$ must yield an ordinary infinitesimal rotation of the spatial axes (together with $t' = t$). Consequently, by the relevant results in Appendix 3A, it follows that

$$R_i = \begin{bmatrix} 0 & 0 & 0 & 0 \\ 0 & & & \\ 0 & & U_i & \\ 0 & & & \end{bmatrix} \tag{3B-2}$$

where the first row and column (to be numbered by the index 0) correspond to the time variable t.

In order to determine the matrices L_i, we refer to relations (3-10), which can now be written

$$\left.\frac{\partial x_i'}{\partial x_j}\right|_{\substack{dt=0\\ \theta_i=0}} = \left.\frac{\partial x_i}{\partial x_j'}\right|_{\substack{dt'=0\\ \theta_i=0}} \tag{3B-3}$$

$$\left.\frac{\partial t'}{\partial t}\right|_{dx_i'=0} = \left.\frac{\partial t}{\partial t'}\right|_{dx_i=0} \tag{3B-4}$$

Using the last of Eqs. (3A-6) it can be concluded from Eq. (3B-4) that

$$(L_i)_{00} = 0 \tag{3B-5}$$

‡ The logical basis of this deduction is discussed more fully in H. M. Schwartz, *Am. J. Phys.*, **30:** 697, (1962); **31:** 140, (1963).

§ Recall discussion in the first part of Sec. 3-4, and the relations (3A-6).

Similar reasoning involving Eq. (3B-3) leads to:

$$(L_i)_{jk} = 0 \tag{3B-6}$$

Again by the last of Eqs. (3A-6), and since $v_i = dx_i/dt \big|_{x_j'=0}$, one finds, remembering Eqs. (3B-1) and (3B-2), that

$$(L_i)_{j0} = -\delta_{ij} \tag{3B-7}$$

It remains to determine the matrix elements $(L_i)_{0j}$. To this end we note that the part $v_i(L_i)_{0j}x_j$ of the expression entering in the transformation equation for the time variable must be independent of the orientation of the spatial axes in S—as follows from the *isotropy* of physical space and the operational meaning of the time variable. Consequently, the quantities $(L_i)_{0j}$ must be the components of a *spatial* second-order tensor with respect to S. Our basic principle of the isotropy of physical space can serve also for indicating the form of this tensor. A little reflection will show that for consistency with this principle, one must have

$$(L_i)_{0j} = \lambda\delta_{ij}, \qquad \lambda \text{ a scalar} \tag{3B-8}$$

The scalar λ is clearly a universal constant and its physical dimensions are those of a reciprocal velocity squared. By reasoning similar to that employed in a related connection in Sec. 3-2, one can subsequently show that λ must be negative. Therefore, writing $\lambda = -\sigma^{-2}$, and combining Eqs. (3B-1), (3B-2), and (3B-5) to (3B-8), we finally arrive at the following expression for the matrix of the general infinitesimal transformation connecting two inertial reference frames:

$$\begin{bmatrix} 1 & -\sigma^{-2}v_j \\ -v_i & \delta_{ij} + \theta_k(U_k)_{ij} \end{bmatrix} \tag{3B-9}$$

The only indefiniteness which still remains is in the choice of the *universal velocity* σ. If it is taken as infinite, it is easily verified that the infinitesimal transformations determined by Eq. (3B-9) generate the group containing the galilean transformations and proper rotations. If σ is chosen finite, then in suitable units it can be taken as unity, and a comparison of Eqs. (3B-9) and (3A-25) then shows‡ [remembering Eq. (3B-1) and taking the results of Appendix 3A into account] that the group generated in this case will coincide with $\mathfrak{L}$ when σ is identified with c.

Problems

3-1 Einstein's original definition of simultaneity involves his prescription for clock synchronization (see [2], paper 3), which, in an idealized sense, can be stated as follows. Two 'identical' clocks K, K', situated at the points

‡ In making this comparison it must be remembered that the *imaginary* time variable is used in the derivation of Eq. (3A-25).

P, P' fixed in the inertial system S, are *synchronous*, when the respective K and K' times t_1, t_1' of the sending of a light signal at P and its arriving at P', are connected by the formula $t_1' = \frac{1}{2}(t_1 + t_2)$ with the K time t_2 of its return to P (upon suitable reflection at P'—the light propagation taking place *in vacuo*). (*a*) Prove the consistency of this definition by showing that it satisfies the conditions of reflexivity and transitivity. Do we require any additional assumptions? Does Einstein's definition involve implicitly the existence (again in an idealized sense) of perfectly rigid bodies when at rest in a given inertial system? What is the relationship of this definition to postulate B? (*b*) Can the optical assumptions concerning light propagation in empty space replace the mechanical assumptions inherent in Newton's first law as they relate to the *straightness* of spatial lines and the *uniformity* of time flow? (*c*) Compare Einstein's method for establishing simultaneity relative to a given inertial system with the method (again purely conceptual) of the infinitely slow transport of a master clock. [See [1], sec 11; and Bohm, *op. cit.* (on page 31), chap. 8.]

3-2 Show that the linear transformations

$$\mathbf{x} \to \mathbf{x}' = T_v\mathbf{x} \qquad \mathbf{x} \equiv (x_0,x_1,x_2,x_3)$$
$$x_0 = ct,\ x_1 = x,\ x_2 = y,\ x_3 = z$$

which leave Eq. (3-2) form invariant, and which correspond to a relative motion of coordinate frames as indicated in Fig. 2-1, are either of the form (3-3) or of the form

$$\begin{aligned} x_0' &= -\lambda\gamma(x_0 - \beta x) \\ x' &= \lambda\gamma(x - \beta x_0) \\ x_k' &= \lambda x_k \qquad k = 2,\ 3 \end{aligned} \tag{i}$$

Show further that from the relations

$$T_v^{-1} = T_{-v}, \qquad \lambda(-v) = \lambda(v) \tag{ii}$$

one can conclude that $\lambda^2 = 1$, the Lorentz equations (2-6) resulting from the choice $\lambda = +1$. Justify Eq. (ii) on the basis of accepted kinematic principles. Lastly, discuss the physical significance of Eqs. (i) with $\lambda = +1$, as well as the significance of the transformations (3-3) and (i) with $\lambda = -1$; also find the determinants of the four possible classes of transformations and examine the group properties of each class. [After justifying the general form of the last two of Eqs. (3-3) for the type of transformations under consideration, one can consider transformations of the form $x_0' = lx_0 + mx$, $x' = px_0 + qx$. Our form-invariance condition, that is equivalent to

$$(\Delta x_0')^2 - \Delta x_i'\,\Delta x_i' = \lambda^2(\Delta x_0{}^2 - \Delta x_i\,\Delta x_i), \qquad \lambda \equiv \lambda(v)$$

then yields the relations $l^2 - p^2 = \lambda^2$, $q^2 - m^2 = \lambda^2$, $lm = pq$. From these equations one finds $l^2 = q^2$, and thence again by these equations (and since

$\beta \equiv v/c = -p/q$) it follows that $m = -\beta l$, $l^2 = q^2 = \lambda^2\gamma^2$. See also footnote, page 85.]

3-3 (*a*) From Eq. (3-13*a*), with the proper substitution for the symbols, deduce the formula

$$\gamma_{u'} = \left(1 - \frac{vu}{c^2}\right)\gamma_v\gamma_u \tag{i}$$

where u, u' are the velocities of a particle as measured in the inertial frames S, S' respectively, and v is the velocity of S' relative to S—all the motions being parallel to a given line. Obtain the generalization of Eq. (i) (consisting in the replacement of vu by v_iu_i) when the motions in question have arbitrary directions, after noting first the law of transformation of the velocity vector $\mathbf{u}$ under the Lorentz transformations (3-29*a*) [generalizing Eq. (3-22)],

$$\mathbf{u}' = \frac{1}{\gamma[1 - (1/c)\boldsymbol{\beta}\cdot\mathbf{u}]}\left[\mathbf{u} - \left(c\gamma - \frac{\gamma - 1}{\beta^2}\boldsymbol{\beta}\cdot\mathbf{u}\right)\boldsymbol{\beta}\right] \tag{ii}$$

where ordinary vector notation is employed in an understandable sense. Deduce these results also by considering the product of the matrices of two transformations of the form (3-29). (*b*) Although the transformation formula (ii) [unlike the special case (3-15)] is not symmetrical in $\mathbf{u}$ and $c\boldsymbol{\beta} = \mathbf{v}$, the general formula (i) (i.e., with vu replaced by $\mathbf{v}\cdot\mathbf{u}$) shows that the *magnitude* of the vector $\mathbf{u}'$ is such a symmetric function. Verify also the following more explicit expressions showing this symmetry,

$$\begin{aligned} \mathbf{u}'^2 &= c^2\left(1 - \frac{(1-\boldsymbol{\alpha}^2)(1-\boldsymbol{\beta}^2)}{(1-\boldsymbol{\alpha}\cdot\boldsymbol{\beta})^2}\right) & \boldsymbol{\alpha} &= \frac{\mathbf{u}}{c} \\ &= c^2\frac{(\boldsymbol{\alpha}-\boldsymbol{\beta})^2 - (\boldsymbol{\alpha}\times\boldsymbol{\beta})^2}{(1-\boldsymbol{\alpha}\cdot\boldsymbol{\beta})^2} & \boldsymbol{\beta} &= \frac{\mathbf{v}}{c} \end{aligned} \tag{iii}$$

(*c*) With the aid of the general formula (i) verify that if an object has a velocity smaller than c relative to one inertial system, its velocity relative to any other inertial system is also smaller than c. What invariance result given in the first part of Sec. 3-4 leads immediately to the same conclusion?

3-4 With the aid of the relativistic law for the composition of velocities show that if there existed an action that could be propagated relative to an inertial system with a speed greater than c, it would be possible to have a situation in which an *effect precedes its cause.*

3-5 If $\mathbf{v}'$, $\mathbf{v}''$ represent the velocities relative to an inertial system S of two particles P', P'', will the velocity of P'' relative to P' *as measured in* S be expressible in terms of $\mathbf{v}'$, $\mathbf{v}''$ according to the classical law of composition of velocities? In particular, can we obtain in this fashion relative velocities whose magnitudes exceed c, and would this entail a contradiction with the theory of relativity? What relevance do these questions have to the customary analysis of the Michelson-Morley experiment?

3-6 (*a*) Show that the transformation equations connecting inertial systems must be linear, from the requirement that straight lines of $\mathfrak{M}$ are transformed into such lines. (See Prob. 1-4. Note that it is tacitly assumed that points having *finite* coordinates are transformed into such points.) (*b*) Deduce this result also by a method similar to that employed in the proof of linearity given on page 9. (*c*) Show that another linearity proof that likewise is based on the homogeneity property of space-time follows from a consideration of the transformations between the differentials of the coordinates.

3-7 Show that the prerelativistic notion of an ideal rigid body is inconsistent with the principles of STR. Does this conclusion imply the complete inadmissibility of postulating rigid measuring rods in the physical constructions of the spatial and temporal relations of STR, or can we employ a suitable restricted kinematic definition of rigidity which in an ideal sense can be consistently applied also in STR?

3-8 Using the transformation equations (2-7) applied to an electromagnetic field having the form of a plane wave, prove that the phase function (3-23) is a relativistic invariant, and thence deduce Eqs. (3-19) and (3-21). As an intermediate step in this proof show that $\mathsf{n} = (\nu,\nu\mathbf{n})$ represents a 4-vector (i.e., a vector in $\mathfrak{M}$), and that the transformation law for $\mathbf{n}$ is similar to that for $\mathbf{u}$ given in Eq. (ii) of Prob. 3-3.

3-9 Find the connection between the vectors $\mathbf{n}, \mathbf{n}'$ of Eqs. (3-19) and (3-20) and prove the consistency of these formulas.

3-10 The relativistic second-order Doppler effect has recently been subjected to an interesting and fairly precise check through Mössbauer resonance absorption measurements with the gamma-ray source and absorber situated at the center and at the rim of a suitable rotor assembly (see references in footnote §, page 49). Analyze the underlying theory of such experiments, and in particular, assuming that the source is in the shape of a small circular band of radius r' concentric with the rim (of radius $r'' \gg r'$), show that the corresponding relative frequency shift, $(\nu'' - \nu')/\nu'$, is given approximately by $-\Omega^2 r''^2/2c^2$, where Ω is the angular velocity of the rotor. [We can employ an extension of the reasoning given on page 47. We must now consider at first the full expansion of $\delta T = \delta(t + R/c)$, namely,

$$\delta T = \delta t + \frac{1}{c}\left[\frac{\partial R}{\partial t}\,\delta t + \frac{\partial R}{\partial T}\,\delta T + \frac{1}{2}\left(\frac{\partial^2 R}{\partial t^2}\,\delta t^2 + \cdots\right) + \cdots\right]$$

However, we can show that the ratio of the terms involving second derivatives to those involving first derivatives is of the order of Ω/ν, a negligible quantity. The stated result follows from the resulting formula by cancellation of the linear terms, and taking account of the smallness of $(r'/r'')^2$.]

3-11 Derive the result referred to in the text concerning cosmic ray muons by making use of the FitzGerald contraction formula instead of the time-dilatation formula. On the other hand, does the latter formula have any bearing on the usual analysis of the Michelson-Morley experiment? The conventional analysis starting with the assumption of a stationary ether explains of course the null result of this experiment in terms of the FitzGerald-Lorentz contraction. In what context would the time-dilatation formula be likewise relevant? (Note that on the assumption of absolute time it can be concluded that $c/c' = \gamma$, where S, S' are the ether and apparatus frames respectively, and c,c' denote the speed of light as measured in these frames.)

3-12 Deduce Eq. (3-29) directly by the method mentioned on page 51. What is the physical significance of the symmetry of the spatial part of the transformation matrix (3-29)? (This question presupposes some knowledge of the strain tensor of classical elasticity. See Sec. 6-1.)

3-13 Prove that the 'length' [as determined by Eq. (3-34a)] of a *timelike* geodesic in $\mathfrak{M}$ connecting two events is *greater* than the length of any other timelike curve of $\mathfrak{M}$ connecting those events. [The definition of a geodesic in $\mathfrak{M}$ and the proof of its *straightness* proceed along lines similar to those discussed in Sec. 1-2. New features arise because the Minkowski metric is *not positive definite* and the "triangle inequality" (see Sec. 1-2) is modified correspondingly.] What is the bearing of this result on the clock paradox?

3-14 Does the relationship designated in Sec. 3-4 as 'quasi-parallelism' possess the properties of reflexivity or of transitivity? Is there any connection between quasi-parallelism and ordinary parallelism as it would be defined in $\mathfrak{M}$? What is the physical significance of the latter?

3-15 (a) Consider the plane through the origin of coordinates in $\mathfrak{M}$ given by the parametric equations

$$x_\alpha = a_\alpha u + b_\alpha v \tag{i}$$

where the 4-vectors a, b are linearly independent. Show that this plane is *timelike, spacelike,* or *null* [i.e., it intersects the light cone centered at the origin of coordinates in two lines, no line, and one (tangent) line, respectively], according as $(\mathsf{a},\mathsf{b})^2 - (\mathsf{a},\mathsf{a})(\mathsf{b},\mathsf{b})$ [notation as in Eq. (3-50)] is respectively positive, negative, or zero. Check that the sign of the last expression or its vanishing do not depend on the choice of the two linearly independent vectors lying in the plane. (b) Show that of two nonnull planes that are mutually perpendicular in $\mathfrak{M}$ one is spacelike and the other timelike. (c) Given a null vector a, consider all nonnull vectors b orthogonal to a. What type of vectors are $\mathfrak{b}$? What vector space is formed by a and the totality of the vectors $\mathfrak{b}$?

3-16 Given two events E, E' for which the $\mathfrak{M}$-distance (or, "interval") is spacelike [i.e., for which the corresponding expression (3-34*a*) is *negative*], show that this interval Δs can be found by the following construction in $\mathfrak{M}$: Consider a free particle world line l passing through one of the events, say, E (i.e., a timelike geodesic in $\mathfrak{M}$ through E), and let E_1, E_2 be the respective intersections with l of the backward and the forward branches of the light cone whose vertex is at E'; then $\Delta s^2 = -\Delta_1 s\, \Delta_2 s$, where $\Delta_1 s$ and $\Delta_2 s$ are the intervals $\overline{E_1E}$ and $\overline{EE_2}$ respectively. Discuss the physical meaning of this construction. How is it related to the 'radar method' of determining distances? [Consider the relations (in obvious notation),

$$0 = \overline{E_1E'}^2 = (\overline{E_1E} + \overline{EE'})^2$$

and $0 = \overline{E'E_2}^2 = (\overline{EE_2} - \overline{EE'})^2$, and note that $\overline{EE_2} \propto \overline{E_1E}$. See [8], chap. 1, sec. 14 and chap. 2, sec. 2.]

3-17 In dealing with relativistic kinematics it is convenient to employ the proper time τ associated with the motion of a particle, which is naturally defined as follows (see discussion in first part of Sec. 3-5)

$$d\tau = \frac{1}{c}\, ds = dt\sqrt{1 - \frac{u^2}{c^2}}, \qquad \mathbf{u} = \frac{d\mathbf{x}}{dt} \tag{i}$$

The relativistic extensions of the vectors of particle velocity and acceleration are then the corresponding 4-vectors U, A whose components (in a given inertial reference frame) are $U_\nu = dx_\nu/d\tau$ and $A_\nu = dU_\nu/d\tau$ ($\nu = 0, 1, 2, 3$) respectively. (*a*) What type of 4-vectors are U and A? [Note that $(\mathsf{U}, \mathsf{A}) = 0$ since $(\mathsf{U},\mathsf{U}) = c^2$.] (*b*) Show that (the notation being self-explanatory)

$$\mathsf{A} = \gamma^2\left(\frac{\gamma^2}{c}(\mathbf{u}\cdot\mathbf{a}), \left[\mathbf{a} + \frac{\gamma^2}{c^2}(\mathbf{u}\cdot\mathbf{a})\mathbf{u}\right]\right) \qquad \gamma \equiv \gamma_u \quad \mathbf{a} = \frac{d\mathbf{u}}{dt} \tag{ii}$$

(*c*) Consider a particle starting from rest at $t = 0$ and being accelerated along the x_1 axis in such a way that (A,A) remains constant. Show that the graph of this motion in the (x_0,x_1) plane is a hyperbola (such motion is therefore also known as "hyperbolic motion"). [Note that according to Eq. (ii), we have $(\mathsf{A},\mathsf{A}) = -(\mathbf{a}^*)^2$ where $\mathbf{a}^*$ is the ordinary acceleration vector as measured in the instantaneous rest system S^* of the particle.] Discuss the properties of this motion when $|\mathbf{a}^*|t/c$ is much greater and much less than 1. Show that the latter case corresponds to the nonrelativistic limit of the familiar parabolic motion. Suppose that the particle starts at the origin with zero velocity. For approximately how long after its departure can signals be transmitted to it from the origin?

3-18 The postulate C on page 63 is rather subtle and will repay careful examination. There is in it very little of the self-evident, and the possibility cannot in fact be ruled out that it is only approximate involving a limitation of the permissible accelerations. Examine recent experiments aiming to check the relativistic time dilatation in an essentially direct manner, and see to what extent postulate C is confirmed. What are some important indirect confirmations of this postulate? (The reader may wish to return to this question after completing the study of Chap. 4. A deeper understanding of the question can be had in the context of the general theory of relativity.)

3-19 (a) Using Eq. (3A-16) prove that one can always choose the parameter for a 1-parameter group so that $h(a,b) = a + b$, and that consequently a 1-parameter group is always "abelian" (i.e., its group composition is a commutative operation). Prove the same result by infinite power series multiplication for a 1-parameter subgroup of an r-parameter group ($r > 1$) obtained by infinite iteration of a given infinitesimal element of the latter group {i.e., by taking $\lim_{n\to\infty} [I + (t/n)Q]^n$, t being the finite parameter of the resulting subgroup where $Q = \alpha_u Q_u$, $\alpha_u\alpha_u = 1$ [see Eq. (3A-5)]}. (b) Consider the "commutator" product $T_1T_2T_1^{-1}T_2^{-1}$, where T_1 and T_2 are elements of a finite-parameter transformation group. Show that this expression yields an infinitesimal transformation when both T_1 and T_2 are infinitesimal, and in particular that the differential operator associated with this infinitesimal transformation [see Eq. (3A-5)] is the commutator bracket expression $[Q_1,Q_2]$ when Q_k is associated with T_k ($k = 1, 2$). [In view of Eq. (3A-6), we must of course here go to small quantities of second order, and take $T = I + \epsilon Q + \epsilon^2(Q^2/2)$, $T^{-1} = I - \epsilon Q + \epsilon^2(Q^2/2)$; see the exponential representation given inside the brackets in part (a).]

3-20 (a) Prove that the Lie group $\mathfrak{L}$ involves six essential parameters. Is the same true of the full homogeneous Lorentz group? (b) Discuss the group of *special* Lorentz transformations as a Lie group. In particular, find the composition function h defined in Eq. (3A-12) and give its physical meaning. Show also that with β as parameter, Eqs. (3A-16) take here the simple form

$$
\begin{aligned}
\frac{\partial x_0'}{\partial \beta} &= -\gamma^2 x_1' \\
\frac{\partial x_1'}{\partial \beta} &= -\gamma^2 x_0' \\
\frac{\partial x_k'}{\partial \beta} &= 0 \qquad k = 2, 3
\end{aligned}
\tag{i}
$$

and that by introducing the parameter ψ given by

$$\int_0^\beta \gamma^2\, d\beta \qquad \text{(ii)}$$

the solution of these equations (omitting the uninteresting last two) with initial conditions, $x_0' = x_0$, $x_1' = x_1$ for $\beta = 0$, can be written in the form (3A-29) or in the equivalent form,

$$x'_\pm = B^{\pm 1} x_\pm, \qquad x_\pm = x_0 \pm x \qquad B = \sqrt{\frac{1-\beta}{1+\beta}} \qquad \text{(iii)}$$

Check that Eqs. (iii) are indeed equivalent to the transformations (2-6) for x_0, x_1‡ and that the above solution in terms of the original parameter (ii) verifies for the present 1-parameter group the result stated in part (*a*) of Prob. 3-19.

3-21 (*a*) Using results given in Appendix 3A (some without proof) show that $\mathfrak{L}$, considered as a continuous manifold, is *connected* (in the same sense that a continuous arc connecting two points in ordinary space is connected). (*b*) Show that the full homogeneous Lorentz group manifold consists of four disjoint pieces, $\mathfrak{L}$, $R^{(x)}\mathfrak{L}$, $R^{(t)}\mathfrak{L}$, and $R^{(x)}R^{(t)}\mathfrak{L}$, where $R^{(x)}$ and $R^{(t)}$ are the inversion transformations (3-52) and (3-49) (together with $x_i' = x_i$). [Recall in this connection the double signs in Eqs. (3-41) and (3-46).] (*c*) Discuss the classical limit (i.e., the limit $c \to \infty$) of the full homogeneous Lorentz group, with due attention to the ordinary rotations and reflections of axes (including the time axis).

3-22 (*a*) In ordinary space, given an arbitrary proper orthogonal transformation, it is always possible to introduce cartesian coordinates so that, in terms of these coordinates, the matrix of the transformation assumes the simple canonical form (the transformation representing a rotation of vectors)

$$\begin{bmatrix} 1 & 0 & 0 \\ 0 & \cos\theta & -\sin\theta \\ 0 & \sin\theta & \cos\theta \end{bmatrix} \qquad \text{(i)}$$

We have, in fact, utilized essentially this result in Appendix 3A in order to prove that the entire group $\mathfrak{R}$ can be generated from its infinitesimal elements. Do we have an analogous result in $\mathfrak{M}$? The matrix (i) represents a rotation in the x_2x_3 plane, the x_1 axis serving thus as the invariant axis of rotation. One might expect that in $\mathfrak{M}$ an analogous canonical transformation would consist of a rotation in a spatial coordinate plane—say, the x_2x_3 plane—and a quasi-rotation in the perpendicular x_0x_1 plane, so that its matrix

‡ Incidentally, the form (iii) suggests the following simple proof that the form invariance of the metric form $x_0^2 - x^2$ implies the Lorentz transformations (in the variables x_0, $x_1 \equiv x$). One must have $x'_+ = ax_+$, $x'_- = (1/a)x_-$ (as $x'_+x'_- = x_+x_-$) and since $dx/dx_0 = \beta$ for $x' = 0$, $(-a + 1/a)/(a + 1/a) = \beta$, i.e., $a = \sqrt{(1-\beta)/(1+\beta)}$ or B given in Eqs. (iii). Note also that Eqs. (iii) represent a reduction of Eqs. (2-6) to principal axes, and that B, B^{-1} are the eigenvalues of the matrix of this transformation.

would have the form

$$T_{\psi\phi} = \begin{bmatrix} \cosh\psi & \sinh\psi & 0 & 0 \\ \sinh\psi & \cosh\psi & 0 & 0 \\ 0 & 0 & \cos\phi & -\sin\phi \\ 0 & 0 & \sin\phi & \cos\phi \end{bmatrix} \tag{ii}$$

Verify that generally the matrix of a Lorentz transformation will indeed assume the form (ii) upon a suitable choice of rectangular coordinates in $\mathfrak{M}$, but that for an exceptional subset of $\mathfrak{L}$ such a reduction is impossible, and instead, with a proper choice of coordinates the canonical form of its matrices is

$$S_\alpha = \begin{bmatrix} 1+\dfrac{\alpha^2}{2} & -\dfrac{\alpha^2}{2} & \alpha & 0 \\ \dfrac{\alpha^2}{2} & 1-\dfrac{\alpha^2}{2} & \alpha & 0 \\ \alpha & -\alpha & 1 & 0 \\ 0 & 0 & 0 & 1 \end{bmatrix}, \qquad \alpha \text{ real and arbitrary} \tag{iii}$$

In proving this result one can employ an extension of the eigenvalue method of establishing the reduction to the canonical form (i) (see Goldstein, *op. cit.*, sec. 4-6). {Our object is, given a matrix T of $\mathfrak{L}$, to bring it as far as possible to its "principal axes." We have therefore to solve completely the eigenvalue problem

$$Tu = \lambda u \tag{iv}$$

where T satisfies Eq. (3-53) and u is a 4-column matrix representing a 4-vector whose components may assume complex values along with the eigenvalue λ. Eqs. (3-53) and (iv) imply (with understandable notation) the following relations. (1) If $\lambda' \neq 1/\lambda''$ then $(\mathsf{u}',\mathsf{u}'') = 0$. (2) Either $\lambda^2 = 1$ or else $(\mathsf{u},\mathsf{u}) = 0$; in particular, if λ is not real, then

$$(\mathsf{u}_{\text{re}},\mathsf{u}_{\text{re}}) = (\mathsf{u}_{\text{im}},\mathsf{u}_{\text{im}}), \qquad (\mathsf{u}_{\text{re}},\mathsf{u}_{\text{im}}) = 0, \qquad \mathsf{u} = \mathsf{u}_{\text{re}} + i\mathsf{u}_{\text{im}} \tag{v}$$

(3) If $\lambda \neq 1$, then there must exist an eigenvalue $1/\lambda$. These relations lead to the following alternatives. (1) All $\lambda = \pm 1$, and either the set of eigenvectors is "complete" (i.e., they can form a vector base for all of $\mathfrak{M}$),‡ or it is not complete—the latter case arising when there exists one and only one null eigenvector [see Prob. 3-15(*c*)], and leading to the canonical matrix (iii). (2) There exists an eigenvalue λ real $\neq 1$, and hence also an eigenvalue $\mu = 1/\lambda$ but no other such pair; and by a proper linear combination of the corresponding eigenvectors u_λ, u_μ, one is led to the upper submatrix in (ii). (3) There exists a complex eigenvalue $\lambda + i\mu$ of unit modulus (and associated

‡ See Appendix 5A and the references given there to the elementary theory of vector spaces. We are now using $\mathfrak{M}$ to denote also the vector space associated with the Minkowski space-time manifold.

complex eigenvector $\mathsf{u} + i\mathsf{v}$), and hence also the eigenvalue $\lambda - i\mu$, but no other such pair; and with the vectors u and v as base one arrives at the lower submatrix in Eq. (ii).} (b) Show that the matrices (iii) form a 1-parameter additive (or, "cyclic") Lie group: $S_{\alpha'}S_{\alpha''} = S_{\alpha'+\alpha''}$; and that $T_\psi S_\alpha T_\psi^{-1} = S_{\sigma\alpha}$, where $T_\psi \equiv T_{\psi\phi}\Big|_{\phi=0}$ and $\sigma = e^{-\psi}$ (Wigner). (*c*) Verify that, interpreted as representing a change of axes $S \to S'$, S_α corresponds to v given by

$$\gamma_v = 1 + \frac{\alpha^2}{2} \tag{vi}$$

with components of velocity of S' relative to S and of S relative to S' (as measured in S and S' respectively), given by

$$\frac{c}{1 + \alpha^2/2}\left(\frac{\alpha^2}{2}, -\alpha, 0\right), \qquad \frac{c}{1 + \alpha^2/2}\left(\frac{\alpha^2}{2}, \alpha, 0\right) \tag{vii}$$

and angle θ of relative rotation of the axes in the common x_1x_2 plane, given by

$$\cos\theta = \frac{4 - \alpha^2}{4 + \alpha^2}, \qquad \sin\theta = \frac{4\alpha}{4 + \alpha^2} \tag{viii}$$

(*d*) Show that one can also obtain the canonical matrices (ii), (iii), starting with the infinitesimal elements of $\mathfrak{L}$ and finding, again by the method of eigenvalues, their canonical matrices $I + H$, where

$$H \equiv H_{\lambda\mu} = \begin{bmatrix} \lambda P & \\ & \mu Q \end{bmatrix}, \qquad P = \begin{bmatrix} 0 & 1 \\ 1 & 0 \end{bmatrix}, \qquad Q = \begin{bmatrix} 0 & 1 \\ -1 & 0 \end{bmatrix} \tag{ix}$$

and

$$H \equiv H_\nu = \nu U, \qquad U = \begin{bmatrix} 0 & 0 & 1 & 0 \\ 0 & 0 & 1 & 0 \\ 1 & -1 & 0 & 0 \\ 0 & 0 & 0 & 0 \end{bmatrix} \tag{x}$$

with λ, μ, and ν infinitesimals. [One can consider the eigenvalue problem

$$Su = \lambda M u, \qquad H = MS, \qquad \tilde{S} = -S \tag{xi}$$

where M is given in Eq. (3-53). It follows that (1) if λ is real and $\neq 0$, then $(\mathsf{u}, \mathsf{u}) = 0$; (2) if $\lambda' \neq -\lambda''$, then $(\mathsf{u}', \mathsf{u}'') = 0$; and (3) if $\lambda = \lambda_{re} + i\lambda_{im}$, then Eqs. (v) hold. One can prove the expansion,

$$\det(S - \lambda M) = -\lambda^4 + (\mathbf{A}^2 - \mathbf{B}^2)\lambda^2 + (\mathbf{A}\cdot\mathbf{B})^2 \qquad \begin{aligned} A_i &= S_{0i} \\ B_i &= \tfrac{1}{2}\epsilon_{ijk}S_{jk} \end{aligned} \tag{xii}$$

which shows that the eigenvalues have the form

$$\lambda = \pm\sqrt{a \pm b} \qquad \begin{aligned} a &= \tfrac{1}{2}(\mathbf{A}^2 - \mathbf{B}^2) \\ b &= +\sqrt{a^2 + d^2} \\ d &= \mathbf{A}\cdot\mathbf{B} \end{aligned} \tag{xiii}$$

Using the above relations (1), (2), and (3), it can then be proved that the case $b \neq 0$ yields the canonical expression (ix), while the case $b = 0$ corresponds to Eq. (x). The finite matrices are obtained from Eqs. (ix) and (x) by letting $\lambda = \psi/N$, $\mu = \phi/N$, $\nu = \alpha/N$ and evaluating the corresponding limits

$$\lim_{N\to\infty} (I + H)^N \tag{xiv}$$

that reduce to the usual exponential series.]

(*e*) Apply the above results to prove that all of $\mathfrak{L}$ can be generated from the infinitesimal transformations of this group.

4

Relativistic Mechanics

The basic assumptions and results of relativistic kinematics are already contained in their essentials in Einstein's first paper on STR, and they form, as we have seen in Chap. 3, a logically coherent and applicationally satisfactory part of present general physical theory. Relativistic mechanics, on the other hand, has required the efforts of many investigators, and is still not an entirely closed subject.

Historically, the equations of relativistic mechanics were first developed in connection with the Lorentz force equations applied to the motion of a charged particle in external electric and magnetic fields. It was early recognized, however, that the scope of relativistic theory may extend beyond the field of electromagnetics, and attempts were made to establish the basic equations of relativistic mechanics on what could be taken as universal principles, such as those of the conservation of energy and momentum. The first publication containing such an approach is that of Lewis and Tolman.‡ This method is discussed in Sec. 4-2.

In the case of the motion of a single particle in a given external field

‡ G. Lewis and R. Tolman, *Phil. Mag.*, **18:** 510 (1909). We may also note a much later contribution on this subject by Einstein in *Bull. Am. Math. Soc.*, **41:** 223 (1935).

of force (of which, of course, the motion of a charged particle in electric and magnetic fields, mentioned above, is a special case), it is possible to arrive at the relativistic generalization of the newtonian equations of motion in a straightforward way, as is shown in Sec. 4-1. The ideas go back to Planck and Minkowski.‡ The relativistic extension of the variational principles of classical mechanics in this case is also straightforward and is discussed in Sec. 4-3, where it is shown how this analytic method enables us to obtain an initial indication of possible significant generalization of the mechanics of STR. A discussion of possible relativistic generalization of the *canonical formalism* of classical mechanics is also included.

The method outlined in Sec. 4-1 is based on a relativistic extension of Newton's second law. When one wishes to treat relativistically the more general dynamical problem of the interaction between physical systems and must therefore deal with a proper extension of Newton's third law, the fact that the crucial assumption I of newtonian theory (discussed in Sec. 1-3) must be replaced in STR by postulate I* of Sec. 3-1, becomes of far-reaching significance. Action at a distance in the newtonian sense is obviously inconsistent with the relativity of simultaneity; in one form or another the forces operating within a given system must be transmitted through some sort of contiguous action.§ In general, therefore, complete relativistic mechanical systems comprise continuous material media and fields. Quite aside from difficult structural questions that must involve consideration of quantum effects, the subject is complex.¶ A much simpler theory can be developed for systems of particles that interact only on strict contact, as is shown in the latter part of Sec. 4-2. Although such systems form a highly idealized mathematical model of existing physical systems, this model is a useful one. Important examples of its applicability are contained in Sec. 4-4. This section also contains a discussion of Einstein's celebrated mass-energy relation.

4-1 RELATIVISTIC EQUATIONS OF MOTION OF A PARTICLE IN A GIVEN FIELD OF FORCE

A possible direct approach to the development of relativistic mechanics consists in generalizing Newton's second law as applied to systems consisting of a particle moving under the influence of a given external field of force. The corresponding newtonian equations of motion

$$\frac{dp_i}{dt} = f_i, \qquad p_i = m\frac{dx_i}{dt} \tag{4-1}$$

‡ See, e.g., [2], paper 5, sec. 4 and the accompanying notes (6) and (7) by Sommerfeld.

§ However, *propagated* action at a distance can be introduced consistently with STR. See Appendix 7A.

¶ An introduction to the classical relativistic theory of continuous media is presented in Chap. 6.

must be extended in such a manner that the resulting set of equations is *relativistically covariant;* i.e., form invariant under the Lorentz group. Recalling the discussion of $\mathfrak{M}$ geometry contained in Sec. 3-4, it is seen that this generalization can be effected by suitably extending the vectors p_i, f_i‡ to corresponding *4-vectors* P_ν, F_ν. In the spirit of the principle C discussed in Sec. 3-5, this extension can be determined by the following condition holding in the inertial systems in which the particle is instantaneously at rest (i.e., in the *comoving* or *rest* systems):

$$P_i = p_i, \qquad F_i = f_i \qquad \text{in rest system} \tag{4-2}$$

In fact, replacing dt, as one obviously should, by the relativistic invariant (see Prob. 3-17)

$$d\tau = \frac{1}{c}\,ds = dt\sqrt{1 - \frac{u^2}{c^2}} \equiv dt\,\frac{1}{\gamma_u}, \qquad u^2 = \frac{dx_i}{dt}\frac{dx_i}{dt} \tag{4-3}$$

the generalized equations corresponding to Eqs. (4-1) can be written consistently with Eqs. (4-2) in the manifestly relativistic form

$$\frac{dP_\nu}{d\tau} = F_\nu, \qquad P_\nu = m\,\frac{dx_\nu}{d\tau} \tag{4-4}$$

where the $\nu = 0$ equation is derivable from the others in a manner presently to be indicated.

This formal derivation of the relativistic equations of motion (4-4) does not of course guarantee their validity. They do indeed satisfy the following two necessary criteria:

1 They are covariant under $\mathfrak{L}$, and thus automatically comply with Einstein's principle of relativity.

2 They reduce to the corresponding newtonian equations (for $\nu = 1, 2, 3$) in the limit of small u/c.

But these criteria are not in themselves sufficient to establish Eq. (4-4) unconditionally; one must also have appeal to experience. For this purpose it is necessary to be sure of the operational or laboratory specifications of the dynamical quantities m and F. With reference to Eq. (4-2) and principle C, these can be treated along the lines discussed in Chap. 1. In particular, the *invariant* quantity m, the *inertial mass* of the particle, can be taken in general to obey postulate III (Sec. 1-6). Because in principle m must be measured at every instant in the rest system of the particle, this quantity, as used in STR, is known as the "rest mass" or also as the "proper

‡ The vectors whose components in a given cartesian frame attached to a given inertial system (at a given instant of time) are p_i, f_i. There is no need in being pedantic in the use of technical designations, provided the context renders their meaning unambiguous.

mass" of the particle. Similar statements apply to the force F. Moreover, when Eq. (4-4) is rewritten, using Eq. (4-3), as

$$\frac{dP_\nu}{dt} = \frac{1}{\gamma_u} F_\nu, \qquad P_\nu = m\gamma_u \frac{dx_\nu}{dt} \tag{4-5}$$

it is seen that one can consider the relativistic momentum P_i (the spatial part of the "4-momentum" P_ν) as a direct generalization of the classical p_i, provided one introduces the generalized inertial mass‡

$$m(u) = \left(1 - \frac{u^2}{c^2}\right)^{-1/2} m \tag{4-6}$$

(which violates postulate III); and that one can similarly write

$$f_i(u) \equiv F_i = \left(1 - \frac{u^2}{c^2}\right)^{-1/2} f_i, \qquad f_i = \frac{dP_i}{dt} \tag{4-7}$$

The 'relative' force $\mathbf{F}$ is generally called "Minkowski force." It is the spatial part of the 4-vector (4-4).

For a complete check of the suitability of Eqs. (4-4) it still remains to consider their significance for $\nu = 0$. To this end we note that [see Eq. (3-50)]

$$(\mathsf{U},\mathsf{U}) = c^2, \qquad U_\nu \equiv \frac{dx_\nu}{d\tau} \equiv \dot{x}_\nu \tag{4-8}$$

so that by Eq. (4-4),

$$0 = (\mathsf{U},\dot{\mathsf{U}}) = (\mathsf{U},\mathsf{F}) \tag{4-9}$$

and hence, by Eqs. (4-3) and (4-7),

$$F_0 = \frac{1}{U_0}\mathbf{F}\cdot\mathbf{U} = \frac{1}{c}\gamma_u \mathbf{f}\cdot\mathbf{u}, \qquad \mathbf{u} = \frac{d\mathbf{x}}{dt} \tag{4-10}$$

Thus, by Eqs. (4-5) and (4-6),

$$c^2 \frac{d}{dt} m(u) = c\frac{dP_0}{dt} = \mathbf{f}\cdot\mathbf{u} \tag{4-11}$$

or, defining the *kinetic energy* K of the particle by the work-energy relation of classical mechanics, $dt\,\mathbf{f}\cdot\mathbf{u} = dK$,

$$\frac{d}{dt}(K - c^2 m(u)) = 0$$

‡ This is sometimes referred to as the "relative mass," or "relativistic mass." Because $m = m(0)$ in the notation of Eq. (4-6), m is frequently written as m_0, and $m(u)$ is then denoted simply by m.

Integrating this equation and noting that in view of condition 2 (page 91) K must vanish with u, one finds‡

$$K = c^2(m(u) - m) \tag{4-12}$$

As a check, we note that

$$K = c^2 m\left(1 + \frac{\beta^2}{2} + O(\beta^4) - 1\right) = \frac{mu^2}{2}(1 + O(\beta^2)), \qquad \beta \equiv \frac{u}{c}$$

again in agreement with (2).

The relation (4-12) suggests that we look upon the kinetic energy of a particle relative to a given inertial system S as the increase in its 'intrinsic' energy E when its speed in S is u, over the corresponding intrinsic *rest energy*

$$E\Big|_{u=0} = mc^2 \tag{4-13}$$

Thus,

$$P_0 = cm(u) = \frac{1}{c}E = \frac{1}{c}(mc^2 + K) \tag{4-14}$$

and the equation $\nu = 0$ of (4-4) represents on this interpretation the energy relation associated with the momentum relation of Newton's second law. That this interpretation is indeed in full agreement with known facts is of course one of the firmly established results of modern physics. It is discussed in Sec. 4-4.

4-2 PARTICLE COLLISIONS AND RELATIVISTIC MECHANICS; CENTER OF MASS

The approach discussed in the preceeding section is incomplete in so far as it accounts only for the action *on* a given particle by some external agency, but not for the resulting back action emanating *from* the particle; in other words, in so far as it encompasses only Newton's second law and not also his third law. As noted in the introductory remarks to this chapter, this restriction is associated with the relativity of simultaneity in the kinematics of STR. In general, the law of action and reaction can be dealt with relativistically in an obvious manner only in connection with continuous media. In the case of discrete interacting particle systems, the third law can be applied in STR simply only under the idealization of strictly *contact* action.§ As we shall see, a consideration of such idealized mechanical systems is actually of interest both on purely conceptual as well as on more practical grounds.

‡ It is to be observed that the 'relativistic kinetic energy,' Eq. (4-12), is not a covariant quantity, being a hybrid sum of a vector component and a scalar (in $\mathfrak{M}$). Need this occasion any surprise?

§ Recent attempts to describe the electromagnetic interaction of point charges relativistically without the intervention of continuous fields, are discussed in Appendix 7A.

On the purely theoretical side, by analyzing the elastic collision of two particles along the lines of reasoning of Lewis and Tolman (reference on page 89), on the assumption of the relativistic covariance of the conservation laws, it is possible to arrive at the fundamental result (4-6) for the generalized inertial mass of a particle relative to an inertial system S in which it has the velocity u, the momentum of the particle in S being taken to have the corresponding classical form

$$\mathbf{P} = m(u)\mathbf{u} \qquad \begin{array}{l} m(u) \text{ a universal function} \\ m(0) = m \end{array} \tag{4-15}$$

In fact, let us consider the expressions relative to two inertial systems S, S' for the conservation of the total momentum of a system consisting of two identical elastically colliding particles A, B,

$$\Delta(\mathbf{P}_A + \mathbf{P}_B) = 0, \qquad \Delta(\mathbf{P}'_A + \mathbf{P}'_B) = 0 \tag{4-16}$$

where Δ denotes the change resulting from the collision. Upon applying formula (ii) in Prob. 3-3 for the transformation of velocities to the second of Eqs. (4-16), the resulting equations can be made to yield the form of the function $m(u)$, when judicious use is made of the arbitrariness in the relative velocity between the frames S, S', and in the velocities of A and B before and after the collision (see Prob. 4-4). After establishing by this method the result (4-6), one can deduce the energy expression (4-14) with the aid of the work-energy relation as follows:

$$\begin{aligned} dE &= \mathbf{f} \cdot \mathbf{u}\, dt = \frac{d\mathbf{P}}{dt} \cdot \mathbf{u}\, dt = d(m(u)\mathbf{u}) \cdot \mathbf{u} \\ &= m\left(1 - \frac{u^2}{c^2}\right)^{-3/2} u\, du = d(c^2 m(u)) \end{aligned} \tag{4-17}$$

In the derivation (4-17) we have used the spatial part of Eqs. (4-5) [see also Eq. (4-7)]. These do not follow from our present assumptions, but in the last analysis must be postulated. On the other hand, with the method of Sec. 4-1, the relativistic covariance of the conservation laws in ideal elastic collisions (of 'point particles') can be in a certain sense deduced, if we generalize the classical notion of *impulsive* forces in the following obvious manner:

$$F_\nu\, d\tau \to I_\nu = \Delta P_\nu \text{ finite} \qquad \begin{array}{l} d\tau \to 0,\ F_\nu \to \infty \\ d\tau \equiv \text{interval of action of the force} \end{array} \tag{4-18}$$

Indeed, if $F_\nu \equiv F_\nu(A,B)$ represents the force exerted by particle A on particle B, then since the interaction is strictly *localized* in space-time, one can assume that $F_\nu(B,A) = -F_\nu$ without violating the principle of relativity. It follows then at once, by Eq. (4-18), that (in understandable notation)

$$\Delta[P_\nu(A) + P_\nu(B)] = 0 \tag{4-19}$$

this being a covariant expression for the conservation of energy and momentum for the system (A,B).

Even if the method of Lewis and Tolman is incomplete as far as the development of the general scheme of relativistic mechanics is concerned, it is nevertheless of heuristic interest. For this reason we shall also briefly indicate another version of this method.‡ We consider again an ideal system of two identical elastically colliding point particles (A,B), but now compare the momenta before the collision and *at the instant of collision.* We suppose that in the inertial system S' the particles move before the collision with equal and oppositely directed velocities, i.e.,

$$\mathbf{u}'_A = -\mathbf{u}'_B \equiv \mathbf{u}'$$

and apply the momentum conservation law in the system S with respect to which S' moves with the velocity $\mathbf{v}$ parallel to $\mathbf{u}'$. We can suppose that at the instant of collision the velocities of A and B vanish in S' (see Prob. 4-5). Consequently

$$m_+\mathbf{u}_+ + m_-\mathbf{u}_- = m_0\mathbf{v} \tag{4-20}$$

where $\mathbf{u}_+$ and $\mathbf{u}_-$ stand for the velocities of A and B before the collision, $m_\pm \equiv m(u_\pm)$, and m_0 is the mass (*relativistic*) of the system (A,B) at the instant of collision, all the quantities being evaluated in S. Equation (4-20), however, does not suffice; we require also the equation:§

$$m_+ + m_- = m_0 \tag{4-21}$$

Equations (4-20) and (4-21) together with the law of transformation of velocities, according to which in the present case

$$\mathbf{u}_\pm - \mathbf{v} = \frac{\pm(\mathbf{v}/v)(1 - c^{-2}v^2)u'}{(1 \pm c^{-2}vu')},$$

yield the equation

$$\frac{m_+}{m_-} = \frac{1 + (vu'/c^2)}{1 - (vu'/c^2)} = \frac{\gamma_+/\gamma_v\gamma_{u'}}{\gamma_-/\gamma_v\gamma_{u'}} = \frac{\gamma_+}{\gamma_-}, \qquad \gamma_\pm \equiv \gamma_{u_\pm}$$

where we have used the relation (i) in Prob. 3-3. Since $m(0) = m$, the result (4-6) now follows from the arbitrariness in $\mathbf{u}_+$ and $\mathbf{u}_-$.

The relation (4-21) leads to a significant observation. At first thought one might suppose that in agreement with Eq. (4-6) we should have:

‡ R. Tolman, *Phil. Mag.*, **23:** 375 (1912).

§ As we know from the discussion in Sec. 4-1, this conservation of total relativistic mass is equivalent to the conservation of total energy of the system. It is moreover easy to prove that this conservation follows necessarily from the momentum conservation by virtue of the assumed covariance of the equations under the Lorentz group.

$m_0 = 2m(v) = 2m\gamma_v$. Actually, by Eq. (4-21), $m_0 = m(\gamma_+ + \gamma_-)$, and

$$\gamma_+ + \gamma_- - 2\gamma_v = \gamma_v \left(\frac{\gamma_+ + \gamma_-}{\gamma_v} - 2 \right) = 2\gamma_v(\gamma_{u'} - 1)$$

[again by Eq. (i), Prob. 3-3], a positive quantity, since $u' \neq 0$. Thus there is an excess of 'mass' in our system at collision. What is the possible origin of this excess? Obviously, it must somehow arise from the interaction that transpires during the collision: it must be associated with the *energy* generated by this interaction. This observation will be expanded in Sec. 4-4 where the mass-energy relation is discussed more fully and where inelastic collisions are also considered.

On the basis of the idealized contact 'point-interactions' one can also develop general theorems for systems of particles that represent a certain relativistic extension of the classical results concerning the center of mass of a particle system.

In newtonian mechanics the center of mass (or, "center of gravity") of an 'isolated' system of particles has the property that the total momentum of the system (a constant of motion) vanishes in the reference frame in which the center of mass is resting. We can take over this defining property in the treatment of the relativistic systems under consideration, namely, of the systems of point particles interacting only during their instantaneous contact and according to the law of action and reaction. For such mechanical systems it is relativistically meaningful to define the *total 4-momentum*.

$$P_\nu = \sum_s P_\nu^{(s)}, \qquad P_\nu^{(s)} = \text{4-momentum of the } s\text{th particle of the system} \tag{4-22}$$

a quantity which is obviously a *vector* in $\mathfrak{M}$, and which, moreover, satisfies in every inertial system S the conservation law

$$\frac{dP_\nu}{dt} = 0 \tag{4-23}$$

as follows from Eq. (4-19). One can therefore find an inertial system, call it S^*, in which the spatial part of Eq. (4-22) always vanishes:

$$P_i^* = 0 \tag{4-24}$$

In other words, one can choose a frame S^* with its time axis in the direction of P. That P is indeed *timelike* follows from the relation [see Eqs. (4-8) and (4-4)]

$$(\mathsf{P},\mathsf{P}) = m^2c^2 \tag{4-25}$$

for a *single* particle, from which one finds, by evaluation at an instant when all the particles of the system are free,‡

$$\Big(\sum_s \mathsf{P}_s, \sum_r \mathsf{P}_r\Big) = \sum_s m_s^2c^2 + \sum_{s \neq r}\sum P_{0s}P_{0r}\Big(1 - \frac{1}{c^2}\mathbf{u}_s \cdot \mathbf{u}_r\Big) > \sum_s m_s^2c^2 \qquad (4\text{-}26)$$

Noting that the transformation equations for momenta, associated with the Lorentz transformation (3-29), are

$$P_i = P_i' + \frac{\gamma - 1}{\beta^2}\beta_i\beta_j P_j' + \gamma\beta_i P_0', \qquad P_0 = \gamma(P_0' + \beta_i P_i') \qquad (4\text{-}27)$$

it is seen, when we identify S' with S^*, that in an arbitrary inertial frame S

$$P_i = \gamma\beta_i P_0{}^* = \beta_i P_0 \qquad (4\text{-}28)$$

This relation brings out the similarity of S^* to the center-of-mass frame of newtonian mechanics. In fact, if one defines by

$$M^* = \frac{1}{c}P_0{}^* \qquad (4\text{-}29)$$

the *rest mass of the system*, then by Eqs. (4-27) and (4-28)

$$M(v) = \frac{1}{c}P_0 = \gamma_v M^*, \qquad P_i = M(v)v_i \qquad (4\text{-}30)$$

These equations are precisely of the form (4-6) and (4-5) (for P_i) for a *single* particle of rest mass M^* and velocity $\mathbf{v}$. At the same time, note the purely relativistic mass-energy effect exhibited in the explicit expression for the 'rest mass' M^*, which follows from Eqs. (4-29), (4-14), and (4-22):

$$M^* = M + \frac{K^*}{c^2} \qquad \begin{aligned} M &= \sum_s m_s \\ K^* &= \sum_s K_s{}^* \end{aligned} \qquad (4\text{-}31)$$

Here m_s and $K_s{}^*$ are respectively the rest mass, and the relativistic kinetic energy with respect to S^*, of the sth particle of the system.§

The relativistic extension of the classical notion of the center of mass of a mechanical system can also be approached through the generalization of the idea of *angular momentum*. It is easy to see that this generalization should be represented in a given inertial frame S by the set of quantities

$$L_{\mu\nu} = \sum_s L_{\mu\nu}{}^{(s)}, \qquad L_{\mu\nu}{}^{(s)} = x_\mu{}^{(s)}P_\nu{}^{(s)} - x_\nu{}^{(s)}P_\mu{}^{(s)} \qquad (4\text{-}32)$$

‡ Only in the very special case that the rest masses of all the particles are zero and their velocities have the same direction is P a null vector. The inequality (4-26) can actually be sharpened as follows, $\Big(\sum_s \mathsf{P}_s, \sum_r \mathsf{P}_r\Big) \geq \Big(\sum_s m_s c\Big)^2$ (see Prob. 4-18).

§ This treatment, applied to systems of free particles, was presented by Einstein in *Ann. Physik*, **23:** 371 (1907).

where $x_i^{(s)} = x_i^{(s)}(x_0)$ describe in S the world line of the sth particle, and the $x_0^{(s)}$ are all taken to have the same value x_0 [so that $L_{\mu\nu} = L_{\mu\nu}(x_0)$]. Indeed, both criteria (1) and (2) (page 91) are satisfied—(2) quite obviously so, and (1) by virtue of the 4-vector character of the $x_\mu^{(s)}$ and $P_\mu^{(s)}$ and the consequent 4-tensor character of the $L_{\mu\nu}$ (see Chap. 5). The latter conclusion holds because, for the point-mass systems under consideration in this section, the relativistic angular momentum (4-32) is *conserved:*

$$\frac{dL_{\mu\nu}}{dt} = 0 \tag{4-33}$$

this being, in fact, true for each particle between collisions and for each colliding pair, as can be seen by noting that the $dx_\mu^{(s)}/dx_0$ are proportional to the $P_\nu^{(s)}$, and by recalling the action-reaction property of our forces (and the result in Prob. 4-5).

A relativistic analog of the newtonian center of mass appears in connection with the components L_{i0} of the tensor (4-32). The three components L_{ij} evidently constitute the relativistic generalization of the corresponding components of the classical angular-momentum vector, and the L_{i0} are the remaining nonvanishing components of the *antisymmetric* tensor (4-32). To see their physical significance, note that $L_{i0} = \sum_s x_i^{(s)}P_0^{(s)} - x_0P_i$, and hence

$$c_i = \frac{P_i}{P_0}x_0 + \frac{L_{i0}}{P_0} \tag{4-34}$$

where

$$c_i \equiv \frac{1}{P_0}\sum_s x_i^{(s)}P_0^{(s)} = \frac{\sum_s m_s(u_s)x_i^{(s)}}{\sum_s m_s(u_s)} \tag{4-35}$$

It is apparent that the c_i represent an immediate generalization of the cartesian coordinates of the classical center of mass. Moreover, taking account of the conservation relations (4-23) and (4-33), it is seen that Eqs. (4-34) express the law of the *uniform straight-line motion* of the generalized center of mass relative to an inertial reference frame. In a number of respects, though, the definition (4-35) is unsatisfactory. The evident noncovariance in its form and the dependence on the choice of inertial system is the most disturbing inadequacy, to whose possible removal we now turn our attention.‡

We note first that, as shown by Eqs. (4-34) and (4-28), all the 'relative center-of-mass points' defined by Eq. (4-35) (in all possible inertial frames)

‡ The ideas of the treatment apparently go back to A. D. Fokker. See his "Relativiteitstheorie," sec. 10.8, Noordhoff, Gronigen, 1929 (unfortunately no English translation exists of this fine Dutch textbook); also J. L. Synge, *Phys. Rev.*, **47:** 760 (1935), and [6], sec. 64, which includes further references. The condition (4-24) defining the center-of-mass frame was introduced by Pauli for a special case in *Z. Physik,* **18:** 272 (1923).

are *at rest* in the inertial system S^* introduced earlier—this property being in fact an added justification for calling S^* the "center-of-mass frame." It is clear that if we can choose, among this family of points, one that is defined uniquely and in a relativistically covariant manner, then it will have a good claim to being designated *the relativistic center of mass* of our system of particles. The natural choice that presents itself is of course c^*, the c associated with S^* (see Prob. 4-9). But does this choice admit of a relativistically covariant description? That the answer is in the affirmative can be seen by observing that for any inertial frame S, the c associated with it has the following property: if we designate by $L_{\mu\nu}(\mathsf{a})$ the angular-momentum tensor *relative to the event* a—what we have called before "angular momentum" was of course only a short designation for angular momentum *relative to the origin of coordinates*—then

$$L_{i0}(\mathsf{c}) = 0, \qquad \mathsf{c} = (x_0, c_1, c_2, c_3) \tag{4-36}$$

This can be proved at once from the generally valid and immediate relation

$$L_{\mu\nu}(\mathsf{a}) = L_{\mu\nu}(O) - (a_\mu P_\nu - a_\nu P_\mu), \qquad O = (0, 0, 0, 0) \tag{4-37}$$

by taking $a_i = c_i$, $a_0 = x_0$ and comparing with Eq. (4-34). Moreover, Eqs. (4-23), (4-33), (4-34), and (4-37) for $\mathsf{a} = \mathsf{c}$, yield the conservation equations:

$$\frac{dL_{\mu\nu}(\mathsf{c})}{dt} = 0 \tag{4-38}$$

It is the relation (4-36), taken with reference to the frame S^*, that leads to the covariant condition we are seeking. This can be seen explicitly by recalling the condition (4-24), which permits writing Eq. (4-36) for S^* as follows: $0 = L_{i0}{}^*(\mathsf{c}^*) = L_{i\nu}{}^*(\mathsf{c}^*)P_\nu{}^*$. Since L_{00} vanishes identically, this can also be written $L_{\mu\nu}{}^*(\mathsf{c}^*)P_\nu{}^* = 0$, and it is then apparent that the equation is form invariant under $\mathfrak{L}$ (see Chap. 5). Our covariant condition is thus:

$$L_{\mu\nu}(\mathsf{c}^*)P_\nu = 0 \tag{4-39}$$

It can be seen from the preceding discussion that the tensor $L_{\mu\nu}(\mathsf{c}^*)$ represents a natural relativistic generalization of the *internal* angular momentum of a mechanical system. This can also be seen more directly in the reference frame S^*, for by Eq. (4-36) the $L_{i0}{}^*(\mathsf{c}^*)$ always vanish, and we are left with the $L_{ij}{}^*(\mathsf{c}^*)$. These are, incidentally, identical with $L_{ij}{}^*(O)$, as follows from Eqs. (4-37) and (4-24). On the other hand, if

$$L_{\mu\nu}(\mathsf{c}^*) = 0 \tag{4-40}$$

so that our mechanical system has no internal angular momentum,‡ the

‡ The condition (4-40) persists in time, since $dL_{\mu\nu}(\mathsf{c}^*)/dx_0 = 0$; which is proved in the same way as Eq. (4-38), bearing in mind that the velocity of the center of mass relative to the inertial system under consideration is given by Eq. (4-28).

relativistic notion of center of mass becomes sharpened in that all the relative centers of mass **c** coincide with **c*** when taken at the same instant of time in any given inertial frame. This can be seen by substituting in Eq. (4-34) for $L_{i0} \equiv L_{i0}(O)$ in terms of $L_{i0}(\mathbf{c}^*)$ and using Eq. (4-37),‡ getting,

$$c_i = \frac{P_i}{P_0} x_0 + \frac{1}{P_0} \{L_{i0}(\mathbf{c}^*) + [(c^*)_i P_0 - x_0 P_i]\} = (c^*)_i + \frac{1}{P_0} L_{i0}(\mathbf{c}^*) \tag{4-41}$$

(See also Prob. 4-9.)

4-3 VARIATIONAL PRINCIPLES IN CLASSICAL AND RELATIVISTIC MECHANICS; CANONICAL FORMALISM

In this section we shall limit our discussion of the stationary action method in STR to mechanical systems consisting of a single particle moving under the influence of a given external field of force. In Sec. 4-1, where the relativistic equations of motion of such systems were developed, nothing was said of the types of force field **F** that are consistent with the relativistic principles. As will now be shown, the general approach afforded by the variational principles enables us to arrive at some indications concerning the analytical structure of the 4-vector field **F** and the possibilities in generalizing the classical mechanics notion of *potential energy*.

First let us note that we can conveniently express the variational principles of newtonian mechanics for a given Lagrangian function

$$L\left(q_a; \frac{dq_a}{dt}; t\right), \qquad a = 1, \ldots, n \tag{4-42}$$

by introducing an evolution parameter w, an increasing function of t, in terms of which the *action integral* assumes the form:

$$I = \int_{t_1}^{t_2} L\, dt = \int_{w_1}^{w_2} \mathfrak{L}(q_A; q'_A)\, dw \qquad \begin{aligned} A &= 0, 1, \ldots, n \\ q_0 &= t \end{aligned} \tag{4-43}$$

where, by Eq. (4-42),

$$\mathfrak{L}(q_A; q'_A) = L\left(q_a; \frac{q'_a}{t'}; t\right) t', \qquad q' \equiv \frac{dq}{dw} \tag{4-44}$$

The variation of I for arbitrary variations δq_A but vanishing δw, is then by the well-known method of integration by parts:

$$\delta I = \int \left(\frac{\partial \mathfrak{L}}{\partial q_A} - \pi'_A\right) \delta q_A\, dw + [\pi_A\, \delta q_A]_1^2 \tag{4-45}$$

‡ Using the notation $(c^*)_\nu$ to indicate the components of **c*** in S, as contrasted with c_ν^*, the components of **c*** in S^*.

Here the summation convention is applied to the index A (ranging over $0, 1, \ldots, n$), and

$$\pi_A = \frac{\partial \mathfrak{L}}{\partial q'_A} \tag{4-46}$$

Hamilton's principle is essentially equivalent to taking $\delta I = 0$ with

$$\delta q_A = 0 \qquad \text{for } w = w_1 \text{ and } w_2 \tag{4-47}$$

The equations of motion are then obtained at once from Eq. (4-45) in the form

$$\pi'_A = \frac{\partial \mathfrak{L}}{\partial q_A} \tag{4-48}$$

Since, as is easily verified,

$$\pi_a = p_a = \frac{\partial L}{\partial(dq_a/dt)}, \qquad \pi_0 = L - p_a \frac{dq_a}{dt} = -H \tag{4-49}$$

and $\partial\mathfrak{L}/\partial q_A = t' \, \partial L/\partial q_A$, it is seen that the set (4-48) is indeed equivalent to the familiar equations

$$\frac{dp_a}{dt} = \frac{\partial L}{\partial q_a}, \qquad \frac{dH}{dt} = -\frac{\partial L}{\partial t} \tag{4-50}$$

In the usual derivation, the last of Eqs. (4-50) is obtained from the others. That Eqs. (4-50) are in fact not independent is shown by the *identity*

$$\left(\frac{\partial \mathfrak{L}}{\partial q_A} - \pi'_A\right) q'_A \equiv 0 \tag{4-51}$$

which follows by Euler's formula from the fact that, as seen in Eq. (4-44), $\mathfrak{L}$ is a homogeneous function of order 1 in the q'_A, so that by the definition (4-46),‡

$$\mathfrak{L} \equiv \pi_A q'_A, \qquad \frac{\partial \pi_A}{\partial q'_B} q'_B \equiv 0 \tag{4-52}$$

Incidentally, the last relation in Eqs. (4-49) also follows straightway from the first of Eqs. (4-52).

‡ It will be recalled that one terms a differentiable function $f(x, y, \ldots)$ "homogeneous of order k" (or, "homogeneous of degree k") when $f(\alpha x, \alpha y, \ldots) = \alpha^k f(x, y, \ldots)$. By taking the derivative of both sides with respect to α and then setting $\alpha = 1$, we obtain Euler's formula

$$\frac{\partial f}{\partial x} x + \frac{\partial f}{\partial y} y + \cdots = kf$$

In Eq. (4-52) this formula is applied for $k = 1$ and for $k = 0$. Identity (4-51) results from the first of the identities (4-52), upon differentiation with respect to w. The second set of identities is applied on page 106.

We may note also that the *principle of least action*, valid when $\partial L/\partial t = 0$ and hence when H and π_0 are constants of motion, follows also readily from Eq. (4-45). The variational boundary conditions (4-47) are now modified by the replacement of the relation for $A = 0$ by the condition:

$$\delta\pi_0 = 0 \text{ for all } w \tag{4-53}$$

Since for the true motion, Eqs. (4-48) are valid, it follows by Eqs. (4-45) and (4-49) (for $a = 1, \ldots, n$), and making use of the first relation in Eqs. (4-52), that for this motion and for the stated variational conditions,

$$\delta \int_1^2 p_a \, dq_a = 0 \tag{4-54}$$

The above formulation of the classical variational principles can be taken over into relativistic mechanics for one-particle systems with obvious identification of the q_A. Referring to Eq. (4-43), it is seen that a sufficient condition for the action I to be a relativistic invariant is that both the parameter w and the Lagrangian function $\mathfrak{L}$ are such invariants. The first requirement is satisfied by taking for w either the proper time τ or any increasing function of τ. We may arrive at some idea regarding the possible structure of $\mathfrak{L}$ if we require that, as in the classical case, $\mathfrak{L}$ is a homogeneous function of the first order in the x'_α. Without entering here into a discussion of the possible significance of this restriction (see footnote ¶ on page 108), let us note that in simplest terms it leads to the expansion

$$\mathfrak{L} = A_\alpha x'_\alpha \pm \sqrt{B_{\alpha\beta} x'_\alpha x'_\beta} + \cdots \qquad \begin{matrix} \alpha,\beta = 1, 2, 3, 4 \\ x_4 = ix_0 \end{matrix} \tag{4-55}$$

where $A_\alpha \equiv A_\alpha(x)$, $B_{\alpha\beta} \equiv B_{\alpha\beta}(x)$, etc., are 4-vectors, symmetric second-rank 4-tensors, etc., respectively.‡

If only the first sum is retained in Eq. (4-55) the equations of motion (4-48) are found to lead to an unacceptable result. Hence we cannot have $B_{\alpha\beta} = 0$, and the simplest choice for the quantities in Eq. (4-55) is as follows:

$$A_\alpha = 0, \qquad B_{\alpha\beta} = -B^2 \, \delta_{\alpha\beta} \tag{4-56}$$

where B is a real, constant 4-scalar. One would expect such $\mathfrak{L}$ to correspond to the simplest motion of a particle, namely, to 'free' motion, and this is indeed immediately verified. In fact, the variational problem can be recognized as that for a timelike geodesic in $\mathfrak{M}$, from which it also follows that the *negative sign* must be taken in Eq. (4-55) if the resulting extremum is to be a *minimum*. (See Prob. 3-13.) On the other hand, it is of course not possible to identify B directly in this case. For such identification it is necessary

‡ We have reintroduced in this expansion the imaginary time variable x_4, in order to make the invariance properties of the terms evident on the basis of cartesian vector (or tensor) algebra. The methods developed in the next chapter obviate the introduction of imaginary quantities.

to have a nonvanishing F and we must therefore consider the question of how this can be introduced by means of the variational formalism.‡

In classical mechanics, one commonly applies the variational formulation to systems that involve forces derivable from a *potential-energy function* (which may, however, in general, have explicit dependence on time). Can we carry this idea over to STR? In the classical theory the potential energy is a *scalar*. But we have seen, in Secs. 4-1 and 4-2, how energy occurs in STR as the time component of a 4-vector. This suggests that we require a 4-vector to serve as a generalization of the classical potential-energy function. The vector A appearing in the relativistic Lagrangian (4-55) is a natural candidate for this role. Retaining only the written terms in Eq. (4-55) (with the negative sign of the square root) and taking for $B_{\alpha\beta}$ the values in Eq. (4-56), we find—by Eqs. (4-46) and (4-48), and applying the understandable relation $\mathfrak{L}_w = \mathfrak{L}_\tau (d\tau/dw)$§—that

$$\pi_\alpha = \frac{\partial \mathfrak{L}_w}{\partial x'_\alpha} = \frac{\partial \mathfrak{L}_\tau}{\partial \dot{x}_\alpha} = A_\alpha + \frac{B}{c}\dot{x}_\alpha, \qquad \dot{\pi}_\alpha = \dot{A}_\alpha + \frac{B}{c}\ddot{x}_\alpha = \pi'_\alpha \dot{w} = \frac{\partial A_\beta}{\partial x_\alpha}\dot{x}_\beta$$

When these equations are compared with the equations of motion (4-4), it can be concluded that the inertial rest mass of the particle should be taken as

$$m = \frac{1}{c}B \tag{4-57}$$

and that the equations of motion then assume the form

$$m\ddot{x}_\alpha = F_\alpha = A_{\beta,\alpha}\dot{x}_\beta - \dot{A}_\alpha = (A_{\beta,\alpha} - A_{\alpha,\beta})\dot{x}_\beta, \qquad A_{\alpha,\beta} \equiv \frac{\partial A_\alpha}{\partial x_\beta} \tag{4-58}$$

That A does indeed represent a generalization of the classical potential can be seen by going to the nonrelativistic limit in Eqs. (4-58) ($\alpha = 1, 2, 3$); when all small terms are properly neglected these equations are found under suitable restrictions to reduce to:

$$f_k = icA_{4,k} = -\frac{\partial V}{\partial x_k}, \qquad A_4 = \frac{i}{c}V \tag{4-58a}$$

Equations of the form (4-58) actually apply in a certain approximation to the motion of a charged particle in an electromagnetic field of 4-potential proportional to A (as discussed in Sec. 7-5). It appears reasonable to

‡ On the other hand, it is not difficult to verify that by applying condition 2 of page 91, the value (4-57) for B can be deduced from the requirement that (except for an inconsequential additive constant) the classical Lagrangian $L = mu^2/2$ should be obtained in the limit of small velocities.

§ Making use also of Eq. (4-8) in the capacity of a *subsidiary condition*. Strictly, we need to justify now the validity of the Euler equations, since our parameter cannot stay unvaried at the final endpoint. See Prob. 1-2 and condition (1-5*a*), and Prob. 4-13.

surmise that a similar relativistic description applies also to the motion of a particle in a gravitational field. Attempts in this direction were indeed made both before and also after the publication of Einstein's theory of gravitation. These are discussed in Appendix 7B.

There is another idea it is instructive to explore here briefly. We have encountered one quantity of the nature of an energy that is not the time component of a 4-vector, but a true relativistic invariant, namely, the intrinsic particle rest energy mc^2. We had assumed that this quantity is an absolute constant. What conclusions would follow from a relaxing of this assumption? Suppose that the inertial mass m is not a constant but a scalar *field* $m(x)$, can such a mechanical system be encompassed by our equations of motion?‡

If we examine the Lagrangian expansion (4-55) to see if a 4-scalar field can be included in it in a simple fashion, it is readily discovered that this is indeed possible. One need only substitute in this expansion the values given in Eq. (4-56), with B taken to be a scalar *field* $B(x)$. Applying Eqs. (4-46) and (4-48), we find, after simplification [using Eq. (4-8)]: $\pi_\alpha = B\dot{x}_\alpha/c$, $\dot{\pi}_\alpha = -c\,\partial B/\partial x_\alpha$. It is thus seen, when we compare these equations with the corresponding ones in Eqs. (4-4), that it is indeed reasonable to consider

$$\frac{1}{c}B(\mathsf{x}) \equiv m(\mathsf{x}) \tag{4-59}$$

as a generalized mass, with the π_α forming a corresponding generalization of the momenta P_α. At the same time, the associated energy $m(x)c^2$ acts as a potential-energy function $\Phi(x)$ whose 4-gradient yields the present Minkowski force vector

$$F_\alpha = \dot{\pi}_\alpha = -\frac{\partial\Phi}{\partial x_\alpha}, \qquad \Phi \equiv cB \tag{4-60}$$

The arbitrary constant involved in Φ can be fixed by making the natural stipulation that $m(\mathsf{x})$ reduce to the ordinary inertial rest mass of the particle m wherever Φ vanishes:

$$m(\mathsf{x}) = m + \frac{1}{c^2}\Phi(\mathsf{x}) \tag{4-61}$$

We have so far made no reference to the relation (4-9). It is immediately verified that it holds in the case of the force (4-58), and this insures the constancy of m. It will in general fail to hold for the force field (4-60), since in this case

$$(\mathsf{F},\mathsf{U}) = -F_\alpha U_\alpha = \frac{\partial\Phi}{\partial x_\alpha}\dot{x}_\alpha = \dot{\Phi} \tag{4-62}$$

‡ See also Prob. 4-6 for an indication of quite another type of rest-mass variability. The macroscopic change in proper mass arising from heat flow is considered in Sec. 6-6.

Moreover, if in Eqs. (4-4) we had allowed for variability in m, then in place of Eq. (4-9), we would have found that

$$(\mathsf{F},\mathsf{U}) = c^2\dot{m} \tag{4-63}$$

so that, with F given by Eq. (4-60), it would have followed that

$$\Phi(\mathsf{x}) = c^2 m(\mathsf{x}) + \text{constant}$$

and we would have come back to our original identification of the Lagrangian factor B in terms of a generalized particle mass.

Again one can show that in the classical limit the equations of motion reduce to the newtonian equations, with Φ playing the role of a potential-energy function, and in the present case the reduction is actually immediate. Equation (4-61) is also interesting in exhibiting another instance of the Einstein mass-energy relation, this time for the case of *potential* rather than kinetic energy. [Cf. remarks made in connection with Eq. (4-21).] No less noteworthy is the association of our field of force with the symmetric second-order tensor of Eq. (4-55), which could be considered as a generalization of the *metric* tensor of our space-time $\mathfrak{M}$ (see Chap. 5). Einstein's general theory of relativity comprises a far-reaching modification of such a generalization, connected with new physical points of view, and leading to a radically new conception of gravitational fields.

In classical physics, the variational formulation and the Euler-Lagrange equations of motion form only the first steps in the advanced analytical theory of mechanics. The developments associated with the names of Hamilton, Poisson, and Jacobi are central to this theory. Moreover, the canonical formalism created by them forms the classical substratum of a good part of quantum mechanics. It is therefore of obvious interest to inquire into the possibility of extending the classical results to STR. It turns out, however, that such an extension encounters analytical complexities even in the simplest case of a single particle moving in an assigned field of force, if we wish to preserve explicit relativistic covariance throughout.

As a preliminary to our inquiry, let us return to the classical equations (4-48) and (4-46) and note how the transition is made to the hamiltonian equations. The significant step, as the reader will recall, and as is shown in every text on analytic mechanics, is to express the quantity H defined in Eq. (4-49) in terms of the canonical momenta p_a, obtaining the *hamiltonian* $H(q;p;t)$, with whose aid the equations of motion (4-50) can then be thrown into the canonical form:

$$\frac{dq_a}{dt} = \frac{\partial H}{\partial p_a}, \qquad \frac{dp_a}{dt} = -\frac{\partial H}{\partial q_a} \tag{4-64}$$

This derivation involves the assumption (usually tacit) that the first set of

Eqs. (4-49) is solvable for the dq_a/dt, which requires that

$$\det \left\| \frac{\partial^2 L}{\partial(dq_a/dt)\, \partial(dq_b/dt)} \right\| \neq 0 \tag{4-65}$$

Since this condition is in general satisfied, the canonical formalism forms part of a fruitful theory in classical mechanics. But when we go over to STR and use the general momenta defined by Eq. (4-46) (with $\{q_A\} = \{x_\alpha\}$, and $\alpha = 0, 1, 2, 3$ or $1, 2, 3, 4$ depending on our choice of the time coordinate), the quantity analogous to H is

$$\mathcal{H} = \pi_\alpha q'_\alpha - \mathcal{L} \tag{4-66}$$

which, as one readily verifies (see Prob. 4-12), is indeed a relativistic scalar. However, by the second set of Eqs. (4-52) it is apparent that $\mathcal{L}$ does not satisfy the condition (4-65) for the solvability of Eqs. (4-46).‡

One way of circumventing this difficulty is to relinquish the immediate covariance in our formalism by choosing t as our evolution parameter and proceeding along the usual lines of the classical theory. Relativistic covariance needs to be assured then only in the final results. One starts, thus, with the usual nonrelativistic *form* of the action integral, namely, the second side of Eq. (4-43); though of course, the action integral itself must be a relativistic invariant; i.e., we must have

$$L\, dt = \mathcal{L}\, dw \tag{4-67}$$

where, as before, both $\mathcal{L}$ and dw are relativistic scalars. The generalized momenta are now the p_i given in Eq. (4-49), and the ordinary velocities dx_i/dt can be solved in terms of these momenta, yielding, upon substitution into the last of Eqs. (4-49), the hamiltonian function $H(x_i, p_i, t)$. The latter is not a scalar in $\mathfrak{M}$, but the time component of a 4-vector whose spatial components are p_i.§ Similarly the three Euler-Lagrange equations, combined with the energy equation derivable from them, give the four components of a 4-vector equation of motion. The ultimate covariance of the calculation is thus secured. These steps are illustrated in the following example.

Consider the Lagrangian (4-55) with $B_{\alpha\beta}$ given in Eqs. (4-56) and (4-57). By Eq. (4-67) with $w = \tau$, one finds *upon applying* Eq. (4-8):

$$L = -mc^2 \sqrt{1 - \frac{u^2}{c^2}} + A_j u_j + icA_4, \qquad u_k = \frac{dx_k}{dt} \tag{4-68}$$

‡ The additional fact that actually $\mathcal{H} = 0$ [by the first of Eqs. (4-52)] is of less moment (see footnote on page 109).

§ See Prob. 4-12. Strictly, in our present coordinates, the time component of the energy-momentum 4-vector is iH/c. Also note that we have previously used P_i for what we now call p_i.

Consequently,

$$p_k = \frac{\partial L}{\partial u_k} = m\gamma_u u_k + A_k, \qquad u_k = \frac{c(p_k - A_k)}{[m^2c^2 + (p_j - A_j)(p_j - A_j)]^{1/2}} \tag{4-69}$$

the latter equations following from the first set by using the relation

$$1 - \frac{u^2}{c^2} = \frac{m^2c^2}{m^2c^2 + (p_j - A_j)(p_j - A_j)} \tag{4-69a}$$

that is deducible from the first set, i.e., from the equation

$$(p_j - A_j)(p_j - A_j) = m^2\gamma_u{}^2u^2$$

By the latter equations and by Eq. (4-69a) (as $\beta^2\gamma^2 + 1 \equiv \gamma^2$),

$$H = p_j u_j - L = mc^2\gamma_u - icA_4 = c[m^2c^2 + (p_j - A_j)(p_j - A_j)]^{1/2} - icA_4 \tag{4-70}$$

Thence, by Eq. (4-64), and using the comma notation for partial derivatives,

$$\frac{dp_k}{dt} = \frac{c(p_r - A_r)}{[m^2c^2 + (p_j - A_j)(p_j - A_j)]^{1/2}} A_{r,k} + icA_{4,k}$$

or, by using Eqs. (4-69) and the notation (4-6),

$$\begin{aligned} \frac{d}{dt}(m(u)u_k) &= A_{r,k}u_r + icA_{4,k} - \frac{dA_k}{dt} \\ &= (A_{r,k} - A_{k,r})u_r + ic(A_{4,k} - A_{k,4}) \end{aligned} \tag{4-71}$$

Similarly, by the second of Eqs. (4-50) and the first part of Eq. (4-70), one finds‡

$$\frac{d}{dt}(m(u)c^2) = ic(A_{4,k} - A_{k,4})u_k \tag{4-72}$$

An additional advantage of the present method is that it permits a certain extension to systems of particles (see Prob. 4-11b). However, both the theoretical scope and the practical usefulness of this extension are limited. Even if one could successfully develop a fully covariant canonical formalism for systems of interacting particles, it is questionable if it would be very useful without the introduction of fields.§ Since strictly relativistic dynamical effects are, in any case, important only in the case of micropar-

‡ It can be easily verified that this result also follows simply by multiplying (and summing) Eq. (4-71) by u_k, as $c^2\gamma_u^{-3}\,d\gamma_u/dt = \mathbf{u} \cdot d\mathbf{u}/dt$.

§ For attempts to develop such a theory, see, e.g., D. G. Currie, T. F. Jordan, and E. C. G. Sudarshan, *Rev. Mod. Phys.*, **35:** 350 (1963) and the references given there, especially to the investigations of Dirac, of Thomas, and of Foldy; D. G. Currie, *J. Math. Phys.*, **4:** 1470 (1963). See also Appendix 7A.

ticles, and consequently, except for special situations, quantum effects must also be accounted for, the classical-relativistic theory can serve mainly as an understructure of the corresponding quantum theory. But in most high-energy problems (at least in the case of electrodynamic phenomena where our knowledge is greatest) field-theoretical considerations appear to be of central importance.‡

We therefore return now to the simple one-body problem to consider how it may be possible to introduce a manifestly relativistic canonical formalism in a consistent manner, but without pursuing this question completely.

We have seen that imposing the condition of first-order homogeneity on our Lagrangian is at the root of the immediate analytical difficulty. Two questions, therefore, pose themselves: What significance if any attaches to the homogeneity condition in the present case? Can one properly modify the standard formalism so that it would apply to the homogeneous case? That the answer to the second question is in the affirmative is well known.§ We indicate a treatment for the Lagrangian (4-55).¶

Let us write our homogeneous Lagrangian (4-55) generally as

$$\mathcal{L} = \mathcal{L}_0 + \mathcal{L}_1 \qquad \begin{aligned} \mathcal{L}_0 &= -\sqrt{B_{\alpha\beta}x'_\alpha x'_\beta} \\ B_{\alpha\beta} &\equiv B_{\alpha\beta}(x) = B_{\beta\alpha} \end{aligned} \tag{4-73}$$

and suppose the parameter w chosen so that the following condition is satisfied along the trajectory (in $\mathfrak{M}$):

$$\mathcal{B} \equiv B_{\alpha\beta}x'_\alpha x'_\beta = 1 \tag{4-74}$$

‡ It should be noted, though, that for 'moderately relativistic' energies, an approximate many-particle canonical formulation has its use. This is exemplified by C. G. Darwin's second-order Hamiltonian for a system of charged particles, *Phil. Mag.*, **39:** 537 (1920). See also [4], sec. 2.6; L. Landau and E. Lifshitz, "The Classical Theory of Fields" (translated by M. Hamermesh), sec. 8-4, Addison-Wesley Press, Inc., Cambridge, Mass., 1951.

§ A mathematically complete treatment of the general topic in the variational calculus (of which our problem is a simple special case) relating both to homogeneity and to existence of subsidiary conditions can be found in C. Carathéodory, "Variationsrechnung und partielle Differentialgleichungen erster Ordnung," chaps. 13 and 18, Verlag Teubner, Leipzig 1935. Many physicists have also attacked this subject independently by various methods. For the treatment of constraint conditions with particular reference to the many-body problem, see e.g., P. A. M. Dirac, *Proc. Cambridge Phil. Soc.*, **29:** 389 (1933); *Proc. Roy. Soc.*, **A246:** 326 (1958).

¶ As to the first question, let us only point out, as is easily proved, that the numerical value and the form of the action integral (4-43) is unaffected by a change of evolution parameter if and only if the Lagrangian is homogeneous of first order [strictly, one need assume only that it is *positively* homogeneous, i.e., that $\mathcal{L}(x;kx') = k\mathcal{L}(x;x')$ for *positive* k]. This leaves it an open question, which the interested reader can pursue for himself, if these conditions on the action integral are generally necessary.

Then the Euler equations are found to reduce to (cf. Prob. 4-13)

$$\frac{d}{dw}\left(-\frac{1}{2}\frac{\partial\mathcal{B}}{\partial x'_\alpha}+\frac{\partial\mathcal{L}_1}{\partial x'_\alpha}\right)+\frac{1}{2}\frac{\partial\mathcal{B}}{\partial x_\alpha}-\frac{\partial\mathcal{L}_1}{\partial x_\alpha}=0 \tag{4-75}$$

Moreover, the possibility of applying the condition (4-74) consistently is assured by the identical vanishing of $d\mathcal{B}/dw$ along the space-time trajectories. This follows from the identity (4-51) as applied to $\mathcal{L}_1$, since by the second-order homogeneity of $\mathcal{B}$, $(\partial\mathcal{B}/\partial x'_\alpha)x'_\alpha = 2\mathcal{B}$, which—combined with the identity $d\mathcal{B}/dw = (\partial\mathcal{B}/\partial x_\alpha)x'_\alpha + (\partial\mathcal{B}/\partial x'_\alpha)x''_\alpha$—leads, by Eq. (4-75), to

$$\frac{d\mathcal{B}}{dw}=\left(\frac{d}{dw}\frac{\partial\mathcal{B}}{\partial x'_\alpha}-\frac{\partial\mathcal{B}}{\partial x_\alpha}\right)x'_\alpha=2\left(\frac{d}{dw}\frac{\partial\mathcal{L}_1}{\partial x'_\alpha}-\frac{\partial\mathcal{L}_1}{\partial x_\alpha}\right)x'_\alpha\equiv 0$$

Considering the expression (4-75), it can be concluded that the Lagrangian (4-73) can be replaced by the effectively equivalent Lagrangian [equivalent under the imposition of the subsidiary condition (4-74)]:

$$\mathcal{L} = -\tfrac{1}{2}\mathcal{B} + \mathcal{L}_1 \tag{4-76}$$

This Lagrangian is no longer homogeneous and one can therefore develop the canonical equations in the usual way. In particular, the hamiltonian function (4-66) is the $\mathfrak{M}$ invariant

$$\mathcal{H} = \mathcal{H}_0 + \mathcal{H}_1 = \mathcal{H}_0 = -\tfrac{1}{2}\mathcal{B}(x;x'(\pi)) \tag{4-77}$$

(in understandable notation, and since $x'_\alpha\,\partial\mathcal{B}/\partial x'_\alpha = 2\mathcal{B}$, while $\mathcal{H}_1 \equiv 0$).‡

In the case of the problem (4-68), treated earlier by nonmanifestly covariant methods, our effective Lagrangian is

$$\mathcal{L} = \tfrac{1}{2}m^2c^2x'_\alpha x'_\alpha + A_\alpha x'_\alpha$$

The condition (4-74), that is, $-m^2c^2x'_\alpha x'_\alpha = 1$, yields the relation $dw = mc^2\,d\tau$ (τ = proper time along the trajectory). Since $\mathcal{L}_w\,dw = \mathcal{L}_\tau\,d\tau$, the above Lagrangian can be replaced—on going over to the parameter τ and writing now $\mathcal{L}$ for $\mathcal{L}_\tau$—by

$$\mathcal{L} = \frac{m}{2}\dot{x}_\alpha\dot{x}_\alpha + A_\alpha\dot{x}_\alpha, \qquad \dot{x}\equiv\frac{dx}{d\tau} \tag{4-78}$$

The covariant canonical momenta are then

$$\pi_\alpha = m\dot{x}_\alpha + A_\alpha \tag{4-79}$$

and

$$\mathcal{H} = \frac{m}{2}\dot{x}_\alpha\dot{x}_\alpha = \frac{1}{2m}(\pi_\alpha - A_\alpha)(\pi_\alpha - A_\alpha) \tag{4-80}$$

‡ As in the case of the nonrelativistic Hamiltonian of a conservative system, $\mathcal{H}$ is a constant of motion; however, though for suitable choice of the parameter it has the physical dimensions of an energy [see Eq. (4-80)], it obviously possesses a different character from the nonrelativistic H in that its value is independent of the trajectories—it is not a 'dynamical variable.'

Hence, the canonical equations of motion are

$$\dot{x}_\alpha = \frac{\partial \mathcal{H}}{\partial \pi_\alpha} = \frac{1}{m}(\pi_\alpha - A_\alpha)$$
$$\dot{\pi}_\alpha = -\frac{\partial \mathcal{H}}{\partial x_\alpha} = \frac{1}{m}(\pi_\beta - A_\beta)A_{\beta,\alpha}, \qquad A_{\beta,\alpha} \equiv \frac{\partial A_\beta}{\partial x_\alpha} \tag{4-80a}$$

The first set of equations merely reproduces Eq. (4-79), while the second set yields, with the aid of the first, the covariant Euler equations for our system,

$$m\ddot{x}_\alpha = (A_{\beta,\alpha} - A_{\alpha,\beta})\dot{x}_\beta \tag{4-81}$$

Comparison of the present results with those deduced by the previous method starting with Eq. (4-69) shows that, in the first place, the final results arrived at in both cases are completely equivalent, as they must be; and secondly, that the present fully covariant method is more elegant, making use as it does throughout of the inherent $\mathfrak{M}$ symmetries. This method permits also easy extension of further results in the classical analytic theory of mechanics. Thus, considering the classical Hamilton-Jacobi equation for a conservative mechanical system (see, e.g., H. Goldstein, *op. cit.*, sec. 9-3), it can be seen that its relativistic analog is, in the present case, simply

$$\left(\frac{\partial \mathcal{W}}{\partial x_\alpha} - A_\alpha\right)\left(\frac{\partial \mathcal{W}}{\partial x_\alpha} - A_\alpha\right) + m^2c^2 = 0 \tag{4-82}$$

[by Eqs. (4-80) and (4-8), and remembering that we are using the imaginary time variable; see Prob. 4-14].

It is not difficult to pursue further the development of this covariant canonical theory (see Prob. 4-14). It must be remembered, though, that the importance of the canonical formalism in classical mechanics is due principally to its applicability to *many*-body systems. Moreover, unlike the classical canonical theory, any covariant relativistic formulation, whatever the chosen method, cannot avoid involving a certain arbitrariness in intermediate steps, owing to the presence of the relation (4-8) between the 4-velocity components, and this mars in part the aesthetic value of the theory.

4-4 APPLICATIONS OF RELATIVISTIC MECHANICS; EINSTEIN'S MASS–ENERGY FORMULA

In Sec. 4-2 we discussed the method of particle collisions in the study of relativistic mechanics. Precisely what is to be understood by the term "particle" was not considered. If we simply adopt classical usage, then the two identical particles in the elastic-collision thought experiment of Lewis and Tolman, for instance, could be identified with two homogeneous, spherical, and perfectly elastic balls. Similarly, in discussing inelastic collisions, we could consider, say, the extreme case of two identical balls of putty that collide with equal and opposite velocities in a given inertial system S and so come to rest in S by coalescing. Now, although such examples are obviously devoid of practical significance, they can very well serve as useful mental models for manifesting novel features presented by relativistic mechanics. Thus, the second example provides a vivid illustration of the conversion of kinetic energy into proper mass arising from the development of internal energy (heat) on impact. The purely academic nature of this imaginary experiment is also evident: the relative increase in proper mass, as is at once verified, amounts only to $\gamma_u - 1 \approx u^2/2c^2$ (where u is the initial speed of each of the balls relative to S), a clearly inappreciable quantity for laboratory measurement.

The foregoing example is, as we know, one of many in which purely relativistic effects are of order u^2/c^2, and hence are of no consequence in the mechanics of gross systems considered in the laboratory. These effects become significant in the laboratory only when we turn to the atomic and subatomic domains. All high-energy collisions of atoms, nuclei, 'elementary particles' (i.e., leptons, nucleons, mesons, and hyperons), and photons (that can also be included among the 'particles') have been found to be governed, as far as the rules of overall conservation of energy and momentum are concerned, by the results of STR. The proof for this is, to be sure, not all direct, yet the consistency of numerous experimental results based on this hypothesis is so overwhelming, that there appears to be no reason at present for doubting its general validity, and this fact can be rightly taken as one of the important triumphs of STR.

The details of the various types of elastic and inelastic collision experiments in atomic, nuclear, and elementary particle physics that bear on our present topic need not concern us here. They can be found in texts on modern atomic physics and more fully in specialized monographs. For our present purpose, it will suffice to consider a few examples that illustrate the scope of application of the relativistic conservation rules. These will also serve to indicate how the results on special systems developed in the second part of Sec. 4-2, can be applied in practice.

Before we take up specific examples, let us examine briefly some general aspects of high-energy particle collisions relating to classical relativistic mechanics.

Let us consider the collision of two particles A, B whose principal interaction takes place only during a very brief time interval when they are in close proximity. Particles of zero rest mass may also be included. Suppose that the system of particles $C_1, \ldots, C_p$ is the result of the collision reaction, where $p \geq 1$. This system is considered outside the space-time interaction region, where it is assumed that no further appreciable mutual interaction exists between any of the particles. Under these conditions, it is not difficult to see that for practical purposes our colliding system can be taken to be of the type discussed in Sec. 4-2. The added feature of possible change in the *number* of the particles of the system, one readily verifies, introduces no difficulties as long as the restrictive conditions regarding the interaction are satisfied. In practice we can, therefore, generally apply the conservation rule (4-19), which in the present case can be written more explicitly

$$P_\nu(A) + P_\nu(B) = \sum_{s=1}^{p} P_\nu(C_s), \qquad p \geq 1 \tag{4-83}$$

the notation being self-explanatory.

Although in general the full treatment of a problem in atomic or subatomic collisions must involve quantum-mechanical considerations, one can always assume, on the basis of all empirical evidence to date, the validity of the classical result (4-83) under the above specified conditions, when all the particles are practically 'free' and their 4-momenta have therefore 'sharp' values from the point of view of quantum mechanics. Even when the required quantum-mechanical theory is largely unavailable, as is still true in the case of subatomic interactions, the relations (4-83) can still be applied, and provide (along with other postulated nonclassical‡ conservation rules) a partial guide in the study of the elementary particle phenomena. Moreover, not only strict collisions but also decay phenomena are subject to the conservation rule (4-83) with the omission of the second term on the left-hand side of the equation and identification of A with the decaying particle.

The notion of *center of mass* discussed in Sec. 4-2 also finds useful application in the atomic domain. It is frequently more convenient to make computations in the center-of-mass system, as will be illustrated in the specific example to follow. Moreover, our results concerning the covariant center of mass provide an explanation of the empirical fact that for some purposes it is possible to treat composite systems, such as many-nucleon nuclei, for example, as individual particles.

It is also possible to apply the results concerning the total angular momentum in its covariant form, discussed in Sec. 4-2, but the treatment of intrinsic angular momenta does not appear to be generally fruitful without the intervention of angular-momentum quantization.§

As our first concrete example, we shall consider briefly the historically important results of cloud-chamber experiments performed by Champion

‡ The word "classical" refers here of course to both newtonian *and relativistic* physics.

§ Attempts have been made from time to time to work out a strictly classical-relativistic theory of the spins of elementary particles. The interested reader can consult, e.g., the first part of F. Halbwachs, "Théorie relativiste des fluides à spin," Gauthier-Villars, Paris, 1960; and a brief review by J. Weyssenhoff in the "Max Planck Festschrift," Veb Deutscher Verlag der Wissenschaften, Berlin, 1958.

in 1932,‡ which provided the first direct and visual evidence for the validity of the relativistic elastic-collision formulas. In this experiment many thousands of cloud-chamber photographs were taken of the collision of a rapidly moving electron obtained from a radioactive source with one practically stationary in the gas. From a careful examination of these photographs, Champion was able to conclude that the measured angle $\alpha = \theta + \phi$ between the asymptotic paths of the two collided electrons was closely approximated by the following formula deducible from Eq. (4-83):

$$\cos\alpha = \frac{(\gamma_u - 1)\sin\theta\cos\theta}{[(\gamma_u + 1)^2\sin^2\theta + 4\cos^2\theta]^{1/2}} \tag{4-84}$$

where the symbols are defined in Fig. 4-1. It is seen that for $u^2/c^2 \ll 1$, we have the known classical result, $\alpha = \pi/2$; whereas for 'relativistic veloci-

‡ F. C. Champion, *Proc. Roy. Soc.*, **A136:** 630 (1932).

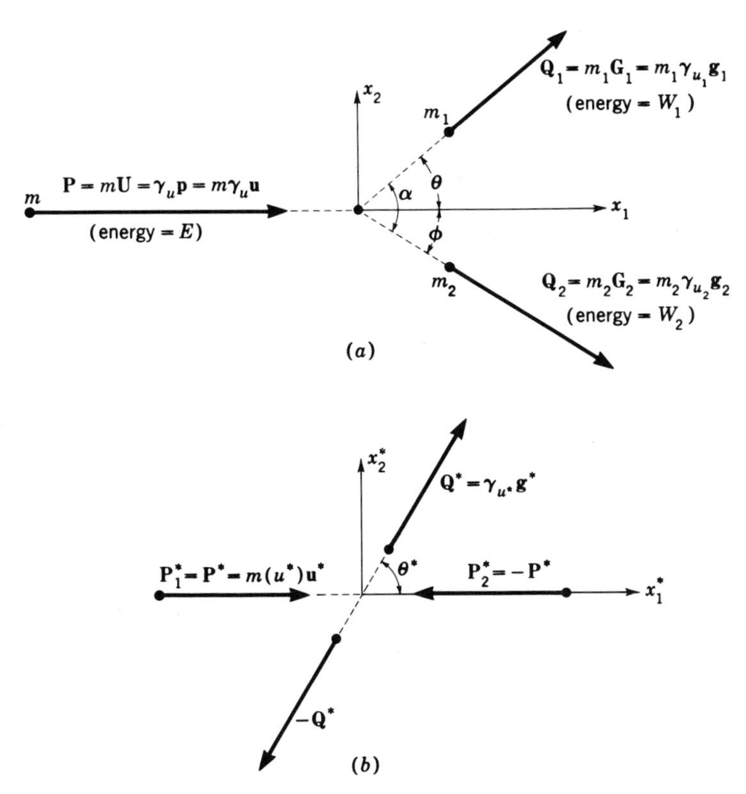

Fig. 4-1 Particle collision in (*a*) laboratory and (*b*) center-of-mass coordinate systems. In Champion's experiment, $m_1 = m_2 = m$.

ties' of the bombarding particle, α is always $<\pi/2$. ($\theta = 0$ is a singular and practically unimportant case.)‡

Instead of deriving Eq. (4-84) we shall derive the following simpler but equivalent formula given by Møller ([6], sec. 32):§

$$\tan\theta \tan\phi = \frac{2}{1+\gamma_u} \tag{4-85}$$

Its derivation is accomplished conveniently by first working out the problem in the center-of-mass system S^* as defined in Sec. 4-2, and then transforming the result to the laboratory system S. (The latter is of course for our purpose practically an *inertial system*.) In S^* one finds at once from the time component of law (4-83), i.e., from conservation of energy, and using Eq. (4-25), or more explicitly,

$$E^2 - c^2\mathbf{P}^2 = m^2c^4 \tag{4-86}$$

that $2[c^2\mathbf{P}^{*2} + m^2c^4]^{1/2} = 2[c^2\mathbf{Q}^{*2} + m^2c^4]^{1/2}$ (see Fig. 4-1); and hence, $|\mathbf{P}^*| = |\mathbf{Q}^*|$, and $|\mathbf{u}^*| = |\mathbf{g}^*|$, as in classical mechanics.

To go over to the laboratory frame, we observe (see Fig. 4-1) that initially the target particle has zero velocity in S and velocity u^* in the negative x^* direction in S^*, so that the velocity of the S^* frame in S is u^* in the positive x direction. Thus, by the velocity-transformation law (3-22), and introducing in the following calculations c as our *unit of velocity*,

$$u = \frac{u^* + v}{1 + vu^*} = \frac{2v}{1+v^2}, \qquad c = 1 \tag{4-87}$$

The relative velocity v of S and S^* can also be obtained immediately by making use of the fact that S^* is the center-of-mass system. By Eq. (4-28), and remembering that we are taking $c = 1$,

$$v = \frac{P_x}{P_0} = \frac{p\gamma_u}{m\gamma_u + m} = u\frac{\gamma_u}{\gamma_u + 1} \tag{4-88}$$

and it is easily checked that Eqs. (4-87) and (4-88) are equivalent. Another application of both relations in Eq. (3-22) now gives, with the notation indicated in Fig. 4-1 (noting that we are taking the angle ϕ given in Fig. 4-1

‡ Although the forces involved in these collisions (Coulomb forces) are not strictly short range, the observations refer of course to practically infinite separations of the electrons. In general one would also have to consider radiative effects, but these are small in collisions involving electron energies of the order of only one Mev.

§ Equation (4-85) implies that $\tan\alpha = [2 + (\gamma + 1)\tan^2\theta]/(\gamma - 1)\tan\theta$, and the same relation follows from Eq. (4-84) with the aid of a few trigonometric identities.

as positive),

$$\tan\theta = \frac{g_y^*}{\gamma(g_x^* + v)} \qquad \gamma \equiv \gamma_v$$
$$\tan\phi = \frac{g_y^*}{\gamma(-g_x^* + v)}$$

so that $\tan\theta\tan\phi = g_y^{*2}/\gamma^2(v^2 - g_x^{*2}) = 1/\gamma^2$, since $v^2 = u^{*2} = g_x^{*2} + g_y^{*2}$. The result (4-85) now follows by applying formula (i) of Prob. 3-3:

$$\gamma_u = (1 + vu^*)\gamma_v\gamma_{u*} = (1 + v^2)\gamma_v{}^2$$

i.e., $1/\gamma^2 = (1 + v^2)/\gamma_u = 2v/u\gamma_u = 2/(\gamma_u + 1)$, where we have used Eqs. (4-87) and (4-88).

We may note that a more symmetrical expression than Eq. (4-84) can be found for $\cos\alpha$ when given in terms of the final electron energies W_1, W_2. It can be obtained quite easily from the conservation of magnitude of total relativistic 3-momentum [as defined in Eq. (4-15)] following from our basic law (4-83). With the notation given in Fig. 4-1, this can be written, $\mathbf{P}^2 = (\mathbf{Q}_1 + \mathbf{Q}_2)^2$, from which one finds directly that

$$\cos\alpha = \frac{P^2 - Q_1^2 - Q_2^2}{2Q_1Q_2}, \qquad P = |\mathbf{P}|, \text{ etc.} \tag{4-89}$$

It should be noted that this expression entails no restrictions on the masses of the particles before or after the collision (or reaction)—it has *general* validity. In the case of elastic collisions of identical particles, substitution of the energy conservation rule

$$E + m = W_1 + W_2, \qquad c = 1 \tag{4-90}$$

and use of Eq. (4-86) leads, by a few simple algebraic steps, to the desired formula:

$$\cos\alpha = \left[\frac{(W_1 - m)(W_2 - m)}{(W_1 + m)(W_2 + m)}\right]^{1/2} \tag{4-91}$$

Another historically important experimental result bearing on our subject is the well-known *Compton effect*—though the primary importance of this experiment was, of course, in its manifesting mechanical *particle* properties of electromagnetic radiation. This result provides a simple example of the application of the law (4-83) to systems involving particles of *zero rest mass.* Compton's formula for the shift $\Delta\lambda$ in the wavelength of the scattered radiation can be obtained in fact from Eq. (4-89) together with the expression for the conservation of momentum along the direction of the scattered photon (particle 1 in Fig. 4-1), $P\cos\theta = Q_1 + Q_2\cos\alpha$, from which it follows that

$$1 - \cos\theta = \frac{Q_2^2 - (P - Q_1)^2}{2PQ_1} = \frac{(W_2^2 - m^2) - (E - W_1)^2}{2EW_1} = \frac{2m(E - W_1)}{2EW_1}$$

[by Eq. (4-86) and (4-90)], and hence,

$$\Delta\lambda = h\left(\frac{1}{W_1} - \frac{1}{E}\right) = \frac{h}{m}(1 - \cos\theta), \qquad c = 1$$

In more recent times, significant applications of the conservation law (4-83) have been made in particular in connection with elementary particle decay phenomena. It is, for instance, easily deduced that in case of the decay of a particle into precisely two given particles, each of these particles carries away a definite characteristic energy (see Prob. 4-18); whereas, if there are more than two decay products, the liberated energy is distributed among the products according to an appropriate statistical law. This criterion has made it possible to conclude, as is well known, that there are at least two neutral particles emitted in muon decay, but only one such particle in pion decay.‡ Even more striking is the more recent discovery of a new *neutral* particle, the hyperon Λ, by cloud-chamber measurements on the products (proton and negative pion) of its decay in flight. The relevant formula is also deducible from Eq. (4-89). Upon substitution of Eq. (4-90) with the second term of the first side absent, and application of the relation (4-86), it leads to (see Fig. 4-1):

$$\cos\alpha = \frac{m_1^2 + m_2^2 - m^2 + 2W_1W_2}{2Q_1Q_2} \tag{4-92}$$

The mass m of the invisible decaying particle can thus be calculated from the measurable data.§

Turning now to other applications and confirmations of relativistic mechanics not immediately involving quantum phenomena, we can limit

‡ See, e.g., A. M. Thorndike, *op. cit.* chap. 5.

§ Equally interesting is the approximate determination of the mass of the neutral pion with the aid of Eq. (4-92)—which, for two zero-rest-mass decay products ($\gamma + \gamma$ in the present case), can be written $1 - \cos\alpha = m^2/2W_1W_2$—from the angle α and the photon energies W_1, W_2 as suitably measured. The reader will find many further interesting applications of the conservation laws (4-83) to elementary particle problems in the literature on the subject. A survey of the field as of 1957 is contained in an extensive paper by C. Franzinetti and G. Morpurgo, *Nuovo Cimento, Suppl.*, **6:** 469 (1957). For an illustration of the use of Eq. (4-83) in the partial analysis of complex elementary particle reactions one can consult, e.g., J. Podolanski and R. Armenteros, *Phil. Mag.*, **45:** 13 (1954); N. G. Birger and Yu. A. Smorodin, *Soviet Phys. JETP*, **9:** 823 (1959); A. M. Baldin, V. I. Gol'danskii, and I. L. Rozenthal, "Kinematics of Nuclear Reactions" Pergamon Press, New York, 1961 (translated by W. E. Jones). A readable introduction to the subject is contained in R. Hagedorn, "Relativistic Kinematics," W. A. Benjamin, Inc., New York, 1963. See also Probs. 4-16 to 4-21.

ourselves to two important groups. The successful operation of ultra-high-energy accelerators serves as a strong confirmation of Eqs. (4-4) and the basic formula (4-6). In the early days of STR considerable effort was expended to check this formula by electron-deflection experiments (see Prob. 4-1, and references to measurements other than those of Kaufmann given in [7], p. 83), which were never of very high accuracy. These are obviously now only of historical interest.

The other domain of application involves the mass-energy relation (4-13).‡ Its first unequivocal verification came with the establishment of the annihilation of electron-positron pairs and of the total conversion of their 'mass equivalents' into the energy of the resulting photons [Blackett and Occhialini, 1933; high-precision measurement by J. Dumond, et al., *Phys. Rev.*, **75**: 1226 (1949)]. But we need not dwell here on this subject, with which, it can be assumed, the reader is already well acquainted. Neither is it necessary here to enter into a discussion of the verification as well as utilization of the mass-energy relation in nuclear physics.§ The only observation that needs to be made in the present connection is that in nuclear mass defects we have an all-important example of the equivalence of inertial rest mass and *potential energy*. We have already made reference to such equivalence in a purely theoretical connection (page 105), but the present is of course a significant realistic case. It is therefore desirable to examine in some quantitative manner how the equivalence in question arises here.

It is obvious that the analysis developed in Sec. 4-2 does not suffice in the present case, in which it is precisely the state of mutual binding of the particles, and not of their dispersal, that is important. Thus, it is necessary to introduce in some form the concept of negative potential energy of nuclear attraction (upon normalizing this energy to zero for infinite separation of the nucleons); but how can this be done in a relativistically covariant way? The answer is not known; the present theory of 'nuclear forces' is in any case still largely phenomenological. However, since the mean kinetic energies of nucleons in a nucleus are only of the order of one percent of the nucleon's rest mass, it can be concluded that classical ideas can be employed approximately in inertial systems in which the mean nucleon velocity is small compared with c, and in particular in the center-of-mass frame S^* of the system of nucleons comprising our nucleus (which is now also defined only approximately). One can therefore introduce the mutual

‡ It is hardly necessary to remind the reader of the significance of this formula both in pure and in applied physics. Some would possibly have preferred there were less to be said of the latter.

§ A systematic discussion of the agreement of nuclear data with the mass-energy law is given by W. Braunbeck, Z. *Physik*, **107**: 1 (1937). More recent data are contained, e.g., in J. Mattauch and F. Everling, Article 8 in "Progress in Nuclear Phys.," vol. 6, Pergamon Press, London, 1957.

potential energy V^* of the nucleon system relative to S^* taken in the classical sense, and, in the spirit of this approximate treatment, now apply the pertinent results developed in Sec. 4-2, modified by the replacement of the internal kinetic energy K^* of Eqs. (4-31) by the total 'semiclassical' internal energy $E^* = K^* + V^*$. The first of Eqs. (4-31) is then replaced by the following relation (where we are otherwise using the notation employed there)

$$M^* = \sum_s m_s + \frac{E^*}{c^2} \tag{4-93}$$

which gives us thus the celebrated connection between the rest masses m_s of the isolated nucleons and the rest mass M^* of the bound system of nucleons—the nucleus. Needless to say, in the actual experimental checking of this formula, the approximate features of the calculation are immaterial. It is the dynamical identification of the mass defect $\Sigma m_s - M^*$ in Eq. (4-93) that can only claim approximate validity.

Although the experimental verifications of Eq. (4-13) are so impressive that we could, if we wished, start with Eq. (4-13) as our basic dynamical assumption from which we could deduce Eq. (4-6) and the equations of motion on the basis of further natural assumptions modeled after their newtonian correspondents,‡ it is of obvious interest rather to deduce this formula as generally as possible from the relativistic principles. This is indeed possible,§ but we shall content ourselves here with calling attention to the interesting history relating to this subject.¶ The equivalence of mass and energy was foreshadowed in the recognition of inertial properties pertaining to electromagnetic radiation, largely implicit in Maxwell's equations, made more evident through Poynting's interpretation of the surface integral known by his name, and further clarified by Poincaré.‡‡ The first paper in which the mass-energy equivalence is enunciated in its full generality as a hypothesis suggested by a thought experiment pointing to its validity in the case of electromagnetic energy is Einstein's paper "Does the Inertia of a Body Depend Upon Its Energy-Content?" ([2], paper 4).

This celebrated paper was apparently written under the influence of Einstein's simultaneous path-breaking work on the light-photon hypothesis. His thought experiment and ensuing analysis can, in fact, be restated as follows. Imagine an excited *localized* physical system A resting in the inertial frame S, whose total energy in S is E, and suppose that A emits

‡ Cf. G. N. Lewis, *Phil. Mag.*, **16**: 705 (1908).

§ The interested reader can consult, e.g., [6], sec. 30, and [7], sec. 41.

¶ A good sketch of this history is contained in M. von Laue, Inertia and Energy, in P. A. Schilpp (ed.), "Albert Einstein: Philosopher Scientist," pp. 503–533, Tudor Publishing Company, New York, 1951.

‡‡ H. Poincaré, La Théorie de Lorentz et la Principe de Réaction, *Archives Néérlandaises des Sciences Exactes et Naturelles*, **5**: 252 (1900).

simultaneously two photons each of energy $w/2$ and moving in opposite directions, so that A remains stationary in S. Considered from another inertial system S' connected with S by the Lorentz equations (2-6), the energy of A before the photon emission is E', and hence $E' - E$ is the kinetic energy of A in S' before the emission process. After emission, this kinetic energy is given by the similar expression, $(E' - w') - (E - w)$, where w' is the energy of the emitted photons relative to S'. By the 4-vector property of a photon's energy-momentum,‡

$$w' = \gamma\left(\frac{w}{2} + \beta P_x + \frac{w}{2} - \beta P_x\right) = \gamma w$$

and hence the loss of kinetic energy to A in S' amounts to $(\gamma - 1)w$. Comparing with Eq. (4-12) it is seen immediately that there is associated with the energy w a proper mass $m_w = w/c^2$.§

Problems

4-1 (*a*) During the first few years after the publication of Einstein's basic paper on STR, this theory was accepted with reservations even by many of its friends, because the published results of W. Kaufman (1901, 1906) on e/m measurements with β particles of radium C (see references on p. 83 of [7]), appeared to favor the following formula for the variation of the mass of the electron with velocity, proposed by M. Abraham [*Ann. Physik*, **10:** 105 (1903)]:

$$m(v) = \frac{3}{4}\frac{m}{\beta^2}\left(\frac{1+\beta^2}{2\beta}\log\frac{1+\beta}{1-\beta} - 1\right), \qquad \beta = \frac{v}{c}$$

Abraham deduced this formula from electromagnetic theory on the assumption of the invariance of the electronic charge and on the basis of a model of a perfectly and permanently rigid spherical electron. Without entering into the details of Abraham's theory, what in his approach do you find consistent and what do you find inconsistent with STR? What fundamental difference attaches to the mass-velocity formulas in these two theories quite aside from the particular functional expressions? Considering the latter, what percentage difference is yielded by the two expressions when the electron's energy is of the order of one Mev, and is this difference consistent with its being masked by experimental errors in deflection experiments per-

‡ Einstein speaks in his first relativity paper—to which he refers in the paper under discussion—of "light complexes," and deduces the transformation of their energy contents by special kinematic and electrodynamic considerations ([2], paper 3, secs. 7, 8). See Prob. 4-22.

§ It may be noted that Einstein's restrictive assumption made on p. 71 of [2] is unnecessary, since he could have referred to the exact relativistic expression for kinetic energy previously obtained by him (p. 63 of [2]). For a discussion of an alternative method of justifying Eq. (4-13), also originally proposed by Einstein, see E. Feenberg, *Am. J. Phys.*, **28:** 565 (1960).

formed at the break of this century? (*b*) Do the interesting measurements of W. Bertozzi, *Am. J. Phys.*, **32**: 551 (1964), have any bearing on the above questions?

4-2 (*a*) By using the transformation equations (3-29*a*) for P show that the force vector **f** as defined in the second set of Eqs. (4-7) obeys the following transformation law under a 'parallel-axis' Lorentz transformation (taking c for the unit velocity):

$$\mathbf{f}' = \frac{1}{\gamma(1 - \mathbf{v}\cdot\mathbf{u})}\left\{\mathbf{f} + \left[\mathbf{f}\cdot\left(\frac{\gamma - 1}{v^2}\mathbf{v} - \gamma\mathbf{u}\right)\right]\mathbf{v}\right\}, \qquad c = 1 \qquad \text{(i)}$$

Rederive this result by considering the 4-vector F of Eq. (4-4). (*b*) Consider the motion of a particle under the action of a force that remains constant in its instantaneous rest system. Show that referred to any inertial frame this motion is "hyperbolic" (see Prob. 3-17) when the initial velocity is in the direction of the force.

4-3 Lewis and Tolman (reference on page 89) have called attention to the following interesting thought experiment bearing on the relativistic transformation properties of force. It involves a rigid lever as indicated in Fig. 4-2, in equilibrium in an inertial system under the two forces f_1, f_2 (as shown

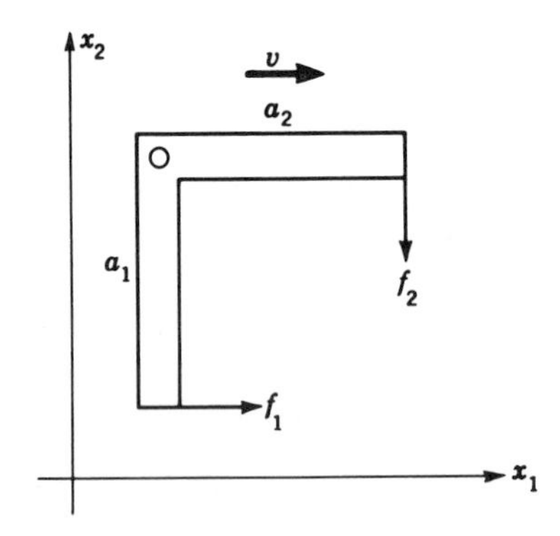

Fig. 4-2 The Lewis-Tolman rigid-lever thought experiment. The lever is free to rotate about the indicated pivot. The arm lengths a_1 and a_2 and the force magnitudes f_1 and f_2 are equal in the rest frame. In Prob. 4-3, the letters f_1, f_2 refer to the force magnitudes in the *moving* system.

in the figure), which is set in uniform motion of speed v. They conclude that from its continuing state of equilibrium one can infer that during the motion $f_1/f_2 = (1 - v^2/c^2)^{1/2}$. Verify this conclusion on the basis of their premises. Do you have any reservations concerning the latter? Show that by applying the transformation formula (i) of Prob. 4-2 we find the ratio $f_1/f_2 = \gamma_v$. (This question is reopened in Prob. 6-16.)

4-4 Consider the following Lewis-Tolman thought experiment. Two identical elastically colliding balls P, Q are projected towards each other with the same speed u along the y direction at the instant $t = t' = 0$ from the origins of two inertial frames S, S' whose coordinates are connected by the transformation (2-6), except that $y' = y + a$ $(a > 0)$. Show that by the relativistic formula of composition of velocities and by simple symmetry considerations one finds the following velocity components u_x, u_y of P and w_x, w_y of Q, indicating by bars the corresponding quantities after the collision: $u_x = 0$, $u_y = u$; $w_x = v$, $w_y = -u/\gamma$; $\bar{u}_x = 0$, $\bar{u}_y = -u^*$; $\bar{w}_x = v$, $\bar{w}_y = u^*/\gamma$; $u'_x = -v$, $u'_y = u/\gamma$; $w'_x = 0$, $w'_y = -u$; $\bar{u}'_x = -v$, $\bar{u}'_y = -u^*/\gamma$; $\bar{w}'_x = 0$, $\bar{w}'_y = u^*$ $(\gamma \equiv \gamma_v)$. Assuming that the momentum of a particle of velocity $\mathbf{u}$ is given by the expression $m(|\mathbf{u}|)\mathbf{u}$, show next that from the conservation of momentum along the x direction for our colliding balls it can be concluded that $u^* = u$, and that the conservation of momentum of this system along the y direction then leads to the relation

$$m(\sqrt{v^2 + (u^2/\gamma^2)}) = \gamma m(u) \tag{i}$$

from which Eq. (4-6) follows by letting $u \to 0$; and finally that (i) is satisfied generally by virtue of the relation (4-6). Precisely what essential assumptions are involved in this derivation of the relativistic mass formula? In particular, is essential use being made of the relativistic covariance of the momentum-conservation law? Would the present derivation be simplified if referred to the center-of-mass system of the colliding particles? (See [7], sec. 38.)

4-5 Show that for the covariant applicability of Newton's third law in the collision of two particles, it is necessary that at the impact event the velocities of the two particles coincide. Show that the latter is a relativistically covariant condition.

4-6 (*a*) In exploring the question whether a rocket approaching "relativistic velocities" is likely ever to become an actuality, one can utilize, by way of an initial orientation, the formula of J. Ackeret [*Helv. Phys. Acta*, **19**: 103 (1946)]:

$$U = \frac{1 - (m_f/m_i)^{2w}}{1 + (m_f/m_i)^{2w}}, \qquad c = 1 \tag{i}$$

where m_i, m_f are respectively the initial and final rest masses of the rocket, U is its final speed relative to its initial rest frame, and w is the exhaust velocity relative to the rocket (which is assumed constant and directed oppositely to the rocket's motion). Derive this formula, assuming that the rocket moves in a straight line in empty space and far removed from all fields. [Apply the law of conservation of 4-momentum to the system consisting at each instant of the rocket and the exhaust material, both being treated as 'particles.' Denoting by m and u the rest mass and the velocity of the former, the resulting differential equation reduces, with the aid of the relativistic law of composition of velocities, to

$$\frac{dm}{m} = -\frac{1}{w}\gamma^2\,du \tag{ii}$$

which integrates under the stated conditions to the expression (i).] (*b*) Suppose that mass ejection takes place at a constant relative rate, as measured in the rocket's rest frame. Show that our idealized spaceship moves with constant proper acceleration. (*c*) Ch. Mauguin [*Compt. Rend.*, **234**: 1004 (1952)] considers space travel (with comfortable return to earth) from the point of view of proper time required to cover distances of thousands of light years when the acceleration referred to in (*b*) is of the order of the acceleration of gravity at the surface of the earth. He finds periods that can accommodate a normal human lifespan, but is pessimistic about the technical possibilities of achieving the required acceleration. Verify his conclusions. Is his pessimism still fully justified today even in the case of travel to the nearest star? [In making numerical estimates bearing on the first part of this question, it is helpful to introduce c/α and c^2/α as units of time and of space, where α is the constant proper acceleration, so that the pertinent equations assume the form (choosing the x axis for the line of motion and assuming that initially $t = 0$, $x = 0$, $dx/dt = 0$), $x = \cosh\tau - 1$, $t = \sinh\tau$ (τ = proper time of the rocket); and to note that our new unit of time is about a year long and our new unit of distance is correspondingly a light-year long.]

4-7 Consider a mechanical system for which the 4-vector of total energy and momentum is well defined. For such a system show that from the conservation of energy one can infer the conservation of momentum as a consequence of relativistic covariance. Do we have an analogous result in newtonian mechanics when invariance under the galilean group is invoked? [Consider energy conservation as expressed by the relation $d(\Sigma mu^2/2)/dt = \Sigma\mathbf{f}\cdot\mathbf{u}$. See M. von Laue, *op. cit.* (on page 118), footnote on p. 516.]

4-8 To what extent are the results concerning angular momenta and the center of mass of the special particle systems discussed in Sec. 4-2 similar to the corresponding results in nonrelativistic mechanics? [Examine in particular the validity of the characteristic relation $d(\Sigma m(u)\mathbf{x})/dt = 0$ holding in the center-of-mass frame.]

4-9 (*a*) Prove that the quantities (4-32) are the components of a covariant entity under the conditions given in the text, when the underlying group with respect to which the covariance is defined is (as always tacitly assumed) the *homogeneous* Lorentz group. (*b*) Prove the essential uniqueness (i.e., up to a shift in the spatial origin in S^*) of the center of mass $\mathbf{c}^*$ defined in Sec. 4-2. (*c*) Show that in any inertial system S we have the following decomposition for the tensor L given in Eq. (4-32):

$$L_{\mu\nu} = L_{\mu\nu}^{(\text{int})} + (c^*)_\mu P_\nu - (c^*)_\nu P_\mu \tag{i}$$

where the "internal" part of L, $L_{\mu\nu}^{(\text{int})}$, is given by $L_{\mu\nu}(\mathbf{c}^*)$, in the notation explained in Sec. 4-2.

4-10 (*a*) A particle of rest mass m is acted upon by a central force $f_i = -\partial V(r)/\partial x_i$ ($r^2 = x_i x_i$), as considered in a given inertial system S, f_i being defined in Eq. (4-7). Applying relativistic mechanics, show that the following quantities are constants of motion in S [using the notation of Eq. (4-6)]:

$$m(u)c^2 + V = E, \qquad m(u)\mathbf{x} \times \frac{d\mathbf{x}}{dt} = \mathbf{J} \tag{i}$$

Proceeding as in the corresponding classical mechanics treatment, deduce the following equation for the trajectory of the particle in terms of polar coordinates r,ϕ in the plane of motion:

$$c^2J^2(s'^2 + s^2) - (E - V)^2 + (mc^2)^2 = 0 \qquad s = \frac{1}{r} \quad s' \equiv \frac{ds}{d\phi} \tag{ii}$$

where, $J = m(u)r^2\, d\phi/dt$. Check that the familiar classical results are obtained in the limit when $E \approx mc^2$, $|V|/E \ll 1$, E as given in Eq. (i).

In particular, when

$$V = -C\frac{1}{r} \tag{iii}$$

and

$$a^2 = 1 - \alpha^2 \neq 0, \qquad \alpha = \frac{C}{cJ}; \qquad J \neq 0 \tag{iv}$$

show that the general solution of Eq. (ii) is

$$s = A \sin(a\phi + B) + \eta, \qquad \eta = \frac{E\alpha^2}{Ca^2} \tag{v}$$

where E, J are the constants of motion given in Eqs. (i), B is arbitrary, and

$$A^2 = \frac{E^2 - m^2c^4a^2}{c^2J^2a^4} \tag{vi}$$

Show further that bound solutions exist only if the force is attractive ($C > 0$), and

$$a^2 \geq 0, \qquad |E| < mc^2 \tag{vii}$$

with the trajectories spiraling about and converging upon the origin (particle 'capture') in the case $a = 0$, while if $a^2 < 0$ the trajectories are not bounded and also present the capture behavior. Indicate the limiting conditions under which one obtains the nonrelativistic elliptic and hyperbolic orbits. (*b*) Deduce from Eq. (v) of the particle's orbit that the advance of the perihelion per revolution (see Fig. 4-3) is (in radians)

$$2\pi\left(\frac{1}{a}-1\right)=\frac{\pi C^2}{c^2J^2}+\cdots \qquad \text{(viii)}$$

If C has the value corresponding to the newtonian attraction of the planet Mercury by the sun, compare Eq. (viii) with the observational value.

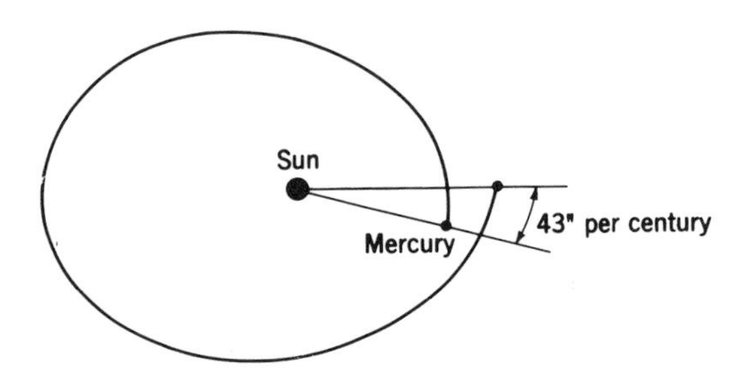

Fig. 4-3 Schematic representation of the perihelion advance of the planet Mercury—the excess over the perihelion shift due to perturbation by other planets.

(This value is about 43″ per century after subtracting the larger shift caused by the newtonian perturbations of the other planets.)

4-11 (*a*) The preceding problem is concerned with the motion of a particle referred to a particular inertial frame S in which there is specified a conservative field of force (in the classical sense).

$$\mathbf{f} = -\operatorname{grad} V(\mathbf{x})$$

Show that this field of force can be cast into a relativistically covariant form. As a check, verify that the resulting Minkowski 4-vector of force transforms properly under the Lorentz transformations (3-29). [Unless you are acquainted with the tensor formalism in $\mathfrak{M}$ (treated in Chap. 5), introduce the imaginary time variable $x_4 = ix_0$, so as to be able to refer to needed analogous results in ordinary tensor algebra (as done in Sec. 4-3). Show that with proper definitions one can write the equations of motion in the form of Eq. (4-58).] (*b*) Consider a mechanical system consisting of N particles and a time-independent potential energy function $V(q_1, \ldots ,q_n)$ involving n independent generalized coordinates, as referred to a given inertial frame S. Show that canonical equations of motion, of the same form as in nonrelativistic mechanics but with relativistic masses, can be deduced from the Lagrangian

$$L = L_0 - V, \qquad L_0 = -\sum_{r=1}^{N}\frac{m_r}{\gamma_r}c^2, \qquad \gamma_r \equiv \gamma_{u_r}, \qquad \mathbf{u}_r = \frac{d\mathbf{x}_r}{dt}$$

Writing the corresponding Hamiltonian as

$$H = p_a\dot{q}_a - L = H_0 + V, \qquad p_a = \frac{\partial L}{\partial \dot{q}_a}, \qquad \dot{q} \equiv \frac{dq}{dt}$$

show that

$$H_0 = p_a\dot{q}_a - L_0 = c^2 \sum_{r=1}^{N} m_r(u_r) \tag{i}$$

(so that H_0 is the total energy of the system relative to S in the absence of all interaction), and that the total energy of the system relative to S is conserved. Show that for $N = 1$ and $n = 3$, the present result is consistent with that considered in (*a*). In what sense, if any, can the above equations be taken to have relativistic significance when $N > 1$? In what essential respect relating to relativistic covariance does the present situation in the case $N > 1$ differ from that considered in (*a*)? [One finds,

$$p_a = \Sigma m_r\gamma_r\dot{\mathbf{x}}_r \cdot \frac{\partial \mathbf{x}_r}{\partial q_a}$$

and Eq. (i) then follows using the identity $\gamma^2\beta^2 + 1 = \gamma^2$. This treatment is discussed in R. C. Tolman, "The Theory of the Relativity of Motion," chaps. 7 and 9, University of California Press, Berkeley, 1917.]

4-12 If $\mathfrak{L}$ is an invariant one-particle Lagrangian, prove that

$$P_\alpha^{(w)} \equiv \frac{\partial \mathfrak{L}^{(w)}}{\partial(dx_\alpha/dw)} = P_\alpha^{(w')}$$

i.e., that $P_\alpha^{(w)}$ is for each value of α (= 1, 2, 3, 4) an invariant with respect to changes of the 4-scalar evolution parameter w; but that the $P_\alpha^{(w)}$ are the components of a 4-vector, and hence the expression (4-66) is a 4-scalar. In particular, show that the quadruplet $(p_k, iH/c)$ referred to on page 106 represents a 4-vector.

4-13 (*a*) In connection with the flexibility inherent in the relativistic canonical formulation, show that, in view of the identity (4-8), that is, $U_\alpha U_\alpha = -c^2$, using the time variable $x_4 = ict$, if for instance

$$\mathfrak{L} = \tfrac{1}{2}mU_\alpha U_\alpha + A_\alpha(\mathsf{x})U_\alpha$$

is a relativistic Lagrangian, then $mf(U_\alpha U_\alpha) + A_\alpha(\mathsf{x})U_\alpha$ is an effectively equivalent $\mathfrak{L}$, provided $f'(-c^2) = \frac{1}{2}$. Compare with the relevant discussion in Sec. 4-3. (*b*) Consider the following alternative method for obtaining the relativistic canonical equations for a one-body problem with a first-order-homogeneous Lagrangian. Since the π_α are homogeneous of order zero in the x'_α (see footnote on page 101), one can eliminate the ratios of

x_1', x_2', x_3', x_4' obtaining a constraint relation

$$\Psi(x_\alpha;\pi_\alpha) = 0 \tag{i}$$

Remembering that with our assumption the action integral can be written

$$I = \int \pi_\alpha \, dx_\alpha \tag{ii}$$

show, by using the method of Lagrange multipliers, that $\delta I = 0$ subject to condition (i), provided

$$\pi_\alpha' = -l \frac{\partial \Psi}{\partial x_\alpha}, \; x_\alpha' = l \frac{\partial \Psi}{\partial \pi_\alpha} \qquad \begin{aligned} l &\equiv l(w) \\ x' &\equiv \frac{dx}{dw} \end{aligned} \tag{iii}$$

and that these equations assume the standard form (of a canonical set with Hamiltonian Ψ) by a proper choice of the parameter w [after proving that there is no essential loss of generality in assuming $l(w) > 0$]. Show further that Eqs. (iii) insure the consistent application of condition (i) (by proving that $d\Psi/dw = 0$). Relate this condition and the present method to the corresponding approach presented in Sec. 4-3. (*c*) When taking $w = \tau$, the proper time along the 4-trajectory, the variational procedure employed in Sec. 4-3 needs to be completed by taking account of the obvious impossibility in general of having $\delta\tau = 0$ at the terminal point of the trajectory [a similar situation arises in the treatment of the principle of least action, Eq. (4-54)]. Show that the results given in Sec. 4-3 are nevertheless correct, in view of the vanishing of $\mathcal{H}$. [When the required variation in $w = \tau$ is included in our analysis, there results an additional term $-\mathcal{H}\,\delta\tau$ inside the square brackets in Eq. (4-45), as can be seen, for instance, by repeating the arguments leading to Eq. (4-45) and the last equation in Eqs. (4-49) with $a \equiv \alpha = 1, 2, 3, 4$; $q_\alpha \equiv x_\alpha$; and $q_0 \equiv \tau$.]

4-14 (*a*) Derive Eq. (4-82) by considering the relativistic analog of "Hamilton's characteristic function" (see, e.g., Goldstein, *op. cit.*, sec. 9-3). (Consider the integral (ii) of Prob. 4-13 taken along a 4-trajectory with lower limit fixed and upper limit a variable point of $\mathfrak{M}$.) Continue the development of the canonical relativistic theory for the one-body problem by suitable extension of the corresponding classical results, and in particular consider the possibility of setting up finite and infinitesimal canonical transformations for this problem and associated Poisson bracket relations. [For the classical theory, see, e.g., Goldstein, *op. cit.*, chap. 8. Incidentally, note that canonical transformations form an example of *infinite* continuous groups: they are characterized by general "generating *functions*" and thus essentially involve not a finite but an *infinite* number of parameters (see Appendix 3A).] (*b*) Deduce the classical limit of the Hamilton-Jacobi equation (4-82). (Eliminate first the rest energy mc^2 by the transformation $S \to S - mc^2t$.)

4-15 It will be observed that if one makes the change $A_\alpha \to A_\alpha + \partial\Psi/\partial x_\alpha$, where Ψ is an arbitrary 4-scalar, the equations of motion (4-58) are not affected (a result familiar from electromagnetic theory). Relate this result to corresponding considerations concerning the Lagrangian. (Bear in mind that adding a complete differential to a Lagrangian does not affect the equations of motion.)

4-16 (*a*) Let a particle of proper mass m and at rest in the laboratory be bombarded by a particle whose kinetic energy K is much greater than its rest mass (i.e., a particle moving in the laboratory with "extreme relativistic" speed). Assuming that the rest masses of the two particles are of the same order of magnitude, show that in the center-of-mass coordinate system the *total energy* of the particles is approximated by the expression $\sqrt{2Km}$ (taking $c = 1$). (*b*) The above result shows the practical limitations that exist in the production of ultrahigh-energy reactions by the bombardment of nearly stationary targets. To obtain substantially greater reaction energies than is now possible, colliding-beam accelerators are therefore under investigation. Moreover, even with stationary targets, if they are many-nucleon nuclei, a nontrivial percentage increase in available energy can result, owing to the distribution of the momenta of the nucleons in the nucleus corresponding to an average kinetic energy of the order of 10 Mev. For the purpose of obtaining an estimate of the optimum reaction energy E^* (the total energy in the center-of-mass frame) that can be thus made available, show that for oppositely directed initial momenta and like rest masses we have

$$E^{*2} = 2\{2 + K_1 + K_2 + K_1K_2 + [(K_1{}^2 + 2K_1)(K_2{}^2 + 2K_2)]^{1/2}\} \qquad \text{(i)}$$

where K_1, K_2 are the kinetic energies of the colliding particles, and we are using c and the initial particle rest mass as units. Find E^* for $K_1 = 20$ and $K_2 = 2$ and compare your result with that corresponding to $K_2 = 0$. In the special case (applicable to the bombardment of nuclei by ultrahigh-energy protons) that $K_1 \gg 1$, $\sqrt{K_2} \ll 1$, show that Eq. (i) yields the approximate formula

$$\frac{E^* - E_0^*}{E_0^*} \approx \sqrt{\frac{K_2}{2}}, \qquad E_0^* \equiv E^* \text{ for } K_2 = 0$$

and apply it to typical cases. (*c*) In the case of a two-particle inelastic collision, show that the "threshold energy" for the reaction (4-83) (i.e., the minimum laboratory kinetic energy of the bombarding particle necessary to initiate the reaction, that is otherwise allowed, the target particle being stationary) is

$$K_{\text{thr}} = \frac{M^2 - m^2}{2m(B)} \qquad \begin{aligned} M &= \sum_s m(C_s) \\ m &= m(A) + m(B) \end{aligned}$$

where B is the target particle in the notation of Eq. (4-83). In theory, what is the least costly way of producing nucleon-antinucleon pairs? [All of the above results can be obtained by suitably evaluating in the center of mass and in the laboratory frames the quantity (P,P), where P is the total 4-momentum of our system. For part (c), note that this quantity is M^2 in the limiting case in question.]

4-17 (a) Show that if it were dynamically possible (i.e., allowed by strong interaction selection rules) for an isolated nucleon to absorb a meson without immediate disintegration, there would have to exist single-nucleon excited states (nucleon isobars). On the other hand, what limitations are imposed by classical (relativistic) considerations on free resonance absorption (the excitation of an isolated atom or nucleus to a given level by absorption of a photon emitted by an identical atom or nucleus excited to the same level)? Show that in the atomic case these limitations are practically negligible. What is the situation in the nuclear case? [Consider the simple considerations involving energy-momentum conservation and natural line width relating to the Mössbauer effect (cf., e.g., Frauenfelder, *op. cit.*). If one wishes to consider the general case of free resonance absorption with arbitrary relative velocity of the two atoms (or nuclei) regardless of practical considerations and also disregarding all but classical (relativistic) particle mechanics restrictions, one can proceed for instance as follows ([8], chap. 6, sec. 17): suppose that the 4-momenta of the emitting and absorbing atoms A, A', before and after the emission and absorption of the photon, are $\bar{\mathsf{P}}$, P, P', $\bar{\mathsf{P}}'$, respectively, and that of the photon is Q. From the relations (taking $c = 1$) $\mathsf{P}^2 \equiv (\mathsf{P},\mathsf{P}) = \mathsf{P}'^2 = m^2$, $\bar{\mathsf{P}}^2 = \bar{\mathsf{P}}'^2 = \bar{m}^2$, $\mathsf{Q}^2 = 0$, $\bar{\mathsf{P}} = \mathsf{P} + \mathsf{Q}$, $\mathsf{P}' + \mathsf{Q} = \bar{\mathsf{P}}'$, one finds $(\mathsf{Q},\bar{\mathsf{P}}) = (\mathsf{Q},\mathsf{P}') = (\bar{m}^2 - m^2)/2$. Hence, in the rest system of A before emission, $Q_0 = (\bar{m}^2 - m^2)/2\bar{m} \equiv a$, $\mathbf{Q}^2 = a^2$, $\mathbf{Q} \cdot \mathbf{P}' = Q_0 P'_0 - a\bar{m} = a(P'_0 - \bar{m})$, and the condition of consistency of the last two equations yields the restriction $(P'_0 - \bar{m})^2 \leq \mathbf{P}'^2$, that reduces to $P'_0 = E' \geq (m^2 + \bar{m}^2)/2\bar{m}$, from which one can find the lower bound of the velocity of A' before absorption relative to A before emission.] (b) Using the Planck-Einstein quantum relation, $E = h\nu$, derive the general Doppler effect and light-aberration formulas from particle mechanics considerations. [The latter formula can be written, in the notation of Sec. 3-3,

$$\mathbf{n}' = \frac{1}{\gamma(1 - \boldsymbol{\beta} \cdot \mathbf{n})} \left[\mathbf{n} + \left(\frac{\gamma - 1}{\beta^2} \boldsymbol{\beta} \cdot \mathbf{n} - \gamma \right) \boldsymbol{\beta} \right]$$

(see Prob. 3-8).]

4-18 (*a*) Prove that the energies of the decay products in the decay of a kaon ($K^{\pm} \rightarrow \mu^{\pm} + \nu$) are unique (in any given frame of reference). (*b*) Show that in the decay of a muon the maximum energies that can be carried away by a neutrino or by the electron are each approximately half the rest energy of the muon. Assume that both neutrinos have vanishing rest mass. [In finding the general formula covering such questions, namely (taking $c = 1$),

$$K_i^{\max} = \Delta M \left(1 - \frac{m_i}{M} - \frac{\Delta M}{2M}\right), \qquad \Delta M = M - \sum_i m_i \tag{i}$$

where $K_i^{\max}$ is the maximum kinetic energy in the center of mass of the system of the ith decay particle of rest mass m_i, and M is the rest mass of the decaying particle, one can make use of the following sharpening of the inequality (4-26):

$$\left(\sum_i \mathsf{P}_i\right)^2 \geq \left(\sum_i m_i\right)^2 \tag{ii}$$

the equality holding when all the particles are at rest relative to each other.]

4-19 (*a*) Consider straight-line elastic collisions of two particles A_1, A_2. Letting ψ stand for the quantity defined in Eq. (3A-30) and denoting by bars quantities after the collision, show that

$$\psi_1 + \bar{\psi}_1 = \psi_2 + \bar{\psi}_2 \tag{i}$$

and that in the nonrelativistic limit, Eq. (i) reduces to the known classical result, $u_1 + \bar{u}_1 = u_2 + \bar{u}_2$ (Jüttner). [In the derivation of this result it is helpful to apply the identity,

$$\tanh \frac{\phi + \psi}{2} = \frac{\cosh \phi - \cosh \psi}{\sinh \phi - \sinh \psi}$$

By using Eq. (i) it is possible to express $\bar{u}_1$ and $\bar{u}_2$ in terms of u_1, u_2 and the rest masses of the particles. However, the expressions are rather complicated. (F. Jüttner, *Z. Math. Phys.*, **62**: 410 (1913–1914).] (*b*) Prove that for any two-particle elastic collision there exists a Lorentz transformation connecting the initial and final states [W. Pauli, *Z. Physik*, **18**: 272 (1923); **22**: 261 (1924). This result is applied in this paper in a very instructive way.]

4-20 Prove in simplest terms that a reaction involving the transformation of a system of particles into a particle of zero rest mass is incompatible with energy-momentum conservation.

4-21 The analysis of the reactions of strongly interacting particles (nuclei, π and K mesons, hyperons) is presently based on a number of symmetry postulates including those of relativistic *kinematics* (by which one understands, in this work, strict kinematics as well as 4-momentum conservation). In particular, it follows that the quantum-mechanical probability amplitude for a given reaction must be a relativistic scalar. Its dependence on 'kinematic' variables must therefore involve 4-scalar combinations. In the simple case of a binary collision [$p = 2$ in Eq. (4-83)] of spinless particles, show that we have two such independent invariants, when we consider the initial and final rest masses m_1, m_2 and $\bar{m}_1$, $\bar{m}_2$ as known parameters. Prove that the invariants can be represented in a symmetric form as follows: let us designate the initial and final 4-momenta of the particles by P_1, P_2, $\bar{\mathsf{P}}_1$, $\bar{\mathsf{P}}_2$, and write $\bar{\mathsf{P}}_1 = -\mathsf{P}_3$, $\bar{\mathsf{P}}_2 = -\mathsf{P}_4$, so that the conservation law (4-83) assumes the symmetric form

$$\sum_{a=1}^{4} \mathsf{P}_a = 0 \tag{i}$$

The invariants are then given by the quantities $s_k = s_{k4}$ ($k = 1, 2, 3$), where $s_{ab} = (\mathsf{P}_a + \mathsf{P}_b)^2$ ($a, b = 1, 2, 3, 4$; $a \neq b$), and

$$\sum_{k=1}^{3} s_k = \sum_{a=1}^{4} m_a^{\,2} \qquad \begin{aligned} m_3 &= \bar{m}_1 \\ m_4 &= \bar{m}_2 \end{aligned} \tag{ii}$$

Prove Eq. (ii). What is the physical significance of the s_k? [One can derive Eq. (ii) by taking the square of Eq. (i). Note that $s_{ab} = s_{cd}$, where a, b, c, d are distinct.]

4-22 In the reformulation of Einstein's deduction (of 1905) of the mass-energy equivalence (for electromagnetic radiation), as given at the end of Sec. 4-4, are we involved in any circular reasoning by assuming that we can attribute to a photon an energy-momentum vector? Compare this assumption with Einstein's original treatment. Is there any tacit assumption involved in our taking $E' - E$ as the kinetic energy of A in S' (Einstein actually put $E' - E$ = kinetic energy + constant, to allow for the arbitrary additive constants in the energy definitions, but this does not essentially affect our question)?

5
Tensor Analysis in Flat Spaces

We have had an indication in the preceding chapters of the important role played by the idea of invariance under appropriate transformation groups in both classical and relativistic physics, and later chapters will only further accentuate its importance. It is therefore desirable to pause at this point to examine the mathematical formulation of this idea available to us for representing the underlying physical relations. The notion of group representations is a useful tool, which is discussed in Sec. 5-1. This section contains also a first introduction to the theory of tensors, whose algebraic properties are discussed in Sec. 5-2.

A heuristically interesting idea, which has had its initial inspiration principally in the investigations of Riemann and of Minkowski, is what may be termed the "geometrization of physics"—the idea that important groups of physical relations are reproduced by corresponding structural relations in the continuous manifold of space plus time. The fruitfulness of this idea has been shown at least by the use made of it by Einstein in evolving his theory of gravitation. Whether or not it has further significant areas of application, as is the sanguine expectation of some physicists, the methodological value of geometric imagery, when suitably applied, is easy to appreciate. The theory of tensors is consequently treated also from a geometric point of view, which is further elaborated in Sec. 5-3. Moreover, by following a general geometric approach, and by introducing general curvilinear coordinates, the present discussion aimed at "flat" spaces applicable to STR can be readily extended to general "Riemannian spaces" of interest in the general theory of relativity. This approach leads also naturally to further developments in the algebra of tensors (Sec. 5-4), and to tensor analysis (Sec. 5-5).

5-1 GROUP REPRESENTATIONS AND TENSORS

The discussion of euclidean geometry contained in Sec. 1-2, and the analogous treatment of $\mathfrak{M}$ suggested in Sec. 3-4 bring out the significance of *invariance* under a characteristic group of coordinate transformations both in ordinary geometry looked at as a branch of physics and in physics generally. Quantities that can be taken to have well-defined geometric or physical meaning must be represented in our analytical scheme by expressions that do not discriminate between the members of the distinguished family of coordinate systems associated, for instance, with the group $\mathfrak{R}$ or $\mathfrak{L}$ respectively. More explicitly, if such a quantity is represented, say, in one distinguished coordinate system S by the set of real numbers or functions $q_1, \ldots, q_p$, and in another system S' by the corresponding set $q'_1, \ldots, q'_{p'}$, then the relationship of the q to S must be precisely the same as that of the q' to S' (and hence in particular we must have $p' = p$); and moreover, if we are given any equation involving the q and representing an objective relation (a "physical law"), then this equation must look the same in all coordinate systems of our basic family—it must be *covariant*, or *form invariant* under the associated group. An immediate example is provided by the "intervals" (i.e., '$\mathfrak{M}$ distances') between pairs of events; 4-vector fields and equations such as Eqs. (4-4) or (4-25) provide others. How can one develop a general scheme for constructing quantities enjoying this type of invariance with respect to a given transformation group, and for the easy identification of such quantities? This is the basic question to whose examination we now turn briefly.

Consider the quantities $q_1, \ldots, q_p$, and $q'_1, \ldots, q'_p$, referred to earlier. We can write

$$q'_a = f_a(q;T), \qquad a = 1, \ldots, p \tag{5-1}$$

where T is the transformation from S to S'. What can we say about the functions f_a? It is clear that the general requirements stated in the preceding paragraph, with the implication in particular that the q refer to *measurable* quantities (at least in principle), imply that the set of transformations of the q represented by Eqs. (5-1) must be an isomorphic map (see Appendix 1A) of our fundamental group $\mathfrak{G} = \{T\}$; it must constitute what algebraists call a "faithful realization" of $\mathcal{G}$. All such realizations of importance presently in both classical and quantum physics involve, moreover, functions f_a that are *linear homogeneous* in the q. Linear homogeneous realizations of a group, whether faithful or not, are known as "representations." The theory of group representations is a highly developed branch of algebra finding increasing application in current basic theoretical physics problems, of which some are touched upon in Chap. 8. For our immediate purpose we need refer to only one result of this theory that points to the general form of the (linear homogeneous) functions f_a of Eq. (5-1).

We need to define first the *direct* (or, *Kronecker*) product of two matrices. If the elements of the square matrices A, A' of respective orders n, n' are A_{ab} and $A'_{a'b'}$, then their "direct product" $A \times A'$ is the square matrix of order nn' whose elements are

$$(A \times A')_{pq} = A_{ab}A'_{a'b'} \qquad \begin{matrix} p = (a,a') \\ q = (b,b') \end{matrix} \tag{5-2}$$

with any given ordering of the indices within the pairs. For instance, for $n = n' = 2$, and with the ordering (1,1), (1,2), (2,1), (2,2), one has

$$\begin{bmatrix} A_{11} & A_{12} \\ A_{21} & A_{22} \end{bmatrix} \times \begin{bmatrix} A'_{11} & A'_{12} \\ A'_{21} & A'_{22} \end{bmatrix} = \begin{bmatrix} A_{11}A'_{11} & A_{11}A'_{12} & A_{12}A'_{11} & A_{12}A'_{12} \\ A_{11}A'_{21} & A_{11}A'_{22} & A_{12}A'_{21} & A_{12}A'_{22} \\ A_{21}A'_{11} & A_{21}A'_{12} & A_{22}A'_{11} & A_{22}A'_{12} \\ A_{21}A'_{21} & A_{21}A'_{22} & A_{22}A'_{21} & A_{22}A'_{22} \end{bmatrix}$$

Consider now the matrices $A, \ldots$ and $A', \ldots$ of two representations $\mathfrak{A}$, $\mathfrak{A}'$ of a given group. It is thus assumed that the association between the elements T of the group and the matrices A is such that if A_1, A_2 correspond to T_1, T_2 then A_1A_2 corresponds to T_1T_2, and similarly for the matrices of $\mathfrak{A}'$. The set of matrices $A \times A'$ forms likewise a representation of our group. In fact, since

$$(A \times A')(B \times B') = AB \times A'B' \tag{5-3}$$

as one easily verifies, the homomorphism or isomorphism, as the case may be, is also evident. The resulting representation is known as the *direct product* (or *Kronecker product*) of the representations $\mathfrak{A}$, $\mathfrak{A}'$, and is written $\mathfrak{A} \times \mathfrak{A}'$.

Considering the case, of principal interest to us at present, of the basic group $\mathcal{G}$ being itself *linear homogeneous*, it is clear that the associated group of matrices $\mathfrak{G}$ constitutes its own representation.‡ We have just seen that with $\mathfrak{G}$ also $\mathfrak{G} \times \mathfrak{G}$ is a representation of $\mathcal{G}$; hence, so is also $\mathfrak{G} \times \mathfrak{G} \times \mathfrak{G}$—which we shorten to read $\mathfrak{G}^{[3]}$; and by induction it follows that $\mathfrak{G}^{[n]}$ is a representation of $\mathcal{G}$ when n is any positive integer (and $\mathfrak{G}^{[1]} \equiv \mathfrak{G}$). In addition, one can obtain another sequence of finite-dimensional representa-

‡ In speaking of a representation we shall have reference indifferently either to the transformations or to the associated matrices.

tions,‡ by observing that by virtue of the matrix relations

$$(AB)^{-1} = B^{-1}A^{-1}, \qquad (\widetilde{AB}) = \tilde{B}\tilde{A}$$

which imply that

$$(\breve{AB}) = \breve{\mathfrak{G}}\breve{\mathfrak{G}}, \qquad \breve{A} \equiv \tilde{A}^{-1} \tag{5-4}$$

one can conclude that if $\{T\}$ is the family of matrices of $\mathcal{G}$, then the corresponding family $\{\breve{T}\}$ forms a representation of $\mathcal{G}$. Denoting this representation by $\breve{\mathfrak{G}}$, it follows then by the same reasoning as employed in connection with $\mathfrak{G}$, that each member of the sequence $\breve{\mathfrak{G}}^{[n]}$ ($n = 1, 2, \ldots$) forms also such a representation; and more generally, that this is true of any succession of direct products of representations $\mathfrak{G}$ and of representations $\breve{\mathfrak{G}}$. Though these do not strictly exhaust the finite-dimensional representations of $\mathcal{G}$, since by means of the notion of *reducibility* of representations (whose discussion, except for an indication in Sec. 5-2, is deferred to Appendix 8A) the process of constructing new representations can be extended, they nevertheless represent the basic set for $\mathcal{G}$ from which all irreducible representations can be derived (provided the matrices of $\mathcal{G}$ are unimodular, i.e., have determinants = 1).§ It is therefore to be expected that the representations $\mathfrak{G}^{[n]}$, $\breve{\mathfrak{G}}^{[n]}$ and the mixed representations $\mathfrak{G} \times \breve{\mathfrak{G}}$, etc., must play a central role in the development of an analytic formalism suitable for describing the invariance properties engendered by the underlying group $\mathcal{G}$. A clue to understanding this role is provided by a consideration of $\mathfrak{G}$. Let us consider the case $\mathcal{G} = \mathfrak{R}$. The representation space (see last footnote) is then seen to coincide with what one commonly understands by the space of ordinary vectors. This suggests that the quantities q_a corresponding to $\mathfrak{G}^{[n]}$ represent, for every fixed $n > 1$, a generalization of the set of vector components when $n = 1$, which can describe an objective quantity in the same sense as the vector components describe a vector quantity. As we shall presently see, with the aid of these quantities and related quantities associated with the $\breve{\mathfrak{G}}^{[n]}$ one can indeed construct very simply *form-invariant* relations needed in the analytic description of geometric and physical laws.

The *object* associated with the set q_a corresponding to $\mathfrak{G}^{[n]}$ is known as a "tensor" of "rank" (or "order") n. To see the origin of this designation let us take again $\mathcal{G} = \mathfrak{R}$ and consider the case $n = 2$. The corresponding transformation (5-1) has then, by the definition of $\mathfrak{G}^{[2]}$ and by Eq. (5-2), the following form

$$q'_{i'j'} = R_{i'i}R_{j'j}q_{ij} \tag{5-5}$$

‡ A representation has the *dimension n* when the "representation space," i.e., the *linear space* that serves as the domain of operation of the transformations or matrices of the representation, is n-dimensional (see Appendix 5A).

§ For a concise but thorough general discussion of group representations and reducibility see, e.g., H. Weyl, *op. cit.* (Theory of Groups and Quantum Mechanics), chaps. 3 and 5.

where T of Eq. (5-1) is now the rotation matrix $\|R_{ij}\|$ given in Eq. (3A-2). It is seen that Eq. (5-5) is just the standard transformation equation defining a second-rank tensor of classical mechanics and electrodynamics.‡

In order to construct form invariants from tensor components, we require, as indicated earlier, related quantities that are associated with the $\breve{\mathfrak{G}}$ representations. One can easily see how to proceed by considering first the case $n = 1$. Thus, let the q_a of Eq. (5-1) be vector components, with p representing then the dimensionality of our underlying space ($p = 4$ for instance in the case of $\mathfrak{M}$). Let $\breve{q}_a$ denote corresponding quantities with respect to $\breve{\mathfrak{G}}$, so that

$$\breve{q}'_{a'} = \breve{T}_{a'a}\breve{q}_a \tag{5-6}$$

whereas

$$q'_{a'} = T_{a'a}q_a \tag{5-7}$$

By definition (5-4) one finds then

$$\breve{q}_{a'}q_{a'} = \breve{T}_{a'a}T_{a'b}\breve{q}_a q_b = \delta_{ab}\breve{q}_a q_b = \breve{q}_a q_a \tag{5-8}$$

which shows that the expression $\breve{q}_a q_a$ is an invariant (or *scalar*) under $\mathfrak{G}$ and at the same time also a *form invariant.*

The generalization of this result to tensors of rank > 1 presents no difficulties. It is considered in Sec. 5-2 as part of the algebra of tensors.

It is to be observed that when $\mathfrak{G} = \mathfrak{R}$, then $\mathfrak{G} \equiv \breve{\mathfrak{G}}$, since an orthogonal matrix R satisfies the condition given in Eq. (3A-2), which can also be written

$$\breve{R} = R \tag{5-9}$$

Therefore, in this case we have only the basic set $\mathfrak{R}^{[n]}$ and these define the family of *tensors* completely. When Eq. (5-9) is not satisfied, as is the case for $\mathfrak{M}$, the situation is more complicated. It is simplified when explicit use is made of the *metric* of our underlying space, permitting the establishment of an association between the q_a and $\breve{q}_a$ such that these quantities can be looked upon as furnishing merely different representations of the *same object.* This is discussed in Sec. 5-3.

For the present we shall disregard this intimate connection and—temporarily following common usage—speak, e.g., of the q_a and $\breve{q}_a$ as representing a "contravariant vector" and a "covariant vector" respectively.

5-2 TENSOR ALGEBRA

The definition of a tensor given in Sec. 5-1 has been largely implicit. Explicit definitions have been given only of tensors of rank one, i.e., of vectors, in terms of the transformation equations (5-7) and (5-6). If we consider only

‡ The designation "tensor" in fact derives originally from the classical theory of elasticity and was at first confined to tensors of rank two. Its present extended use is due to Einstein ([2], paper 7, sec. 6).

the separate representations $\mathfrak{G}^{[n]}$ and $\breve{\mathfrak{G}}^{[n]}$ it is seen by reference to the definitions given in Sec. 5-1, that for tensors of rank n the transformation equations corresponding to Eqs. (5-7) and (5-6) can be written

$$\begin{aligned} q'_{a_1' \cdots a_n'} &= T_{a_1'a_1} \cdots T_{a_n'a_n} q_{a_1 \cdots a_n} \\ \breve{q}'_{a_1' \cdots a_n'} &= \breve{T}_{a_1'a_1} \cdots \breve{T}_{a_n'a_n} \breve{q}_{a_1 \cdots a_n} \end{aligned}$$

These two sets of transformation equations define a *contravariant tensor of rank n* and a *covariant tensor of rank n* in the same sense as Eqs. (5-7) and (5-6) define the corresponding vectors.

However, in the case of $n > 1$ we have also the mixed representations involving $\mathfrak{G}$ and $\breve{\mathfrak{G}}$ products, and it is clear that the above notation is not a convenient one for tensors associated with such representations. It seems simplest to represent the contravariant or covariant character of a tensor by the placement of the associated set of indices. A general, though not universal, procedure is to indicate contravariant character by *upper* and covariant character by *lower* indices. With this convention, which we now adopt, our former $q_{a_1 \cdots a_n}$ are represented by $q^{a_1 \cdots a_n}$, while in place of $\breve{q}_{a_1 \cdots a_n}$ we now write $q_{a_1 \cdots a_n}$. Generally, the "components" of a "mixed tensor" will have the form $q^{a_1 \cdots a_n}_{b_1 \cdots b_m}$, corresponding to contravariance of rank n and covariance of rank m; with the transformation law

$$q^{a_1' \cdots a_n'}_{b_1' \cdots b_m'} = T^{a_1'}_{a_1} \cdots T^{a_n'}_{a_n} \breve{T}^{b_1}_{b_1'} \cdots \breve{T}^{b_m}_{b_m'} q^{a_1 \cdots a_n}_{b_1 \cdots b_m} \tag{5-10}$$

where we have appropriately changed the notation of the transformation matrix elements (thus arranging for summation to take place between corresponding upper and lower indices). These equations cover all possible cases if we allow the values $n = 0$ or $m = 0$, with the absence then of the corresponding indices.

Equation (5-10) leads at once to two combination rules for tensors. If we sum the components of two tensors u, v of the *same type* $\{n,m\}$ (i.e., contravariant of rank n and covariant of rank m, including also the cases $n = 0$ or $m = 0$ with the convention explained above) it is clear that the resulting quantities obey again the transformation law (5-10), and consequently represent the components of a tensor of the type $\{n,m\}$—the "sum" $u + v$ of the two given tensors. We have here clearly a generalization of the addition of ordinary vectors.

The other operation can be applied to two tensors of arbitrary type, and is likewise an extension of a known result in ordinary vector algebra—that the six products $u_i v_j$ of the components of two vectors $\mathbf{u}$, $\mathbf{v}$ are the components of a tensor. Let $u^{a_1 \cdots a_n}_{b_1 \cdots b_m}$, $v^{c_1 \cdots c_q}_{d_1 \cdots d_p}$ be the components of two tensors and consider the products $u^{a_1 \cdots a_n}_{b_1 \cdots b_m} v^{c_1 \cdots c_q}_{d_1 \cdots d_p}$. It is immediately verified that they satisfy transformation equations of the form of Eq. (5-10) by virtue of the tensor characters of u and v. This resultant tensor, known as the "product" (sometimes also as the "outer product" or "direct product") uv of the two tensors, is seen to be of type $\{n + q, m + p\}$.

The extension of the invariantive operation involved in Eq. (5-8) is also immediate. Let us note that the invariant $\breve{q}_a q_a$, i.e., $q_a q^a$ in our present notation—or better, $u_a v^a$—can be obtained by first forming the product $u_a v^b$ and then summing with respect to the indices a, b. The proof, as we have seen, follows entirely from the relation [using for the transformation matrix elements the notation introduced in Eq. (5-10)]

$$T_a^c \breve{T}_c^b = \delta_a^b \equiv \delta_{ab} \tag{5-11}$$

It requires little more to prove the following general result.

Given a mixed tensor of type $\{n,m\}$ with n and $m \geq 1$, one obtains a tensor of type $\{n-1,\ m-1\}$ (calling a *scalar* a "tensor of rank zero") when one picks any pair of indices, one upper and one lower, and sums with respect to them; that is to say, one obtains in this fashion the components of a derived tensor. This tensor, of rank smaller by two than that of the original tensor, is said to be derived by "contraction" from the original tensor (or, more explicitly, by contraction with respect to a given pair of indices). For example, given the tensor u^a_{bc} (i.e., the tensor whose components relative to a given coordinate system‡ are u^a_{bc}), one can obtain the two vectors u^a_{ac} and u^a_{ba}.

In classical physics, it will be recalled, two types of second-rank tensors occur frequently—the "symmetric" and "antisymmetric" tensors, whose components are symmetric or antisymmetric in their indices. This symmetry notion carries over to general tensors. Since any linear combination of tensors of the same type is a covariant expression, i.e., retains its form in all coordinate systems, this is true in particular of the expressions

$$q_{\cdots}^{\cdots a \cdots b \cdots} + \alpha q_{\cdots}^{\cdots b \cdots a \cdots}, \qquad q^{\cdots}_{\cdots a \cdots b \cdots} + \alpha q^{\cdots}_{\cdots b \cdots a \cdots} \tag{5-12}$$

(in understandable abbreviated notation), and of course their vanishing in one coordinate system implies their vanishing in every other coordinate system. Taking $\alpha = -1$ and $+1$, it follows that the *symmetry* or *antisymmetry* of a tensor in a pair of upper or lower indices is a *covariant property*.

The above proof is actually not complete. We must also show that the second terms of Eqs. (5-12) are tensors when that is true of the first terms. It will obviously suffice to do this for a contravariant tensor of second rank, as the same proof would apply generally. Suppose, then, that u^{ab} are the components of a tensor and consider the quantities $v^{ab} \equiv u^{ba}$. We find: $v'^{ab} = u'^{ba} = T_c^b T_d^a u^{cd} = T_c^a T_d^b u^{dc} = T_c^a T_d^b v^{cd}$. The v^{ab} obey, therefore, the transformation law of tensor components, and our proof of sym-

‡ The fact that the system is a member of the family associated with $\mathcal{G}$ will be tacitly assumed in the sequence. Though we have not stated it explicitly, it is clear that the association of a given set of tensor components with a member of $\mathcal{G}$ (as demanded by our definition in terms of *group representations*) draws with it its association with a corresponding coordinate system, the system obtained from a standard system by applying that transformation of $\mathcal{G}$.

metry covariance is complete. It is important to note that using indices of the same character is essential. For a mixed tensor u^a_b the set $v^a_b \equiv u^b_a$ does not in general represent a tensor, as one readily verifies by going through the above steps.

We may touch here parenthetically on one instance of the *reducibility* of group representations. Since any tensor u of second rank that is not mixed—say, a covariant tensor—admits of the unique decomposition‡

$$u_{ab} = \tfrac{1}{2}(u_{ab} + u_{ba}) + \tfrac{1}{2}(u_{ab} - u_{ba}) \equiv u_{(ab)} + u_{[ab]} \tag{5-13}$$

it can be concluded, with the aid of the preceding result, that the representation space $\mathfrak{I}$ of $\breve{\mathfrak{G}}^{[2]}$ breaks up into the subspaces $\mathfrak{S}$ and $\mathfrak{A}$, corresponding to the symmetric and antisymmetric tensors, with each serving as a new representation space (i.e., each being an *invariant subspace* under $\breve{\mathfrak{G}}^{[2]}$). By the latter property, the representation $\breve{\mathfrak{G}}^{[2]}$ is not merely reducible, but also "decomposable," or "completely reducible": each vector u of the linear space $\mathfrak{I}$ is, according to Eq. (5-13), represented uniquely as a sum of a vector $u_{(s)}$ from $\mathfrak{S}$ and a vector $u_{(a)}$ from $\mathfrak{A}$ ($\mathfrak{I}$ is the *direct sum* of $\mathfrak{S}$ and $\mathfrak{A}$: $\mathfrak{I} = \mathfrak{S} + \mathfrak{A}$), and every transformation from $\breve{\mathfrak{G}}^{[2]}$ sends $u_{(s)}$ into a vector of $\mathfrak{S}$ and $u_{(a)}$ into one in $\mathfrak{A}$. The transformations thus *induced* in $\mathfrak{S}$ and $\mathfrak{A}$ by the given transformation of $\breve{\mathfrak{G}}^{[2]}$ are in the present case easily found. If the latter transformation corresponds to the element T of $\mathfrak{G}$, one verifies by a few simple steps, using Eq. (5-13), that the transformations induced in $\mathfrak{S}$ and $\mathfrak{A}$ respectively are given by $T^{(a}_{a'}T^{b)}_{b'}$ and $T^{[a}_{a'}T^{b]}_{b'}$, using the notation shown in Eq. (5-13). It is also easy to see that when a *base* of $\mathfrak{I}$ is *adapted* to the above decomposition, i.e., is chosen so that each base vector lies wholly either in $\mathfrak{S}$ or in $\mathfrak{A}$, then (upon suitably numbering these base vectors) our representation matrices Q assume the "decomposed" form

$$Q = \begin{bmatrix} Q_{(s)} & \\ & Q_{(a)} \end{bmatrix}, \qquad \text{zeros outside the submatrices } Q_{(s)},\, Q_{(a)} \tag{5-14}$$

The matrix (5-14) admits actually of further decomposition when the group is orthogonal or quasi-orthogonal (Prob. 5-1).

Of the symmetric or antisymmetric (or "alternating") tensors of rank higher than second (by which we mean what should be termed, more precisely, *totally* symmetric or antisymmetric tensors, i.e., tensors whose components are symmetric or antisymmetric in every pair of covariant or contravariant indices), the latter form a particularly interesting class, discussed in Sec. 5-4. Here we consider an interesting subclass of these, comprising tensors with the remarkable property of having each of their components unchanged by any of the transformations; we shall call such tensors "unchanging tensors."§

‡ Introducing a convenient and frequently used symbolism for denoting the "symmetric part" and the "antisymmetric part" relative to a set of indices.

§ They are frequently called "numerical tensors."

Before we discuss these alternating tensors, let us first note a second-rank unchanging tensor that is already implicit in Eq. (5-11), or in the equivalent equation

$$T^a_c \check{T}^c_b = \delta^a_b \tag{5-15}$$

In fact, if we rewrite Eq. (5-15) as $\delta^a_b = T^a_c \check{T}^d_b \delta^c_d$, and compare these equations with Eq. (5-10), it is seen that the set of numbers δ^a_b serve as the components of a mixed unchanging tensor.

In Sec. 5-3 we shall consider the geometric significance of the above unchanging tensor. We shall likewise see, in Sec. 5-4, that the alternating unchanging tensors are also associated with basic geometric relations. But at present our concern is only with their algebraic properties.

The basic unchanging alternating tensor in the case of $\mathfrak{R}$ has the components ϵ_{ijk} [defined in connection with Eq. (3A-8)]. The proof follows immediately from the definition of the Levi-Civita symbols and from rules concerning the expansion of determinants:

$$R^r_i R^s_j R^t_k \epsilon_{rst} = \epsilon_{ijk} \det \|R^i_j\| = \epsilon_{ijk} \tag{5-16}$$

By a precisely similar proof one finds that in the general case of p-dimensional underlying space, the quantities $\epsilon_{a_1 \cdots a_p}$, defined analogously to the ϵ_{ijk}, are the components of an unchanging alternating tensor of rank p, it being assumed that the group $\mathcal{G}$ is *unimodular*. When the matrices of $\mathcal{G}$ do not satisfy condition (5-9), one has of course to distinguish between the above quantities and the quantities $\epsilon^{a_1 \cdots a_p}$ and, in the proof of their tensor character, make use of the fact that with T also $\check{T}$ is unimodular.

Further mixed alternating unchanging tensors (i.e., alternating separately in the set of covariant and in the set of contravariant indices) are obtained by taking the product $\epsilon^{a_1 \cdots a_p}\epsilon_{b_1 \cdots b_p} \equiv \delta^{a_1 \cdots a_p}_{b_1 \cdots b_p}$, and successive contractions of this product, $\delta^{a_1 \cdots a_{p-1}a}_{b_1 \cdots b_{p-1}a} \equiv \delta^{a_1 \cdots a_{p-1}}_{b_1 \cdots b_{p-1}}$, etc.

What if $\mathcal{G}$ is *not unimodular?* For instance, we may wish to consider the full Lorentz group instead of $\mathfrak{L}$, or the orthochronous Lorentz group, or the full three-dimensional orthogonal group. In the latter case, say, Eq. (5-16) shows that the tensorlike character of the quantities can be preserved provided the transformation law is broadened by the inclusion of a determinant factor as in Eq. (5-16), with due attention to the distinction between T and $\check{T}$. This suggests the possibility of the following generalization of the transformation law (5-10):

$$q'^{a_1' \cdots a_n'}_{b_1' \cdots b_m'} = (\det T)^{-w} T^{a_1'}_{a_1} \cdots T^{a_n'}_{a_n} \check{T}^{b_1}_{b_1'} \cdots \check{T}^{b_m}_{b_m'} q^{a_1 \cdots a_n}_{b_1 \cdots b_m} \tag{5-17}$$

The mathematical entities thus defined, are known as "relative tensors of weight w." Important examples are discussed in Sec. 5-4. It is readily verified that the $\epsilon^{i_1 \cdots i_p}$ and the $\epsilon_{i_1 \cdots i_p}$ form the components of a relative tensor of weight $+1$ and of weight -1 respectively [since $\det \check{T} = \det T^{-1} = (\det T)^{-1}$]; while for $\delta^{a_1 \cdots a_p}_{b_1 \cdots b_p}$, $w = 0$, that is, they represent a proper tensor.

The latter conclusion follows from the following general result concerning relative tensors, whose proof is immediate:

The algebraic operation rules on proper tensors are applicable to relative tensors with the stipulation that weights are unchanged in addition, and are added in multiplication.

From the point of view of group representations, the relative tensors can be understood in terms of the following considerations. When the matrices of $\mathcal{G}$ are not unimodular, we have for each w the one-dimensional representation, $T \rightarrow (\det\ T)^w$; since $[\det\ (T_1T_2)]^w = (\det\ T_1)^w(\det\ T_2)^w$. This representation is, of course, in general not faithful; however, its direct product with a faithful representation is, in general, faithful. It is readily verified that the transformation laws of the form of Eq. (5-17) correspond to such products.

5-3 METRIC CONSIDERATIONS; GENERAL COORDINATES

In the preceding discussion essential use was made of the underlying basic group we had denoted by $\mathcal{G}$, of which the example of immediate interest to us is of course the Lorentz group $\mathcal{L}$, though subgroups of $\mathcal{L}$ such as $\mathcal{R}$, and wider groups than $\mathcal{L}$ such as the full Lorentz group, must also claim our attention. The particular cases of $\mathcal{G}$ we have so far considered were introduced in association with a basic form invariant that determines the *metric properties* of the space under consideration, i.e., in terms of which a *geometry* based on the notion of *length* is impressed on the underlying *point continuum.* This was discussed at some length in Sec. 1-2 for $\mathcal{R}$ and the associated metric formula (1-2), while for $\mathcal{L}$ and the metric (3-34a) the corresponding considerations were indicated in Sec. 3-4. The metric aspects of our underlying spaces need now to be incorporated in our discussion of tensors. It will be again convenient to develop the discussion at first in general terms.

Before we proceed, it may not be amiss to point out that our present long excursion into abstract mathematics must not cause us to lose sight of the purpose of this mathematics: to help describe groups of physical phenomena in a compact and fruitful manner. Except as it relates to $\mathcal{R}$, our terminology must not be taken to imply that we are in the process of converting physics into geometry. Let us take electrodynamics as a typical and all-important example. The electromagnetic field is represented by an alternating second-rank tensor under $\mathcal{L}$, and this fact as such is indeed important, and can be couched, if we like, in suggestive geometric language. However, in itself it is still very far from giving us the essentials of the physical entity in question (as it can be given by physical theory), which involves significant additional considerations of a purely physical character, as partly reflected for instance in the *physical dimensions* of the components of the electromagnetic tensor.

With this all-important reminder let us resume our general mathematical discussion. Let us write the metric form associated with $\mathcal{G}$ and referring to the point pairs of the underlying space $\mathfrak{F}$ (e.g., $\mathfrak{M}$, in the case of $\mathfrak{L}$) as‡

$$\Delta s^2 = g_{ab}\,\Delta x^a\,\Delta x^b, \qquad g_{ab} = g_{ba} \tag{5-18}$$

The g_{ab} are *constants,* which means that $\mathfrak{F}$ is *homogeneous:* all points are metrically equivalent. In the case of euclidean space, it is also, as we know, *isotropic:* the structure of Δs^2 is independent of direction, i.e., independent of the ratios of the Δx^a. Not so the space $\mathfrak{M}$, for, as we have seen, it permits three distinct types of directed segments.

In this connection, let us note parenthetically that, in general, if the metric structure of a given space has, in terms of coordinates x, the general expression (5-18), one can always introduce by a suitable linear transformation new coordinates y, in terms of which Eq. (5-18) assumes the canonical form§

$$\begin{gathered} \Delta s^2 = \sum_{a=1}^{p} g_a(\Delta y^a)^2 \\ g_a = \begin{cases} +1 \text{ for } a = 1, \ldots, r \\ -1 \text{ for } a = r+1, \ldots, p \end{cases} \end{gathered} \tag{5-19}$$

(p being the dimensionality of $\mathfrak{F}$) and to adopt the associated family of transformations for our basic group $\mathcal{G}$, and the associated family of coordinate systems for the distinguished coordinate frames, as discussed for the euclidean case in Sec. 1.2.

On the other hand, if we reexamine the discussion concerning tensors given in Sec. 5-2, it is seen that their definition entails only the *linearity* of the transformations of $\mathcal{G}$ and, in fact, from this point of view, the natural choice of $\mathcal{G}$ is the group of *all* nonsingular p-dimensional linear transformations.¶ Under these transformations, the *general* form of the metric (5-19) is again Eq. (5-18) with constant g_{ab}. In terms of the geometry induced by Eq. (5-19), the general linear coordinates not belonging to the distinguished family form the family of *oblique rectilinear* coordinates. It thus appears desirable to reconsider the theory of tensors in terms of these coordinates. Such consideration is moreover essential as a basis for extension to the case of general (i.e., nonrectilinear) coordinates that are necessary in the general theory of relativity.

‡ We now write, following common usage, x^a rather than x_a, so that the tensor character of Δx^a agrees with our convention concerning tensor indices.

§ We have tacitly assumed that the quadratic form given in Eq. (5-18) is nondegenerate, i.e., that $\det \|g_{ab}\| \neq 0$. One can therefore apply a classical algebraic theorem that asserts the possibility of the reduction (5-19), and invariance of the number r. See, e.g., [10], pp. 30–31; or, M. Bôcher, "Introduction to Higher Algebra," secs. 45 and 50, The Macmillan Co., New York, 1927.

¶ This group is also known as the "affine group," and the associated geometry (when no metric is assumed) as "affine geometry" (see Appendix 5A). See, e.g., [10], sec. 2.

We begin with the notion of *vectors* in $\mathfrak{F}$. These are defined exactly as are vectors in ordinary space, in terms of the differences of coordinates of two points, i.e., in terms of *rectilinear directed segments* of the space. A general "vector base" is given by any set $\{\mathsf{e}_a\}$ of p *linearly independent* vectors,‡ in terms of which any vector A can be written

$$\mathsf{A} = A^a \mathsf{e}_a \tag{5-20}$$

The set of quantities A^a specifies the vector fully relative to the given base: it coincides with what we called earlier a *contravariant* vector. How would one now specify a *covariant* vector? If no account is taken of the metric, i.e., from the point of view of pure affine geometry, it would be necessary to introduce what is known as the space *dual* to the given one, and a vector A_a would then be defined in terms of a given base in that space in similar fashion to Eq. (5-20). But this general nonmetric approach is not needed in the present discussion. The metric form, Eq. (5-19), is a vital part of our present development and it leads to a simplification of the theory of tensors.

This simplification consists in the following: we no longer have two types of vectors, but only one type; instead, we have two types of components of a given vector. In other words, there exists in $\mathfrak{F}$ only one kind of vector *object,* but it can be specified relative to a given base in two alternative ways. In Eq. (5-20) we have one way, corresponding to *parallel projection* with respect to the directions of the e_a. This is the only suitable geometric construction possible under strictly affine geometry. But with the availability of a metric, one can also employ *perpendicular* projection, and construct the quantities§

$$A_a = \mathsf{A} \cdot \mathsf{e}_a \tag{5-21}$$

The *scalar product* in Eq. (5-21) is determined by the metric of $\mathfrak{F}$ in the same way as the scalar product of ordinary vectors is determined by the euclidean metric. We shall have the explicit formulation presently. The quantities A_a are thus uniquely specified given A, and the converse is also true. The A_a are the *covariant components* of the vector A, whose *contravariant components* are A^a.

To prove that the A_a determine A uniquely, let us note first that

$$\mathsf{e}_a \cdot \mathsf{e}_b = g_{ab} \tag{5-22}$$

This follows at once from Eq. (5-18), which, in accordance with our present

‡ See Appendix 5A. We shall employ sans serif letters to denote vectors in $\mathfrak{F}$ as well as in $\mathfrak{M}$. Incidentally, a convenient way of designating vectors and second-rank tensors in ordinary space and in space-time respectively, is by placing the arrow-symbols, $\rightharpoonup$, $\Rightarrow$ $\rightarrow$, $\Rightarrow$ above the corresponding letters.

§ However, we are not assuming in general that e_a are *unit* vectors.

definition of a vector, implies that

$$\mathbf{A}^2 \equiv \mathbf{A} \cdot \mathbf{A} = g_{ab}A^aA^b \tag{5-23}$$

so that by Eq. (5-20), we have $\mathbf{A}^2 = \mathbf{e}_a \cdot \mathbf{e}_b A^a A^b$, and hence Eqs. (5-22). The latter equations and Eqs. (5-21) and (5-20) lead at once to the relation

$$A_a = g_{ab}A^b \tag{5-24}$$

Since,

$$\det \|g_{ab}\| \equiv g \neq 0 \tag{5-25}$$

the A^b and hence $\mathbf{A}$ are uniquely determined by the A_a.

If we introduce the quantities g^{ab} by the equations

$$g^{ab}g_{bc} = g_{cb}g^{ba} = \delta^a_c \tag{5-26}$$

we get the explicit solution

$$A^a = g^{ab}A_b \tag{5-27}$$

Combining Eqs. (5-20) and (5-27), we find $\mathbf{A} = g^{ab}A_b\mathbf{e}_a$. Hence by introducing the system of vectors

$$\mathbf{e}^a = g^{ba}\mathbf{e}_b \tag{5-28}$$

one can express a vector in terms of its covariant components similarly to Eq. (5-20):

$$\mathbf{A} = A_a\mathbf{e}^a \tag{5-29}$$

The system $\{\mathbf{e}^a\}$ therefore forms a *base*. It is known as the base "reciprocal" (or "dual") to $\{\mathbf{e}_a\}$. The relationship between these two bases is a reciprocal one in an obvious sense, reflecting the relations (5-26), which state that the matrices $\|g_{ab}\|$ and $\|g^{ab}\|$ are *reciprocals* of each other. This is also seen from the equations

$$\mathbf{e}_a \cdot \mathbf{e}^b = \delta^b_a \tag{5-30}$$

These follow directly from Eqs. (5-28), (5-22) and (5-26), when account is taken of the *symmetry* of the matrix g^{ab}, the latter being an immediate consequence of the assumed symmetry of g_{ab} and the defining Eqs. (5-26).

General tensors can now be defined conveniently by two alternative methods. The most immediate method is to define, say, the *contravariant components* $Q^{a_1 \cdots a_n}$ of a tensor Q of rank n by the condition:

$$Q^{a_1 \cdots a_n} A^{(1)}{}_{a_1} \cdots A^{(n)}{}_{a_n}, \quad \text{invariant for arbitrary vectors } \mathbf{A}^{(1)}, \ldots, \mathbf{A}^{(n)} \tag{5-31}$$

with similar definitions for the components of any other character of the same tensor Q; e.g., the covariant components involve the invariant expression $Q_{a_1 \cdots a_n} A^{(1)a_1} \cdots A^{(n)a_n}$, the mixed components $Q_{a_1}{}^{a_2 \cdots a_n}$, the expression $Q_{a_1}{}^{a_2 \cdots a_n} A^{(1)a_1} A^{(2)}{}_{a_2} \cdots A^{(n)}{}_{a_n}$, etc. It is clear that, by virtue of the relations (5-24) and (5-27), any set of components of Q can be obtained from any other, and in fact we have generally:

$$Q^{\cdots a \cdots}_{\cdots\ \cdots} = g^{ab} Q^{\cdots\ \cdots}_{\cdots b \cdots}, \qquad Q^{\cdots\ \cdots}_{\cdots a \cdots} = g_{ab} Q^{\cdots b \cdots}_{\cdots\ \cdots} \tag{5-32}$$

with understandable abbreviated notation. The tensor Q therefore determines all the possible types of components, and is completely determined by any one given set. The operations shown in Eqs. (5-32) are referred to as "raising" and "lowering" of indices.

It should be noticed that in the present treatment the *relative position* of the covariant and contravariant indices in the *mixed components* is important if the tensor is not totally symmetric. For example, suppose that Q is of second rank and is not symmetric. Then we have the following generally distinct sets of components: Q^{ab}, Q_{ab}, $Q^a{}_b$, $Q_a{}^b$. Only if Q is symmetric, then $Q^a{}_b = g_{bc}Q^{ac} = g_{bc}Q^{ca} = Q_b{}^a$, and we can write simply Q^a_b. Similar relations hold for tensors of higher rank that are symmetric with respect to given pairs of indices.

The second method of defining tensors is in terms of their transformation properties under the group $\mathcal{GL}_p$ of nonsingular, p-dimensional, homogeneous linear transformations in $\mathfrak{F}$, similarly to the definition (5-10) given earlier for transformations under $\mathcal{G}$. (See Prob. 5-5.)

Referring to our definition of vectors in $\mathfrak{F}$, it can be seen that an arbitrary transformation of $\mathcal{GL}_p$ can be represented by a change of vector base

$$\mathbf{e}_a \rightarrow \mathbf{e}'_a = M^b{}_a \mathbf{e}_b, \qquad \det \|M^b{}_a\| \neq 0 \tag{5-33}$$

(Here $M^b{}_a$ are of course not the components of a tensor,‡ and the row index b is raised merely for visual convenience since, with our present tensor index notation, repeated summable indices occur generally in pairs of lower and upper indices.) The corresponding change in the contravariant components of a vector are then given, in view of Eq. (5-20), by the equations

$$A'^a = N^a{}_b A^b, \qquad \|N^a{}_b\| = \|M^a{}_b\|^{-1} \tag{5-34}$$

In order to find the corresponding change in the covariant components of the vector A, we need the transformation equations for the base reciprocal to $\{\mathbf{e}_a\}$. If we write, $\mathbf{e}'^a = P^a{}_b \mathbf{e}^b$, we find by Eqs. (5-30) and (5-33), that $\delta^a_b = \mathbf{e}'^a \cdot \mathbf{e}'_b = P^a{}_c \mathbf{e}^c \cdot M^d{}_b \mathbf{e}_d = P^a{}_c M^d{}_b\, \delta^c_d = P^a{}_c M^c{}_b$, or, $\|P^a{}_b\| = \|M^a{}_b\|^{-1}$. Hence, by the last equation in Eq. (5-34),

$$\mathbf{e}'^a = N^a{}_b \mathbf{e}^b \tag{5-35}$$

and consequently

$$A'_a = M^b{}_a A_b \tag{5-36}$$

Equations (5-34) and (5-36) agree, as they should, with Eqs. (5-7) and

‡ Unless Eqs. (5-33) represent a mapping of vectors, as is seen by Eq. (5-36) and the tensor quotient theorem (given in Prob. 5-2).

(5-6) when we take $T_{ab} = N^a{}_b$, since $\|M^b{}_a\| = \|\check{N}^a{}_b\|$. Thus the present transformation law for tensor components is similar to Eq. (5-10); for example,

$$Q'^a{}_b{}^c = N^a{}_d M^e{}_b N^c{}_f Q^d{}_e{}^f \tag{5-37}$$

It is now clear that the set of quantities g_{ab} entering in Eq. (5-18) form the components of a symmetric tensor whose components take on the same special set of values given in Eq. (5-19) in every coordinate frame of our distinguished family. Understandably, this tensor is known as the "metric" or "fundamental" tensor G of our space $\mathfrak{F}$. The contravariant components of G are the g^{ab} defined in Eq. (5-26). Indeed, by Eqs. (5-29), (5-28), (5-22), and (5-26),

$$\mathbf{A} \cdot \mathbf{A} = A_a A_b g^{ac} g^{bd} \mathbf{e}_c \cdot \mathbf{e}_d = g^{ab} A_a A_b \tag{5-38}$$

By Eq. (5-26) it also follows that the mixed components of G are the Kronecker delta symbols δ^a_b. This is the unchanging tensor referred to in Sec. 5-2, whose geometric significance has now been manifested.‡

We are now in a position to develop rapidly the theory of tensors referred to *general curvilinear* coordinate systems in $\mathfrak{F}$. Our starting point is again the distinguished family of coordinate systems for which the metric form is given by Eq. (5-19). A general system of coordinates x is defined in terms of a set of distinguished coordinates y by functions

$$x^a = x^a(y) \tag{5-39}$$

which are subject only to continuity and differentiability conditions and to the obviously necessary condition of the nonvanishing of the Jacobian:

$$\left\| \frac{\partial x^a}{\partial y^b} \right\| \neq 0 \tag{5-40}$$

insuring that the correspondence (5-39) is one to one.

As to the metric form, Eq. (5-19), itself, it is clear that unless all the functions $x^a(y)$ are linear, i.e., except for the special case treated previously, it is necessary to go over to the corresponding *differential* expression,

$$ds^2 = \sum_{a=1}^{p} g_a (dy^a)^2 \tag{5-41}$$

‡ From the point of view of affine geometry involving a pair of mutually dual spaces, an essentially similar connection exists with reference to the basic invariant expression contained in Eq. (5-8).

Note also that the tensor character of g^{ab} follows also from the following general result holding for tensors taken in the sense of Sec. 5-2: given an arbitrary covariant tensor A_{ab} such that det $\|A_{ab}\| \neq 0$, then the quantities B^{ab} defined in terms of A_{ab}, similarly to the definition (5-26) of the g^{ab} in terms of the g_{ab}, form the components of a contravariant tensor. This result follows at once from an application of the quotient theorem of tensor calculus (Prob. 5-2).

Since, by Eqs. (5-39) and (5-40),

$$dy^a = \frac{\partial y^a}{\partial x^b}\, dx^b, \qquad y^a = y^a(x) \tag{5-42}$$

it follows that in the general coordinates x,

$$ds^2 = g_{ab}\, dx^a\, dx^b \tag{5-43}$$

where

$$g_{ab} = \sum_{c=1}^{p} g_c \frac{\partial y^c}{\partial x^a} \frac{\partial y^c}{\partial x^b} \tag{5-44}$$

and except when the functions (5-39) are linear, the quantities g_{ab} vary with x. But it must be borne in mind that this variability of the g_{ab} is due solely to the choice of x, and that because of the particular expression (5-44) in which these functions can be put, resulting from the existence of the special $\{y\}$ with the associated line element (5-41), our space is both homogeneous as well as *flat*.

It is also clear that in the general case the notion of vector components can be arrived at by reasoning similar to that used earlier in this section, but with the finite Δx^a replaced by the corresponding *differentials*. The components A^a, or A_a, of a given vector A, relative to the given system $\{x\}$, thus also in general vary with x, even if A itself is independent of position in the space.

With the representation of a vector in general coordinate frames established, one can find the representation of tensors of any rank in such frames by any of the methods discussed earlier. The method of vector bases is both interesting and instructive. In the general case, the choice of $\{x\}$ determines a vector base $\{\mathsf{e}_a(x)\}$ at every point x of $\mathfrak{F}$. The case of curvilinear coordinates in an ordinary euclidean plane affords a simple but adequate example (see Fig. 5-1). Generally, the analytic expression for $\mathsf{e}_a(x)$ can be obtained by noting that $\partial y^a/\partial x^b$ represent for fixed b and fixed x the components of a vector t_b in the frame $\{y\}$; it is in fact, as is easily verified, the vector in the direction of the *tangent* to the curvilinear coordinate line obtained by keeping all x coordinates but x^b constant (Fig. 5.1). It is this vector t_b that can be taken for our $\mathsf{e}_b(x)$. In fact, consider the general vector relation corresponding to Eq. (5-42), $A^a{}_{(y)} = (\partial y^a/\partial x^b)A^b{}_{(x)}$ ($A^a{}_{(y)}$, $A^a{}_{(x)}$ being the coordinates of A in $\{y\}$ and in $\{x\}$ respectively), and let $\{\mathsf{u}_a\}$ constitute a base in $\{y\}$. We have then the equation

$$\mathsf{A} = \mathsf{u}_a A^a{}_{(y)} = \mathsf{u}_a \frac{\partial y^a}{\partial x^b} A^b{}_{(x)} = \mathsf{t}_b A^b{}_{(x)}$$

and since the vector A is arbitrary our assertion follows.

When we go over from the system $\{x\}$ to another curvilinear system $\{x'\}$, it is found by applying the rule of differentiation of a function of functions to $y^a(x) = y^a(x(x'_1, \ldots, x'_p))$, that

$$\mathsf{e}_a(x) = \frac{\partial y^c}{\partial x^a}\,\mathsf{u}_c = \frac{\partial y^c}{\partial x'^b}\frac{\partial x'^b}{\partial x^a}\,\mathsf{u}_c = \frac{\partial x'^b}{\partial x^a}\,\mathsf{e}'_b(x') \tag{5-45}$$

where x and x' refer to the *same point* of $\mathfrak{F}$. This is then the transformation of bases induced at every point by the transformation $x \to x'$. Comparing it with the inverse of the base transformation (5-33), it is seen that

$$\frac{\partial x'^b}{\partial x^a} = N^b{}_a \equiv N^b{}_a(x) \tag{5-46}$$

These results agree with Eqs. (5-33) and (5-34), in view of the relations

$$dx'^a = \frac{\partial x'^a}{\partial x^b}\,dx^b \tag{5-47}$$

The base field $\{\mathsf{e}^a(x)\}$ reciprocal to $\{\mathsf{e}_a(x)\}$ can be obtained, for instance, by referring to Eq. (5-30). Since $(\partial x^b/\partial y^c)(\partial y^c/\partial x^a) = \delta^b_a$ it can be concluded (see Prob. 5-8) that

$$\mathsf{e}^a(x) = \frac{\partial x^a}{\partial y^b}\,\mathsf{u}^b, \qquad \{\mathsf{u}^a\} \text{ reciprocal of } \{\mathsf{u}_a\} \tag{5-48}$$

The consistency with Eq. (5-36) is again easily verified, while Eqs. (5-35) for change of base follow at once from Eq. (5-47) in view of Eq. (5-48).

With the construction of our *base fields* and their transformation equations, our problem of defining tensor components relative to a general coordinate frame $\{x\}$ is solved, inasmuch as we can follow the procedure employed in the case of rectilinear coordinates. The only new feature is

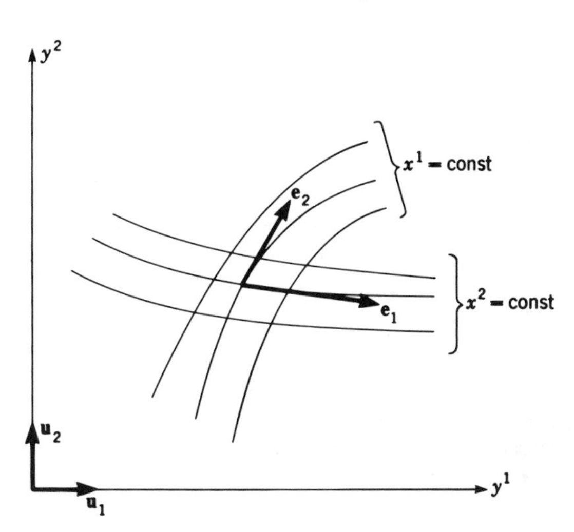

Fig. 5-1 Curvilinear coordinates and associated bases in a euclidean plane.

that the components vary in general from point to point, even if the tensor itself does not.

5-4 FURTHER ALGEBRAIC AND GEOMETRIC CONSIDERATIONS; PSEUDOTENSORS

The preceding two sections contain a brief outline of the essentials of tensor algebra. In this section we consider at greater length a class of alternating (i.e., totally antisymmetric) tensors and associated entities termed *pseudotensors* that are simply related to relative tensors. These quantities have both geometric and physical interest.

An immediate generalization of the geometric object consisting of a directed segment and represented by a vector, is the object formed by the ordered set of two noncollinear directed segments issuing from a point, as represented by an ordered pair of nonparallel vectors. More precisely, this object is specified in terms of its vectors A,B by (1) the *plane* Π through the origin determined by A,B (or, more precisely, by the 2-dimensional linear subspace of our vector space, containing A and B); (2) the *area* of the parallelogram formed by the corresponding segments; and (3) the *orientation* of Π *in* $\mathfrak{F}$ associated with the order: A, then B.

It can be conjectured that the object thus defined, which we denote by $[\mathsf{A},\mathsf{B}]$, is represented analytically by a second-rank tensor. By its geometric properties the two-vector function $[\mathsf{A},\mathsf{B}]$ must satisfy the following rules:

$$\begin{aligned} [\mathsf{A}+\mathsf{C},\mathsf{B}] &= [\mathsf{A},\mathsf{B}] + [\mathsf{C},\mathsf{B}] \\ [\alpha\mathsf{A},\mathsf{B}] &= \alpha[\mathsf{A},\mathsf{B}] \qquad \alpha \textit{ scalar} \\ [\mathsf{B},\mathsf{A}] &= -[\mathsf{A},\mathsf{B}] \end{aligned} \tag{5-49}$$

Thus, relative to a chosen base $\{\mathbf{e}_a\}$,

$$[\mathsf{A},\mathsf{B}] = [A^a\mathbf{e}_a,B^b\mathbf{e}_b] = A^aB^b[\mathbf{e}_a,\mathbf{e}_b] = A^{[a}B^{b]}[\mathbf{e}_a,\mathbf{e}_b] \tag{5-50}$$

where we use the notation introduced in Eq. (5-13): $2A^{[a}B^{b]} \equiv A^aB^b - A^bB^a$. Now, the latter quantities are seen to be the components of a tensor T determined by the vectors A,B, and satisfying the rules (5-49). Their agreement with points (1) and (3) of the foregoing definition can also be easily verified. As to (2), let us now specialize $\mathfrak{F}$ to be *euclidean*, i.e., let us assume that all g_a in Eq. (5-19) are positive, until we deal with $\mathfrak{M}$ later in this section. Then, denoting the square of the area in question by the symbol $[\mathsf{A},\mathsf{B}]^2$, and writing as usual A^2 for the scalar product $\mathsf{A}\cdot\mathsf{A}$, one has

$$\begin{aligned} [\mathsf{A},\mathsf{B}]^2 &= \mathsf{A}^2\mathsf{B}^2\sin^2(A,B) = \mathsf{A}^2\mathsf{B}^2(1-\cos^2(A,B)) = \mathsf{A}^2\mathsf{B}^2 - (\mathsf{A}\cdot\mathsf{B})^2 \\ &= A^aA_aB^bB_b - A^aB_aA_bB^b = A^aB^b(A_aB_b - A_bB_a) = 2A^{[a}B^{b]}A_{[a}B_{b]} \\ &= \tfrac{1}{2}T^{ab}T_{ab} \end{aligned} \tag{5-51}$$

In particular, if the base is *orthonormal* [i.e., $g_{ab} = \delta_{ab}$ in Eq. (5-22)], and if

$[\mathsf{A},\mathsf{B}]$ lies in a coordinate plane, say, $A_a = \delta_{a1}$, $B_a = \delta_{a2}$, then

$$[\mathsf{A},\mathsf{B}]^2 = (T_{12})^2 = (A_1B_2 - A_2B_1)^2$$

—a familiar result of elementary analytic geometry.

We may note incidentally that the notation $[\mathsf{A},\mathsf{B}]$ for the tensor T is consistent with the usual commutator notation if we let AB stand for the *product* of the two vectors (in which case one must insist that a dot be used to indicate the scalar product; and the product AB should then perhaps be identified more specifically as, say, the "tensor product"). It is also of interest to observe that with this notation we have, similarly to Eq. (5-50), the expansion

$$\mathsf{AB} = A^aB^b\mathbf{e}_a\mathbf{e}_b \tag{5-50a}$$

so that $\{\mathbf{e}_a\mathbf{e}_b\}$ forms a base in the linear space associated with the direct product with itself of our underlying representation, just as $\{[\mathbf{e}_a,\mathbf{e}_b]\}$ serves as a base in the representation space corresponding to $\mathcal{A}$ in the discussion following Eq. (5-13).

Returning to our general discussion, let us at first further particularize it by taking $p = 3$; i.e., by turning our attention for the moment to the space of our daily experience and of elementary geometry and vector algebra. By considering this very familiar case in some detail in terms of the present approach, it will then be possible to survey rather easily the other principal results pertaining to the general case.

The nonidentically vanishing components T_{ij} of the tensor $[\mathbf{A},\mathbf{B}]$, are recognized as the components of the *vector product* $[\mathbf{A} \times \mathbf{B}]$. What then is the relationship between these two entities? The vector product, as is well known, is not a strict vector under the full orthogonal group, but is an "axial vector": under the reversal of the direction of one or of all coordinate axes, or—what amounts to the same thing—under a change of orthonormal vector base of the form

$$\mathbf{u}_i \to \mathbf{u}'_i = \epsilon_{(i)}\mathbf{u}_i \qquad \begin{array}{l}\text{no summation}\\ \epsilon_{(i)} = \pm 1\\ \epsilon_{(1)}\epsilon_{(2)}\epsilon_{(3)} = -1\end{array} \tag{5-52}$$

its components are unchanged, whereas those of a true vector (a "polar vector") would be multiplied by the corresponding $\epsilon_{(i)}$. With this property in mind, our question can be answered at once when we recall the transformation rule obeyed by the unchanging relative tensor ϵ_{ijk} (see page 139). Indeed, the relative vector $\mathbf{C}$ with components‡

$$C_i = \tfrac{1}{2}\epsilon_{ijk}T_{jk} \tag{5-53}$$

‡ $\mathbf{C}$ is a relative vector having the same weight as ϵ_{ijk}, by the rule for the product of two relative tensors (an ordinary—or "absolute"—tensor is of course a relative tensor of weight zero), and since, quite obviously, the *contraction* rule works for relative tensors in the same way as for ordinary tensors. Note also that we do not distinguish notationally between absolute and relative tensors; such distinction is sometimes to be found in the literature.

has the same transformation properties as $[\mathbf{A} \times \mathbf{B}]$, and of course the identical components. The two mathematical objects can therefore be identified.

When we go over from the orthogonal group to the wider linear group $\mathcal{GL}_3$ it becomes necessary to distinguish between covariance and contravariance, and we seem to be faced with a notational difficulty: the ϵ^{ijk} are not the contravariant components of the relative tensor whose covariant components are ϵ_{ijk}. This is obvious, for we have seen generally that the weights of $\epsilon_{\cdots}$ and $\epsilon^{\cdots}$ are -1 and $+1$ respectively, whereas the rule of raising and lowering indices, as one easily verifies, applies to relative just as well as to absolute tensors, so that the weight of a relative tensor is a property of the tensor and not of the components used to specify it. Moreover, we have the explicit relation

$$g_{ir}g_{js}g_{kt}\epsilon^{rst} = g\epsilon_{ijk} \tag{5-54}$$

and this indeed suggests the way out of our minor difficulty, when we also observe that under a change of base (5-33), the fundamental determinant g given in Eq. (5-25) undergoes the transformation

$$g \rightarrow g' = (\det M)^2 g, \qquad M = \|M^i{}_j\| \tag{5-55}$$

This relation follows from the transformation law for the metric tensor, $g'_{ij} = M^r{}_i M^s{}_j g_{rs}$, which can be written in matrix form, $G' = \tilde{M}GM$ with $G = \|g_{ij}\|$.

By Eq. (5-55), and referring to the defining Eqs. (5-17), g is seen to be a relative scalar of weight 2, since M corresponds to $\check{T}$. Hence $\sqrt{g}$ has the weight 1; however, it obeys a law of transformation that differs from Eqs. (5-17) by involving the *absolute value* of det M.‡ By this result and by Eq. (5-54) it follows that the quantities

$$E^{ijk} = \frac{1}{\sqrt{g}}\epsilon^{ijk}, \qquad E_{ijk} = \sqrt{g}\,\epsilon_{ijk} \tag{5-56}$$

represent respectively the contravariant and covariant components of a tensorlike quantity that is subject to a transformation law differing from that of ordinary tensors by involving on the right side of Eqs. (5-10), as an additional factor, the sign of the determinant of T. Such objects will be called "pseudotensors."§ For instance, a *pseudoscalar* Ψ has the following

‡ Note that g is positive in the present case in view of the law (5-55) and since $g = 1$ in orthonormal coordinates. However, generally, and in particular in the case of $\mathfrak{M}$, we must take $\sqrt{|g|}$. Moreover, when g is negative, the notation in Eqs. (5-56) is again not fully consistent. This point is discussed later in the section when we consider the space $\mathfrak{M}$.

§ This term is also used with other meanings in the mathematical literature. Note also that under the special groups, for which det $M = \pm 1$, i.e., those of greatest interest in physical theory, the only tensors that are not absolute are the relative tensors of odd weight, and they are all pseudotensors.

transformation law under (5-33):

$$\Psi' = \text{sgn}\,(\det M)\Psi, \quad \text{sgn}\,\alpha \equiv \frac{|\alpha|}{\alpha} \tag{5-57}$$

With the aid of the pseudotensor E we can write in place of Eq. (5-53):

$$C_i = \tfrac{1}{2}E_{ijk}T^{jk} \tag{5-58}$$

which represents an association of a *pseudovector* **C** with the alternating tensor T. This, then, is the general algebraic significance of the ordinary vector product. Its geometric significance we already know; geometric properties cannot be affected by changes in coordinate systems; they are indeed precisely the kind of invariants that are our chief interest in developing the present formalism. However, we rederive them in terms of oblique coordinate frames as a useful illustration of a treatment that can be extended to the general case.

We have to prove three properties of **C**: (1) its *perpendicularity* to the plane Π formed by the vectors **A**, **B**; (2) the equality of the square of its *length*, $\mathbf{C}^2 = C_iC^i$, to $[\mathbf{A},\mathbf{B}]^2$; and (3) its specifying the *orientation* of Π.

Property (1) is proved immediately by noting that, by virtue of the "ϵ properties" of the E components, it follows from Eq. (5-58) that

$$C_iA^i = 0, \qquad C_iB^i = 0 \tag{5-59}$$

If one wishes, one can replace this pair by the equivalent equations (the equivalence being easily proved)

$$C_iT^{ij} = 0 \tag{5-59a}$$

To prove (2), we have only to utilize the following identity, which can be easily verified,

$$E_{ijk}E^{irs} = \epsilon_{ijk}\epsilon^{irs} \equiv \delta^{rs}_{jk} = 2\delta^{\,r}_{[j}\,\delta^{s}_{k]} = 2\delta^{[r}_{j}\,\delta^{s]}_{k} \tag{5-60}$$

By this identity,

$$\mathbf{C}^2 = C_iC^i = \tfrac{1}{4}\delta^{rs}_{jk}T^{jk}T_{rs} = \tfrac{1}{2}T^{jk}T_{jk} \tag{5-61}$$

which, by Eq. (5-51), is the desired result. Note that $\mathbf{C}^2$ is an *absolute* scalar; and, of course, quite generally, the product of two pseudotensors is an absolute tensor.

Before supplying the proof of property (3), a word of explanation should be given as to its meaning. For this purpose we need first to explain what is meant by the *orientation relative to a given base* of a volume determined by an ordered set of three noncoplanar vectors **A**, **B**, **C**.

Let us observe that we can associate with this ordered set an alternating tensor [**A**,**B**,**C**] in a manner quite similar to that of the association of [A,B] with the geometric object discussed at the beginning of this section. Now, point (1) in the specification of that object is simply our condition of noncoplanarity, i.e., of the linear independence of the three vectors. Points (2) and (3) refer in the present case to the *oriented* (or *directed*) volume of the parallelepiped formed by the vectors.

What do we mean by the latter quantity? The answer is provided by the familiar and basic notion of right- and left-handedness of a coordinate system, or, equivalently, by the positive or negative sense of screw motion. The volume in question is taken as positive, if the order of our vectors corresponds to that of the coordinate vectors which we *agree* to call right-handed or "positive." If we denote by $\{\mathbf{A},\mathbf{B},\mathbf{C}\}$ the determinant formed with the components of **A**, **B**, **C** relative to an *orthonormal base,* we know from solid analytic geometry that it represents the volume of the corresponding parallelepiped; but it also has the right *sign* to represent an oriented volume, by virtue of the *permutation properties* of determinants that correspond precisely to those involved in the definition of coordinate orientation. In order to find the representation of this volume in an arbitrary base $\{\mathbf{e}_i\}$, let us recall the determinant properties:

$$\begin{aligned} \{\mathbf{A}+\mathbf{D},\mathbf{B},\mathbf{C}\} &= \{\mathbf{A},\mathbf{B},\mathbf{C}\} + \{\mathbf{D},\mathbf{B},\mathbf{C}\}, \text{ etc.} \\ \{\alpha\mathbf{A},\mathbf{B},\mathbf{C}\} &= \alpha\{\mathbf{A},\mathbf{B},\mathbf{C}\}, \text{ etc.,} \qquad \alpha \text{ a scalar} \\ \{\mathbf{B},\mathbf{A},\mathbf{C}\} &= -\{\mathbf{A},\mathbf{B},\mathbf{C}\}, \text{ etc.} \end{aligned} \tag{5-62}$$

the "etc." referring to similar relations involving the other letters and pairs of letters. Using rules (5-62) one finds

$$\begin{aligned} \{\mathbf{A},\mathbf{B},\mathbf{C}\} &= \{A^i\mathbf{e}_i,B^j\mathbf{e}_j,C^k\mathbf{e}_k\} \\ &= A^iB^jC^k\{\mathbf{e}_i,\mathbf{e}_j,\mathbf{e}_k\} = \{\mathbf{e}_1,\mathbf{e}_2,\mathbf{e}_3\}\epsilon_{ijk}A^iB^jC^k \end{aligned} \tag{5-63}$$

which gives us the desired representation.

Equation (5-63) can be put into a more useful form when we observe that (writing e_{ij} for the jth components of $\mathbf{e}_i$ in our standard orthonormal base, and remembering the determinant product rule)

$$\{\mathbf{e}_1,\mathbf{e}_2,\mathbf{e}_3\}^2 = (\det \|e_{ij}\|)^2 = \det \|e_{ik}e_{kj}\| = \det \|e_{ik}e_{jk}\| = \det \|\mathbf{e}_i \cdot \mathbf{e}_j\| = \det \|g_{ij}\|$$

that is, that

$$\{\mathbf{e}_1,\mathbf{e}_2,\mathbf{e}_3\} = \sqrt{g} \tag{5-64}$$

The positive sign is here taken, it should be noted, when $\{\mathbf{e}_i\}$ has positive orientation with respect to a chosen *standard* base. In fact, under the change of base (5-33),

$$\begin{aligned} \{\mathbf{e}_1',\mathbf{e}_2',\mathbf{e}_3'\} &= \{M^i{}_1\mathbf{e}_i,M^j{}_2\mathbf{e}_j,M^k{}_3\mathbf{e}_k\} \\ &= \epsilon_{ijk}M^i{}_1M^j{}_2M^k{}_3\{\mathbf{e}_1,\mathbf{e}_2,\mathbf{e}_3\} = \det M\{\mathbf{e}_1,\mathbf{e}_2,\mathbf{e}_3\} \end{aligned} \tag{5-65}$$

By Eqs. (5-64) and (5-56), Eq. (5-63) assumes the simpler form

$$\{\mathbf{A},\mathbf{B},\mathbf{C}\} = E_{ijk}A^iB^jC^k \tag{5-66}$$

This expression is thus a *pseudoscalar*, in accordance with the fact that it represents a geometric quantity that reverses its sign with that of the base orientation.

The property (3) of the pseudovector **C** is now readily shown. This vector *corresponds* to the orientation in the plane Π as determined by the vectors **A**,**B**, when the orientation of the ordered triplet **A**,**B**,**C** is positive; and indeed, by Eqs. (5-66) and (5-58), which can also be written $C_i = E_{ijk}A^jB^k$,

$$\{\mathbf{A},\mathbf{B},\mathbf{C}\} = E_{ijk}A^iB^jC^k = C^kE_{kij}A^iB^j = C^kC_k = \mathbf{C}^2 \tag{5-67}$$

This lengthy discussion concerning such a well-known elementary topic may appear to be somewhat in the nature of shooting cannon at a sparrow. However, as already noted, this detailed treatment in terms of general linear bases of a familiar and easily visualizable case makes it possible to proceed more rapidly with the discussion of the general case, all the listed formulas admitting ready generalization.

Thus, quite generally, one can consider in $\mathfrak{F}$ the r-dimensional linear structures $[\mathsf{A}_1, \ldots, \mathsf{A}_r]$ $(r \leq p)$, which describe what one may call an oriented *r-extension* in $\mathfrak{F}$, and which, as in the case $r = 2$ discussed earlier, are determined by (1) the r-dimensional vector subspace Π_r spanned by $\mathsf{A}_1, \ldots, \mathsf{A}_r$ (we are assuming this vector set *linearly independent*), (2) the r-dimensional volume of the "r-parallelepiped" determined by the vectors, and (3) the orientation of Π_r in our space—with respect to a standard base, of course.

The relations (5-49) generalize in an obvious manner to $r > 2$ and lead, as in Eq. (5-50), to the similar result

$$[\mathsf{A}_1, \ldots, \mathsf{A}_r] = A^{[a_1}_{(1)} A^{a_2}_{(2)} \cdots A^{a_r]}_{(r)}[\mathsf{e}_{a_1}, \ldots, \mathsf{e}_{a_r}] \tag{5-68}$$

where the bracket enclosing the indices acts on these similarly to the case $r = 2$; i.e., it indicates the taking of the "alternating part"—the sum divided by $r!$ of all possible terms corresponding to permutations P of $(a_1, \ldots, a_r)$ and taken with the sign given by the parity of P. Similar generalizations can be found quite easily for Eq. (5-51) as well as for all the equations developed in the above special case. It will suffice to consider a few representative results in this general setting before turning to the particular space of chief interest to us, namely, $\mathfrak{M}$.

The generalization of the relationship (5-58) to the structures represented by the alternating tensor (5-68) is given by

$$T^*_{a_{r+1}\cdots a_p} = \frac{1}{r!}E_{a_1\cdots a_p}T^{a_1\cdots a_r} \tag{5-69}$$

the alternating pseudotensor E being defined similarly to Eq. (5-56). The alternating pseudotensor T^* is usually called the "dual" of T.‡ That there

‡ It is important to note that this designation as well as the following results apply to general totally antisymmetric tensors, and not only to those of the form of Eq. (5-68).

is indeed a reciprocity between the two tensors T^* and T follows at once from the following identity extending Eq. (5-60):

$$E^{b_1 \cdots b_r a_{r+1} \cdots a_p} E_{a_1 \cdots a_p} = \epsilon^{b_1 \cdots a_p} \epsilon_{a_1 \cdots a_p} = (p - r)! \, \delta^{b_1 \cdots b_r}_{a_1 \cdots a_r} \tag{5-70}$$

where the unchanging absolute tensor components $\delta^{\cdots}_{\cdots}$ are $+1$, -1, or 0, according to whether the upper and lower sets of indices are an even, an odd, or no permutation of each other. This identity applied to Eq. (5-69) gives:‡

$$T^{a_1 \cdots a_r} = \frac{1}{(p - r)!} E^{a_1 \cdots a_p} T^*_{a_{r+1} \cdots a_p} \tag{5-71}$$

With the help of Eq. (5-71) it is not difficult to show that the geometric structure represented by the pseudotensor T^* satisfies properties that are direct extensions of the properties (1), (2), (3) obeyed by the pseudovector **C** of our earlier discussion. The extensions of Eq. (5-59) are immediate. By Eqs. (5-69) and (5-70), and the extension to rank >2 of Eq. (5-51) (see Prob. 5-11),

$$\frac{1}{s!} T^*_{a_1 \cdots a_s} T^{*a_1 \cdots a_s} = \frac{1}{r!} T^{a_1 \cdots a_r} T_{a_1 \cdots a_r}, \qquad r + s = p \tag{5-72}$$

corresponding to Eq. (5-61). Finally, analogously to Eq. (5-67), we have

$$E_{a_1 \cdots a_p} T^{a_1 \cdots a_r} T^{*a_{r+1} \cdots a_p} = (p - r)! \, T^{a_1 \cdots a_r} T_{a_1 \cdots a_r} \tag{5-73}$$

and the correctness of the correspondence in the orientations of T^* and T (i.e., of the structures described by them) follows from the positiveness of this expression.

Returning now to the space of central interest to us, namely, $\mathfrak{M}$, it remains only to clear up those points that involve essentially the *nondefiniteness* of the metric.

One such point had already been noted previously. In formulas such as Eq. (5-56) one must take the absolute value of the determinant g. Since $g = -1$ for $\mathfrak{M}$ in the distinguished coordinate frames—we shall henceforth call them "lorentzian"—it follows by Eq. (5-55) that g is negative generally, and corresponding to the second set of Eqs. (5-56), for instance, one should take

$$E_{\lambda\mu\nu\sigma} = \sqrt{-g} \, \epsilon_{\lambda\mu\nu\sigma} \tag{5-74}$$

When one now applies the equation similar to Eq. (5-54), one finds that by raising the indices of $E_{\lambda\mu\nu\sigma}$ one gets

$$E^{\lambda\mu\nu\sigma} = -\frac{1}{\sqrt{-g}} \epsilon^{\lambda\mu\nu\sigma} \tag{5-75}$$

‡ As obviously $\delta^{b_1 \cdots b_r}_{a_1 \cdots a_r} T^{a_1 \cdots a_r} = r! T^{b_1 \cdots b_r}$, which, incidentally, explains the designation "generalized Kronecker deltas" applied to the quantities $\delta^{\cdots}_{\cdots}$.

instead of an equation completely similar to the first set in Eq. (5-56). This difference must be borne in mind when applying our general results to $\mathfrak{M}$.

The occurrence of the minus sign in Eq. (5-74) and its consequences do not exhaust the novel features presented by $\mathfrak{M}$. In addition to the product of the g_a of Eq. (5-19), the actual occurrence of one positive and three negative g_a in our metric form‡ lead to specific differences in sign in the quantities (5-72), depending on the *types* of vectors of which the special alternating tensors are composed; the possibility also exists that these quantities vanish, i.e., that the "extensions" of the corresponding geometric structures are *null*.

For $r = 2$ it follows from the latter part of Eq. (5-51) and from the result (*a*) in Prob. 3-15, that $[\mathsf{A},\mathsf{B}]^2$ is negative, positive, or zero, according to whether the associated plane through the origin of coordinates in $\mathfrak{M}$ is "timelike," "spacelike," or "null"; i.e., according to whether this plane intersects the light cone about the origin in two lines, no line, or one line, respectively.

Similar conclusions can be drawn in the case $r = 3$ by observing that the expression corresponding to Eq. (5-72) for this case can also be written (see Prob. 5-11) in determinant form:

$$[\mathsf{A},\mathsf{B},\mathsf{C}]^2 = \begin{vmatrix} \mathsf{A}^2 & \mathsf{A}\cdot\mathsf{B} & \mathsf{A}\cdot\mathsf{C} \\ \mathsf{B}\cdot\mathsf{A} & \mathsf{B}^2 & \mathsf{B}\cdot\mathsf{C} \\ \mathsf{C}\cdot\mathsf{A} & \mathsf{C}\cdot\mathsf{B} & \mathsf{C}^2 \end{vmatrix} \tag{5-76}$$

Note that for three 4-vectors whose associated 3-flat through the origin intersects the light cone only in the origin, this gives a negative value, so that we get an imaginary volume, a result due, of course, merely to our present choice of signs for the g_α (see preceding footnote).

Let us check the consistency of our formalism in this particular case by evaluating the associated pseudovector T^* and establishing its type. A word of caution is in order here. We cannot apply Eq. (5-72) as it is. It would in fact give us a *negative* squared interval for T^* and this is impossible as this vector is "perpendicular" to the *spacelike* $[\mathsf{A},\mathsf{B},\mathsf{C}]$. Actually

$$\mathsf{T}^{*2} = -[\mathsf{A},\mathsf{B},\mathsf{C}]^2 \tag{5-77}$$

as it should be, and this result is indeed deduced, just as Eq. (5-72), with due regard to the minus sign in Eq. (5-75).

‡ The choice of the "signature" $(+\,-\,-\,-)$ rather than $(-\,+\,+\,+)$ is of course a mere convention, and the second choice is in fact also used by many authors. The small relative advantages of each require no comment. [In the mathematical literature the word "signature" usually refers to the difference between the number of positive and the number of negative g_a in Eq. (5-19).]

5-5 TENSOR ANALYSIS IN FLAT SPACES

When we are dealing with a tensor *field* $Q(x)$, the components $Q^{\cdot\cdot\cdot}_{\cdot\cdot\cdot}(x)$ being differentiable functions over a given region of $\mathfrak{F}$, then relative to rectilinear coordinate frames one can derive new tensors simply by differentiation. A familiar example is the formation of the *gradient* by differentiation of a scalar. The proof in the general case is as follows. Differentiate with respect to x'^a both sides of the transformation law for a scalar,

$$Q'(x') = Q(x), \qquad x' \text{ and } x \text{ refer to the same point of our region} \tag{5-78}$$

getting, $\partial Q'/\partial x'^a \equiv Q'_{,a} = (\partial Q/\partial x^b)\, \partial x^b/\partial x'^a \equiv Q_{,b}\, \partial x^b/\partial x'^a$. But

$$\frac{\partial x^b}{\partial x'^a} = M^b{}_a \tag{5-79}$$

as follows, e.g., by Eq. (5-46), since $M = N^{-1}$. Hence,

$$Q'_{,a} = M^b{}_a Q_{,b} \tag{5-80}$$

Remembering the transformation law (5-36), it is seen that the "gradient" $Q_{,a}$ is a covariant vector in the sense used earlier in the chapter. With our later convention, upon the availability of a metric, we can say that $Q_{,a}$ are the covariant components of a vector Grad Q.‡

In the case of a tensor field of arbitrary rank it is clear that, in rectangular coordinates, one can conclude, by similar steps, that if $Q^{\cdot\cdot\cdot}_{\cdot\cdot\cdot}$ are the components of this field, then $Q^{\cdot\cdot\cdot}_{\cdot\cdot\cdot,a}$, are the components of a tensor field of rank higher by one. Because of this property of raising the rank, this process of tensor derivation is known as "extension."

When our tensor field is referred to general bases, we have seen that the rule concerning the gradient of a scalar retains its validity; however, since now the transformation matrices M and N are, in general, nonconstant point functions, it is obvious that the process of extension in the case of tensors of rank >0 requires modification.

Let us first examine the change in a vector field $\mathsf{A}(x)$ corresponding to an infinitesimal displacement $d\mathbf{x}$. Remembering that we are now dealing in general with x-dependent bases, one finds, by Eq. (5-20),

$$d\mathsf{A} = d(A^a \mathbf{e}_a) = dA^a \mathbf{e}_a + A^a d\mathbf{e}_a = dA^a \mathbf{e}_a + A^a \mathbf{e}_{a,b}\, dx^b$$

Therefore, by Eqs. (5-21) and (5-22),

$$(d\mathsf{A})_c = \mathbf{e}_c \cdot d\mathsf{A} = g_{ca}\, dA^a + [ab,c] A^a\, dx^b \tag{5-81}$$

where,

$$[ab,c] \equiv \mathbf{e}_{a,b} \cdot \mathbf{e}_c \tag{5-82}$$

or, as one finds by differentiating Eq. (5-22) and using the symmetry prop-

‡ This is the notation we shall also use in $\mathfrak{M}$. In ordinary three-dimensional space we shall use lower case letters for such symbols.

erty of g_{ab}

$$[ab,c] = \tfrac{1}{2}(g_{ac,b} + g_{bc,a} - g_{ab,c}) \tag{5-83}$$

This derivation also involves the basic symmetry property

$$[ab,c] = [ba,c] \tag{5-83a}$$

stemming from the corresponding symmetry of $\mathbf{e}_{a,b}$. The latter symmetry follows at once when $\mathbf{e}_a$ is referred to a cartesian frame as discussed on page 146: $\mathbf{e}_a = y^c{}_{,a}\mathbf{u}_c$, $\mathbf{e}_{a,b} = y^c{}_{,ab}\mathbf{u}_c = y^c{}_{,ba}\mathbf{u}_c = \mathbf{e}_{b,a}$. The quantities (5-83) are known as the "Christoffel symbols of the first kind." Equation (5-81) can also be written,

$$(d\mathsf{A})^d = g^{dc}(d\mathsf{A})_c = (A^d{}_{,b} + \Gamma^d_{ab}A^a)\, dx^b \tag{5-84}$$

where we have introduced the "Christoffel symbols of the second kind"

$$g^{dc}[ab,c] \equiv \Gamma^d_{ab} \tag{5-85}$$

Since $d\mathsf{A}$ is a vector, and since the vector $d\mathbf{x}$ is arbitrary, it follows (see Prob. 5-2) that

$$A^d{}_{,b} + \Gamma^d_{ab}A^a \equiv A^d{}_{;b} \tag{5-86}$$

represent the components of a tensor of character indicated by the position of the indices. They are known as "covariant derivatives."

Equation (5-86) obviously represents the desired generalization of the "extension rule" in the case of the contravariant components of a vector. In the special case of rectilinear bases, $\Gamma^a_{bc} \equiv 0$, and the quantities reduce to the ordinary partials. What is one to understand by the *covariant derivative* in the case of general tensor components? It should, naturally, obey the rules of ordinary differentiation. This turns out to be now also sufficient to define it uniquely. We list the basic rules (these can be, and often are, taken for defining postulates of covariant differentiation):

1 $f_{;a} = f_{,a}$, f a scalar
2 $A^a{}_{;b} = A^a{}_{,b} + \Gamma^a_{cb}A^c$
3 $(U^{\cdots}_{\cdots} + V^{\cdots}_{\cdots})_{;a} = U^{\cdots}_{\cdots;a} + V^{\cdots}_{\cdots;a}$
4 $(U^{\cdots}_{\cdot}V^{\cdots}_{\cdots})_{;a} = U^{\cdots}_{\cdot}V^{\cdots}_{\cdots;a} + U^{\cdots}_{\cdot;a}V^{\cdots}_{\cdots}$

The rules (1) and (2) have already been considered, while (3) and (4) have the same structure as the corresponding rules for ordinary derivatives.

By combining rules (1), (2), and (4), and evaluating $(A_aA^a)_{;b}$ one finds

$$A_{a;b} = A_{a,b} - \Gamma^c_{ab}A_c \tag{5-87}$$

The covariant derivatives for tensors of higher rank can now be found easily by mathematical induction. The general result can be written in understandable condensed form as follows:

$$Q^{\cdots}_{\cdots;a} = Q^{\cdots}_{\cdots,a} + \Sigma Q^{\cdots a_{r-1} c a_{r+1} \cdots}_{\cdots} \Gamma^{a_r}_{ca} - \Sigma Q^{\cdots}_{\cdots b_{s-1} d b_{s+1} \cdots} \Gamma^{d}_{b_s a} \tag{5-88}$$

This formula can also be proved by direct application of rules (1) to (4) and Eq. (5-87), as illustrated by the following steps for mixed components of a second-rank tensor Q, A,B being *arbitrary* vectors:

$$\begin{aligned}(Q^a{}_b A_a B^b)_{;c} &= Q^a{}_{b;c} A_a B^b + Q^a{}_b (A_{a;c} B^b + A_a B^b{}_{;c}) \\ &= \cdots + Q^a{}_b [B^b (A_{a,c} - A_d \Gamma^d_{ac}) + A_a (B^b{}_{,c} + B^d \Gamma^b_{dc})] = (Q^a{}_b A_a B^b)_{,c} \\ &= Q^a{}_{b,c} A_a B^b + Q^a{}_b (A_{a,c} B^b + A_a B^b{}_{,c})\end{aligned}$$

or

$$[Q^a{}_{b;c} - (Q^a{}_{b,c} - Q^a{}_d \Gamma^d_{bc} + Q^d{}_b \Gamma^a_{dc})] A_a B^b = 0$$

which implies, in view of the arbitrariness of the vectors, that

$$Q^a{}_{b;c} = Q^a{}_{b,c} + Q^d{}_b \Gamma^a_{dc} - Q^a{}_d \Gamma^d_{bc} \tag{5-88a}$$

in agreement with Eq. (5-88).

The covariant derivatives $A^a{}_{;b}$ were defined so that $(d\mathsf{A})^a = A^a{}_{;b}\, dx^b$, the tensor with the mixed components $A^a{}_{;b}$ forming the *extension* of the vector A. Do we also have $(d\mathsf{A})_a = A_{a;b}\, dx^b$? For this to be true $A_{a;b}$ must be the covariant components of the extension tensor: $A_{a;b} = g_{ac} A^c{}_{;b}$, which requires that

$$g_{ab;c} = 0 \tag{5-89}$$

and by Eqs. (5-88), (5-85), and (5-83) one finds that this is indeed a true identity.

The covariant derivatives of relative tensors can be found by a method similar to that used for absolute tensors.‡ The result differs from Eq. (5-88) only by an additional term on the right-hand side, of the form

$$-wQ^{\cdots}_{\cdots} \Gamma^c_{ac} \tag{5-88b}$$

It will suffice to indicate the derivation of this term in the case of a relative scalar.

For a relative scalar Q of weight w, we have the factor $(\det M)^w$ on the right-hand side of Eq. (5-78), M being the matrix (5-79). Therefore,

$$Q'_{,a} = (\det M)^w M^b{}_a (Q_{,b} + wQ(\ln \det M)_{,b}) \tag{5-90}$$

and our problem is reduced to the evaluation of the derivatives of det M.

In general, given a nonsingular differentiable matrix function

$$A = \|A^a{}_b(x)\|$$

‡ One can dispense with these derivatives both in STR as well as in the general theory. The few steps devoted here to this topic have however independent interest and entail no serious digression.

the derivatives of its determinant can be found by using the expansion $\epsilon_{a_1 \cdots a_p} A^{a_1}{}_1 \cdots A^{a_p}{}_p$, differentiating term by term, and noting that $\epsilon_{a_1 \cdots a_p} A^{a_1}{}_1 \cdots A^{a_{q-1}}{}_{q-1} A^{a_{q+1}}{}_{q+1} \cdots A^{a_p}{}_p$ give the cofactors

$$(\det A)(A^{-1})^q{}_{a_q}$$

of the qth column of A. The result is

$$(\det A)_{,a} = (\det A) A^b{}_{c,a} (A^{-1})^c{}_b \tag{5-91}$$

Hence, when $A = M$, one gets

$$(\ln \det M)_{,a} = M^b{}_{c,a} N^c{}_b \tag{5-92}$$

It remains to evaluate the derivatives $M^b{}_{c,a}$. Moreover, the result must be in such a form that upon substitution in Eq. (5-90) one can read off the desired transformation law. We note that by Eqs. (5-92), (5-79), and (5-46), the sum $M^b{}_a (\ln \det M)_{,b}$ occurring in Eq. (5-90), can be written

$$\frac{\partial x^b}{\partial x'^a} \frac{\partial^2 x^c}{\partial x'^d \, \partial x^b} \frac{\partial x'^d}{\partial x^c} = \frac{\partial^2 x^c}{\partial x'^a \, \partial x^c} = M^c{}_{a,c} \tag{5-93}$$

This suggests the following steps.

Differentiating Eq. (5-33), one gets

$$\mathbf{e}'_{a,b} \equiv \frac{\partial \mathbf{e}'_a(x')}{\partial x'^b} = (M^c{}_{a,d} \mathbf{e}_c + M^c{}_a \mathbf{e}_{c,d}) M^d{}_b$$

which, when multiplied scalarly by $\mathbf{e}'_c$, give, upon use of Eqs. (5-33) and (5-82), the transformation equations

$$[ab,c]' = M^g{}_a M^d{}_b M^e{}_c [gd,e] + g_{ge} M^g{}_{a,d} M^e{}_c M^d{}_b \tag{5-94}$$

These show, incidentally, that $[ab,c]$ [and hence also Γ^a_{bc}, as also shown directly in Eq. (5-95)] are not the components of a tensor except relative to rectilinear coordinate frames. Multiplying-summing Eqs. (5-94) by g'^{fc} on the left and $g^{rs} N^f{}_r N^c{}_s$ on the right, one finds the transformation law for the Christoffel symbols of the second kind;

$$\Gamma'^f_{ab} = \Gamma^r_{cd} N^f{}_r M^c{}_a M^d{}_b + M^c{}_{a,d} M^d{}_b N^f{}_c \tag{5-95}$$

Contraction with respect to the indices f,b then gives

$$\Gamma'^b_{ab} = \Gamma^d_{cd} M^c{}_a + M^c{}_{a,c} \tag{5-96}$$

Comparing now with our previous result, Eq. (5-93), and substituting in Eq. (5-90), one gets immediately the stated transformation law for the derivatives of the relative scalar Q.

As an immediate application of these transformation equations for relative tensors we prove the following two useful results:‡

$$\text{Div } \mathsf{A} \equiv A^a{}_{;a} = \frac{1}{\sqrt{|g|}}(\sqrt{|g|}\, A^a)_{,a} \tag{5-97}$$

$$(\text{Div } T)^a \equiv T^{ab}{}_{;b} = \frac{1}{\sqrt{|g|}}(\sqrt{|g|}\, T^{ab})_{,b}, \qquad T^{ab} = -T^{ab} \tag{5-98}$$

These results follow from the following formulas for relative tensors of weight 1, or *tensor densities* (using now the customary Gothic letters for denoting such tensors):

$$\mathfrak{A}^a{}_{;a} = \mathfrak{A}^a{}_{,a} \tag{5-99}$$

$$\mathfrak{T}^{a_1 \cdots a_{n-1} b}{}_{;b} = \mathfrak{T}^{a_1 \cdots a_{n-1} b}{}_{,b}, \qquad \mathfrak{T} \text{ alternating} \tag{5-100}$$

These relations are immediate consequences of the transformation law for the derivatives of relative tensors when $w = 1$, remembering, in the case of Eq. (5-100), the symmetry of Γ^a_{bc} in the lower indices. Equations (5-97) and (5-98) are seen to follow from Eqs. (5-99) and (5-100) (for $n = 2$) when it is observed that in accordance with Eq. (5-55), if Q is a tensor then $\sqrt{|g|}\, Q$ is a tensor density (see above definition),§ and that by Eq. (5-89), we have the identities

$$g_{;a} = 0 \tag{5-101}$$

and hence also $\sqrt{|g|}_{;a} = 0$.

By referring to Eq. (5-89) in support of Eq. (5-101) we have made the tacit assumption that we also have the identities.

$$\epsilon^{a_1 \cdots a_p}{}_{;b} = 0 \tag{5-102}$$

But these identities, that are useful also in other connections, follow in a few simple steps from rule (5-88) with the addition of Eq. (5-88*b*), when we remember that the $\epsilon^{\cdots}$ are alternating *unchanging* tensor densities (i.e., $w = 1$) and that the Γ^a_{bc} are symmetric in the lower indices.

The fundamental identities (5-101) can also be proved directly with little difficulty. By means of Eqs. (5-91), (5-26), (5-83), and (5-85) one

‡ Again we may note that the explicit use of relative tensors can be here avoided. As the reader can confirm with little difficulty, the results, Eqs. (5-97) and (5-98), can be obtained by direct—though not essentially different—means.

§ The designation "density" is due to the occurrence of such tensors as integrands in volume integrals with volume elements that are corresponding tensor quantities of weight -1 (the latter being therefore known as "capacities"). The fact that the transformation law for $\sqrt{|g|}\, Q$ involves the absolute value of the determinant of the transformation matrix does not matter here, as one easily verifies; and, in fact, rules (5-97) and (5-98) can be also readily checked using the result, Eq. (5-103).

can in fact show that

$$\frac{g_{,a}}{g} = (\ln |g|)_{,a} = g^{bc}([ab,c] + [ac,b]) = 2\Gamma^b_{ab} \tag{5-103}$$

and this is seen to be identical with Eq. (5-101) when one remembers that g is a relative scalar of weight 2.

In addition to the "gradient" and the "divergence," the differential operator "rotation" (or "curl") of classical vector analysis also admits of ready extension to general $\mathfrak{F}$, and in particular to $\mathfrak{M}$. This extension as applied to a vector is obviously as follows:

$$(\text{Rot } \mathsf{T})_{ab} = A_{b;a} - A_{a;b} = A_{b,a} - A_{a,b} \tag{5-104}$$

the last expression resulting from the cancellation of the two Γ terms owing to the symmetry property of the Γ symbols.

One can generalize this operation so as to apply to tensors of any rank by noticing that the components of Eq. (5-104) can also be written $-\delta^{cd}_{ab}A_{c,d}$. The generalization of this expression to a tensor Q of arbitrary rank n, $(-1)^n/n!\, \delta^{b_1 \cdots b_{n+1}}_{a_1 \cdots a_{n+1}} Q_{b_1 \cdots b_n;b_{n+1}}$, is an *alternating* tensor of rank $(n + 1)$, that may be called the *rotation* of Q. Moreover, by the antisymmetry of the δ symbols and the symmetry property of the Γ symbols, it follows from rule (5-88) that

$$(\text{Rot } Q)_{a_1 \cdots a_{n+1}} = \frac{(-1)^n}{n!} \delta^{b_1 \cdots b_{n+1}}_{a_1 \cdots a_{n+1}} Q_{b_1 \cdots b_n,b_{n+1}}, \qquad n \leq p - 1 \tag{5-105}$$

In particular, when $n = 2$ and the tensor Q is alternating‡ we have the useful formula

$$(\text{Rot } T)_{abc} = T_{ab,c} + T_{bc,a} + T_{ca,b}, \qquad T_{ab} = -T_{ba} \tag{5-106}$$

In ordinary vector analysis, it will be recalled, the differential operations Div and Rot can be introduced in an invariant way, i.e., independently of any specific coordinate system, guided by the integral theorems of Gauss and of Stokes; and these theorems are of course of great importance in themselves. The above generalizations of the differential operations to general $\mathfrak{F}$, and in particular to $\mathfrak{M}$, can also be defined in terms of limiting processes based on the generalizations of the integral theorems of Gauss and of Stokes. When thus defined these theorems follow immediately from the definition of multiple integrals as limiting sums.

The usual deductions starting with the differential definitions of Div and Rot as given above can be worked out with little difficulty when one observes that in all cases these differential operations involve tensor components that are equivalent to expressions involving ordinary derivatives. The latter point makes it possible to employ *integration by parts* as applied

‡ Rot Q depends in any case only on the "alternating part" of Q.

to multiple integrals. The requirement of general covariance, on the other hand, can be satisfied only if our integrals are sums over *scalars*, since in a general coordinate frame the addition of tensor components at two different points is in general meaningless. The type of multiple integrals that can occur in each case is thus determined by the required invariance properties of the associated integration elements. The latter can be ascertained by applying the theory of linear structures in $\mathfrak{F}$ developed at length in Sec. 5-4. If we are integrating over a surface or hypersurface of dimensionality r, let us call it an "r-surface" for short (which is in particular a curve if $r = 1$ or a spatial region of $\mathfrak{F}$ when $r = p$), then the *oriented* r-surface element $dS_{(r)}$ can be represented by the quantities $[d_1\mathbf{x}, \ldots, d_r\mathbf{x}]$ [in the notation of Eq. (5-68)], for a suitable choice of the vector differentials spanning $dS_{(r)}$.

In this manner one can obtain the generalizations of the theorems of Gauss and of Stokes applied to regions of $\mathfrak{F}$ of dimensionality $\leq p$, of which the following, written for $\mathfrak{M}$, are the most frequently used:

$$\int_{R_4} \text{Div}\, \mathbf{A}\, dV = \int_{B_3} \mathbf{A} \cdot d\mathbf{S}, \qquad B_3 = \text{boundary of the 4-region } R_4 \tag{5-107}$$

$$\frac{1}{2} \int_S (\text{Rot}\, \mathbf{A})_{\lambda\mu}\, dS^{\lambda\mu} = \oint_C \mathbf{A} \cdot d\mathbf{s}, \qquad C = \text{one-dimensional boundary of the 2-region } S \tag{5-108}$$

The proof of these particular integral identities can be carried out in close analogy to the proofs of the corresponding theorems in ordinary euclidean space; only one must take care that due attention is paid to the signs of the various types of geometric magnitudes that are involved, arising from the particular signature of the indefinite metric of $\mathfrak{M}$.‡

APPENDIX 5A FINITE-DIMENSIONAL VECTOR SPACES

Vector spaces of finite or infinite dimensions over the field of real or complex numbers play an important role in all parts of mathematical physics. We present here an outline of a few basic definitions and results concerning finite-dimensional vector spaces. Both [10] and H. Weyl's "The Theory of Groups and Quantum Mechanics," Dover Publications, Inc., N.Y., contain instructive and pithy introductions to the subject. Fuller treatments are to be found in most advanced modern algebra books.

Consider the system of ordinary vectors, the vectors used by the physicist, and abstract from all their properties save those pertaining to vector addition and multiplication by a scalar. The resulting mathematical

‡ For a discussion of the general integral identities see, e.g., J. L. Synge and A. Schild, "Tensor Calculus," chap. 7, University of Toronto Press, Toronto, 1949; N. Coburn, "Vector and Tensor Analysis," chap. 8, The Macmillan Company, New York, 1955; see also Prob. 5-17.

system is what one understands by an *abstract three-dimensional vector space V_3 over the field F of real numbers*. The three-dimensionality itself is defined abstractly by the property of V_3 of containing three but no more than three *linearly independent* vectors—p vectors $\mathsf{v}_1, \ldots, \mathsf{v}_p$ of a vector space being "linearly independent" if

$$\alpha_1 \mathsf{v}_1 + \cdots + \alpha_p \mathsf{v}_p = \mathsf{0} \equiv \text{zero vector} \quad \text{implies } \alpha_1 = 0, \ldots, \alpha_p = 0, \qquad \alpha\text{'s in } F \tag{5A-1}$$

Replacing in the last definition, the number 3 by an arbitrary positive integer n gives us the abstract *n-dimensional* vector space V_n over the field F.

Thus, V_n consists of a collection of objects $\{\mathsf{v}\}$, called "vectors," among which is defined a binary operation $+$, called "vector addition" (or, just "addition"), the resulting system forming an abelian (i.e., commutative) group, with $\mathsf{0}$ as the identity and $-\mathsf{v}$ the inverse of v. There is also defined a process of multiplication between elements of F and of V_n obeying the associative and distributive laws of arithmetic, with $1\mathsf{v} = \mathsf{v}$. In addition, V_n is subject to the dimensionality property: the relation (5A-1) can be satisfied when $p = n$ but not when $p > n$.

Isomorphism of vector spaces over the same field is defined similarly to isomorphism for groups. Just as an abstract group, so also an abstract V_n admits of many concrete manifestations or *realizations*. An important class of realizations is obtained by introducing in V_n a coordinate system, or *base*,‡ namely, a set of *n linearly independent* vectors $\{\mathsf{u}_a\}$ $(a = 1, \ldots, n)$ (whose existence is insured by our definition). Since every set of $(n + 1)$ vectors $\mathsf{v}, \mathsf{u}_1, \ldots, \mathsf{u}_n$ is by our assumption linearly dependent, it follows that

$$\mathsf{v} = \alpha_a(\mathsf{v})\mathsf{u}_a, \qquad \text{summation over } a = 1, \ldots, n \tag{5A-2}$$

where not all α_a are zero unless $\mathsf{v} = \mathsf{0}$. It is easy to verify that the correspondence $\mathsf{v} \rightarrow (\alpha_1(\mathsf{v}), \ldots, \alpha_n(\mathsf{v})) \equiv \{\alpha_a(\mathsf{v})\}$ is an isomorphism in which $\mathsf{v}_1 + \mathsf{v}_2 \rightarrow \{\alpha_a(\mathsf{v}_1) + \alpha_a(\mathsf{v}_2)\}$, $\lambda\mathsf{v} \rightarrow \{\lambda\alpha_a(\mathsf{v})\}$ (λ in F), and $\mathsf{0} \rightarrow (0, \ldots, 0)$; also, $\mathsf{u}_a \rightarrow \{\delta_{ab}\}_{b=1,\ldots,n}$. We have therefore as many such realizations as there are independent bases, and, of course, we can obtain all such bases from any given one by nonsingular linear homogeneous transformations

$$\mathsf{u}_a \rightarrow \mathsf{u}'_a = A_{ba}\mathsf{u}_b, \qquad \det A \neq 0 \tag{5A-3}$$

In what sense does one apply the term vector *space?* Is there a geometric complement to our algebraic point of view? When we recall our previous observations regarding the connection between space, or geometry, and invariance under a characteristic group of transformations, it can be seen that the group of transformations (5A-3)—the group denoted by the symbol $\mathfrak{GL}_n$ in Sec. 5-3—is the characteristic group of the present space V_n. This group is known as the *affine* group, and the same designation is applied

‡ The equivalent term "basis" is perhaps in more common use.

to the associated space or geometry. The characteristic property of this geometry is that *linear* structures have an invariantive meaning; and that the same is true also of the notion of *finiteness:* vectors having finite components in one base retain this property in every base. We get a more visual grasp of these properties if we consider V_3 and identify the vector components with the coordinates of a "point," the point representing the origin being a special point of the space, just as the vector $\mathsf{0}$ to which it corresponds is a special vector—its components are the same in all bases. In this space we not only have *straight lines*, but also *parallelism*, since the property of two lines not having a *finite* point of intersection is an invariant one.

One can also introduce other meaningful—and, for some purposes, useful—relations in affine geometry; but for these the interested reader must be referred to the literature on the subject, and in particular for the concept of "dual" vector spaces, of which we have had an indication in our discussion of tensors in Sec. 5-2.

Let us note in conclusion that the family of tensors of a given rank r and given character over the underlying space $\mathfrak{F}_p$, introduced in Sec. 5-3, provides an important example of realizations $\mathfrak{B}_n$ of V_n (with $n = r^p$). A base in each $\mathfrak{B}_n$ can be given by a symbolic product of one of the following forms:

$$\mathsf{e}_{a_1} \cdots \mathsf{e}_{a_r}, \quad \text{or} \quad \mathsf{e}^{a_1} \cdots \mathsf{e}^{a_r}, \quad \text{or} \quad \mathsf{e}_{a_1}\mathsf{e}^{a_2}\mathsf{e}_{a_3} \cdots \mathsf{e}_{a_r}, \quad \text{etc.} \tag{5A-4}$$

taken in the sense of Eq. (5-50a). The transformations (5A-3) connecting these bases are induced by the transformations (5-33) or (5-35).

Problems

5-1 (a) If $\mathcal{G}$ is an orthogonal or quasi-orthogonal group [i.e., its matrices satisfy Eq. (5-9) with real or complex elements], show that the representation matrices $Q_{(s)}$ given in Eq. (5-14) can be further decomposed. (Make use of the invariance of u_{aa} in this case.) (b) If $\mathcal{G}$ is also four-dimensional and unimodular, show that $Q_{(a)}$ of Eq. (5-14) can be further reduced by noting that every second-rank antisymmetric tensor A associated with $\mathcal{G}$ admits the covariant decomposition

$$A = A^{(+)} + A^{(-)}, \qquad A^{(\pm)*} = \pm A^{(\pm)}, \qquad A^*_{\alpha\beta} \equiv \tfrac{1}{2}\epsilon_{\alpha\beta\gamma\delta}A_{\gamma\delta} \tag{i}$$

5-2 If A_aB^a is a scalar for every vector B, then A_a are necessarily the covariant components of a vector. This result is merely a special case of the first definition of tensors given in Sec. 5-3. A general result, known as the "quotient theorem" of tensor calculus states similarly that $T^{\cdot\cdot\cdot}_{\cdot\cdot\cdot}$ are the components of a tensor if the quantities obtained through "inner multiplication" (i.e., multiplication followed by contraction of one or more pairs of indices, each pair including one index from each factor) with *arbitrary* tensor components of a given character, are the components of a tensor.

Prove this result. [It is obtained most simply by using the definition given in the paragraph that includes Eq. (5-31).]

5-3 Verify that the two definitions of a tensor given in Sec. 5-3 are equivalent.

5-4 Is it possible that at any point of the space $\mathfrak{F}$ as defined in Sec. 5-3, the condition (5-25) is violated? What is the geometric significance of this condition? [Consider the generalization of the result (5-64).]

5-5 Show that for a space $\mathfrak{F}$ as defined in Sec. 5-3, the definition of a tensor in terms of its transformation properties under the underlying group $\mathcal{G}$ (given in Sec. 5-2) and under the general linear group $\mathcal{GL}_p$ (of Sec. 5-3), leads to the same 'object'. Give the geometric interpretation of the relationship between the two definitions. (Consider first the simple example of $\mathfrak{F}$ coinciding with a euclidean plane, when there is available an easy graphic representation of all the relevant ideas.)

5-6 Prove the companion relationship to Eq. (5-22), namely,

$$\mathbf{e}^a \cdot \mathbf{e}^b = g^{ab}$$

and show that these quantities are tensor components by applying the second definition given in Sec. 5-3.

5-7 In the case of euclidean spaces establish the precise geometric significance of *reciprocal bases* and of the covariant and contravariant components of a vector, and check explicitly all the pertinent formulas in the 2-dimensional case. Are any modifications indicated in the case of $\mathfrak{M}$?

5-8 Prove the validity of Eq. (5-48) and its consistency with Eq. (5-36). [Recall the definition of $\mathbf{e}_a(x)$ in terms of the cartesian base $\{\mathbf{u}_a\}$. Consistency with Eq. (5-36) can be shown directly using Eqs. (5-29) and (5-79).]

5-9 Find the expansion of the determinant (5-63) relative to the base $\{\mathbf{e}^i\}$ and deduce the associated results similar to (5-64) to (5-66).

5-10 Show that the geometric structures represented by tensors of the form (5-50) are characterized by items (1) to (3) given on page 148.

5-11 Generalize the result (5-51) to the tensors T given by (5-68) (also known as "r-vectors," i.e., "bivectors" when $r = 2$, etc.) and prove for euclidean $\mathfrak{F}_p$, that (Élie Cartan)

$$V_r^2 \equiv [\mathsf{A}_1, \ . \ . \ . \ , \mathsf{A}_r]^2 = \frac{1}{r!} T^{a_1 \cdots a_r} T_{a_1 \cdots a_r} \qquad 2 \le r \le p \qquad \text{(i)}$$

where $T^{a_1 \cdots a_r} = r! A^{[a_1}_{(1)} \cdots A^{a_r]}_{(r)} \equiv \delta^{a_1 \cdots a_r}_{b_1 \cdots b_r} A^{b_1}_{(1)} \cdots A^{b_r}_{(r)}$. Show that (i) can also be written as a determinant:

$$V_r^2 = \begin{vmatrix} \mathsf{A}_1 \cdot \mathsf{A}_1 & \cdots & \mathsf{A}_1 \cdot \mathsf{A}_r \\ \cdots & \cdots & \cdots \\ \mathsf{A}_r \cdot \mathsf{A}_1 & \cdots & \mathsf{A}_r \cdot \mathsf{A}_r \end{vmatrix} \qquad \text{(ii)}$$

[It may be simpler to prove (ii) first and then deduce (i). One can prove (ii), e.g., by mathematical induction by noting that, $V_r^2 = V_{r-1}^2(\mathsf{A}_r - \mathsf{B}_r)^2$, where B_r is the projection of A_r on Π_{r-1}, the vector space determined by the vectors $\mathsf{A}_{(1)}, \mathsf{A}_{(2)}, \ldots, \mathsf{A}_{(r-1)}$; and showing that $(\mathsf{A}_r - \mathsf{B}_r)^2 = D_r/D_{r-1}$, where D_r denotes the determinant (ii).] What modifications are required in $\mathfrak{M}$?

5-12 (*a*) Consider an alternating second-rank tensor T in $\mathfrak{M}$. Show that

$$\begin{aligned} T^*_{0i} &= \sqrt{-g}\, T^{jk} \\ T^*_{ij} &= \sqrt{-g}\, T^{0k} \end{aligned} \qquad i, j, k = 1, 2, 3 \text{ and cyclic permutations} \qquad \text{(i)}$$

so that if we write formally,

$$(T^{01}, T^{02}, T^{03}) = \mathbf{U}, \qquad (T^{23}, T^{31}, T^{12}) = \mathbf{V} \qquad \text{(ii)}$$

we have the condensed formula

$$T^*_{\mu\nu}T^{\mu\nu} = 4\sqrt{-g}\mathbf{U} \cdot \mathbf{V} \qquad \text{(iii)}$$

(Note that $\epsilon_{0ijk} \equiv \epsilon_{ijk}$.) (*b*) Given an arbitrary tensor $T^{\mu\nu}$ in $\mathfrak{M}$, show that under the subgroup of Lorentz transformations that represent spatial rotations, T^{00}, T^{0i}, T^{i0}, T^{ij} transform as a three-dimensional scalar, vector, vector, and tensor respectively; and that in particular when $T^{\mu\nu} = -T^{\mu\nu}$, T is associated with the 3-vectors (ii) (of which the second is *axial*). Show further that under an arbitrary Lorentz transformation (3-29), the transformation of T is given by the following transformations of the associated 3-vectors:

$$\begin{aligned} \mathbf{U}'_\parallel &= \mathbf{U}_\parallel, \qquad & \mathbf{U}'_\perp &= \gamma[\mathbf{U} + (\boldsymbol{\beta} \times \mathbf{V})]_\perp \\ \mathbf{V}'_\parallel &= \mathbf{V}_\parallel, \qquad & \mathbf{V}'_\perp &= \gamma[\mathbf{V} - (\boldsymbol{\beta} \times \mathbf{U})]_\perp \end{aligned} \qquad \text{(iv)}$$

where the symbols $\parallel$ and $\perp$ denote the respective parts of the vector parallel and normal to $\mathbf{v}$.

5-13 Prove that

$$\mathsf{A}_{,a} \cdot \mathsf{e}_b = A_{b;a}$$

[Use (5-20).]

5-14 Prove the identity

$$\text{Rot Rot } T = 0 \qquad \text{(i)}$$

holding for an arbitrary tensor field T. In what sense can (i) be considered as a generalization of the familiar identity

$$\text{Rot Grad } T = 0$$

[Consider taking $n = 0$ formally in the right-hand side of Eq. (5-105).]

5-15 Prove the identities

$$E^{a_1 \cdots a_p}{}_{;b} = 0 \tag{i}$$

and with their aid show that

$$(\text{Rot } T)^* = (-1)^{p-1} \text{ Div } T^* \qquad T \text{ alternating tensor} \tag{ii}$$

where $(\text{Div } T)^{a_1 \cdots a_{n-1}} = T^{a_1 \cdots a_n}{}_{;a_n}$.

5-16 Consider in $\mathfrak{M}$ the 'tensor functionals' of the form

$$\mathfrak{F}^{\cdots}_{\cdots}(S) \equiv \int_S T^{\cdots\mu}_{\cdots} \, dS_\mu$$

where the 3-surfaces S are spacelike and the meaning of the symbols is the usual one. Prove that in rectangular coordinates, and with suitable restrictions on the functions $T^{\cdots}_{\cdots}$,

$$\frac{D\mathfrak{F}^{\cdots}_{\cdots}}{DS_{\mathsf{x}}} = T^{\cdots\mu}_{\cdots}{}_{,\mu}(\mathsf{x}) \tag{i}$$

where the 'functional derivative' D/DS_{x} with respect to the surface S at the event x is, in general, defined as follows (see Fig. 5-2):

$$\frac{D\mathfrak{F}}{DS_{\mathsf{x}}} = \lim_{(dV) \to \mathsf{x}} \frac{\mathfrak{F}(S') - \mathfrak{F}(S)}{dV}$$

where by $(dV) \to \mathsf{x}$ we understand that the space-time volume enclosed between the surfaces S and S' tends to zero by collapsing on the point x.

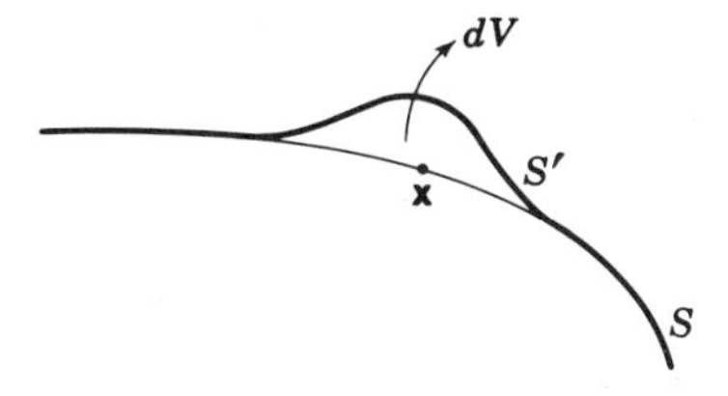

Fig. 5-2 Schematic representation of the neighboring 3-surfaces and enclosed differential element of space-time 'volume,' referred to in Prob. 5-16.

[The result can be deduced from an extension of the integral identity (5-107) to tensors of arbitrary order.] What special case of (i) can be extended to general coordinates?

5-17 (*a*) Show that the integration element $dx^1 \cdots dx^p$ in p-dimensional space behaves as a relative scalar of weight -1 (such scalars are therefore sometimes termed "capacities"). (*b*) Consider the integral

$$\int A_{i_1 \cdots i_n}(x^1, \ldots, x^p) \frac{\partial(x^{i_1}, \ldots, x^{i_n})}{\partial(u^1, \ldots, u^n)} du^1 \cdots du^n \tag{i}$$

taken over a given n-dimensional region determined by the parametric equations $x^a = x^a(u^1, \ldots, u^n)$. What type of quantities are represented by the functional determinants in (i)? Is there any loss of generality in assuming that the $A \ldots$ are alternating quantities in all their indices? Show that the integral (i) is an invariant under changes of the parameters, and under changes of the x if A is a tensor. [The integrals of the form (i) are used in an interesting way to introduce the ideas of tensor analysis by F. D. Murnaghan, "Vector Analysis and the Theory of Relativity," chap. 1, The Johns Hopkins Press, 1922. He proves that if the domain of integration in (i) is a closed n-dimensional surface ($n \leq p - 1$), then the integral of Rot A [see (5-105)] over the enclosed $(n + 1)$-dimensional region is identical with (i) multiplied by $(n + 1)$ (i.e., the two integrals are identical if the summations in (i) and in the corresponding integral for Rot A are taken for $i_1 < i_2 < \cdots$). This result constitutes obviously a complete generalization of Stokes' integral identity.]

5-18 In any *flat* space $\mathfrak{F}_p$ one finds by evaluation in rectilinear coordinate frames, that

$$T^{\cdots}_{\cdots;ab} = T^{\cdots}_{\cdots;ba} \tag{i}$$

where T is an arbitrary tensor field. In particular,

$$A^a{}_{;[bc]} \equiv \tfrac{1}{2}(A^a{}_{;bc} - A^a{}_{;cb}) = 0 \tag{ii}$$

On the other hand, in an arbitrary Riemannian space [i.e., a space for which a metric is defined by Eq. (5-43), with no restriction in general on the tensor field g except for appropriate regularity conditions], one has the identity

$$A^a{}_{;[bc]} = \tfrac{1}{2}R^a{}_{sbc}A^s \tag{iii}$$

where

$$R^a{}_{bcd} \equiv 2(\Gamma^a_{b[c,d]} + \Gamma^s_{b[c}\Gamma^a_{d]s}) \tag{iv}$$

is the so-called "Riemann curvature tensor" of the space. (*a*) Prove (iii), (iv), and the fact that R is a tensor. Show that for flat Riemannian spaces R vanishes everywhere. (*b*) Prove that conversely, if $R = 0$ everywhere in a given Riemannian space [or if the identity (ii) is satisfied for every vector field A], then the space is necessarily flat. Prove this result by making use of the integrability conditions (3A-14) of a system of total differential equations (3A-13). [Consider the system of differential equations $U^a{}_{;b} = 0$. Its integrability conditions, i.e., the necessary and sufficient conditions that it have p independent vector field solutions $U^a_{(b)}$, where p is the dimensionality of the space, reduce to: $R^a{}_{scb}U^s = 0$. Set $U^a_{(b)} = M^a{}_b \equiv \partial x^a/\partial x'^b$ [see

(5-79)] and deduce that $\Gamma'^{a}_{bc} \equiv 0$ by using Eq. (5-95); thence conclude that $g'_{ab,c} \equiv 0$.}

5-19 We have introduced in this chapter general coordinates in $\mathfrak{M}$ in a purely formal fashion. The usefulness of curvilinear coordinates in ordinary space is well known, and in particular, spherical and cylindrical coordinates find frequent applications in mathematical physics. It was pointed out that general coordinates in space-time are necessary in the analysis of general relativity. What can one say about their physical significance in STR? In particular, what restrictions, if any, need to be imposed on the coordinate transformations for consistency with the principles of the STR? As an instructive special case, consider coordinates that imply a rotation of our system with respect to an inertial frame and examine the 'instrumental' significance of these coordinates (in terms of *standard* length and time measurements in an inertial system). (See related questions in Prob. 6-6 and the references given there.)

5-20 With the aid of the special pseudotensor $E^{\lambda\mu\nu\sigma}$ introduced in Sec. 5-4, we can characterize the intrinsic angular momentum defined in Sec. 4-2, by means of the 4-pseudotensor

$$S^{\lambda} = \tfrac{1}{2}E^{\lambda\mu\nu\sigma}L_{\mu\nu}P_{\sigma} \tag{i}$$

assuming that $P_{\sigma}P^{\sigma} \neq 0$. Show that this vector does indeed determine $L^{(\text{int})}_{\mu\nu}$ as defined in Prob. 4-9. [One way of showing this is by proving that

$$L_{\mu\nu} = \frac{1}{P_{\sigma}P^{\sigma}}(T_{\mu}P_{\nu} - T_{\nu}P_{\mu} + E_{\mu\nu\sigma\tau}S^{\sigma}P^{\tau}), \qquad T_{\mu} = L_{\mu\nu}P^{\nu} \tag{ii}$$

and then showing, using (i) of Prob. 4-9, that

$$T_{\mu} = P_{\sigma}P^{\sigma}(c^{*})_{\mu} - (c^{*})_{\sigma}P^{\sigma}P_{\mu}$$

and hence, $T_{[\mu}P_{\nu]}/P_{\sigma}P^{\sigma} = (c^{*})_{[\mu}P_{\nu]}$; so that by (ii) and (i) of Prob. 4-9,

$$L^{(\text{int})}_{\mu\nu} = \frac{1}{P_{\sigma}P^{\sigma}}E_{\mu\nu\sigma\tau}S^{\sigma}P^{\tau}$$

while again, by (i) of Prob. 4-9, one finds that S^{λ} is given by (i) with $L_{\mu\nu}$ replaced by $L^{(\text{int})}_{\mu\nu}$. The identities $T_{\mu}P^{\mu} = 0$, $S_{\mu}P^{\mu} = 0$ enter in this proof.]

6
Relativistic Mechanics of Continuous Media

In Chap. 4 it was noted that the assimilation of Newton's third law within relativistic mechanics leads naturally to a consideration of continuous media. We have now acquired in the tensor formalism a convenient tool with which to undertake their study. A general introduction to the subject is presented in Secs. 6-2 and 6-3, following a review in Sec. 6-1 of some of the underlying ideas in the nonrelativistic theory.

The formalism for continuous material media is readily adapted to the treatment of classical fields, of which the most important example is the electromagnetic field, treated in Chap. 7. The variational principle, discussed in Sec. 6-7, facilitates the analysis of such fields.

A number of interesting special topics can be included in the present discussion. Only two are considered in any detail: the relativistic equations for perfect fluids (Sec. 6-5), which have been studied in both the special and the general theories of relativity; and the explanation of the null result of the Trouton-Noble experiment (Sec. 6-4), which has historical interest (see Sec. 2-2). A few general remarks concerning continuous systems are presented in Sec. 6-6, which also contains a discussion of the first two laws of thermodynamics as applied to an element of a continuous medium.

If we exclude astrophysics, there are as yet no clear-cut indications of statistical macroscopic systems for which relativistic theory finds significant practical application; though with eventual advances in plasma physics such theory may assume more than academic interest. In addition to part of Sec. 6-6, a few of the problems to this chapter relate to simple elements of relativistic thermodynamics and statistical mechanics.

In Secs. 6-5 and 6-7, the results are obtained in terms of general coordinates in $\mathfrak{M}$. They can therefore be applied directly to problems in which it is convenient to use curvilinear spatial coordinates, and formally they also apply with few exceptions in the general theory of relativity.

6-1 ELEMENTS OF CLASSICAL MECHANICS OF CONTINUOUS MEDIA

The term "continuous mechanical medium," as used in classical theory, represents from our modern point of view a pure abstraction. This abstraction serves, however, as an excellent practical macroscopic model for all extended material systems, such as fluids and solids, under the following condition: on a gross scale, the system can be treated with negligible error as a geometrically continuous aggregate.

With this understanding, it can be seen that the kinematic specification of such a medium must involve the field

$$\mathbf{x} = \mathbf{x}(\mathbf{a},t) \tag{6-1}$$

where $\mathbf{a}$ is the position vector of a representative point of the medium at some initial instant, and $\mathbf{x}$ is the corresponding position vector at the time t. But, precisely what do we mean in this case by the "corresponding" position? Perhaps the simplest explanation is as follows. We must imagine that in some way we can identify an arbitrarily small portion δV of the medium in the vicinity of the point $\mathbf{a}$ and including that point, so as to be able to follow its progress in the course of time.‡ This is a fundamental and often tacit assumption that underlies the macroscopic theory of material continua. In line with this assumption, Newton's second law as applied to the motion of such systems can be written

$$\frac{d}{dt}(\rho\mathbf{v}\;\delta V) = \mathbf{F}(\delta V) \tag{6-2}$$

Here δV on the left-hand side of the equation represents the *volume* of the infinitesimal region described earlier (and also subsequently) by the same symbol; $\rho = \rho(\mathbf{x},t)$ is the density of inertial mass at the indicated space-time

‡ In an actual material system we cannot of course take arbitrarily small spatial regions without entering the atomic domain. In our idealized model, however, this difficulty does not exist, and we are free to apply the limiting processes of the differential and integral calculus (as well as assume—as is usual, tacitly—all needed regularity conditions on our functions).

point, that is, inside δV; the vector

$$\mathbf{v} = \frac{\partial \mathbf{x}}{\partial t}\bigg|_{\mathbf{a}\text{ constant}} \tag{6-3}$$

represents the velocity of δV; and $\mathbf{F}(\delta V)$ denotes the resultant of all the forces that act on the matter inside δV.

The force $\mathbf{F}(\delta V)$ consists in general of two parts, a force acting throughout δV and proportional to the volume δV for which we shall write $\mathbf{f}\,\delta V$, and the resultant of forces acting across the surface of δV, which we shall temporarily denote by $\mathbf{F}_S(\delta V)$. The former force is known as "body force" or "volume force" and is exemplified by the gravitational attraction on the mass inside δV or the Coulomb force on electric charges continuously distributed throughout δV; the latter force represents the "stress" transmitted through the surface δS of δV. The stress is a manifestation on the gross scale, consistent with the continuum model, of the underlying interaction on the atomic scale of the portions of the system lying contiguously to δS on both sides of it. Hydrostatic pressure and elastic stresses set up in a strained piece of metal are examples of this type of force.

In more precise terms, the force density vector $\mathbf{f}$ at a given point P is defined by the following limiting process

$$\mathbf{f} = \mathbf{f}(P) = \lim_{\delta V \to P} \frac{\text{resultant of body forces over } \delta V}{\delta V} \tag{6-4}$$

all the quantities being evaluated at a given instant. Clearly, this direct limiting procedure cannot be followed in the case of the surface force $\mathbf{F}_S(\delta V)$. Before going to the limit it must be transformed into an equivalent expression proportional to δV. To this end, consider the force due to the stress acting across an oriented surface element dS *from the positive side* of this element (see Fig. 6-1). It is a vector $\mathbf{T}(dS)$ which depends on the magnitude and the aspect of dS. Consequently, we can conclude on reasonable regularity assumptions that its components must have the form

$$T^i(dS) = T^i_{\ jk}\, dS^{jk}$$

where the dS^{ij} are the tensor components of dS (see Sec. 5-4). By an application of the quotient theorem of tensor analysis (Prob. 5-2), it follows that

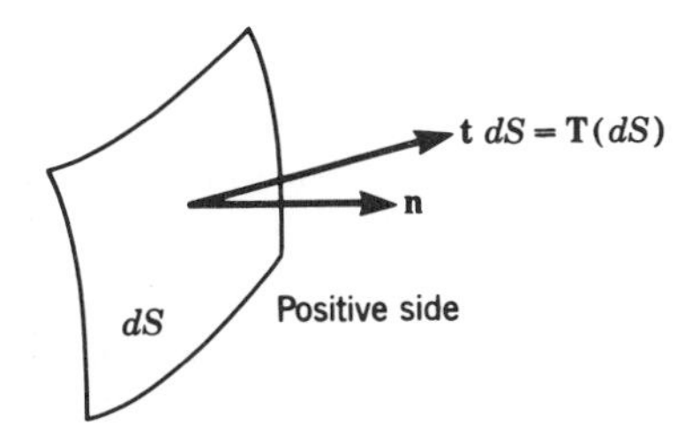

Fig. 6-1 Orientation convention for the stress vector in a material medium. For the relative directions of the vectors $\mathbf{n}$ and $\mathbf{t}$ as shown in the figure, the mutual interaction of the material on the two sides of the element dS represents a net attraction.

T must be a tensor of rank three antisymmetric in the lower indices. This can also be written in terms of pseudotensors as follows:‡

$$T^i(dS) = T^{ij}\,dS_j \qquad \begin{aligned} T^{ij} &= E^{jrs}T^i{}_{rs} \\ dS_j &= \tfrac{1}{2}E_{jlm}\,dS_{lm} \end{aligned} \tag{6-5}$$

Note that we do not distinguish pseudotensors notationally; it will be clear from the context what the character of the tensor quantities is in each case. Moreover, in most ordinary situations the distinction is not important. Note also that Eq. (6-5) can be taken to hold in *general* coordinates [when **x**, **a** in (6-1) must be thought of as replaced by x^i and a^i]. As will be seen from what follows, by applying the tensor algorithm, many equations can be dealt with in general coordinates as easily as in rectangular coordinates. However, it must be remembered that integrations can be performed in general only on scalar quantities. Thus, in applying Gauss' theorem to (6-5) to find the relation

$$\lim_{\delta V\to P} \frac{F^i_S(\delta V)}{\delta V} = \lim_{\delta V\to P} \frac{1}{\delta V}\int_{\text{surface of }\delta V} T^{ij}\,dS_j = T^{ij}{}_{;j}(P,t) \tag{6-6}$$

holding at a given point P and a given instant t, it is necessary, when the coordinates are not rectangular, to proceed as follows. One replaces T^{ij} by the vector A_iT^{ij}, where A_i is an *arbitrary* vector field of vanishing covariant derivatives, and after applying Gauss' integral identity, the result (6-6) follows by virtue of the arbitrariness of the $A_i(P)$ (remembering that upon integration one is taking the limit $\delta V \to P$).

Combining the results (6-2), (6-4), and (6-6), one can put the newtonian equations of motion of a continuous mechanical system in the following form:§

$$\rho\frac{dv^i}{dt} = f^i + T^{ij}{}_{;j} \tag{6-7}$$

In this derivation one makes use of the relation

$$\frac{d}{dt}(\rho\,\delta V) = 0 \tag{6-8}$$

‡ The quantity $T^i(dS)/dS = t^i$, it will be recalled, is known as the "stress vector." Dividing both sides of Eq. (6-5) by dS one obtains the familiar relation: $t^i = T^{ij}n_j$, $n_i = dS_i/dS$ = unit pseudovector normal to dS. Note that the stress tensor T^{ij} is also frequently defined with the opposite sense.

§ The notation d/dt now indicates the time differentiation shown in (6-3), i.e., along a flow line (it represents the so-called "substantial derivative"); so that when x,t rather than a,t are taken for the independent variables, one has the relation (6-12), in which $\partial/\partial t$ stands for $\partial/\partial t\big|_{x\text{ const.}}$. The two points of view correspond respectively to the so-called *lagrangian* and *eulerian* approaches in hydrodynamics (an historically unjustified designation). See, e.g., Coburn, *op. cit.* (on page 162), sec. 30.

This relation expresses the conservation of the mass inside δV; it is the well-known "equation of continuity."

The equations of motion (6-7) are obviously not very useful unless we have sufficient information concerning the connection between the fields T^{ij} and (6-1), a connection that must involve parameters of inner structure of the material system and of its thermodynamic state or history. It is not necessary for us to enter here into a discussion of this general subject. For our present purpose it will suffice merely to recall a few basic definitions pertaining to two important special cases; namely, the practically nonviscous fluids ("perfect fluids") that are treated by the classical theory of hydrodynamics, and the practically elastic solids whose deformations are kept within the elastic limits, and whose behavior is treated by the classical theory of elasticity.‡ The equations of motion of perfect fluids are treated relativistically in Sec. 6-5. There is little scope to a relativistic theory of elasticity in the classical sense, and our interest is only in recalling the analytic description of deformation. The topic of deformability of elastic bodies considered relativistically and, more especially, of suitable definitions in STR of rigid bodies, or at least of "rigid motions," has attracted many investigators. (See Prob. 6-6 and references given there.)

We consider first the perfect fluid. It is characterized by the property of not being able to sustain any tangential stresses.§ According to Eq. (6-5), if we denote by n_i the *unit* pseudovector dS_i/dS (see footnote on page 174), it is seen that the resolved part along the surface element dS of the stress vector $\mathbf{T}(dS)/dS$ is $T^{ij}n_j - T^{kj}n_k n_j n^i$. If this is to vanish for all possible $\mathbf{n}$, we can take in particular $n_j = (g^{rr})^{-1/2}\,\delta_{rj}$ (no summation over the r), and obtain $T^{ir} = (T^{rr}/g^{rr})g^{ir}$ (see Prob. 6-2). The quantity in parentheses must obviously be a pseudoscalar and is therefore independent of the value of the index r. We shall denote it by $(-p)$, so that, as is immediately verified, p represents a *pressure*. The stress in a perfect fluid is thus always represented by the pseudotensor

$$T^{ij} = -pg^{ij} \tag{6-9}$$

‡ In the English language the following are still the authoritative treatises on these subjects (after three quarters of a century): H. Lamb, "Hydrodynamics," Dover Publications Inc., New York; A. E. H. Love, "Treatise on the Mathematical Theory of Elasticity," Dover Publications Inc., New York. Volume 2 of the well-known series on theoretical physics by A. Sommerfeld, entitled "Mechanics of Deformable Bodies," Academic Press Inc., New York, 1950 (translated by G. Kuerti), can be consulted with profit, especially on the subject of hydrodynamics. Another useful modern textbook on the latter subject is L. D. Landau and E. M. Lifshitz, "Fluid Mechanics," Pergamon Press, London, 1959 (translated by J. B. Sykes and W. H. Reid), which includes a chapter on relativistic fluid dynamics (chap. 15). A treatment of hydrodynamics topics making extensive use of tensor calculus methods is contained in Coburn, *op. cit.*, beginning with sec. 56. A few results concerning general fluids are referred to in Prob. 6-5.

§ A tangential or "shearing stress" through an element of area, it will be recalled, is the resolved part along this area of the total stress across the area.

In addition to Eqs. (6-7) and (6-9), a coupling between the inner force field p and the vector field (6-1) is also provided by the thermodynamic "equation of state" of the fluid

$$p = p(\rho, T), \qquad T \equiv \text{absolute temperature} \tag{6-10}$$

The connection with the field (6-1) is effected through the intermediacy of the equation of continuity (6-8). Remembering the nature of the time differentiation in that equation, one finds for $(1/\delta V)\, d(\delta V)/dt$, or, more precisely, for the limit of this expression as $\delta V \to P$ (the "dilatation rate"), the value $v^i{}_{;i}$, the velocity vector $\mathbf{v}$ being given in Eq. (6-3) (see Prob. 6-3). The equation of continuity can thus be written

$$\frac{d\rho}{dt} + \rho v^i{}_{;i} = 0 \tag{6-11}$$

Since

$$\frac{d}{dt} = \frac{\partial}{\partial t} + v^i \frac{D}{Dx^i}, \qquad \frac{DT^{\cdot\cdot\cdot}_{\cdot\cdot\cdot}}{Dx^i} \equiv T^{\cdot\cdot\cdot}_{\cdot\cdot\cdot;i} \tag{6-12}$$

Eq. (6-11) can also be put in the more familiar form

$$\frac{\partial \rho}{\partial t} + (\rho v^i)_{;i} = 0 \tag{6-13}$$

The system of equations (6-7), (6-9), (6-10), and (6-11) forms the starting point of any analysis in hydrodynamical problems involving perfect fluids.‡

In the continuum mechanics of elastic solids it is necessary in general to deal with the full complications of the tensor T. On the other hand, significant simplification results from the assumption that all the deformations of the solid are small. This assumption has adequate validity in the domain of strict elasticity and leads to the linearity of the equations of motion. In order to formulate this restriction quantitatively, one must have an expression for a suitable measure of deformation. Such a measure can be seen to be provided by the change in length per unit length of an

‡ We have five equations and six quantities x^i, p, ρ, T; one further condition is therefore required for a definite solution, such as restricting the changes of state to have isothermal or adiabatic character, or by including an equation governing thermal conduction when the temperature distribution is nonuniform. Moreover, if the fluid is not homogeneous in its microparticle composition, additional equations are required corresponding to the additional variables of the system, the relative concentrations. In practice, one needs, of course, also to consider initial and boundary conditions and possibly also surfaces of specific discontinuity, such as those connected with shock waves. This and the nonlinearity of Eqs. (6-7) [that is recognized by expanding these equations according to the symbolic identity (6-12)] contribute to the mathematical difficulties of the subject. Our concern in this book is however only with the relativistic extension of the hydrodynamic equations of motion and not with their solutions.

arbitrary line element of the body, and one requires therefore an expression for this change in terms of the field (6-1).‡

Consider then a given line element Δa^i in the original unstrained state of the body at time t_0, say, and let Δx^i be its position at a later time $t = t_0 + \Delta t$, as a result of the motion of the elements of the body leading to the infinitesimal displacements $d^i = x^i(a,t) - x^i(a,t_0) = x^i(a,t) - a^i$ (see Fig. 6-2). Then,

$$x^i(a + \Delta a,t) = a^i + \Delta a^i + d^i(a + \Delta a) = a^i + \Delta a^i + d^i + d^i{}_{;j}\,\Delta a^j$$

i.e., $\Delta x^i = \Delta a^i + d^i{}_{;j}\,\Delta a^j$. Hence [remembering that $(\mathbf{A})^2 = A^iA_i$]

$$\frac{|\Delta\mathbf{x}| - |\Delta\mathbf{a}|}{|\Delta\mathbf{a}|} = \frac{(\Delta\mathbf{x})^2 - (\Delta\mathbf{a})^2}{(\Delta\mathbf{a})^2}\,\frac{|\Delta\mathbf{a}|}{|\Delta\mathbf{x}| + |\Delta\mathbf{a}|}$$
$$= \frac{2d_{i;j}\,\Delta a^i\,\Delta a^j + d^i{}_{;j}\,d_{i;k}\,\Delta a^j\,\Delta a^k}{(\Delta\mathbf{a})^2}\left[\frac{1}{2} + 0\left(\frac{|\Delta\mathbf{x}| - |\Delta\mathbf{a}|}{|\Delta\mathbf{a}|}\right)\right]$$

is the desired expression, and it is seen that the assumption of small deformation entails the smallness of the tensor $d_{i;j}$. It follows that

$$\frac{|\Delta\mathbf{x}| - |\Delta\mathbf{a}|}{|\Delta\mathbf{a}|} = d_{i;j}\,\frac{\Delta a^i}{|\Delta\mathbf{a}|}\,\frac{\Delta a^j}{|\Delta\mathbf{a}|} = e_{ij}\,\frac{\Delta a^i}{|\Delta\mathbf{a}|}\,\frac{\Delta a^j}{|\Delta\mathbf{a}|} \tag{6-14}$$

where
$$e_{ij} = \tfrac{1}{2}(d_{i;j} + d_{j;i}) \tag{6-15}$$

are the components of the symmetric "deformation," or "strain" tensor. (See Prob. 6-6.)

The connection between the stress and the strain fields within the elastic limits can be written generally as an expansion

$$T^{ij} = C^{ijrs}e_{rs} + \cdots \tag{6-16}$$

it being assumed that no stresses exist in the unstrained state of the body. The retention of only the linear terms corresponds to a generalization of Hooke's law, which is found empirically to hold with good approximation

‡ For an elementary discussion of the kinematics of deformation, see, e.g., Sommerfeld, *op. cit.*, sec. I.1. The notion of elastic-strain tensor is not used in the rest of the book and this topic can be omitted if desired, in which case Probs. 6-1 and 6-6 need also to be omitted.

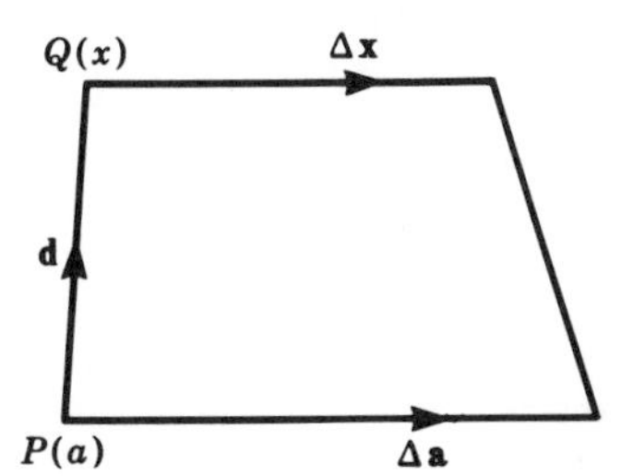

Fig. 6-2 Change of a line element in a deforming continuous material medium.

within the elastic limits. This can also be taken to follow from our assumption on the smallness of the strain components. The tensor character of the coefficients C is apparent from the expression (6-16), while their dependence on structural and thermodynamic parameters must be determined empirically or by an underlying atomic theory.

The values of the *Hooke's constants* C of Eq. (6-16) as actually occur in practice are such that the maximum velocities of disturbance propagation in the corresponding media are small compared to the velocity of light. The theory of relativity has therefore little to say in the practical theory of elasticity. On the other hand, if one wishes to consider the deformation relative to an inertial system S of a practically rigid body (say, a metal block kept as far as possible in a constant environment), that is, in an *arbitrary* state of motion relative to S, then two new features present themselves. The strain arising from the Lorentz contraction relative to S will in principle be in general *finite;* but such strain can be treated by a straightforward extension of the classical results (see Prob. 6-6). A more serious difficulty is that the distribution of strain throughout the body may not be compatible with continuous deformation in the sense of *euclidean geometry*. This is shown most simply by the example, first pointed out by P. Ehrenfest, of rotational motion of a rigid body about an axis passing through an interior point (see Prob. 6-6).‡

6-2 RELATIVISTIC EQUATIONS FOR CONTINUOUS MEDIA

One can arrive at the relativistic equations of the mechanics of continuous media following a number of alternative approaches.§ The one we choose is patterned after the method employed in Sec. 4-1 to obtain the relativistic generalization of the newtonian mechanics of a particle with the aid of the rules (1) and (2) of page 91. These must, however, be used with care in the present case.¶ Our problem would be more taxing if, as in the program of

‡ Considerations of this nature pointed to the need, under certain circumstances, of an extension of our geometric concepts, as incorporated in the general theory of relativity.

§ Perhaps the most direct physical approach is that employed by Tolman ([9], chap. 3, part 2), based on operational definitions of stress components in arbitrary and in comoving inertial frames. M. v. Laue, who, along with M. Abraham and M. Planck, was among the first to develop the central ideas of the relativistic mechanics of continuous media, devotes in his text [5] considerable space to the details of the subject, developing the basic relations principally from a study of charged material systems in interaction with electromagnetic fields.

¶ A partial motivation for v. Laue's starting with continuous media in his development of relativistic mechanics is in fact the failure of (2) to apply fully to the mechanics of continuous media, at least in principle. More recently we have also come to recognize that there may exist continuous media having a sensible essentially non-newtonian behavior even in locally comoving frames, such as plasmas of sufficiently high temperature, with the underlying average microscopic velocities not negligible in comparison with the speed of light.

v. Laue, we were to start with the continuous medium as the primary entity from which one must deduce, as a limiting case, the equations of motion of a particle, and in particular, the mass-energy relation (4-14), i.e.,

$$E = m(u)c^2 \tag{6-17}$$

But our procedure will be, on the contrary, to accept those equations of motion as well as the relation (6-17). In fact, this relation, taken in an extended sense to apply to any form of energy whatever, will be adopted as one of our basic assumptions.

We consider first the mass-conservation equation (6-13), confining ourselves for the present to *lorentzian coordinates*, by which we understand rectangular coordinates in $\mathfrak{M}$,‡ and also replace the symbol $\mathbf{v}$ by $\mathbf{u}$ to agree with the notation employed in Sec. 4-1. Recalling the definition (4-8) of the 4-velocity, it is seen that Eq. (6-13), with mass taken to mean *relative* mass, can be rewritten in the following form

$$S^{\nu}{}_{,\nu} = 0 \tag{6-18}$$

where

$$S^{\nu} = \rho U^{\nu} \tag{6-19}$$

and

$$\rho = \frac{1}{\gamma_u}\,\rho(u) \equiv \sqrt{1 - \frac{u^2}{c^2}}\,\rho(u) \tag{6-20}$$

is the proper mass density, the latter as measured in the given inertial frame S [$\rho(u)$ being the relative mass density in S].

Although Eq. (6-18) has the appearance of a covariant equation, the appearance is misleading, for S^{ν} is not a 4-vector: the quantity (6-20) is not a relativistic invariant, since the "density" arises from division by a volume of ordinary and not of Minkowski space. At the same time, if, in agreement with the relation (6-17), we write for the energy density in S associated with the mass density,

$$h(u) = c^2\rho(u) \tag{6-21}$$

and if we suppose that no other forms of energy are involved in our mechanical system, and that

$$\mathbf{f} = 0 \tag{6-22}$$

then, under these restrictions, Eq. (6-18) represents also (when multiplied by c^2) the equation of conservation of energy. One may expect that an equation of the form (6-18), but with a more general expression than (6-19) for S^{ν}, can be taken to represent in relativistic mechanics the conservation of energy of general continuous systems. This consideration suggests that Eq. (6-18), while not itself covariant, forms part of a larger covariant set

‡ We limit ourselves, in this and in the next section, to these special coordinates; but formally, many of the results can be recast into a generally covariant form merely by replacing the commas representing ordinary partials by semicolons to denote covariant partial derivatives.

of equations. Moreover, since it should be possible in any case to obtain the equations of motion (6-7) as some limit of the corresponding relativistic equations, it can also be expected that the covariant set in question should embrace the generalization of both Eqs. (6-13) and (6-7).

We have one further indication. From relativistic one-particle mechanics we know that the 4-momentum vector P incorporates both the ordinary momentum vector (with the relativistic mass) and the energy. We are thus led to anticipate that as a companion set to Eq. (6-13), the equations (6-7) express the conservation of momentum in differential form in the nonrelativistic limit; and an examination of the structure of Eq. (6-13) suggests that such a conservation equation should admit of an analogous form, namely,

$$\frac{\partial g^i}{\partial t} + P^{ij}{}_{,j} = f^i \tag{6-23}$$

where $\mathbf{g} \equiv$ momentum density vector $= \rho\mathbf{u}$
$P^{ij} \equiv j$th component of velocity of ith component of momentum density. (6-24)

Such a transformation of Eq. (6-7) can, in fact, be easily effected by applying Eqs. (6-12) and (6-13). One finds

$$P^{ij} = -T^{ij} + \rho u^i u^j = -T^{ij} + g^i u^j \tag{6-25}$$

the last expression following by substitution of the first of Eqs. (6-24). The second term of this expression is manifestly in agreement with the definition (6-24). That the first term, too, agrees with this definition can be seen by noting that $-T^{ij}$ represents the time rate of change of the ith component of momentum across unit area perpendicular to the x^j axis and in the direction of the axis [see Eq. (6-5)], which is clearly equivalent to the flux in question.

Turning now to Eqs. (6-23), subject to restriction (6-22), we observe that if the tensor P can be extended to a *space-time tensor*, then these equations can be written as the spatial part of the covariant set of equations

$$P^{\mu\nu}{}_{,\nu} = 0 \tag{6-26}$$

provided we set

$$P^{i0} = cg^i \tag{6-27}$$

If our program of relativistic extension is to work, and if Eq. (6-18) forms part of it, then the latter equation must also be contained in the set (6-26), and therefore as its remaining, $\mu = 0$ equation. This is indeed the case if

$$P^{0\nu} = cS^\nu \tag{6-28}$$

where the S^ν have now, in general, an extended meaning, and need not admit the restrictive form (6-19). The essential thing is that the quantities

$$J^\nu = c^2 S^\nu \qquad (S^i = g^i) \tag{6-29}$$

represent, in accordance with the relation (6-17), the densities of energy (times c) and of energy current, i.e., the energy density 4-current. Our conjectured 4-tensor field P must have, therefore, the following general form:

$$\|P^{\mu\nu}\| = \begin{bmatrix} h & \frac{1}{c} J^j \\ cg^i & P^{ij} \end{bmatrix}, \qquad h = \frac{1}{c} J^0 \tag{6-30}$$

Our major task still remains: to find the structure of its components that is consistent with the relativistic principles, including the fundamental relation (6-17), and such that Eq. (6-26) (when no external forces are present) agrees with observation in the case of continuous media to which our description applies (in the macroscopic phenomenological sense in which such theory can apply), and hence in particular reduce to the corresponding newtonian equations under proper limiting conditions.

Let us begin with **g** given in the first of Eqs. (6-24), and inquire if this equation can be retained in relativistic mechanics. Quite obviously ρ must be replaced by $\rho(u)$ as defined in (6-20), so that with any given element of the medium of volume δV that can be treated as a 'particle' in the spirit of our macroscopic model there is associated a momentum vector $\rho(u)\, \delta V\, \mathbf{u}$ in agreement with Eq. (4-5). However, when we take into account the basic relativistic relation (6-17), we perceive that the circumstances under which the momentum density in a continuous medium can be thus represented are quite special, ruling out the flow within the medium of any type of energy except that associated with the gross inertial mass of its material, and hence also precluding in general the existence in it of any state of stress. In fact, if a state of stress does exist, it can give rise to a contribution to **g** stemming from the work performed by the internal stress on the moving element of the material. Thus if at a given point P of the medium at a given instant, $\mathbf{u} \neq 0$, and if $-\mathbf{t}(\mathbf{n})$ is the stress force (as measured in our inertial frame S) then acting at P across the element of area δS normal to the unit vector $\mathbf{n}$ and towards the positive side of δS (as determined by the sense of $\mathbf{n}$), then the resulting work in time δt is $-\mathbf{t}(\mathbf{n}) \cdot \mathbf{u}\, \delta S\, \delta t$, so that an energy of amount $-\mathbf{t}(\mathbf{n}) \cdot \mathbf{u}$ streams through δS per unit area per unit time, and hence, by (6-17), the contribution to the momentum density in question is $-\mathbf{t}(\mathbf{n}) \cdot \mathbf{u}/c^2$. We conclude [as $t^i(\mathbf{n}) = T^{ij}n^j$] that in the presence of stress (but in the absence of any additional forms of energy propagation), the expression given in (6-24) must be replaced by‡

$$g^i = \frac{1}{c^2} (h\delta^i_j - T^{ji})u^j \tag{6-31}$$

‡ Here we have one indication how rule (2) can be in default, at least in principle. Even for relatively moderate velocities the nonclassical second term (6-31) can be sensible if the strength of the stress is sufficiently great.

where h is defined in (6-30) and includes a contribution to the energy density arising from the state of stress [see Eq. (6-46) and Prob. 6-7].

One important consequence of the result (6-31) is immediate. If we accept formula (6-25) as holding generally (taking of course the last and not the middle expression), it is seen that its last term is in general not symmetric. Consequently, if

$$P^{ij} = P^{ji} \tag{6-32}$$

which, as we shall presently show, can be taken to be a generally valid relation, then the tensor T^{ij} cannot be in general symmetric. It will be symmetric, of course, at any given space-time point when measured in the comoving inertial frame S^* at that point (under usual circumstances—see Prob. 6-4), but it will in general lose this symmetry when referred to a frame moving with respect to S^*. Are we to infer that body torques are generated in an elastic body, otherwise free of external forces, when it is set in uniform straight-line motion? We shall return to this question at a later point.

The validity of the *symmetry* relation (6-32) follows from (6-17) as applied in (6-29), bearing in mind the meaning of the symbols as used in (6-30). In fact, by Eqs. (6-27), (6-28), and (6-29),

$$P^{i0} = P^{0i} \tag{6-33}$$

and since this relation must hold in *every* inertial system it can be concluded (see Prob. 6-9) that also (6-32) must hold. It follows that

$$P^{\mu\nu} = P^{\nu\mu} \tag{6-34}$$

This result was obtained as a consequence of the basic relation (6-29). It is instructive to note that conversely, that relation can be deduced from the limited assumption of the validity of Eqs. (6-32) in the comoving inertial frames, when the following condition is satisfied:

$$\begin{aligned} \mathbf{g}(\mathsf{x}) &= 0 \\ \mathbf{J}(\mathsf{x}) &= 0 \end{aligned} \quad \text{in } S^*(\mathsf{x}), \text{ the comoving inertial frame at the space-time point } \mathsf{x} \tag{6-35}$$

The proof is very simple. By (6-35) and our assumption, it follows that the symmetry property (6-34) holds in $S^*(\mathsf{x}) \equiv S^*$, and therefore also in every inertial coordinate system owing to the covariance of such symmetry. We have then in particular (6-33) and hence (6-29). It should be noted also that the assumption that (6-32) holds in S^* reduces, in view of (6-25), to the assumption that T^{ij} is symmetric in S^*. This amounts to requiring the validity of rule (2) (page 91) with respect to this particular classical property of the stress tensor (in usual situations), a requirement that appears to be entirely reasonable. If this is accepted, then the present arguments are seen to be in the nature of a plausibility proof of the *inertia-of-energy* relation (6-29) under our restrictive assumptions.

Our general discussion is still incomplete in at least two significant respects: the 4-tensor character of (6-30) has only been assumed, not proven; and the structure of the component P^{00}, the energy-density field h, is still to be specified. By "general discussion" we mean here only that the continuous mechanical systems under consideration can involve any (otherwise permissible) internal state of stress. Otherwise we assume the restriction (6-35) (its removal is discussed in Sec. 6-6); we also assume, as is generally done tacitly, that both the spatial and the temporal rates of change of a typical state of our medium are within limits that permit the mental isolation of an element at each event $\mathbf{x}$ in the history of the medium, presenting the same macroscopic behavior as does the medium as a whole.

It would be much in order at this point to pause before we continue with our largely mathematical analysis and discuss actual instances of such systems as occur in practice and for which relativistic considerations are important. These instances however are scarce. Much of the original work in this field, done in the early stages in the development of relativity theory, had for its aim little more than showing that one can construct a relativistic set of equations that apply to sundry 'continuous' substances in given thermodynamic states such as fluids and elastic bodies, in the sense that they reduce to the known classical equations under proper limiting conditions. It is only in the case of charged media involving electromagnetic interactions that relativistic effects may be recognized. A historically important example is presented by the analysis of the Trouton-Noble experiment, discussed in Sec. 6-4. Further discussion relating to such systems is presented in Sec. 7-3. For the present we continue with our restricted 'general discussion' without any attempt to anchor it on the firm ground of concrete illustration. In justification of the pains we are nevertheless taking in developing this topic, it is to be noted that even if the results may not have much immediate practical interest, the method of their derivation, related to the heuristic rules (1), (2), and of which important instances have already been encountered in Chap. 4, has independent value.

Returning to our immediate questions, we could begin with the determination of the 'general' form of P^{00} along lines pursued in finding the expression (6-31). But although this method is instructive,‡ our general goal can be attained faster by applying ourselves first to the question of covariance of the set $P^{\mu\nu}$; the structure of P^{00} is then obtained as a by-product of our analysis.

An immediate question that may well have occurred to the reader is how one would, in the first place, have arrived at the expectation that the sundry quantities $P^{\mu\nu}$, as introduced previously, should combine to form a second-rank 4-tensor. A simple answer that can be given is provided by the special case referred to earlier of a material medium with no internal stresses, that we may picture to ourselves as approximated by, say, a very

‡ See, e.g., [9], pp. 67–68; and Prob. 6-7.

rarified gas of inert molecules, or an astronomical dust cloud—a 'continuous' aggregate of so-called "incoherent matter."‡ We have already given in Eqs. (6-28) and (6-19) the form of $P^{0\nu} = P^{\nu 0}$ for such a system, while by Eqs. (6-25) and (6-31), $P^{ij} = \rho(u)u^i u^j$. Hence, we can write in this case:

$$P^{\mu\nu} = \rho(u)u^\mu u^\nu = \frac{1}{\gamma_u}\rho U^\mu U^\nu \equiv \rho^* U^\mu U^\nu \tag{6-36}$$

where, it will be remembered, $u^\mu = dx^\mu/dt$, $U^\mu = dx^\mu/d\tau$, and ρ^* is readily shown to be a 4-scalar (see Prob. 6-8).§ Since U is a 4-vector, it follows by the multiplication theorem of tensor calculus that $P^{\mu\nu}$ given in (6-36) are indeed the components of a second-rank tensor in space-time.

The preceding result does not prove, but only makes plausible the covariant character of $P^{\mu\nu}$ in the general case. We shall gain confidence in this conclusion from two considerations. In Sec. 6-7 it will be shown that a second-rank 4-tensor whose components have the energy-momentum current density significance of the elements in (6-30), arises naturally from a variational approach to continuous media and fields (of which an important application to the electromagnetic field is discussed in Chap. 7). More directly, we shall show now that the quantities P^{0i} and P^{ij} relative to a given inertial frame S, which are obtained from the $P^{*\mu\nu}$ defined in S^*, by the second-rank tensor transformation corresponding to the Lorentz transformation from S^* to S, are fully consistent with the relations between the $P^{\mu\nu}$ we have obtained earlier by a direct physical analysis.

Before we can apply our transformation we must of course know the structure of $P^{*\mu\nu}$, but that follows readily from the restrictive assumptions we have made about the nature of our continuous systems. Taking into account the conditions (6-35) and Eq. (6-25), we can conclude that

$$\|P^{*\mu\nu}\| = \begin{bmatrix} h^* & 0 & 0 & 0 \\ 0 & & & \\ 0 & & -T^{*ij} & \\ 0 & & & \end{bmatrix} \tag{6-37}$$

The structure of the matrix (6-37) suggests that we split it into two parts:

$$P^{*\mu\nu} = H^{*\mu\nu} + G^{*\mu\nu}, \qquad G^{*\mu 0} = G^{*0\mu} = 0, \qquad G^{*ij} = -T^{*ij} \tag{6-38}$$

Correspondingly, we write

$$P^{\mu\nu} = H^{\mu\nu} + G^{\mu\nu} \tag{6-39}$$

The matrix $\|L^\mu{}_\nu\|$ of a general 'parallel-axis' transformation of $\mathfrak{L}$ from S^* to S, corresponding to the matrix N in (5-34), is given by (3-29) with

‡ Some care is obviously required here in applying the continuum model.

§ All the tensors occurring in our discussion are, of course, in general tensor *fields*. The omission of tiresome reference to this fact in each instance need occasion no misunderstanding. Similarly, we write S^* for $S^*(\mathbf{x})$ and $\mathbf{u}$ for $\mathbf{u}(\mathbf{x})$.

$\mathbf{v} = -\mathbf{u}$, since the velocity of S relative to S^* is $-\mathbf{u}$. Thus,

$$\begin{aligned} L^0{}_\nu &= L^\nu{}_0 = \frac{1}{c} U^\nu \equiv W^\nu \\ L^i_j &= \delta_{ij} + \frac{\gamma - 1}{\beta^2} \beta^i \beta^j \end{aligned} \qquad \gamma \equiv \gamma_u,\ \beta^i \equiv \frac{u^i}{c} \tag{6-40}$$

where we have introduced the *unit* 4-velocity W,

The transformation of $H^{\mu\nu}$ given in (6-39) can now be written at once. By Eqs. (6-37), (6-38), and (6-40):

$$H^{\mu\nu} = L^\mu{}_0 L^\nu{}_0 h^* = h^* W^\mu W^\nu \tag{6-41}$$

The transformation of $G^{\mu\nu}$ can be found in a few simple steps. By (6-38),‡

$$G^{00} = L^0{}_\mu L^0{}_\nu G^{*\mu\nu} = -L^0{}_i L^0{}_j T^{*ij} = -T^{*ij} W_i W_j \equiv g \tag{6-42}$$

and with omission of obvious intermediate steps:

$$G^{0k} = W_i \left(\delta_{kj} + \frac{\gamma - 1}{\beta^2} \beta^k \beta^j \right) T^{*ij}, \qquad \text{as } W_i = -W^i$$

$$G^{rk} = -\left(\delta_{ri} + \frac{\gamma - 1}{\beta^2} \beta^r \beta^i \right) \left(\delta_{kj} + \frac{\gamma - 1}{\beta^2} \beta^k \beta^j \right) T^{*ij}$$

(Note that we are now summing over repeated Latin indices regardless of their position, and that $\beta^i \beta^i = \beta^2$.) Introducing the quantities

$$z^i = T^{*ji} W_j \tag{6-43}$$

we find, remembering (6-42), and since $(\gamma - 1)/\beta^2\gamma^2 = 1/(\gamma + 1)$, that

$$G^{0k} = z^k + \frac{g}{\gamma + 1} W^k \tag{6-44}$$

and $$G^{rk} = -T^{*rk} + \frac{1}{\gamma + 1} (W^r z^k + W^k z^r) + \frac{g}{(\gamma + 1)^2} W^r W^k \tag{6-45}$$

(using also the symmetry of T^*). The transformation equations for P are then obtained according to (6-39), by combining Eqs. (6-41) to (6-45):

$$h = P^{00} = \gamma^2 h^* + g \tag{6-46}$$

$$P^{0i} = \left(\gamma h^* + \frac{g}{\gamma + 1} \right) W^i + z^i \tag{6-47}$$

$$P^{ij} = \left(h^* + \frac{g}{(\gamma + 1)^2} \right) W^i W^j + \frac{1}{\gamma + 1} (W^i z^j + W^j z^i) - T^{*ij} \tag{6-48}$$

‡ The symbol g introduced in (6-42) is not to be mistaken for the magnitude of the vector $\mathbf{g}$.

In order to examine the consistency of our result, we proceed to extract from it the connection between T^{ij} and T^{*ij}. To this end, we combine Eqs. (6-25) and (6-47), and find (remembering that $P^{0i} = P^{i0} = cg^i$):

$$P^{ij} = -T^{ij} + \left(h^* + \frac{g}{\gamma(\gamma+1)}\right) W^i W^j + z^i \beta^j$$

Comparing this with (6-48), it then follows that

$$T^{ij} = T^{*ij} + \frac{\gamma g}{(\gamma+1)^2}\beta^i\beta^j + \frac{1}{\gamma+1}z^i\beta^j - \frac{\gamma}{\gamma+1}\beta^i z^j \tag{6-49}$$

That these relations are indeed in agreement with the operational definitions of stress components in S and in S^* can be verified by referring to the relativistic kinematic transformations and transformations of force components. Such verification is considerably simplified if we choose our spatial axes so that $\beta^i = (\beta,0,0)$, when (6-49) are found to reduce to

$$\|T^{ij}\| = \begin{bmatrix} T^{*11} & \gamma T^{*12} & \gamma T^{*13} \\ \frac{1}{\gamma}T^{*21} & T^{*22} & T^{*23} \\ \frac{1}{\gamma}T^{*31} & T^{*32} & T^{*33} \end{bmatrix} \tag{6-50}$$

It can also be easily verified that Eq. (6-47) follows as a necessary consequence of Eqs. (6-49) and (6-31), which can be considered as an additional check on the consistency of our results. We may take it then as a well-founded conclusion that the set $P^{\mu\nu}$ given in (6-30) represents a second-rank 4-tensor. This tensor is known, in view of the significance of its components, as the "energy-momentum tensor," although other designations are also to be encountered in the literature.

The all-important symmetry property of the energy-momentum tensor has already been commented upon. Let us also note again that the stress 3-tensor T^{ij} is in general *not symmetric*, although T^{*ij} is in general symmetric. This striking purely relativistic effect is in clear evidence in Eqs. (6-49) and even more directly in Eq. (6-50). On the other hand, the tensor $G^{\mu\nu}$ given in Eqs. (6-44) and (6-45) [and by Eqs. (6-39) and (6-41) it is indeed a 4-tensor] is obviously symmetric. Some authors call it the covariant "stress tensor" in consideration of the fact that in the local rest frame its in general nonvanishing components represent the stress tensor (or, its negative, with our sign convention). Note also that in view of the definitions (6-39) and (6-41), the relation (6-25) can also be written (as $W^j = \beta^j W^0$)

$$T^{ij} = G^{0i}\beta^j - G^{ij} \tag{6-25a}$$

6-3 INTEGRAL CONSERVATION LAWS

We have seen the significance of the symmetry property (6-34) in discussing the differential equations of motion. Observationally, one deals with integrated results, with the motion of matter in the bulk, rather than with that of its infinitesimal elements.‡ We therefore take up now the derivation of the integral conservation formulas for continuous media, and in particular examine the problem of the conservation of total angular momentum, which can be expected to be related to Eqs. (6-34).

Consider a spatial volume V in our medium *fixed* in a given inertial frame S taken at a given time t. Integrating Eqs. (6-26) over this volume, one obtains, after a familiar integral transformation,

$$0 = \int_V P^{\mu\nu}{}_{,\nu}\, dV = \int_V \left(P^{\mu i}{}_{,i} + \frac{1}{c}\frac{\partial P^{\mu 0}}{\partial t}\right) dV = \int_B P^{\mu i}\, dS_i + \frac{d}{dt}\int_V g^\mu\, dV \tag{6-51}$$

We consider the case when either the system is confined for the entire time interval under consideration inside a bounded volume V relative to S, or else the components of the energy-momentum tensor vanish rapidly enough at spatial infinity so that the surface integrals in (6-51) tend to zero as the surface B recedes to infinity in all directions—we shall say in either case that the mechanical system is "bounded," this condition being independent of the choice of S (Prob. 6-10). Then, by (6-51), it follows that

$$G^\mu = \int g^\mu\, dV \tag{6-52}$$

are *conserved*.§ They are obviously the relativistic generalizations of the total momentum and the total energy (divided by c) of the system.

To deduce the corresponding conservation theorems for angular

‡ We should be reminded again that the theory whose broad lines we are here discussing aims at exactness only in what concerns Einstein's restricted principle of relativity, and that otherwise it has a phenomenological and essentially macroscopic character associated with some sort of space-time averaging of an underlying more basically irreducible atomistic structure. This is certainly true of material systems whether neutral or electrically charged. But also in the case of pure "fields" one has a somewhat similar situation when one is neglecting quantum effects, which, in effect, endow a field in a certain sense with a microstructure.

§ When the region of integration is not indicated, it will be understood to consist of all of space for a given instant of time. When the system is bounded in a finite volume, the integral will of course reduce to one over that volume. In the contrary case, one can always perform the integrations first over a finite volume and in the end let that volume expand to cover all of space, it being assumed that the integral converges. The reader need hardly be reminded also that in the above analysis we are tacitly assuming that the functions $P^{\mu\nu}$ obey within the domain V the necessary regularity conditions required for the validity of the partial integrations involved in the application of Gauss' theorem. In practice, singularities arising from boundary conditions can occur and require special handling.

momentum and center of mass (see Sec. 4-2), one considers the tensor

$$R^{\lambda\mu\nu} = x^\lambda P^{\mu\nu} - x^\mu P^{\lambda\nu} \tag{6-53}$$

(Note that the restriction to rectilinear space-time coordinates is here essential.) One finds as an immediate consequence of the Eqs. (6-26), that

$$R^{\lambda\mu\nu}{}_{,\nu} = P^{\mu\lambda} - P^{\lambda\mu} \tag{6-54}$$

Therefore the vanishing of these equations is fully equivalent with the validity of the symmetry relation (6-34). On the other hand, it is evident that the proof of the conservation of the quantities (6-52) carries over to the quantities

$$L^{\lambda\mu} = \frac{1}{c}\int R^{\lambda\mu 0}\, dV = \int (x^\lambda g^\mu - x^\mu g^\lambda)\, dV \tag{6-55}$$

under similar conditions on the mechanical system.

The importance of the conserved quantities (6-52) and (6-55) is due to their covariance under the Lorentz group (i.e., their 4-tensor character) for the mechanical systems we have called *bounded*. This covariance can be proved easily with the aid of the following lemma, which actually also provides an alternative proof of the conservation of (6-52) and (6-55). This lemma can be stated as follows.

Let w^μ be a vector field in $\mathfrak{M}$ that satisfies the two conditions

1 $w^\mu{}_{,\mu} = 0.$

2 w behaves spatially as does the 4-tensor P for bounded systems (see page 187).

Then $\int w^0\, dV$, with the region of integration the three-dimensional hyperplane $t = C$, is an invariant in $\mathfrak{M}$ and a conserved quantity (i.e., time independent).

The proof of this lemma follows readily by applying Gauss' theorem (5-107) to the integral of $w^\mu{}_{,\mu}$ over a region in $\mathfrak{M}$ (see Fig. 6-3) bounded by

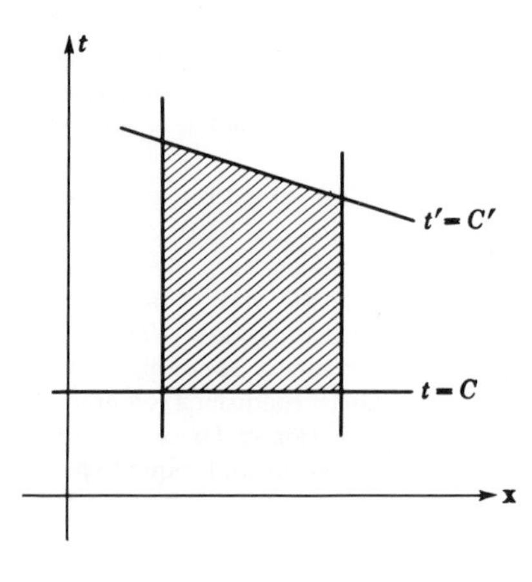

Fig. 6-3 Schematic representation of the integration 4-region in the proof of the lemma given on this page.

two hyperplanes $t = C$ and $t' = C'$, (t and t' being the time variables in two arbitrarily chosen inertial frames S and S'), and laterally by a hypersurface, which, together with the above planar regions, encloses our 4-region completely, and on which, in accordance with condition (2), either $w^\mu = 0$ or the hypersurface integral vanishes in the limit of going to infinity spatially. One finds then, in view of condition (1), the primed quantities being taken in S', that (see Prob. 6-14)

$$\int_{t=C} w^0 \, dV = \int_{t'=C'} w^\mu \, dS_\mu = \int_{t'=C'} w'^0 \, dV'$$

and, as the constants C and C' as well as the systems S, S' are arbitrary, our lemma is proved.

In order to prove that G^μ are the components of a 4-vector for bounded systems one need only take $w^\mu = A_\nu P^{\nu\mu}$, where A is an *arbitrary constant* vector, and observe that by the above lemma

$$A_\nu \int P^{\nu 0} \, dV$$

is a 4-scalar. By an application of the quotient theorem of tensor analysis it can then be concluded that the integrals are 4-vector components. In an exactly similar way one proves the tensor character of the quantities (6-55).‡

We have so far confined our discussion to *closed* (i.e., *isolated*) systems, namely systems that have no interaction with other systems. The generalization of the classical equations (6-7) when the volume force $\mathbf{f} \neq 0$, must obviously have the following form, in agreement with the covariant result (6-26),

$$P^{\mu\nu}{}_{,\nu} = f^\mu \tag{6-56}$$

This agrees when $\mu = i$—considering the physical meaning of the left-hand side of the equation—with the interpretation of f^i as the components of a force density, i.e., an ordinary spatial density of the vector of force indicated in (4-7) by $\mathbf{f}$.§ For $\mu = 0$, the left-hand side of this equation represents, as we know, the time rate of change of the energy density in the medium (divided by c). Consequently, f^0 must represent the corresponding time rate of work done by the external forces per unit volume; i.e., we should have¶

$$f^0 = \frac{1}{c} \mathbf{f} \cdot \mathbf{u} \tag{6-57}$$

This agrees with the result (4-10) in the relativistic mechanics of a particle, a fact which can be taken as a partial confirmation of the consistency of Eqs. (6-56).

‡ This line of proof is due to H. Weyl. See [7], p. 61.

§ A little care is required in recognizing the 4-vector character of f^μ as thus defined. See Prob. 6-11.

¶ Assuming that no heat transfer is taking place. See page 198 and Eq. (6-84).

If we reexamine the proof involving Eq. (6-51), it can be concluded that, in the case of continuous mechanical systems that are bounded but not closed, and for which the symmetry condition (6-34) is satisfied, we have the following integral results:

$$\frac{dG^\mu}{dt} = F^\mu, \qquad F^\mu = \int f^\mu \, dV \tag{6-58}$$

and

$$\frac{dL^{\mu\nu}}{dt} = M^{\mu\nu}, \qquad M^{\mu\nu} = \int (x^\mu f^\nu - x^\nu f^\mu) \, dV \tag{6-59}$$

We are of course assuming also that the integrals defining the components of the "total 4-force" F and of the "total 4-torque" M are convergent.

The above equations have a seductive resemblance to the corresponding classical ones. However, their usefulness in relativistic mechanics is rather restricted; only under very special conditions do they form a covariant set (see Prob. 6-13).

If one takes the view, seriously entertained at the turn of this century, that all physical phenomena can be ultimately explained in terms of "fields," or, in any case, in terms of continuous material media and fields; one is led to look upon the right-hand side of Eq. (6-56) as expressing the energy-momentum flux density coming from the outside field.‡ Therefore, if we represent the corresponding energy-momentum tensor by Θ, then

$$-\Theta^{\mu\nu}{}_{,\nu} = f^\mu \tag{6-60}$$

When these equations are substituted into Eqs. (6-56), one obtains

$$\Pi^{\mu\nu}{}_{,\nu} = 0, \qquad \Pi^{\mu\nu} = P^{\mu\nu} + \Theta^{\mu\nu} \tag{6-61}$$

i.e., equations of the form (6-26) for the total energy-momentum tensor Π of the *complete* system comprising the two interacting fields.

6-4 THEORY OF THE TROUTON-NOBLE EXPERIMENT

Of the immediate applications of the above theory, we shall only consider at this point the simple dynamical explanation provided by it for the negative result of the Trouton-Noble experiment (see Sec. 2-2).§ This experiment consisted in performing torsion-balance measurements of high precision to determine if one could detect body rotation in a suspended charged plane condenser. It was expected that this would be experienced owing to the earth's motion, on the assumption that Maxwell's theory applies to a

‡ Using here the word "field" as a generic term to represent all types of continuous systems.

§ This experiment was repeated with great care by C. T. Chase, *Phys. Rev.*, **30**: 516 (1927).

distinguished frame of reference.‡ Since the principle of relativity denies the existence of such a frame, one might regard the null result of the Trouton-Noble experiment as fully explained. The matter is, however, not that simple. On this very principle, according to which Maxwell's equations hold with respect to *any* given inertial frame S, it must follow that when a charged condenser is stationary in a frame moving relative to S with a nonzero component of velocity parallel to the plates, then there should be a torque exerted on the condenser—*as measured in* S. What, then, becomes of this torque? An indication is provided by the observation that it is necessary to consider in their dynamical aspects the *complete* system consisting of both condenser and the associated electromagnetic field. It can be shown that this system can be taken as approximately "bounded" in the sense defined earlier. Therefore, by virtue of the condition (6-61) of completeness, it follows that the total angular momentum of this system is conserved and thus, if the condenser is thought to be set into its uniform motion relative to S from an initial state of rest in S, its initial value zero in S will remain unchanged.

One might ask, in concrete terms where does the compensation of the torque due to the field come from? This brings us to the question raised earlier in connection with the asymmetry in general of the "relative stress tensor" T^{ij} (see Prob. 6-15). As a consequence of this asymmetry, an elastic body in a state of stress, but otherwise free of external forces, in an inertial frame S, will experience internally developed turning moments when it is set in motion relative to S. This inference is readily established when we note that for such a body

$$\frac{d}{dt}\int_{V\,(\text{moving})} [\mathbf{x} \times \mathbf{g}]\, dV = \int [\mathbf{u} \times \mathbf{g}]\, dV + \int \left[\mathbf{x} \times \frac{d}{dt}(\mathbf{g}\, dV)\right]$$

the notation being schematic. Since by our assumption, $d(\mathbf{g}\, dV)/dt = 0$, we find, for the time rate of change of the total angular momentum of the material system, the value $\int[\mathbf{u} \times \mathbf{g}]\, dV$ which is in general nonvanishing since, as we know, $\mathbf{g}$ is in general not parallel to $\mathbf{u}$. In particular when, as in the case of the condenser problem, $\mathbf{u}$ can be taken with sufficient approximation as constant throughout the body, this value reduces to $[\mathbf{u} \times \mathbf{G}]$. It is the resultant torque that arises in this fashion that compensates precisely the torque due to the field.§

‡ This can be seen in a number of ways. One can, e.g., note that the opposite charges on the plates, by virtue of the component of the earth's velocity parallel to the plates, constitute a nearly closed current loop (by convection); and that the resulting magnetic field together with the electric field of the condenser, which is nearly normal to it, produce an electromagnetic momentum giving rise to a time-varying angular momentum about a given point, so that the condenser must experience a turning torque about that point.

§ For calculational details see, e.g., [7], sec. 44. See also Prob. 6-16.

6-5 RELATIVISTIC MECHANICS OF PERFECT FLUIDS

One can give a relativistically meaningful definition of a perfect fluid by requiring the condition (6-9) to hold at each space-time point in the rest system of the element of fluid at that point. In the notation (6-37) this means that

$$T^{*ij} = -p^* \delta_{ij} \tag{6-62}$$

By applying Eqs. (6-46) to (6-48) we find, in a few simple steps, the following expression for the energy-momentum tensor of a perfect fluid in any given inertial frame of reference S:

$$P^{\mu\nu} = -pg^{\mu\nu} + (h^* + p)W^{\mu}W^{\nu} \tag{6-63}$$

where $g^{\mu\nu}$ is the metric tensor in $\mathfrak{M}$, p is the pressure as measured in S, h^* is the rest energy density, and the unit velocity 4-vector field W is defined in (6-40). In the derivation of (6-63) we use the fact that the quantities g, z^i defined in Eqs. (6-42) and (6-43) assume the following form in the case (6-62):

$$g = \beta^2\gamma^2 p^* \qquad \gamma \equiv \gamma_u$$
$$z^i = \gamma p^* \beta^i \qquad \beta^i = \frac{u^i}{c} \tag{6-64}$$

With the aid of Eqs. (6-64), (6-49), and (6-62) we also find directly that $T^{ij} = -p^*\delta_{ij}$.‡ It follows that (see Prob. 6-7)

$$p = p^* \tag{6-65}$$

and one has the important conclusion that the pressure p is a 4-scalar field. In Eqs. (6-63) we have included this result.

Equations (6-63) are written in a form that is valid in *general* coordinates in $\mathfrak{M}$. They will thus be found to retain validity also in the general theory of relativity when the metric tensor g is allowed to be a suitable general space-time field.

It is of interest to observe that in the present special case it is possible to deduce Eqs. (6-63) very simply, without having to apply the Lorentz transformation directly, but making use only of the requirement of covariance.§ Indeed, we have available for the construction of P the scalars p, h^* and the tensors g, W, from which the most general second-rank 4-tensor expression that can be formed is $P^{\mu\nu} = ag^{\mu\nu} + bW^{\mu}W^{\nu}$, where a, b are 4-scalars. But in the rest frame S^* we find by Eqs. (6-37), (6-62), and (6-65): $P^{*00} = h^* = a + b$, $P^{*ij} = p\delta_{ij} = -a\delta_{ij}$; hence, $a = -p$ and $b = h^* + p$. Note also that in the present case one can see the tensor

‡ As is also seen at once from Eq. (6-50), which, when combined with (6-62), gives $T^{ij} = T^{*ij}$.

§ See [3], pp. 53–54.

character of $P^{\mu\nu}$ directly from its expression (6-63). The 'incoherent matter' continuous system whose energy-momentum tensor has the form (6-36) represents obviously the limiting case $p = 0$ of a perfect fluid.

The relativistic equations of motion for perfect fluids are given by Eqs. (6-56), now rewritten for *general* coordinates:

$$f^{\mu} = P^{\mu\nu}{}_{;\nu} = -g^{\mu\nu}p_{,\nu} + \frac{1}{c^2}\,U^{\mu}\frac{de}{d\tau} + \frac{e}{c^2}\left(\frac{dU^{\mu}}{d\tau} + U^{\mu}U^{\nu}{}_{;\nu}\right), \qquad e = h^* + p$$

$$\frac{dF}{d\tau} \equiv F_{;\nu}\frac{dx^{\nu}}{d\tau} = F_{;\nu}U^{\nu} \tag{6-66}$$

(where the thermodynamic quantity e can be recognized as the *enthalpy* density in S^*). An immediate deduction from these equations is obtained by multiplying with U^{μ} (and summing). As $g^{\mu\nu}p_{,\nu}U_{\mu} = p_{,\mu}U^{\mu} = dp/d\tau$, and $U_{\mu}U^{\mu} = c^2$, one finds

$$f^{\mu}U_{\mu} = \frac{dh^*}{d\tau} + eU^{\nu}{}_{;\nu} = (h^*U^{\nu})_{;\nu} + pU^{\nu}{}_{;\nu} \tag{6-67}$$

It is now tempting to take the equation

$$U^{\nu}{}_{;\nu} = 0 \tag{6-68}$$

assumed to hold throughout the space-time extent of the fluid, as the relativistic condition of its "incompressibility." Equation (6-67) then assumes the suggestive form [see the corresponding classical relations (6-8) and (6-11), and Probs. 6-3 and 6-8]

$$f^{\mu}U_{\mu} = \frac{dh^*}{d\tau} = (h^*U^{\nu})_{;\nu} = \frac{1}{\delta V^*}\frac{d}{d\tau}(h^*\,\delta V^*) \tag{6-69}$$

that is seen to be equivalent to Eq. (4-63), in view of the basic relation (6-17), and since f^{μ} also represents the Minkowski force per unit rest volume (see Prob. 6-11).‡

The definition (6-68) would indeed appear to be in agreement with the heuristic rules (1), (2) of page 91. Equation (6-68) is manifestly covariant, and in each local rest frame $S^*(\mathbf{x})$ it is equivalent, upon evaluating the 4-scalar in lorentzian coordinates, to the classical condition of incompressibility (see Prob. 6-3),

$$\operatorname{div} \mathbf{u}^* = 0 \tag{6-70}$$

But the observant reader may well wonder at the legitimacy of applying rule (2) in this manner; and indeed we have here again an example of the need to exercise caution in applying this rule in the mechanics of continuous systems. Practically, condition (6-68) may perhaps do little harm; but in

‡ In this connection note also the resemblance of the first term on the right-hand side of Eq. (6-66) to the corresponding term in Eq. (4-60).

principle, condition (6-70) implies *infinite* incompressibility, and such a state of matter, just as that of infinite rigidity, cannot be consistent with the kinematic principles of STR. Specifically, one can show, along lines of proof of the classical theory,‡ that when the equation of state (6-10) of the fluid has in the rest frame S^* the form $p = p(\rho^*)$, then the velocity of propagation in this fluid of a small disturbance (i.e., the sound-wave velocity) is given by $\sqrt{dp/d\rho^*}$, and would therefore become infinite under condition (6-70) [see Eq. (6-11)].

The energy-conservation equation (6-67) can be looked upon, when divided by c, as the projection in $\mathfrak{M}$ along W of the 4-vector Eq. (6-66). The equations of motion themselves assume a simpler form when we take the projection of (6-66) that is orthogonal to W, i.e., the 4-vector projection into the spatial directions of the corresponding local rest frame. Indicating by $\mathsf{f}_\perp$ this projection of f, we have

$$f_\perp{}^\mu = \mathcal{P}^\mu_\nu f^\nu, \qquad \mathcal{P}^\mu_\nu = \delta^\mu_\nu - W^\mu W_\nu \tag{6-71}$$

where the symmetric projection tensor $\mathcal{P}$ is seen to obey the conditions

$$\mathcal{P}^\mu_\nu U^\nu = \mathcal{P}^\mu_\nu U_\mu = 0, \qquad \mathcal{P}^\mu_\nu \frac{dU^\nu}{d\tau} = \frac{dU^\mu}{d\tau} \tag{6-72}$$

Equations (6-66) therefore yield:

$$\frac{e}{c^2}\frac{dU^\mu}{d\tau} \equiv \left(\rho^* + \frac{p}{c^2}\right)\frac{dU^\mu}{d\tau} = (g^{\mu\nu}p_{,\nu})_\perp + f^\mu_\perp \tag{6-73}$$

These equations, together with (6-67), are fully equivalent to Eqs. (6-66), and the significance of the terms is in clear evidence. In particular, referred to the local rest frame of the fluid at a given space-time point, Eqs. (6-73) reduce to the identity $0 = 0$ for $\mu = 0$, and to the 3-vector equation

$$\left(\rho^* + \frac{p}{c^2}\right)\frac{d\mathbf{u}^*}{dt^*} = -\boldsymbol{\nabla}^* p + \mathbf{f}^* \tag{6-74}$$

which is seen to coincide with the corresponding classical hydrodynamic equation when the purely relativistic term p/c^2 is neglected. In connection with this term note again the resemblance between the 4-scalar p and the potential energy 4-scalar Φ in Eqs. (4-60) and (4-61).

Another useful way of looking at the energy-conservation equation (6-67) results from applying the decomposition (6-39). By Eqs. (6-63) and (6-71),

$$G^{\mu\nu} = -p\mathcal{P}^{\mu\nu} \tag{6-75}$$

‡ See, e.g., Lamb, *op. cit.*, secs. 276 to 278.

Moreover, by (6-39), (6-41), and (6-56) we have generally

$$\begin{aligned} H^{\mu\nu}{}_{;\nu} &= (\rho^* U^\mu)_{;\nu} U^\nu + \rho^* U^\mu U^\nu{}_{;\nu} = \frac{1}{\delta V^*}\frac{d}{d\tau}(\rho^* U^\mu \delta V^*) \\ &= -G^{\mu\nu}{}_{;\nu} + f^\mu \equiv f^\mu_{\text{elast}} + f^\mu \end{aligned} \tag{6-76}$$

where, following Møller, we have denoted $-G^{\mu\nu}{}_{;\nu}$ by the suggestive symbol f^μ_{elast}, with understandable connotations; while from the first part in (6-76) we can also see why the tensor $H^{\mu\nu}$, first introduced by Minkowski, is known as the "kinetic energy-momentum tensor." Since

$$\mathcal{P}^{\mu\nu}{}_{;\nu} = -(dU^\mu/d\tau + U^\mu U^\nu{}_{;\nu})/c^2$$

it follows from Eq. (6-75), with the aid of (6-72), that

$$U_\mu f^\mu_{\text{elast}} = -pU^\mu{}_{;\mu} = -p\nabla^* \cdot \mathbf{u}^* \tag{6-77}$$

This equation and (6-76) lead at once to Eq. (6-67), as $H^{\mu\nu}{}_{;\nu}U_\mu$ is identical with the right-hand side of (6-69). At the same time, the last term in (6-77) can be recognized as having the form of the classical expression for the time rate of work per unit volume performed by the elastic forces on an element of fluid.

One can generally bring the relativistic equations of motion of continuous media into closer correspondence with the nonrelativistic equations by decomposing the proper energy density h^* into two parts of which one is *conserved:*

$$h^* = \eta^* + \frac{1}{c^2}\eta^*\phi, \qquad (\eta^* U^\mu)_{;\mu} = 0 \tag{6-78}$$

(see Prob. 6-8) where the conserved rest energy density η^* is associated with the system of micromasses referred to the local rest frames, and ϕ—which is seen to have the physical dimensions of energy per unit mass—can be usually identified with an internal potential-energy function. Moreover, in many situations where the continuum model can be properly applied, η^* will stay constant simply because the individual rest masses of the microparticles are unchanging. The potential-energy significance of ϕ is easily shown for a perfect fluid subject to no body forces, or only to such f as satisfy the condition $(\mathsf{f},\mathsf{U}) = 0$, and for which the equation of state is of the form $h^* = h^*(p)$ [so that also $\eta^* = \eta^*(p)$, $\phi = \phi(p)$]. In fact, by (6-67) and the assumption (6-78), it follows then that (using the notation $\dot\phi$ for $d\phi/d\tau$), $0 = \dot\eta^* + (\phi\dot\eta^* + \eta^*\dot\phi)/c^2 + e(-\dot\eta^*/\eta^*) = \eta^*\dot\phi/c^2 - p\dot\eta^*/\eta^*$, i.e., that $d\phi = c^2 p\, d\eta^*/\eta^{*2}$, and a further application of (6-78)—i.e., of the relation $\dot\eta^*/\eta^* = -U^\mu{}_{;\mu}$—together with Eq. (6-77), leads to the equation

$$\frac{\eta^*}{c^2}\frac{d\phi}{d\tau} = U_\mu f^\mu_{\text{elast}} \tag{6-79}$$

Remembering the physical significance of the last term in (6-77), we thus see that ϕ can be identified with the compressional potential energy of the fluid per unit of the mass η^*/c^2 as referred to the local rest frame (see the similar classical result in Prob. 6-5).

We have so far said nothing specific about the possible body forces f^μ. A case of possible importance is that of electromagnetic forces, whose macroscopic theory is considered in Sec. 7-3. In classical hydrodynamics it is of course the force of gravity that is of chief interest, but this force is outside the domain of STR, except in treatments of limited acceptance (see Appendix 7B). As a matter of fact, the relativistic theory of fluids is an important topic in the general theory of relativity, which represents the generally accepted relativistic theory of gravitation.

6-6 FURTHER REMARKS CONCERNING CONTINUOUS SYSTEMS; ELEMENTS OF RELATIVISTIC THERMODYNAMICS

The previous discussion can be continued in a number of directions. One can investigate the relativistic mechanics of real fluids, taking proper account of dissipative effects such as viscosity and heat conduction, and generally incorporate in a covariant manner the reversible and irreversible thermodynamic relations governing the changes of state of gross physical systems. One may also introduce the methods of statistical mechanics and kinetic theory with suitable assumptions concerning the underlying microscopic interactions. The simple example of the perfect fluid also affords a good starting point for further study of the general mathematical structure of the energy-momentum tensor of continuous media. On the other hand, the physical significance of the theory calls for careful examination. Without aiming at any extensive discussion, we now turn to a consideration of these questions.

Regarding the relativistic treatment of real fluids, it has already been noted that the early development of the theory was motivated mainly by the wish to check the consistency of relativistic physics with established classical results, situations involving fluids that essentially require relativistic theory were hardly known then, and in fact such situations are still, as far as terrestrial physics is concerned, mainly the subject of incipient investigations relating to ultrahot plasmas. We therefore limit our discussion relating to real fluids largely to a consideration of the two laws of thermodynamics as applied to general continuous media.‡

‡ Further details may be found, e.g., in [9], chap. 5; [5], secs. 20d, 23, 24; [7], secs. 45–49; and in the references given there to the earlier investigations. An early treatment with inclusion of heat conduction is contained in G. Nordström, *Ann. Physik*, **40**: 856 (1913). A more recent reference of interest, containing a relativistic treatment of viscous fluids, is C. Eckart, *Phys. Rev.*, **58**: 919 (1940). Chapter 15 in the text by Landau and Lifshitz referred to in the footnote on page 175 also contains pertinent material. A study of con-

The relativistic formulation of the first law of thermodynamics, when applied to special continuous systems such as those considered in Prob. 6-13, can be obtained by a straightforward extension of the classical law

$$dE = \delta W + \delta Q \tag{6-80}$$

where dE is the differential change in the total energy of our thermodynamic system during a given process, while δW and δQ are (in appropriate energy units) the work done on the system by outside forces and the heat entering the system across its boundary during that process. This was shown in the first investigations on this subject by Planck, Einstein, Tolman, and others. (See Prob. 6-17 and the references given there.) However, if one wishes to treat more general situations, with an eye to possible future applications of the relativistic theory, it is best to start with the differential rather than the integral form of the law, i.e., as applied to an element of the medium. Such a result must, of course, be derivable from the covariant system (6-56), which, as we know, includes a differential expression of the principle of energy conservation. The derivation is however not too immediate, and it will be instructive to examine it with some care, even if some parts of the following discussion concerned with heat conduction cannot be presently expected to be of much practical interest.

The first thing to observe is that it will not do simply to take the $\mu = 0$ equation in (6-56): that equation refers to changes taking place within an element of volume stationary in our frame S, whereas what is wanted are of course the changes taking place within a 'moving volume element.' Equation (6-56) needs therefore to be transformed accordingly. With the help of Eqs. (6-31) and (6-25) they can indeed be put in the suggestive form (returning now to lorentzian coordinates)

$$\frac{\delta h}{\delta t} \equiv \frac{1}{\delta V}\frac{d}{dt}(h\,\delta V) = \frac{\partial h}{\partial t} + (hu^i)_{,i} = (T^{ij}u^i)_{,j} + cf^0 \tag{6-81}$$

$$\frac{\delta g^i}{\delta t} = T^{ij}{}_{,j} + f^i \tag{6-82}$$

(see Prob. 6-15).

The left-hand side of (6-81) is seen to correspond, after multiplication by δV and dt, to the left-hand side of (6-80), remembering the meaning of h. The first term on the right upon multiplication by δV is seen, with the aid of Gauss' integral identity applied to an element of volume δV, to represent the time rate of work done on our element of the medium by its immediate

---

ditions that must be satisfied by the equation of state of a fluid so as to insure sound and shock wave speeds $<c$ can be found in the following papers: A. H. Taub, *Phys. Rev.*, **74:** 328 (1948); W. Israel, *Proc. Roy. Soc. London*, **A259:** 129 (1960). For references to a discussion of relativistic shock waves occurring in astrophysics, see, e.g., R. A. Gross, *Rev. Mod. Phys.*, **37:** 724 (1965), sec. 4.

surroundings. The last term, when multiplied by δV, represents, according to (4-10), the time rate of work done on the element by the body forces. This term can also include the time rate of *heat* generated in our element per unit of volume by the exterior forces, such as the Joule heat generated in a conducting medium by external electromagnetic fields. To see how such a process can be incorporated in our formalism, let us note that on our idealized mechanical continuum model, the generation of heat within the volume element amounts to an increase in the energy equivalent of the rest mass of this 'particle' [see in this connection, Eq. (4-31) or the approximate relation (4-93)]. Now, in the case of the dynamics of a material particle, an increase in its rest mass under the action of an external force **f** is represented by Eq. (4-63), i.e., (replacing the symbol f used in Sec. 4-1 by k to distinguish it from the present symbol for force density) by the equation

$$ck^0 = \mathbf{k} \cdot \mathbf{u} + c^2 \frac{1}{\gamma} \frac{dm}{dt} \tag{6-83}$$

remembering that F^μ in (4-63) equals γk^μ. The symbol γ stands here and in the rest of this section for $\gamma_u \equiv (1 - u^2/c^2)^{-1/2}$. Upon division by the volume δV of our element and identifying $\mathsf{k}/\delta V$ with f, we get from (6-83) the desired general expression

$$cf^0 = \mathbf{f} \cdot \mathbf{u} + q, \qquad q = \frac{c^2}{\gamma\, \delta V} \frac{dm}{dt} \tag{6-84}$$

that includes the density of heat q generated in the element per unit of time.

In general, heat transfer may also take place as a result of thermal conduction across the boundary of the element. Such conduction would of course be present also in the local rest frame. This possibility is left out of consideration when one assumes the conditions (6-35) or the form (6-37) of the proper energy-momentum tensor. It is therefore necessary, in order to encompass general heat-flow processes, to add to the terms given in (6-38) a rest heat-flow tensor of the form

$$\|C^{*\mu\nu}\| = \begin{bmatrix} 0 & \frac{1}{c} C^{*i} \\ \frac{1}{c} C^{*j} & 0_{ij} \end{bmatrix}, \qquad 0_{ij} = 0 \tag{6-85}$$

in S^*, where the factor $1/c$ is introduced so that the vector $\mathbf{C}^*$ has the proper physical dimensions, ergs/cm^2 sec, to represent energy flux. Since (remembering that $W^{*\mu} = \delta_0^\mu$)

$$cC^{*\mu\nu} = W^{*\mu}C^{*\nu} + W^{*\nu}C^{*\mu}, \qquad C^{*\nu} = (0, C^{*i})$$

it follows that generally, the heat-flow tensor has the form

$$cC^{\mu\nu} = W^{\mu}C^{\nu} + W^{\nu}C^{\mu} \tag{6-86}$$

where the heat-flow 4-vector C^{ν} is expressed in terms of $\mathbf{C}^*$ by the transformation (6-40):

$$C^0 = W^i C^{*i} \equiv w, \qquad C^i = C^{*i} + \frac{w}{\gamma + 1} W^i \tag{6-87}$$

If we now retrace the derivation of (6-81), involving the intermediate result

$$cf^0 = \frac{\delta h}{\delta t} + (c^2 g^i - hu^i)_{,i} \tag{6-88}$$

we must be careful to note that relation (6-31), valid when $\mathbf{C}^* = 0$, need no longer hold. To begin with, the relation (6-49) has limited validity. In fact, from Eqs. (6-25) and (6-86) one finds that now

$$T^{ij} = T_0^{ij} + \frac{1}{c} W^i(w\beta^j - C^j) \tag{6-89}$$

where T_0^{ij} is the expression on the right in (6-49). With a similar notation, we have then by Eqs. (6-27), (6-31), and (6-86),

$$\begin{aligned} cP^{0i} &= c^2 g^i = c^2 g_0^i + wW^i + \gamma C^i \\ &= -T_0^{ji} u^j + h_0 u^i + \cdots \\ &= \left[-T^{ji} + \frac{W^j(w\beta^i - C^i)}{c} \right] u^j + \left(h - \frac{2\gamma w}{c} \right) u^i + \cdots \\ &= hu^i - T^{ji}u^j + (1 - \beta^2)\gamma C^i - (1 - \beta^2)\, wW^i \end{aligned}$$

that is,

$$c^2 g^i - hu^i = -T^{ji}u^j + \frac{1}{\gamma}(C^i - w\beta^i) \tag{6-90}$$

An extension of the differential law (6-81) in the presence of heat conduction is thus obtained by combining Eqs. (6-88) and (6-90):

$$\frac{\delta h}{\delta t} = (T^{ij}u^i)_{,j} + cf^0 - \left(\frac{C^i - w\beta^i}{\gamma} \right)_{,i} \tag{6-91}$$

The last term in this expression must of course represent the algebraic energy increase within the substance element under consideration per unit of time and of volume due to thermal conduction. Indeed in the local rest system

S^* this term reduces to $-\nabla^* \cdot \mathbf{C}^*$, the same as the corresponding expression in the classical theory.‡

In making the comparison with the classical law (6-80), we have been referring to E as the total energy of the system under consideration. Conventionally, one considers systems that are at rest as a whole in the frame of reference and E is then the total *internal* energy. It is possible to transform our differential law (6-91) so that it also refers to the internal energy inside the particular element that we have mentally isolated within our material medium. This internal energy, in one sense, can be conveniently identified with the energy $h^* \, \delta V^*$ contained in the element when referred to its rest frame. Starting with the law (6-91) in terms of $\delta h/\delta t$, we must therefore find the corresponding law in terms of [see the last part in Eq. (6-69)]

$$\frac{1}{\delta V}\frac{d}{dt}(h^* \, \delta V^*) = \frac{1}{\delta V^*}\frac{d}{d\tau}(h^* \, \delta V^*) = (h^* U^\mu)_{,\mu} \tag{6-92}$$

This expression is seen moreover to represent a 4-scalar.

The desired result can be obtained from the following observations. Since $\delta V^* = \gamma \, \delta V$, the expression (6-92) can be written in the notation introduced in (6-81),

$$(h^* U^\mu)_{,\mu} = \frac{\delta}{\delta t}(\gamma h^*) = \gamma \frac{\delta h^*}{\delta t} + h^* \frac{d\gamma}{dt} \tag{6-93}$$

Using the relations

$$G^{\mu\nu} U_\nu = 0, \qquad C^\mu U_\mu = 0, \qquad C^{\mu\nu} U_\nu = C^\mu \tag{6-94}$$

that follow at once by evaluating these covariant expressions in S^*, one finds in a few steps that (Prob. 6-18)

$$\mathbf{g} \cdot \mathbf{u} = h - h^* - \frac{w}{c\gamma}, \qquad w \text{ defined in (6-87)} \tag{6-95}$$

Lastly, by (6-82), $T^{ij}{}_{,j} u^i = -f^i u^i + \partial(g^i u^i)/\partial t + (g^i u^i u^j)_{,j} - g^i \partial u^i/\partial t - g^i u^i{}_{,j} u^j$, that is,

$$T^{ij}{}_{,j} u^i = -\mathbf{f} \cdot \mathbf{u} + \frac{\delta}{\delta t}(\mathbf{g} \cdot \mathbf{u}) - \mathbf{g} \cdot \frac{d\mathbf{u}}{dt} \tag{6-96}$$

Combining Eqs. (6-93), (6-91), (6-95), and (6-96), and also applying the useful identity

$$\gamma_{,\nu} = \gamma^3 \beta^i \beta^i{}_{,\nu} \tag{6-97}$$

‡ See, e.g., Landau and Lifshitz, *op. cit.*, chap. 5; C. Eckart, *Phys. Rev.*, **58**: 267 (1940); also Prob. 6-5. The reader who wishes to refresh his memory on the underlying ideas relating to the laws of thermodynamics can consult, e.g., J. C. Slater, "Introduction to Chemical Physics," chap. 1, McGraw-Hill Book Company, Inc., New York, 1939. The extension of these laws to general thermodynamic systems with inclusion of irreversible processes is discussed, e.g., in I. Prigogine, "Thermodynamics of Irreversible Processes," 2d ed., Interscience Publishers, New York, 1961.

the following result is obtained:

$$(h^*U^\nu)_{,\nu} = \gamma \left[T^{ij}u^i_{,j} - (G^{0i} + C^{0i}) \frac{d\beta^i}{dt} + q - \frac{\delta}{\delta t}\left(\frac{w}{c\gamma}\right) - \left(\frac{C^i - w\beta^i}{\gamma}\right)_{,i} \right] \tag{6-98}$$

Here $G^{\mu\nu} \equiv G_0^{\mu\nu}$ in the notation used earlier, so that

$$P^{\mu\nu} = H^{\mu\nu} + G^{\mu\nu} + C^{\mu\nu} \tag{6-99}$$

The expression on the right in Eq. (6-98) is complicated and its covariance is not easily recognized. The complication is of course simply a reflection of the involved situation that is being described in the three-dimensional language of the observer for which the medium element is in motion. On the other hand, it can be expected that formal simplification would result if this expression were transformed into an explicitly covariant form, though practically the terms given in (6-98) may well have more immediate interest.‡

Bringing the right-hand side of (6-98) directly into an explicitly covariant form is somewhat lengthy, and we leave the details to be worked out in Prob. 6-18, noting here only that by straightforward algebra one finds that

$$\gamma \left(T_0^{ij}u^i_{,j} - G^{0i}\frac{d\beta^i}{dt} \right) = G^{\mu\nu}U_{\mu,\nu} \tag{6-100}$$

[see (6-89)] and that with further reduction of the other terms in (6-98) one arrives at the desired expression

$$(h^*U^\nu)_{,\nu} = G^{\mu\nu}U_{\mu,\nu} + \gamma q - C^\mu{}_{,\mu} + \frac{1}{c^2} C^\mu \frac{dU_\mu}{d\tau} \tag{6-101}$$

We shall discuss the term γq presently; the covariance of the other terms is apparent.

Now that we have the expression (6-101), the question naturally arises if it cannot be derived more simply and more directly by working entirely with space-time quantities. Not surprisingly, this is indeed the case. In fact, starting with the general differential system (6-56), and using the relations (6-94), we find

$$f^\mu U_\mu = (P^{\mu\nu}U_\mu)_{,\nu} - P^{\mu\nu}U_{\mu,\nu} = (H^{\mu\nu}U_\mu)_{,\nu} + C^\nu{}_{,\nu} - P^{\mu\nu}U_{\mu,\nu}$$

But, by (6-41), $(H^{\mu\nu}U_\mu)_{,\nu} = (h^*U^\nu)_{,\nu}$ and $H^{\mu\nu}U_{\mu,\nu} = 0$, since $U^\mu U_{\mu,\nu} = 0$; while, by this identity and (6-86), $C^{\mu\nu}U_{\mu,\nu} = C^\mu\, dU_\mu/c^2\, d\tau$. When we collect our terms and also note that, by (6-84), $f^\mu U_\mu = \gamma q$, we rediscover Eq. (6-101), and incidentally have another instance of the power of tensor analysis in $\mathfrak{M}$ in the treatment of general problems in STR.

‡ Moreover, in any practical application, it would also be necessary to add to our system of equations a 4-vector equation involving C so that the resulting system suffices to determine all our unknown quantities. Such an equation representing a possible covariant extension of the classical Fourier formula has been suggested by Eckart, *op. cit.*

Our covariant derivation of (6-101) resembles the earlier derivation of the corresponding equation (6-67) for a perfect fluid with no thermal conduction. The relations (6-78) for the existence of a conserved part of the rest energy density can be expected to be pertinent in most situations where the theory of continuous media applies. The left-hand side of Eq. (6-101) can then be replaced by

$$\frac{1}{c^2}(\eta^*\phi U^\mu)_{,\mu} = \frac{1}{c^2}\eta^*\frac{d\phi}{d\tau} = \frac{1}{c^2}\gamma\eta^*\frac{d\phi}{dt} \tag{6-102}$$

In (6-102) we see both the invariant character of the quantity ϕ and its analogy with the nonrelativistic intrinsic energy per unit mass.

The only strictly thermodynamic quantities that appear explicitly in formula (6-101) are those relating to heat, namely, q and C^μ. We shall presently discuss the relativistic formulation of the second law of thermodynamics and shall require the law of transformation under the Lorentz group of what in STR can be taken to correspond to δQ in (6-80). As far as the quantity q is concerned, the transformation law is obtained at once from the expression given in (6-84), which shows that the 4-scalar

$$q^* = \gamma q \tag{6-103}$$

can be taken as the amount of heat generated in the medium (by an external source) per unit of time and of volume, all quantities being taken relative to the relevant local rest frame. This result agrees with the covariance character of Eqs. (6-101) and (6-98); moreover, the terms involving the 4-vector C in these equations show, as they must, the same transformation behavior. If we designate by δQ the heat generated in the medium element under consideration in time dt by the external source, then, since $dt\,\delta V = d\tau\,\delta V^*$ is a 4-scalar, so is δQ^*, and, by (6-103)

$$\delta Q = \sqrt{1 - \frac{u^2}{c^2}}\,\delta Q^* \tag{6-104}$$

This transformation law can be taken to hold generally. In particular, it can be verified independently for the heat transferred through the boundary of finite systems such as those considered in Prob. 6-13 (see Prob. 6-17).

The simplest expression of the second law in classical thermodynamics is given, as we know, by the inequality

$$dS \geq \frac{\delta Q}{T} \tag{6-105}$$

where the equality sign holds only if the differential change dS in the *entropy* of the given thermodynamic system takes place in a reversible process, δQ representing the algebraic amount of heat entering the system during the process, and T being the absolute temperature during the infinitesimal duration of the process. This inequality, when properly interpreted, can be expected to retain its validity in relativistic physics. In the case of general continuous media, it is assumed, of course, *ipso facto* that we are dealing with states such that the general ideas of thermodynamics can be consistently applied to every constituent 'macroscopic element.' Thus the law (6-105) must be assumed to hold in all local rest frames:

$$dS^* \geq \frac{\delta Q^*}{T^*} \tag{6-106}$$

The only question that needs to be answered, then, is how the quantities that enter into this formula transform under the Lorentz group. Since we already have, in (6-104), the transformation law for δQ, we require those for S and T. We can invoke statistical mechanics and kinetic theory considerations in attempting to discover these laws. By far the simplest procedure is to postulate the general validity of (6-105), and deal with only one of these two transformation laws. Moreover, if we allow ourselves to bring in statistical mechanics ideas in the present discussion—and there is little point in purism here—we can see very easily that entropy must transform as a 4-scalar, i.e., that

$$S = S^* \tag{6-107}$$

In fact, whatever the statistical mechanics approach, entropy is always expressed in terms of probabilities relating to a statistical distribution connected with the thermodynamic state in question.‡ But, a probability as used in physics is ultimately a matter of counting; it cannot therefore change under a Lorentz transformation, since the Lorentz group is continuous.

From (6-105) and (6-106), and Eqs. (6-104) and (6-107), the transformation law for temperature follows:

$$T = \sqrt{1 - \frac{u^2}{c^2}}\, T^* \tag{6-108}$$

This is the more useful form of the transformation rule; if one wishes to refer to two arbitrary inertial frames, one needs only to apply the corresponding transformation formula for $1/\gamma_u$ as given in Prob. 3-3.

Since entropy is an *extensive* quantity, we can define an entropy density s such that the entropy in a volume element δV is $s\delta V$, and the inequality (6-105), when applied to such an element, can be written: $d(s\,\delta V) \geq \delta Q/T$. But $d(s\,\delta V) = d(s^*\,\delta V^*) = d\tau\,\delta V^*(s^*U^\mu)_{,\mu} = dt\,\delta V(s^*U^\mu)_{,\mu}$ [see (6-92)], where the 4-scalar s^*, as the notation indicates, represents the entropy density in the frame S^*. In terms of

$$S^\mu \equiv s^*W^\mu, \qquad s^* = \frac{1}{\gamma}s \tag{6-109}$$

‡ See, e.g., Slater, *op. cit.*, chap. 3; R. C. Tolman, "The Principles of Statistical Mechanics," sec. 122, Oxford University Press, London, 1942; or any current text on statistical mechanics.

which can be taken to represent the *entropy flux* 4-*vector*, we have then the following differential expression for the second law of thermodynamics ([9], sec. 71)

$$\delta^4 x S^\mu{}_{,\mu} \geq \frac{\delta Q}{T} \qquad \text{(6-110)}$$
$$\delta^4 x = \delta x^0 \, \delta x^1 \, \delta x^2 \, \delta x^3, \qquad \delta x^0 \equiv dx^0$$

Quite obviously this expression holds also in general coordinates when the comma is replaced by a semicolon and for $\delta^4 x$ we take the corresponding expression for the element of volume in $\mathfrak{M}$. A similar statement holds also very obviously for the differential expression (6-101) of the first law of thermodynamics.

Both from purely theoretical as well as possible practical considerations, there is considerable interest in a relativistic extension of not only classical thermodynamics but also of statistical mechanics and kinetic theory. To give an adequate presentation here of these subjects would, however, prolong this section disproportionately without introducing essentially new relativistic ideas or methods, for the amalgamation of the basic concepts of statistical physics and of STR, without bringing in many-particle interaction treatments essentially beyond that given in Sec. 4.2, presents no problems in principle. For an indication of known results, the interested reader may be referred, e.g., to the following sources: [7], secs. 48 and 49; R. C. Tolman, "The Theory of the Relativity of Motion," chap. 8, University of California Press, Berkeley, 1917; [8], chap. 8; J. L. Synge, "The Relativistic Gas," North-Holland Publishing Company, Amsterdam, 1957; D. ter Haar, "Elements of Statistical Mechanics," app. 7, Holt, Rinehart and Winston, Inc., New York, 1961; and the references given in these sources. A few problems at the end of this chapter deal with some questions in relativistic statistical physics.

Before concluding this outline of general questions in the macroscopic theory of mechanics of continuous media, we need consider (in addition to the variational method to be discussed in Sec. 6-7) two further topics. Both the analytic structure of the energy-momentum tensor of continuous systems as well as the physical significance and scope of our continuum theory invite closer examination. We close this section with a very brief consideration of these questions.

One immediate question relating to the energy-momentum tensor of continuous systems that naturally presents itself when we consider the central role of this tensor in the equations of motion of such systems is the extent to which the physical (macroscopic) state of a system determines the energy-momentum tensor associated with it. We have seen, for instance, how the definition of a perfect fluid leads to the form (6-63). In what sense can we be sure that this form is unique? Similar questions arise more importantly when we have to deal with more complex types of continuous systems. This problem has been considered by Fock, who has proved a general result that actually embraces a wider class of physical systems than forms the subject of our present discussion. For a complete statement of this result and a sketch of its proof we must refer the reader to Fock's exposition ([4], sec. 31). It will suffice here to indicate the gist of his theorem; a possible application is referred to in Sec. 7.2.

Fock's theorem deals with physical systems whose equations of motion are given by a finite set of first-order differential equations in the same number of unknown functions $\phi_1, \phi_2, \ldots$, that characterize the *state* of the system, and which can be solved for the time derivatives of the ϕ, their solution being unique for properly given initial and boundary conditions (consistent with the principle of causality). It is supposed that there exist quantities $P^{\mu\nu}$ satisfying the following conditions: they form the components (lorentzian) of a symmetric tensor; they satisfy the differential system (6-26); they are "functions of the state," i.e., they depend on $\phi_1, \phi_2, \ldots$, but not explicitly on their time derivatives or on the x^μ; the expressions (6-52) and (6-55) are finite first integrals of the system; P^{00} can be interpreted as the energy density of the physical system. The conclusion is that the tensor $P^{\mu\nu}$ is essentially unique.

Another question concerning the mathematical structure of the energy-momentum tensor, namely, the eigenvalue problem connected with it, has been discussed rather extensively in the literature,‡ much of it in connection with certain considerations in the general theory of relativity. An indication of the type of results that can be obtained is afforded by the simple example of a perfect fluid. If the energy-momentum tensor is given by (6-63), it is found immediately that

$$\begin{aligned} P^{\mu\nu}W_\nu &= h^*W^\mu \\ P^{\mu\nu}X_\nu &= -pX^\mu, \qquad (\mathsf{X},\mathsf{W}) = 0 \end{aligned} \tag{6-111}$$

Thus in this case P has two real eigenvalues, h^* and $-p$, the latter being triply degenerate with the corresponding eigenvector set spanning the vector space of all spacelike vectors, and the former being associated with the timelike eigenvector W.

An immediate extension of this result is obviously obtained when we give up the degeneracy restriction, so that the first equation in (6-111) is retained, but the last vector equation is replaced by

$$P^{\mu\nu}X_{(k)\nu} = p_{(k)}X^\mu_{(k)}, \qquad k = 1, 2, 3; \text{no summation over } k \tag{6-112}$$

where the $p_{(k)}$ are real and $\{\mathsf{X}_{(k)}\}$ span the spacelike subspace of the Minkowski vector space. It can be surmised that this extension corresponds to going over to a material medium (fluid or solid) with a general stress tensor

‡ See, e.g., [8], chap. 8, sec. 11; Halbwachs, *op. cit.* (on page 112), app. B; A. Lichnerowicz, "Théories relativistes de la gravitation et de l'electromagnétisme," sec. 5, Masson et Cie, Paris, 1955.

T^{ij}; i.e., that the result holds for a general energy-momentum tensor of the form (6-39). The verification is quite easy. Since the expression on the left in the first of the vector equations in (6-111) is covariant, we can evaluate it in the local rest frame S^* using (6-37): $P^{*\mu\nu}W^*_\nu = P^{*\mu 0} = h^*\delta^\mu_0 = h^*W^{*\mu}$. Again, if X is spacelike, then $X^*_0 = 0$ and $P^{*\mu\nu}X^*_\nu = P^{*\mu i}X^*_i = 0$ if $\mu = 0$, i.e., the transformed vector is also spacelike; while $P^{*ij}X^*_j = -T^{*ij}X^*_j$ and, by our assumption of symmetry of T^*, we have the well-known classical result of the existence of three real eigenvalues $p_{(k)}$ (in general distinct): $T^{*ij}X^{*j}_{(k)} = p_{(k)}X^{*i}_{(k)}$. Hence

$$P^{*\mu\nu}X^*_{(k)\nu} = p_{(k)}X^{*\mu}_{(k)} \qquad X^{*0}_{(k)} = 0 \quad k = 1, 2, 3$$

and Eqs. (6-112) follow.

Suppose now that we are dealing with a continuous medium of an arbitrary kind (it may be composed of 'matter,' of pure fields, or of both), and we wish to study its properties as reflected in relevant properties of its energy-momentum tensor P. Guided by the above results, we can recognize the importance of the existence of real eigenvalues of P and eigenvectors that form a base for the complete Minkowski vector space, and in particular include a timelike eigenvector. This analysis is especially of interest when the data on the medium do not provide for an associated velocity field $\mathbf{u}(\mathbf{x})$ that has been at the base of much of our preceding developments. The normalized timelike eigenvector, when it exists, can then take over the role of our W. The conditions that P must satisfy in order that its eigenproblem have the above properties, and a full analysis of these questions, are to be found in the works of Lichnerowicz and of Synge referred to earlier and in the further references contained therein.

The formal aspects of the relativistic mechanics of continuous systems have occupied us for the greater part of our general discussion of these systems. As to the underlying physical content, it will be recalled that our initial stimulus for the introduction of the ideas of continuum mechanics came from the need to take account of Newton's law of action and reaction in a relativistically consistent manner. As the final stage in the development of these ideas, we have been led to the general equations of motion of the form (6-61). In these the explicit notion of *force* apparently has disappeared; the central notion is that of conservation of energy and momentum in a continuous manner throughout a space-time region.

Looking back at the development of the basic ideas of newtonian mechanics, it would appear that a refinement in our theoretical-conceptual structure of mechanics has thus been achieved. This point of view has indeed partly inspired the creation of the general theory of relativity, where the stressing of what may be called the pure field approach finds its culmination. However, when we are not concerned with the approximate gross effects resulting from space-time averaging over an underlying fine-grained structure, but in principle are dealing with what appear to be the ultimate physical systems—whether these consist of what we call matter, or of fields, or of both (if it makes sense to speak of them separately)—the strict elimination of discreteness may be neither possible nor desirable.

6-7 VARIATIONAL FORMULATION OF THE MECHANICS OF CONTINUOUS MEDIA

Let us recall first (see Sec. 4-3) that Hamilton's principle—as applied in nonrelativistic mechanics to a system of a finite number of particles, characterized by a lagrangian function $L(q_a;dq_a/dt;t)$—leads to the Euler equations of the variational problem that constitute the newtonian-lagrangian equations of motion of the system; and that when $\partial L/\partial t = 0$, one obtains the theorem of conservation of energy as a consequence of these equations. Let us now suppose that a field (in the wider sense of the term) can be treated as a mechanical system having an infinite number of degrees of freedom and that we can proceed by analogy with the treatment of finite systems, appropriately modified to insure complete relativistic covariance. It is apparent that the noncovariant variable t occurring in the Lagrangian should be replaced by the 4-vector $\mathbf{x}$, the system variables q being represented by *field-variables* $q(\mathbf{x})$, and the integral to be varied (the "action integral") assuming the form of a four-dimensional integral (the factor $1/c$ insuring that I has the physical dimensions of action)

$$I = \frac{1}{c}\int \mathfrak{L}\sqrt{-g}\,d^4x, \qquad d^4x = dx^0\,dx^1\,dx^2\,dx^3 \qquad \text{(6-113)}$$

with the "lagrangian density" $\mathfrak{L}$ a scalar in $\mathfrak{M}$.

To continue with the analogy, we now expect to obtain the *equations of motion* of our field (the "field equations") as the generalized Euler equations of the hamiltonian-type variation of the action integral (6-113), and to deduce from them the energy-momentum conservation theorems when $\partial\mathfrak{L}/\partial x^\mu = 0$.‡ As to the dependence of $\mathfrak{L}$ on the field functions, it will simplify matters and suffice for our immediate purpose if we take it to involve only the q^a and their covariant derivatives, with the $q^a(a = 1, \ldots, N)$

‡ If we use *general* coordinates only for ordinary space we can write

$$I = \int L\,dt \qquad \begin{aligned} L &= \int \mathfrak{L}\sqrt{G}\,d^3x \\ G &= \det \|g_{ij}\| \end{aligned}$$

so that L corresponds to the classical Lagrangian. In the case of the nonrelativistic mechanics of a field one can introduce the "hamiltonian density" to correspond in a similar fashion to the Hamiltonian of the system. We can see then that the transition from the classical hamiltonian density to the energy-momentum tensor of relativistic theory corresponds in a sense to our transition from t to $\mathbf{x}$, remembering that the energy density of a continuous system is the time-time component of the energy-momentum tensor.

representing an ordered array of the components of a tensor which, for definiteness, we take to have contravariant character.

The derivation of the Euler equations of our variational problem proceeds along lines entirely similar to those employed in the corresponding problem for the classical finite systems. The variation being of the hamiltonian type, both the 4-region of integration as well as x^μ remain unvaried. Since the $g_{\mu\nu}$ and hence the Γ are also unvaried, it follows that $\delta(q^a{}_{;\mu}) = (\delta q^a)_{;\mu}$, and hence

$$\delta I = \frac{1}{c}\int \left[\frac{\partial \mathfrak{L}}{\partial q^a}\,\delta q^a + \frac{\partial \mathfrak{L}}{\partial q^a{}_{;\mu}}\,(\delta q^a)_{;\mu}\right]\sqrt{-g}\,d^4x \tag{6-114}$$

The last term in the integrand inside the brackets can be written

$$(\Pi_a{}^\mu\,\delta q^a)_{;\mu} - \Pi_a{}^\mu{}_{;\mu}\,\delta q^a \tag{6-115}$$

where

$$\Pi_a{}^\mu = \frac{\partial \mathfrak{L}}{\partial q^a{}_{;\mu}} \tag{6-116}$$

To the integral involving the first term of (6-115) one can apply Gauss' theorem (5-107), obtaining a surface integral that is zero by virtue of the vanishing of the δq^a on the boundary. Setting the variation δI of our action integral equal to zero therefore yields the field equations,

$$\frac{\partial \mathfrak{L}}{\partial q^a} - \Pi_a{}^\mu{}_{;\mu} = 0 \tag{6-117}$$

The quantities (6-116) clearly represent a generalization of the classical "canonical momenta."

The energy-momentum tensor of our system—if we are to be guided again by analogy—can be expected to have the form:‡

$$P_\mu{}^\nu = q^a{}_{;\mu}\Pi_a{}^\nu - \delta^\nu_\mu\mathfrak{L} \tag{6-118}$$

This choice does indeed satisfy the conservation relations (6-26), which, in general coordinates, have of course the form

$$P^{\mu\nu}{}_{;\nu} = 0 \tag{6-119}$$

In fact,

$$P_\mu{}^\nu{}_{;\nu} = q^a{}_{;\mu\nu}\Pi_a{}^\nu + q^a{}_{;\mu}\Pi_a{}^\nu{}_{;\nu} - \delta^\nu_\mu[(\partial\mathfrak{L}/\partial q^a)q^a{}_{;\nu} + \Pi_a{}^\sigma q^a{}_{;\sigma\nu}] = \Pi_a{}^\nu(q^a{}_{;\mu\nu} - q^a{}_{;\nu\mu})$$

[by Eq. (6-117)], and hence Eq. (6-119) is satisfied since, owing to the flatness of $\mathfrak{M}$ (see Prob. 5-18):

$$q^a{}_{;\mu\nu} = q^a{}_{;\nu\mu} \tag{6-120}$$

It remains to prove that the quantities (6-118) are the components of a tensor. In view of our assumptions, it is only necessary to prove that the quantities (6-116) are tensor components of the character indicated by

‡ That it is indeed a tensor will be shown presently.

the position of the indices. This can be seen to follow from the invariance properties of the integrand in Eq. (6-114) and the quotient theorem of tensor calculus, by virtue of the tensor character of $\partial \mathfrak{L}/\partial q^a$. From

$$\partial \mathfrak{L}'/\partial q'^a = (\partial \mathfrak{L}/\partial q^b)(\partial q^b/\partial q'^a)$$

and our assumption concerning the q^a it can indeed be easily verified that the $\partial \mathfrak{L}/\partial q^a$ form the covariant components of a tensor.

As to the symmetry condition (6-34), whose significance was pointed out in Sec. 6-2, it is clear that nothing can be said here without further assumptions on the lagrangian density $\mathfrak{L}$; and in fact, in general, the tensor given by (6-118), known as the "canonical energy-momentum tensor," will not be symmetric. What we can do in such cases is discussed in connection with the variational treatment of the electromagnetic field (Sec. 7-2) and in Sec. 8-3.

It would be in place now to apply the present general theory to specific instances of continuous material media such as fluids of given type and given thermodynamic behavior. This application is possible, but it is complicated by the necessity of adjoining special conditions of constraint, owing to the largely phenomenological character of the equations of motion of such systems. The interested reader can find a discussion of this subject as it applies to nonrelativistic hydrodynamics, and references to earlier work, in C. Eckhart, *Phys. Fluids*, **3**: 421 (1960). Relativistic extensions present no difficulties in principle. An early example was given by E. Lamla [*Ann. Physik*, **37**: 772 (1912)], who based his work on Planck's relativistic extension of the variational treatment of thermodynamic systems developed by Helmholtz [M. Planck, *Ann. Physik*, **26**: 1 (1908); also [5], sec. 23f; [7], sec. 47; Tolman, *op. cit.*, chap. 11].‡

Problems

6-1 The components (6-15) form the symmetric part of the matrix $\|d_{i;j}\|$. Using rectangular coordinates, show that the antisymmetric part,

$$\frac{(\text{rot } \mathbf{d})_{ij}}{2} = \frac{(d_{j,i} - d_{i,j})}{2}$$

evaluated at a given space-time point, describes the rigid-body rotation of the element of volume of the medium at that point; and at the same time rederive the relation (6-14). Show also that at a space-time point where the deformation tensor is zero, $\lim_{\Delta t \to 0} (\Delta \mathbf{x} - \Delta \mathbf{a})/\Delta t = \mathbf{\Omega} \times \Delta \mathbf{a}$, where

$$\mathbf{\Omega} = \text{rot}\,\frac{\mathbf{v}}{2}$$

‡ Recent contributions to this subject: I. M. Halatnikov, *Zh. Eksperim. i Teor. Fiz.*, **27**: 529 (1954) (in Russian); Chan-Chin Wei, *Phys. Rev.*, **113**: 1414 (1959).

is the "vorticity vector" (explaining the designations *rot* or *curl*). Compare with the discussion of infinitesimal rotations in Appendix 3A. Give the results also in general coordinates.

6-2 Check the formulas on page 175 leading to Eq. (6-9). Does this result follow more simply by working first in cartesian coordinates?

6-3 Show that the "dilatation rate," as defined on page 176, has the value $v^i{}_{;i}$. [One can prove this for instance by considering the time rate of change of a given 'moving' volume of fluid expressed as a surface integral (noting that $3\int d^3x = \int \text{div}\, \mathbf{x}\, d^3x$), and applying the formula (i) of Prob. 2-1.] Prove (6-13) directly with the aid of Gauss' theorem.

6-4 Under what conditions will the stress pseudotensor of classical elasticity theory be symmetric? [The angular-momentum theorem of newtonian mechanics as applied in an obvious manner to continuous media leads, with the aid of the equations of motion (6-7) and the ubiquitous integral identity of Gauss, to the general relation

$$T^{ij} - T^{ji} = Q^{ij} \tag{i}$$

where Q represents the external torque tensor per unit volume not associated with a nonvanishing body force, if such is present. (A simple example of the presence of such torques is provided by a dielectric substance polarized in an external electric field, the direction of the polarization not being parallel to that of the field.) If, in addition, the medium is possessed of an intrinsic angular momentum (spin) $\mathbf{s}$ per unit mass, then the term $\rho\, d\mathbf{s}/dt$ needs to be added to the left-hand side of Eq. (i).]

6-5 (*a*) In a viscous fluid we have, in place of the stress-strain tensor relation (6-16) that holds in elastic solids, a similar relation connecting the stress components [additional to what is given by (6-9)] with the components of the "velocity strain tensor." The latter are obtained from (6-15) by replacing d^i by the v^i given in (6-3). As an interesting simple application of the method of tensor analysis, show how one can obtain the form of such a relation, assumed to be linear, in the case of completely homogeneous and isotropic conditions, with no dissipative forces arising upon uniform dilatation [i.e., when $v_{1,1} = v_{2,2} = v_{3,3}$ and $v_{i,j} = 0\ (i \neq j)$, as referred to cartesian coordinates]. [One finds, taking T_{ij} symmetric, that

$$T_{ij} = \eta(v_{i;j} + v_{j;i}) - (p + \tfrac{2}{3}\eta v^k{}_{;k})g_{ij} \tag{i}$$

where η is the "coefficient of viscosity" ([3], p. 21).] (*b*) Show that if ϵ is the *internal energy* per unit mass (in the thermodynamic sense) in a continuous medium for which the classical equations of motion (6-7) hold, and if $\mathbf{q}$ is the heat-flux density vector, then

$$\rho \frac{d\epsilon}{dt} = T^{ij}v_{i;j} - \text{div}\, \mathbf{q} \tag{ii}$$

so that in particular, for a viscous and incompressible fluid with negligible heat flow,

$$\rho \frac{d\epsilon}{dt} = 2\eta v_{(i;j)} v^{(i;j)}, \qquad v^{i;j} \equiv g^{jk} v^i{}_{;k}$$

(the meaning of the parentheses is explained on page 138). This equation shows that $\eta > 0$, since the internal energy increases as a result of the heat developed by viscosity. In confirmation of this conclusion prove also, as a consequence of Eq. (6-7), that

$$\frac{\partial}{\partial t} (\tfrac{1}{2}\rho v^2) + (\tfrac{1}{2}\rho v^2 v^i - T^{ji} v_j)_{;i} = -T^{ij} v_{i;j} + f^i v_i \qquad \text{(iii)}$$

and hence that for the above special fluid with η constant, and assumed confined within the volume V and free of body forces, we have

$$-\frac{\partial}{\partial t} \int_V \tfrac{1}{2}\rho v^2 \, dV = 2\eta \int_V v_{(i;j)} v^{(i;j)} \, dV \qquad \text{(iv)}$$

(showing the dissipation of gross kinetic energy into heat through internal friction). [The derivation of (iii) involves Eqs. (6-12) and (6-13). In the proof of (iv) one uses the pertinent boundary condition of the vanishing of the normal component of $\mathbf{v}$ on the boundary of V. To obtain Eq. (ii), one can first derive the expression of the first law of thermodynamics as applied to a (macroscopically) infinitesimal drop of the medium of volume δV (remembering the underlying physical picture of the continuous medium model),

$$\frac{d}{dt}\left[\rho\left(\frac{v^2}{2} + \epsilon\right)\delta V\right] = [f^i v_i + (T^{ij} v_i)_{;j} - \operatorname{div} \mathbf{q}]\, \delta V$$

and then find $d(\rho v^2 \, \delta V/2)/dt$ using Eqs. (6-7) and (6-8).] (*c*) Prove that for a perfect fluid for which the equation of state (6-10) does not involve T and in which no heat transfer takes place, there exists an intrinsic potential energy per unit mass ϕ defined by the differential equation

$$d\phi = -p \, d\left(\frac{1}{\rho}\right)$$

Interpret the right-hand side of this equation.

6-6 (*a*) When one does not restrict the deformation of a body to be small, as was done in Sec. 6-1, one can still define the deformation tensor e_{ij}, and in a manner similar to that outlined there. Note that Eq. (6-14) is equivalent to the equation

$$|\Delta \mathbf{x}|^2 - |\Delta \mathbf{a}|^2 = 2e_{ij} \, \Delta a^i \, \Delta a^j \qquad \text{(i)}$$

(the symbol Δ indicating differentials) and show that this relation can be retained in the case of finite deformations, i.e., when the restriction on

$\mathbf{d} = \mathbf{x} - \mathbf{a}$ to be infinitesimal is abandoned; provided

$$e_{ij} = \tfrac{1}{2}(d_{i;j} + d_{j;i}) + d_{k;i}\, d^k{}_{;j} \tag{ii}$$

where the covariant derivatives are taken with respect to the metric tensor $g_{ij}(a)$ in the initial state of the body. {Introduce in the deformed state (at the given time t) a set of *general* coordinates by assigning to the point $\mathbf{x}(\mathbf{a},t)$, i.e., the point Q of Fig. 6-2, the coordinates a^i [these being the coordinates used in (i)], where the position vectors are of course taken with respect to a fixed cartesian frame. Recall (5-22) and the expression for the local base vectors in terms of the rectangular and general coordinates (see page 146): $\mathbf{e}_i(a) = \partial\mathbf{a}/\partial a^i$, and similar expressions for the base vectors in the deformed state; and use the result in Prob. 5-13.} (*b*) Whether the deformation of a body is finite or not, the tensor e cannot be assigned arbitrarily. This is fairly obvious from the geometric significance of this tensor. Show that the analytical conditions that must be satisfied by e (the "compatibility relations") can be obtained from the theorem that the vanishing of the Riemann curvature tensor (see Prob. 5-19 for its definition) is a sufficient (as well as obviously necessary) condition for the flatness of a riemannian space. (*c*) Consider now a body, which, in an idealized sense, can be taken as perfectly rigid when at rest in a given inertial frame S, and suppose that the geometric state of this body (i.e., its spatial configuration at each instant of time) is surveyed from S after it has been put in some given accelerated motion relative to S. What general conclusions can be drawn concerning the results of such observation when the deformation arising from the relativistic contraction is accounted for on the basis of hypothesis C of Sec. 3-5? In particular, examine quantitatively the case of uniform rotation about a given axis in S. [See [3], pp. 59–60. For earlier references bearing on this question and on the related problem of a consistent and meaningful definition of *rigidity* in STR, see [7], sec. 45; for later work see, e.g., H. Arzeliès, "La Cinématique Relativiste," chap. 9, Gauthier-Villars, Paris, 1955.]

6-7 (*a*) Deduce the result (6-46) holding in an inertial frame S, by a direct examination of the energy content of a given element of volume in the medium as it would be defined in S. {Note that Eqs. (6-49), (6-42), and (6-43) imply the relation

$$g = -T^{ij}W_iW_j \tag{i}$$

[which can also be checked directly with the aid of Eq. (6-50) and a suitable choice of orientation of the spatial axes]. Recall the discussion relating to the last term in (6-31), and consider the unbalance in S in the rate of inflow of energy into the medium element under consideration arising from the work of the stresses. For an alternative instructive proof see [9], pp. 67–68.} (*b*) Find the pressure p on a surface σ of a rigid body moving with uniform velocity $v \sim c$ through a large body of gas at rest in an inertial frame S^* and having there the temperature T. Assume that σ is perpendicular to the direction of **v**, and that T and the rest density ρ^* of the gas correspond to standard conditions. Verify directly that p is the same whether measured in S^* or in the rest frame S of the body. [One can show by means of familiar reasoning that under the specified (as well as tacitly implied) conditions we have in S^* or in S the formula $p = 2\rho^* v^2 \gamma_v^2$ holding to high approximation.] (*c*) Prove the result (6-65), i.e., the relativistic invariance of pressure, by a direct consideration of the laboratory definition of pressure as force per unit area. (It will help to consider the law of transformation of the force components along and perpendicular to the direction of **u**, with a corresponding treatment of the element of area under consideration.)

6-8 (*a*) Prove that $\rho^* = \rho/\gamma_u$, where ρ is defined in (6-20), is a relativistic scalar, so that

$$(\rho^* U^\nu)_{,\nu} = 0 \tag{i}$$

is a relativistically covariant equation. Show that this equation represents the conservation of proper mass by reducing it to the form (6-13) (for rectangular coordinates), as well as by showing that in the local rest frame S^*

$$(\rho^* U^\nu)_{,\nu} = \frac{1}{\delta V^*} \frac{d}{dt^*} (\rho^* \, \delta V^*) \tag{ii}$$

Derive also from (i) the standard integral conservation equation by applying Gauss' theorem in $\mathfrak{M}$. (*b*) It has been assumed that we are employing lorentzian coordinates. What changes are required if we use general coordinates? What physical restrictions need to be introduced in the latter case?

6-9 Prove that the validity of the symmetry relations (6-33) in every inertial system entails the validity of the covariant symmetry relations (6-34). {A convenient way of proving this result is to make use of infinitesimal Lorentz transformations [see Eq. (3A-10)]. We need assume actually no more than the linearity of the transformations.}

6-10 Prove that the condition of being a *bounded* system as defined on page 187, is a covariant condition. (It may be helpful to consider first the case of quantities vanishing at finite spatial distance and make use of a schematic graphical representation in space-time with suppression of two spatial dimensions.)

6-11 Show that the quantities f^μ occurring in (6-56) form a 4-vector by considering directly the explicit definition of these quantities. (Show that f^μ can also be interpreted as the components of Minkowski force per unit rest volume.)

6-12 (*a*) Show that the results given in Sec. 4-2 concerning angular momenta and definitions of center of mass for discrete particle systems can be extended to continuous mechanical systems that are both closed and bounded and for which the vector G defined in Eq. (6-52) is timelike. Give simple examples when the latter condition is satisfied. [The extension of (4-35), for instance, is

$$c^i \equiv c^i(S;x^0) = \frac{1}{E}\int x^i h(\mathbf{x})\, d^3x, \qquad E = cG^0 = \int h\, d^3x$$

and moreover $dc^i/dt = u^i = c^2G^i/E$, so that these points are all at rest in the "rest frame" S^* of the mechanical system defined by the vanishing of G^i; $c^i(S^*) \equiv c^{*i}$ has distinguishing properties; etc.] (*b*) From the results concerning the center of mass $\mathbf{c}^*$, show that if our mechanical system is restricted further to have positive energy density h in every inertial frame, then when it possesses nonvanishing internal angular momentum its size is bounded below in the following way: the radius R of a sphere about the center of mass in S^* enclosing the mechanical system completely, must satisfy the inequality

$$R \geq \frac{1}{cM^*}\sqrt{\tfrac{1}{2}L^{ij}(\mathbf{c}^*)L_{ij}(\mathbf{c}^*)} \equiv \rho, \qquad M^*c^2 = G^\lambda G_\lambda \tag{i}$$

(Møller). [Show first, using lorentzian coordinates and applying the tensor transformation corresponding to the coordinate transformation matrix (6-40), where $U^\lambda = G^\lambda/M^*$, that (with definitions given in Sec. 4-2) $L^{i0}(\mathbf{c}^*) = L^{*ik}(\mathbf{c}^*)W^k$, then use (4-41) to prove that ρ as defined in (i) gives the maximum for all possible inertial frames S of the distances as measured in S^* between the simultaneous positions of the centers of mass associated with S and S^*; and lastly make use of the assumed special property of h.]

6-13 (*a*) Consider a continuous mechanical system that satisfies, when referred to a suitably chosen inertial system of coordinates S^*, the following two conditions: (1) S^* is the "rest frame" of the mechanical system, i.e., $\mathbf{G}^* = 0$; (2) it is "static," i.e., its state does not vary with time. However, it need not be closed (it could be, for instance, a fluid enclosed in a vessel—the outside forces, disregarding gravity, deriving from the pressure of the container walls). Prove, using lorentzian coordinates, that for such a system we have in an arbitrary inertial frame [see (6-52); $E = cG^0$]

$$E = \gamma(E^* + \sigma)$$
$$G^i = \frac{1}{c^2}\left[\left(\gamma E^* + \frac{\gamma - 1}{\beta^2}\sigma\right)u^i + S^{*ij}u^j\right] \tag{i}$$

where

$$S^{\lambda\mu} \equiv \int_{t=\text{const.}} P^{\lambda\mu}\, d^3x, \qquad \sigma \equiv S^{*ij}\beta_i\beta_j, \qquad \beta \equiv \beta_u, \qquad \gamma \equiv \gamma_u \tag{ii}$$

and $\mathbf{u}$ is the velocity of S^* relative to the given frame; and that these quantities are time independent. If the mechanical system is also bounded and closed, show that $S^{*ij} = 0$, so that Eqs. (i) and (ii) reduce to the 'particle' form

$$G^\lambda = M^* U^\lambda, \qquad M^* = \frac{1}{c^2} E^* \tag{iii}$$

In the case of a perfect fluid, show that (i) and (ii) become

$$E = \gamma(E^* + \beta^2 P^*), \qquad G^i = \frac{1}{c^2}\gamma(E^* + P^*)u^i, \qquad P = \int p\, d^3x \tag{iv}$$

from which it follows that

$$E + P = \gamma(E^* + P^*), \qquad G^i = \frac{1}{c^2}(E + P)u^i \tag{v}$$

which is the same transformation as is obeyed by the 4-momentum $((E + P)/c, G^i)$ of a particle of rest mass $(E^* + P^*)/c^2$. (*b*) For continuous systems referred to above, for which Eqs. (iii) apply when they are closed, prove that Eq. (6-58) is a relativistically covariant equation if the external forces are such that the internal macroscopic state of the system as measured in S^* does not change in the course of the action and if the resulting acceleration is uniform throughout the medium at each instant of S^* time; and that in fact Eq. (6-58) assumes, then, in any inertial frame, the 'particle' form [bearing in mind the difference in meaning of the same symbols appearing in (4-7) and in (6-58)], $\mathsf{F} = M^*\, d\mathsf{U}/dt$, M^* as given in (iii) (v. Laue). If the spatial dimensions of the medium are appreciable, does our assumption concerning the uniformity of the acceleration bring us into conflict with relativistic kinematics? Do we have here an indication of a possible logical advantage in starting the development of relativistic mechanics with a consideration of particles?

6-14 With the aid of Gauss' theorem in $\mathfrak{M}$ show that for bounded and closed continuous media, the integrals (6-52) and (6-55) can be expressed in the explicitly covariant form,

$$G^\mu = \frac{1}{c}\int_{S_3} P^{\mu\nu}\, dS_\nu, \qquad L^{\lambda\mu} = \frac{1}{c}\int_{S_3} R^{\lambda\mu\nu}\, dS_\nu \tag{i}$$

where S_3 is a spacelike hypersurface.

6-15 (*a*) The tensors T^{ij} and P^{ij} have been termed "relative" and "absolute" stress tensors by v. Laue. In order to see the fitness of this appellation, show that Eq. (6-56) can also be written with the aid of Eqs. (6-25) and (6-31), as

$$\frac{\delta h}{\delta t} = (T^{ij}u^i)_{,j} + cf^0, \qquad \frac{\delta g^i}{\delta t} = T^{ij}{}_{,j} + f^i$$

$$\frac{\delta h}{\delta t} \equiv \frac{1}{\delta V}\frac{d}{dt}(h\,\delta V) = \frac{\partial h}{\partial t} + (hu^i)_{,i} \tag{i}$$

(the volume δV referring to a given element of the medium), and that consequently,

$$\frac{dE}{dt} = \int T^{ij} u_i \, dS_j + cF^0, \qquad \frac{dG^i}{dt} = \int T^{ij} \, dS^j + F^i \tag{ii}$$

the surface integrals being taken over the spatial boundary of a given portion of the medium, the integrated quantities E, etc., referring to that portion. Note also that, as observed by v. Laue, the expressions (i) and (ii) correspond to the lagrangian approach in hydrodynamics [see footnote on page 174; compare (i) with the classical equations of motion (6-7), remembering Eq. (6-8)]. In this connection show also that (with understandable notation)

$$\frac{d}{dt} \int_{V(\text{moving})} (\mathbf{x} \times \mathbf{g})^i \, dV = \epsilon_{ijk} \int x^j T^{ks} \, dS^s + \int_{V(\text{moving})} (\mathbf{x} \times \mathbf{f})^i \, dV \tag{iii}$$

whereas

$$\frac{d}{dt} \int_{V(\text{fixed})} (\mathbf{x} \times \mathbf{g})^i \, dV = -\epsilon_{ijk} \int x^j P^{ks} \, dS^s + \int_{V(\text{fixed})} (\mathbf{x} \times \mathbf{f})^i \, dV \tag{iv}$$

[In the derivation of (iii), use Eqs. (6-25) and (6-32), while Eqs. (6-32) and (6-56) enter in the derivation of (iv).] (*b*) Examine critically the relativistic definitions of the spatial tensors T^{ij} and P^{ij} in terms of measurements that can be carried out in an arbitrarily given inertial frame, at least in principle. In particular, consider the sense in which the operation of the principle of action and reaction can be taken to be fully consistent with the requirements of STR, bearing in mind the macroscopic nature of our theoretical model of a continuous mechanical system.

6-16 Consider again the Tolman-Lewis right-angled lever referred to in Prob. 4-3 (see Fig. 4-2). The result given there presented a seeming paradox. How is it resolved? [Since we are dealing with an elastically strained body, the considerations of this chapter apply, which point to an increase in the angular momentum of our mechanical system at the rate of $(f_1 v/c)^2 a_1 v = f_1 a_1 \beta^2$ per sec (as measured in the 'stationary' frame), bearing in mind the idealization involved in the problem. See [9], pp. 79–80; [5], sec. 22c.]

6-17 (*a*) Consider a simple thermodynamic system consisting of a homogeneous fluid whose state can be fully specified by two variables such as, say, the pressure p and temperature T. By using the first law of thermodynamics assumed to hold in the local rest frame S^* and the relativistic energy-momentum relations for continuous media developed in this chapter, show that the transformation law for the quantity of heat Q exchanged in a given process is given by the formula

$$Q = \frac{1}{\gamma} Q^*, \qquad \begin{array}{l} \gamma \equiv \gamma_u \\ \mathbf{u} \text{ velocity of } S^* \text{ relative to } S \end{array}$$

(agreeing with the result obtained in Sec. 6-6). [Use the relations (v) of Prob. 6-13, which here reduce to

$$\begin{aligned} E + pV &= \gamma(E^* + p^*V^*) \\ \mathbf{G} &= \frac{1}{c^2}(E + pV)\mathbf{u} \end{aligned} \qquad V = \text{volume of the fluid} \tag{i}$$

and note that the quantity δW in Eq. (6-80), which is $-p\,\delta V^*$ in S^*, is in an arbitrarily given inertial frame S equal to $-p\,\delta V + \mathbf{u}\cdot d\mathbf{G}$, since a force $d\mathbf{G}/dt$ is operative in S, the velocity $\mathbf{u}$ remaining constant during the process in question.] (*b*) If the system consists of black-body radiation in an enclosure, deduce from the known results $E^* = aV^*T^{*4}$, $p^* = \frac{1}{3}aT^{*4}$, where a is the Stefan-Boltzman constant, that

$$E = \gamma\left(1 + \frac{1}{3}\frac{v^2}{c^2}\right)E^*, \qquad \mathbf{G} = \frac{4}{3c^2}\gamma E^*\mathbf{u} \tag{ii}$$

[Details concerning relativistic thermodynamics can be found, e.g. in [9], chap. 5; [5], secs. 23–24; [7], sec. 46; and in included references. Not surprisingly, the results (ii) were first found directly from electromagnetic theory without explicit use of the transformation formulas of STR (and hence with greater labor). For references see [7], p. 138.]

6-18 (*a*) Prove Eq. (6-95). (*b*) Show that Eq. (6-98) reduces to Eq. (6-101).

6-19 Suppose that a rectangular bar resting in the inertial frame S^* is uniformly compressed by constant pressure p^* acting simultaneously at both ends of the bar over its transverse area A^* for the duration $t^* = 0$ to $t^* = t_1^*$. Thus, if $2\delta l^*$ is the resulting decrease in the length of the bar, the total work done upon it by the pressures is $\delta W^* = 2p^*A^*\,\delta l^* = p^*\,\delta V^*$. Consider a reference frame S moving with constant speed v relative to S^* in the longitudinal direction of the bar. (*a*) Find the work δW of compression as would be determined in S, and compare with pertinent results in Sec. 6.6. (*b*) H. Arzeliès [*Nuovo Cimento*, **35**: 792 (1965)] finds the expression

$$\delta W = p^*A^*\gamma_v[(\delta l^* + vt_1^*) - (-\delta l^* + vt_1^*)] = \gamma_v\,\delta W^* \tag{i}$$

concluding that all the previously accepted transformation rules of relativistic thermodynamics [such as (6-104) and (6-108)] need revision. Accepting (i), explain Arzeliès' conclusion. However, examine critically the assumptions that must be invoked to arrive at (i), and compare them with those that underlie the conventional approach to the subject.

6-20 The relativistic extension under proper conditions of the classical Maxwell-Boltzmann kinetic theory methods presents no difficulties in principle, and with use of our covariant methods the derivations are straightforward. A simple example is presented in [1], sec. 53, where the macroscopic energy-momentum tensor $P^{\mu\nu}$ is derived in the following fashion. Consider an element of the medium of unit volume, small in the macroscopic sense but large on the atomic scale, and let **u** denote the velocity of its center of mass. Writing $\mathbf{v} = \mathbf{u} + \mathbf{w}$ for the velocity of a representative particle in the system forming this element, we set

$$P^{\mu\nu} = \Sigma m(v)(u^\mu + w^\mu)(u^\nu + w^\nu) \qquad \begin{aligned} u^\mu &= (c,\mathbf{u}) \\ w^\mu &= (0,\mathbf{w}) \end{aligned} \tag{i}$$

where the summation is extended over all particles of the element in the spirit of kinetic theory. It is concluded that

$$P^{\mu\nu} = \rho(u)u^\mu u^\nu + \Sigma m(v)w^\mu w^\nu \tag{ii}$$

(*a*) What are the simplifying assumptions tacitly made in posing (i)? Have the results discussed in Sec. 4-2 any relevance? Can you justify (ii)? What transport property is represented by the last term in (ii)? Supposing that (because of a possible misinterpretation of notation) we have misread the intent in the above formulation as here presented, rederive $P^{\mu\nu}$ on the assumption of a maxwellian distribution with respect to the local rest frames S^*, by first finding $P^{*\mu\nu}$ and then transforming to the given frame. Compare your result with (ii) and with Eqs. (6-39) to (6-45), and interpret its physical significance. Reformulate the above problem for greater explicitness by introducing the distribution function $f(\mathbf{x},\mathbf{V})$ for our system, assuming that it consists of only one type of particle. [$f(\mathbf{x},\mathbf{V})\, dx^1\, dx^2\, dx^3 \cdot dV^1\, dV^2\, dV^3 \equiv f\, d^3x\, d^3V$ = number of particles at the time t in the volume $d^3x\, d^3V$, $\mathbf{V} = \gamma_v \mathbf{v}$.] What advantage is there in using $f(\mathbf{x},\mathbf{V})$ rather than $f(\mathbf{x};\mathbf{v})$? Could we use as readily a distribution function involving the 4-momentum rather than the 4-velocity of a particle? [See Taub, *op. cit.* (on page 197); Synge *op. cit.* (on page 204). A very clear presentation of relevant ideas and results in the classical theory can be found, e.g., in D. J. Rose and M. Clark, Jr., "Plasmas and Controlled Fusion," chaps. 4 and 6, The M.I.T. Press and John Wiley & Sons, Inc., New York, 1961. On the relativistic Boltzmann equation see, e.g., Yu. L. Klimontovich, *Soviet Phys. JETP*, **37** (**10**) : 524 (1960); S. Yadavalli, *J. Franklin Inst.*, **271** : 368 (1961); I. Abonyi, *Cahier Phys.*, **171–172** : 461 (1964); *Beiträge aus der Plasmaphysik* Heft 1/2 (1965); and references given in these papers.]

6-21 Consider an isolated ideal monatomic gas. Applying the Maxwell-Boltzmann theory find approximately for what values of the parameter mc^2/kT (m = rest mass of an atom, k = Boltzmann's constant, T = absolute temperature) do deviations from classical theory become appreciable. Show that the mean value of $\mathbf{P} \cdot \mathbf{v}$ is $3kT$, and compare this result with the classical equipartition law. (See the references given on page 204.)

6-22 (*a*) The following is an instructive and frequently used example to bring out the significance of the quantities that occur in the variational principle for continuous systems discussed in Sec. 6-7. We start with an infinite (but discrete) nonrelativistic system of particles, each of mass m, and all moving on a straight line (which we take as the x axis). We assume further that each particle interacts with its immediate neighbors according to a linear elastic law, so that the potential-energy function of the system is $\frac{1}{2} \sum_n k(\phi_{n+1} - \phi_n)^2$, where ϕ_n is the displacement of the nth particle from its equilibrium position x_n. The Lagrangian of the system is therefore

$$L = \tfrac{1}{2} \sum_n [m(\dot{\phi}_n)^2 - k(\phi_{n+1} - \phi_n)^2] \tag{i}$$

If one now lets the interparticle distance $a \to 0$, and assumes that at the same time $m \to 0$ and $k \to \infty$, so that m/a and ka have the finite limits λ and κ, one finds that L given in (i) has the limit

$$L = \frac{1}{2} \int \left[\lambda \left(\frac{\partial \phi}{\partial t} \right)^2 - \kappa \left(\frac{\partial \phi}{\partial x} \right)^2 \right] dx \tag{ii}$$

Verify this result. Find the Euler-Lagrange equations for the Lagrangian (i), and show that their limit is given by the one-dimensional wave equation

$$\frac{\partial^2 \phi}{\partial t^2} - v^2 \frac{\partial^2 \phi}{\partial x^2} = 0, \qquad v^2 = \frac{\kappa}{\lambda} \tag{iii}$$

which is the Euler-Lagrange equation corresponding to (ii). [See Goldstein, *op. cit.*, sec. 11-1 for an illustration in terms of an elastic rod.] (*b*) Introduce in the above example the further assumption that each particle is bound elastically to its equilibrium position, so that a term of the form $-\sum_n k'{\phi_n}^2/2$ has to be added to (i). Carry out a similar limiting process as given in (*a*) and show that (ii) is modified to

$$L = \frac{1}{2} \int \left[\lambda \left(\frac{\partial \phi}{\partial t} \right)^2 - \kappa \left(\frac{\partial \phi}{\partial x} \right)^2 - \kappa' \phi^2 \right] dx, \qquad \kappa' = \lim \frac{k'}{a}$$

with the Euler-Lagrange equation

$$\frac{1}{v^2} \frac{\partial^2 \phi}{\partial t^2} - \frac{\partial^2 \phi}{\partial x^2} + \mu^2 \phi^2 = 0, \qquad \mu^2 = \frac{\kappa'}{\kappa} = \lim \frac{1}{a^2} \frac{k'}{k} \tag{iv}$$

v being defined in (iii). Generalizing this to three-dimensional space, and taking $v = c$ in (iv), obtain

$$\Box\phi + \mu^2\phi = 0, \qquad \Box \equiv \frac{1}{c^2}\frac{\partial^2}{\partial t^2} - \nabla^2 \tag{v}$$

which has the form of the well-known Klein-Gordon equation in quantum mechanics (see Schiff, *op. cit.*, sec. 42). Show that the associated lagrangian density $\mathfrak{L}$ has in general coordinates the form

$$\mathfrak{L} = \tfrac{1}{2}(g^{\sigma\tau}\phi_{;\sigma}\phi_{;\tau} - \mu^2\phi^2) \tag{vi}$$

and that the canonical energy-momentum tensor deducible from (vi) is

$$P_{\mu\nu} = \phi_{;\mu}\phi_{;\nu} - \tfrac{1}{2}g_{\mu\nu}(g^{\sigma\tau}\phi_{;\sigma}\phi_{;\tau} - \mu^2\phi^2) \tag{vii}$$

so that it is already symmetric. Show also that the energy density associated with (vii) is *positive*. Do you find anything paradoxical in the fact that starting with newtonian considerations we arrived at a relativistically covariant result?

7
The Electromagnetic Field

We have noted repeatedly the central place occupied by electromagnetic theory in the development of STR. This is explained of course in part by the fact that Maxwell's equations of the pure electromagnetic field are already fully relativistic. For this reason and because of the familiarity we have by now acquired with relativistic methods, our first task, that of casting the Maxwell-Lorentz theory into a manifestly covariant form in $\mathfrak{M}$, will require little effort, and little more is needed to find its *generally* covariant form (Sec. 7-1). Mathematically, we are then partially tooled up for the general relativistic treatment of the electromagnetic field. Partly to the same end we examine at some length the corresponding variational formulation (Sec. 7-2), although a more conclusive discussion is possible only within the context of the general theory of relativity.

Of the many special topics in electrodynamics only a few need occupy us here. The problems presented by electromagnetic phenomena in continuous media have historical interest and, as noted previously, their study is also of some interest in connection with the currently developing investigations in 'relativistic plasmas.' The discussion in Sec. 7-3 is intended to serve only as an introduction to some of the elements of what is a fairly extensive and not entirely closed subject.

The motion of a charged particle in a given electromagnetic field is of course another topic of historic as well as general interest, especially when one allows also for accelerations such that reactive radiation forces are appreciable. This topic is treated extensively in modern textbooks on electrodynamics, and its calculational and applicational details need not concern us here. The central concepts and specific relativistic methods that enter in the analysis of this problem are however of interest in our general study of relativistic theory. They are discussed in Secs. 6-4 and 6-5, the former section dealing mainly with the problem of radiation from an accelerated point charge, and including also a brief excursion on a rigorous basis for the widely used δ symbolism that is very convenient in the treatment of point particles. The interaction of a number of fast moving elementary charges presents problems for which no definitive and universally accepted general theory is known, if indeed such a theory on purely classical-relativistic ideas can have any far-reaching scope. A sketch of some current developments on this question is contained in Sec. 6-5 and in Appendix 7A.

The incorporation of gravitation within STR has challenged theorists from the earliest days of the development of relativity. There exist subtle and compelling arguments why the confines of the special theory are too narrow to permit this, and Einstein's general theory of relativity is a brilliant outgrowth of these arguments. Most physicists today accept his theory as presenting a correct basis for the treatment of gravitation. Nevertheless, theories of gravitation within STR have been proposed even after the advent of Einstein's general theory. Aside from their historic interest, the former are conceptually simpler than the latter theory, and one would wish in any case to examine them critically before giving oneself over completely to the demands of the latter theory. This topic is therefore considered briefly in Appendix 7B, inasmuch as the first attempts at developing a relativistic theory of gravitation were guided by the similarity in form between gravitational and Coulomb interactions. For purposes of comparison, a very brief sketch of the elements of the general theory of relativity is also included.

7-1 COVARIANT FORMULATION OF THE MAXWELL-LORENTZ EQUATIONS

It is possible to arrive at the desired covariant formulation in lorentzian coordinates in a number of alternative ways. The one we choose is based on the observation that, according to its definition as force per unit charge, the electric field intensity $\mathbf{E}$ is a *polar* vector, and therefore, by the second of Eqs. (2-1), $\mathbf{B}$ is an axial vector, or in other words, a pseudovector associated with an *antisymmetric* tensor B_{ij} (see relevant discussion in Sec. 5-4). By reasoning now familiar to us we can expect that our covariant formulation involves an antisymmetric 4-tensor $B_{\alpha\beta}$ whose spatial part coincides with B_{ij}. An examination of the first of Eqs. (2-1) then discloses that it corresponds to the set $\alpha = i$, $\beta = j$, $\gamma = k$ of the covariant set of equations‡

$$B_{\alpha\beta,\gamma} + B_{\beta\gamma,\alpha} + B_{\gamma\alpha,\beta} = 0 \tag{7-1}$$

The remaining equations obtained by taking $\alpha = i$, $\beta = j$, and $\gamma = 0$, are

$$B_{ij,0} + B_{j0,i} + B_{0i,j} = 0$$

These are seen to reproduce the second vector equation in (2-1), provided

$$\mathbf{E} = (B_{10}, B_{20}, B_{30}) \tag{7-2}$$

Let us now consider first the sourcefree case, i.e., the case of vanishing ρ in Eqs. (2-2). If the original Maxwell equations in free space are indeed relativistically covariant, and if our extension $B_{\alpha\beta}$ constitutes a 4-tensor, then the set (2-2) should also be embraced in a covariant equation involving this tensor. It is at once verified that the last equation in (2-2) (with $\rho = 0$) represents the $\alpha = 0$ part of the 4-vector equation

$$B^{\alpha\beta}{}_{,\beta} = 0 \tag{7-3}$$

It remains therefore to verify that the spatial part coincides with the first vector equation in (2-2) (with $\rho = 0$). This is easily done when due attention is paid to our choice of metric in $\mathfrak{M}$. Thus,

$$B^{1\alpha}{}_{,\alpha} = B^{1i}{}_{,i} + B^{10}{}_{,0} = B_{12,2} - B_{31,3} - B_{10,0} = \frac{\partial B_z}{\partial y} - \frac{\partial B_y}{\partial z} - \frac{\partial E_x}{c\,\partial t} = 0$$

represents the x component of the first equation in (2-2), and the other two equations follow similarly.

Turning now to the inhomogeneous Maxwell-Lorentz equations (2-2), it is clear that for their covariant formulation we require a relativistically consistent definition of charge and current densities. It will be remembered that in the original Lorentz theory, electric charges and their velocities are assumed to be continuously distributed (throughout the "electrons"!). We could refer therefore to the relevant discussion in Sec. 6-2. However, it suffices to recall that $(c,\mathbf{u}) = \mathsf{U}/\gamma_u$, in order to see that Eqs. (2-2) can be written [in generalization of (7-3)]:

$$\operatorname{Div} B = \frac{4\pi}{c}\,\mathsf{s} \tag{7-4}$$

where

$$\mathsf{s} = \rho\mathsf{U}, \qquad \rho = \frac{1}{\gamma_u}\,\rho(u) \tag{7-5}$$

‡ See Eqs. (5-106). Though we are now using the first letters of the Greek alphabet, we are not now following the temporary convention tacitly introduced in connection with Eq. (3-33): we are continuing to employ the *real* time variable, so that now α, β, etc. range over 0, 1, 2, 3 and not over 1, 2, 3, 4, as, e.g., in Eq. (3-34).

$\rho(u)$ representing the quantity denoted by ρ in (2-2). Equation (7-4) is manifestly covariant, provided s is in fact a 4-vector, i.e., provided ρ in (7-5) is a 4-scalar. Comparing the last of Eqs. (7-5) and Eq. (6-20) and, recalling the significance of the symbols in the latter equation,‡ it is clear that the assumption of the relativistic invariance of the quantity ρ given in (7-5) is equivalent to the assumption of invariance of electric charge, i.e., to the assumption that the quantity of electric charge associated with a given body (i.e., a 'lastingly identifiable' object such as a condenser or an electron) is, unlike the relative inertial mass of a body, the same whatever the inertial frame in which it is measured (see Prob. 7-1).

An alternative approach for arriving at Eqs. (7-1) is to start with the representation of the field vectors in terms of electromagnetic potentials:

$$\mathbf{E} = -\frac{1}{c}\frac{\partial \mathbf{A}}{\partial t} - \nabla\phi, \qquad \mathbf{B} = \text{rot}\,\mathbf{A} \tag{7-6}$$

One finds that with the identification

$$A^\alpha = (\phi,\mathbf{A}) \tag{7-7}$$

Equations (7-6) can be represented by the 4-tensor equation

$$\text{Rot}\,\mathsf{A} = -B \tag{7-8}$$

Equations (7-1) then follow directly from the identity (i) in Prob. 5-14. One must now, of course, prove in an independent fashion that the A^α defined in (7-7) form a 4-vector (see Prob. 7-2). On the other hand, if we do not go back to the conventional equations, but start with the covariant Eq. (7-8) as the definition of A, we need to ascertain the adequacy of this definition. It can in fact be shown that Eq. (7-1) serves as the integrability condition for this equation in A (see [8], chap. 9, sec. 8).

We have still to consider the Lorentz force formula (2-3). This, as we know, is not a covariant equation. As noted previously, it was only after the work of Poincaré (1905), Einstein (1905), and Planck (1906) that we knew how to handle this equation correctly as part of a relativistic formulation of mechanics that was itself evolving from those searching studies of the Maxwell-Lorentz equations. With the knowledge we now have at hand, though, our task is straightforward. We observe that the right-hand side of Eq. (2-3) has the form, $B_{i\nu}W^\nu/\gamma_u$ ($W^\nu \equiv U^\nu/c$). Since $\mathbf{f}$ in Eq. (2-3) represents the newtonian force per unit charge, one can conclude by Eqs. (7-5) and (4-7), that in terms of the *Minkowski* force per unit rest volume, Eq. (2-3) can be rewritten (retaining the symbol f for the latter force) as

$$f_i = \rho B_{\nu i} W^\nu$$

‡ Since we shall not have occasion (except in Prob. 7-7) to consider the densities of mass and of charge simultaneously, our use of the same symbol ρ for both quantities is permissible.

allowing also for the fact that with our choice of Minkowski metric signature,

$$f_i = -f^i \tag{7-9}$$

Since ρ is an invariant, it is now apparent that these equations form the spatial part of the covariant set

$$f_\alpha = \rho B_{\beta\alpha} W^\beta = \frac{1}{c} B_{\beta\alpha} s^\beta \tag{7-10}$$

The time component of this equation represents—as it should, and as is immediately verified—the time rate of work done by the electromagnetic field on unit element of volume of the charges, as measured in the given inertial frame.

In the rest system of the charges at a given space-time point, we find by Eqs. (7-10), (7-2), and (7-9) that

$$\mathbf{f} = \rho \mathbf{E} \tag{7-11}$$

But this is just the *Coulomb force* per unit volume. The Lorentz force is thus only an aspect of the Coulomb force as surveyed from a reference frame that is moving uniformly relative to the element of charge being acted upon. This is a noteworthy result, though upon reflection it need not greatly surprise us.

It is instructive to deduce the electromagnetic-force formula (7-10) by direct transformation from the local rest frame S^*, in which we have (7-11) and hence $f^{*\mu} = (0,\rho B^*{}_{i0}) = (0,\rho B^{*0i})$. By Eqs. (3-29) [see also (6-40)] we find, in a few simple steps, that (with $\gamma \equiv \gamma_u$)

$$B^{*0i} = \gamma B^{0i} + \frac{1}{\gamma + 1} W^j W^i B^{j0} - W^j B^{ji} \tag{7-12}$$

We need only recall the transformation law for tensors, remembering that

$$B^{\alpha\beta} = -B^{\beta\alpha} \tag{7-13}$$

and the remark enclosed in parentheses in the text above (6-43), as well as the identity $\gamma^2\beta^2 = \gamma^2 - 1$ ($\beta \equiv \beta_u$). Applying now Eqs. (3-29) to the 4-vector $\mathfrak{f}$, and using (7-12), it follows that

$$f^0 = W^i \rho B^{*0i} = \rho\left(\gamma - \frac{\gamma^2\beta^2}{\gamma + 1}\right) W^i B^{0i} = \rho B^{0i} W^i = \rho B_{\nu 0} W^\nu$$

$$f^i = \left(\delta_{ij} + \frac{1}{\gamma + 1} W^i W^j\right) \rho W^{*0j} = \rho\left[\gamma B^{0i} + \left(\frac{\gamma - 1}{\gamma + 1} - \frac{\beta^2\gamma^2}{(\gamma + 1)^2}\right) W^i W^j B^{0j}\right.$$
$$\left. - W^j B^{ji}\right] = \rho(B_{i0} W^0 + B_{ik} W^k) = \rho B_{i\nu} W^\nu$$

and by (7-9) it is seen that these equations coincide with Eq. (7-10).

In the deduction of the above relativistic equations we have had the benefit of the known results in relativistic mechanics. We can understand now how the reverse road was taken and traversed successfully by men of genius. In this connection, it should also be noted that in those days—a good half century ago—it was natural to consider all available evidence as lending support to the belief that, with the possible exception of the gravitational forces, all others were ultimately reducible to electromagnetic interactions. In any case, it was possible to generalize from the transformation properties involving electromagnetic forces to those involving forces of any origin on the basis of the cogent argument that the equilibrium of a set of forces of whatever nature must be an invariant relation.

Returning to the Maxwell-Lorentz equations, we note two important consequences of the antisymmetry property (7-13) of the electromagnetic field tensor. Since $B^{\alpha\beta}{}_{,\beta\alpha} = B^{\alpha\beta}{}_{,\alpha\beta} = 0$, it follows by (7-4) that

$$\operatorname{Div} \mathsf{s} = 0 \tag{7-14}$$

This is the equation of conservation of electric charge (see Probs. 6-8 and 7-1). The other consequence of (7-13) follows from Eq. (7-10). It is seen at once that

$$f_\mu U^\mu = 0 \tag{7-15}$$

The significance of this relation has been discussed in Secs. 4-3 and 6-6.

The Lorentz force formula (7-10) enables us also to derive the energy-momentum tensor T of the electromagnetic field. Eliminating the material "state variables" s^α by means of Eq. (7-4), we find

$$4\pi f_\alpha = B^{\beta\gamma}{}_{,\gamma} B_{\beta\alpha} = (B^{\beta\gamma} B_{\beta\alpha})_{,\gamma} - B^{\beta\gamma} B_{\beta\alpha,\gamma} = \cdots + B^{\beta\gamma} B_{\alpha\beta,\gamma}$$

In order to obtain an equation of the form (6-60), we transform the last term with the aid of Eqs. (7-1) and (7-13):

$$B^{\beta\gamma} B_{\alpha\beta,\gamma} \equiv \tfrac{1}{2} B^{\beta\gamma}(B_{\alpha\beta,\gamma} + B_{\gamma\alpha,\beta}) = -\tfrac{1}{2} B^{\beta\gamma} B_{\beta\gamma,\alpha} = -\tfrac{1}{4}(B^{\lambda\mu} B_{\lambda\mu})_{,\alpha}$$

Hence

$$f^\alpha = -T^{\alpha\beta}{}_{,\beta} \tag{7-16}$$

$$T^{\alpha\beta} = \frac{1}{4\pi}\,(B^{\alpha\mu} B_\mu{}^\beta + \tfrac{1}{4} g^{\alpha\beta} B_{\lambda\mu} B^{\lambda\mu}) \tag{7-17}$$

It is immediately checked that the tensor T is *symmetric*. We have discussed the significance of this property in Sec. 6-2, and we may note again that the corresponding ideas in the mechanics of general continuous media were suggested by the structure of the electromagnetic energy-momentum tensor. To see this structure in more familiar three-dimensional form, we substitute Eqs. (7-2), etc., into (7-17) and, noting that

$$B_{\lambda\mu} B^{\lambda\mu} = 2\Big(\sum_{i<j} B_{ij} B^{ij} + B_{i0} B^{i0}\Big) = 2(\mathbf{B}^2 - \mathbf{E}^2) \tag{7-18}$$

we find

$$4\pi T^{ij} = B^{ik}B_k{}^j + B^{i0}B_0{}^j - \tfrac{1}{2}\delta_{ij}(\mathbf{B}^2 - \mathbf{E}^2) = \delta_{ij}\mathbf{B}^2 - B^iB^j - E^iE^j - \tfrac{1}{2}\,\delta_{ij}(\mathbf{B}^2 - \mathbf{E}^2)$$

$$4\pi T^{0i} = B^{0j}B_j{}^i = \epsilon_{ijk}B^kE^j$$

$$4\pi T^{00} = \mathbf{E}^2 + \tfrac{1}{2}(\mathbf{B}^2 - \mathbf{E}^2)$$

that is,

$$T^{ij} = -\frac{1}{4\pi}\,[E^iE^j + B^iB^j - \tfrac{1}{2}\delta_{ij}(\mathbf{E}^2 + \mathbf{B}^2)]$$

$$T^{0i} = \frac{1}{4\pi}\,[\mathbf{E} \times \mathbf{B}]^i, \qquad T^{00} = \frac{1}{8\pi}\,(\mathbf{E}^2 + \mathbf{B}^2) \tag{7-19}$$

These are recognized as, respectively, the (negative) Maxwell stress components, the Poynting flux-vector components (divided by c), and the energy density of the field. The physical interpretation of these quantities agrees, as it should, with what we found in Sec. 6-2 to be required for any continuous medium.

Before concluding the present formal discussion, a word of caution may not be amiss. It is easy to be carried away by the mathematical elegance of the tensor equations; one must not lose sight of the complex of physical relations underlying these equations and their form invariance. One must also remember that this form invariance has not been proved by our rewriting the Maxwell-Lorentz equations in a manifestly covariant form,‡ but that this covariance is an assumption arrived at, as we know, by a process of induction from the crucial optical and electromagnetic experiments referred to in Chap. 2, and forming part of Einstein's comprehensive invariance principle at the base of STR.

In this connection we need also to be reminded of the observation made in Sec. 3-4 regarding the practical importance of the ordinary three-dimensional representation of physical quantities. Thus, Eqs. (7-1), from a purely mathematical point of view, have a formal significance, which we have considered previously. But from the physicist's and engineer's point of view, these equations embrace on the one hand the equation, div $\mathbf{B} = 0$ that implies the nonexistence of magnetic monopoles, and on the other hand the vector equation $-\partial\mathbf{B}/c\;\partial t = \text{rot}\;\mathbf{E}$ that leads to the design of generators and dynamos.

Our preceding discussion assumed lorentzian coordinates. The transition to general coordinates formally is immediate. The equations (7-1), as we know, are already in generally covariant form. Similarly, Eq. (7-8)

‡ Such a proof is, in any case, no more possible than the proof in any strict sense that the newtonian equations of motion must be invariant under the galilean group. In the latter case, as touched upon in Chap. 1, the operational definitions that give physical content to the newtonian equations are subtly interrelated with operational definitions relating to the galilean transformations. A similar interrelationship quite obviously exists between the electromagnetic equations and the Lorentz group.

can be retained as it is, and its explicit form as well involves only ordinary partials [see Eq. (5-104)]:

$$B_{\alpha\beta} = A_{\alpha,\beta} - A_{\beta,\alpha} \tag{7-8a}$$

As to the force equations, (7-10) remain unchanged, while in (7-16) we have to change the comma to a semicolon to represent covariant differentiation. Similarly, the only change that needs to be introduced into Eq. (7-4) arises when it is expressed in terms of its components; we have then, as in the case of the sourcefree equations (7-3), to substitute covariant for ordinary differentiation.

The full theoretical significance of the *generally* covariant electromagnetic equations we have obtained can be appreciated only in connection with the general theory of relativity, where the metric tensor is no longer in general that of flat Minkowski space. These equations can however be useful also in the domain of application of special relativity, when one deals with problems for which it is convenient to apply spatial curvilinear coordinates rather than the customary cartesian coordinates. The formalism developed in Chap. 5 can then have practical utility. For both these reasons, and because little additional effort is required, we employ general coordinates also in our treatment of the following topic (but see Prob. 7-5).

7-2 VARIATIONAL FORMULATION OF THE MAXWELL-LORENTZ THEORY

In order to set up an action principle for the electromagnetic field in free space, we must know the lagrangian density to be inserted into the action integral (6-113). Our immediate task is then to find this function of our field quantities. First we must of course determine the "canonical field variables" of our problem, that is, the functions $q^a(x)$ in the notation of Sec. 6-7. The field functions $B^{\alpha\beta}$ do not appear to be immediately suitable, considering that the differential field equations are all of the *first order* in the field components. The electromagnetic potentials A^α do not suffer from this apparent difficulty: the field equations expressed in terms of these functions are of second order. Moreover, the field equations (7-1) are automatically satisfied by virtue of the definition (7-8), so that the potentials have to satisfy only the set (7-4) (with $\mathbf{s} = 0$):

$$A^{\mu}{}_{;}{}^{\nu}{}_{;\nu} - A^{\nu}{}_{;}{}^{\mu}{}_{;\nu} = 0 \tag{7-20}$$

However, our field variables have one feature that needs to be noted: they are not independent. In our discussion of the general variational theory the independence of the q^a was tacitly assumed, and it is to be expected that when this restriction is violated provision must be made by means of proper subsidiary conditions or otherwise to make the theory consistent.‡

‡ We have met with a similar problem in Sec. 4-3 when dealing with the variational treatment of the relativistic mechanics of a particle subject to a given external field of force.

The dependence in the present case is connected with the indeterminacy in the A^μ stemming from their definition (7-8), by virtue of which the "gauge transformation"

$$A_\mu \to A_\mu + \chi_{,\mu} \tag{7-21}$$

where $\chi(\mathsf{x})$ is an arbitrary (differentiable) 4-scalar field, leads to no change of physical state. It is hence possible to impose a condition on the A components corresponding to the arbitrariness in the function χ. An examination of Eq. (7-20) suggests the choice

$$A^\mu{}_{;\mu} = 0 \tag{7-22}$$

This is the well-known "Lorentz condition," by which (7-20) simplifies to take the form of the *wave equations*,

$$A^{\mu}{}_{;\nu}{}^{\nu} \equiv \Box A^\mu = 0 \tag{7-23}$$

(see Prob. 7-5). As the reader knows, or can easily check, the arbitrariness in A is actually not completely eliminated: the gauge group merely contracts by the functions χ having to satisfy the wave equation.

We are now ready to attempt to find a solution to our problem. The lagrangian density we are seeking must satisfy the following conditions: it must be an invariant in $\mathfrak{M}$; it must be a "gauge invariant," i.e., an invariant under the group of transformations (7-21) (this is strictly not necessary to begin with, but convenient); and it must lead to the second-order field equations, which are, moreover, *linear* equations. It is not difficult to arrive at the conclusion that the search of lagrangian density narrows down essentially to a consideration of the following two field functions (see Prob. 7-6)

$$J \equiv B_{\lambda\mu}B^{\lambda\mu}, \qquad K = B^*{}_{\lambda\mu}B^{\lambda\mu} \qquad B_{\lambda\mu} \equiv 2A_{[\lambda,\mu]} \tag{7-24}$$

of which the first is a gauge invariant scalar and the second a similar pseudoscalar. The invariant $B^*{}_{\lambda\mu}B^{*\lambda\mu}$ gives nothing new since it is merely $-J$ [see (5-72), remembering (5-75)].

If we did not already know the Euler equations for our system, both invariants (7-24) would come under study. We might note that for $\mathfrak{L}$ proportional to K the canonical momenta given by Eqs. (6-116), are proportional to

$$\begin{aligned}
\frac{\partial(E_{\alpha\beta\gamma\delta}B^{\gamma\delta}B^{\alpha\beta})}{\partial A_{\lambda;\mu}} &\propto E_{\alpha\beta\gamma\delta}g^{\gamma\nu}g^{\delta\sigma}g^{\alpha\rho}g^{\beta\tau}\,\frac{\partial(A_{[\nu;\sigma]}A_{[\rho;\tau]})}{\partial A_{\lambda;\mu}} \\
&\propto E_{\alpha\beta\gamma\delta}g^{\gamma\nu}g^{\delta\sigma}g^{\alpha\rho}g^{\beta\tau}(\delta_{\lambda[\nu}\delta_{\sigma]\mu}B_{\rho\tau} + B_{\nu\sigma}\delta_{\lambda[\rho}\delta_{\tau]\mu}) \\
&= E_{\alpha\beta\gamma\delta}(B^{\alpha\beta}g^{\gamma[\lambda}g^{\mu]\delta} + B^{\gamma\delta}g^{\alpha[\lambda}g^{\mu]\beta}) \propto B^{*\lambda\mu}
\end{aligned}$$

and would therefore according to Eqs. (6-117) yield the field equations

$$B^{*\lambda\mu}{}_{;\mu} = 0 \tag{7-25}$$

But by (ii) of Prob. 5-15, Eqs. (7-25) are fully equivalent to Eqs. (7-1), and the latter as we know are merely identities in the field variables A_λ. On the other hand, if we choose

$$\mathfrak{L} = aJ \tag{7-26}$$

then, by steps similar to the above, one finds

$$\Pi^{\lambda\mu} = 4aB^{\lambda\mu} \tag{7-27}$$

and the Euler equations (6-117) now reproduce the field equations (7-4) (with $\mathsf{s} = 0$), or Eqs. (7-23), subject to the restriction (7-22) on the field variables.

If we now evaluate the corresponding canonical energy-momentum tensor, we find by Eqs. (6-118), (7-26), and (7-27), that

$$P^{\alpha\beta} = 4a(A_{\gamma;}{}^{\alpha}B^{\gamma\beta} - \tfrac{1}{4}g^{\alpha\beta}J) \tag{7-28}$$

an expression that is not symmetric (nor gauge invariant for that matter). We seem therefore to have reached a certain impasse. The fact is, when we considered the general theory in Sec. 6-7 we stopped short of discussing this important property of symmetry in connection with the general canonical tensor. It is quite easy to see that in general this symmetry will not obtain. One proceeds then as follows. One adds to the canonical tensor the divergence of a tensor of the third rank that is antisymmetric in its last two indices,

$$\Omega^{\alpha\beta\gamma}{}_{;\gamma} \equiv \Omega^{\alpha\beta}, \qquad \Omega^{\alpha\beta\gamma} = -\Omega^{\alpha\gamma\beta} \tag{7-29}$$

and so constructed that the resulting tensor

$$P_{(s)}{}^{\alpha\beta} = P^{\alpha\beta} + \Omega^{\alpha\beta}$$

is symmetric.‡ The conservation condition (6-119) is obeyed by this new tensor as well as by the canonical one, since, in view of Eqs. (7-29), $\Omega^{\alpha\beta}{}_{;\beta} = 0$ [upon applying (i) of Prob. 5-18—so that we are assuming here the metric of $\mathfrak{M}$]. Again, the conservation of the new total 4-momentum of the field [Eq. (6-52)] is insured by the form (7-29) of Ω, which leads in the proof of conservation of (6-52), outlined in Sec. 6-3, to a further integration by parts, with the final integrals being taken over 2-surfaces whose contribution vanishes by virtue of the assumption of "boundedness" (as defined in Sec. 6-3) that, in any case, underlies the deduction of our integral conservation principles.

In the present case (7-28), one finds by Belinfante's prescription that one can take

$$\Omega^{\alpha\beta\gamma} = 4aA^{\alpha}B^{\beta\gamma} \tag{7-29a}$$

‡ How this can be done generally within the framework of special relativity, has been shown by F. Belinfante. See, e.g., G. Wentzel, "Quantum Theory of Fields," app. I, Interscience Publishers, Inc., New York, 1949; also [4], sec. 31. The significance of the quantities Ω is discussed in Sec. 8-3.

provided we take into account the field equations $B^{\alpha\beta}{}_{;\beta} = 0$; for then, $\Omega^{\alpha\beta} = 4aA^{\alpha}{}_{;\gamma}B^{\beta\gamma}$, and

$$P^{\alpha\beta}{}_{(s)} = 4a[(A_{\gamma;}{}^{\alpha} - A^{\alpha}{}_{;\gamma})B^{\gamma\beta} - \tfrac{1}{4}g^{\alpha\beta}J] = 4a(B_{\gamma}{}^{\alpha}B^{\gamma\beta} - \tfrac{1}{4}g^{\alpha\beta}J)$$

is indeed symmetric. Moreover, if we compare this tensor with T given in Eq. (7-17), it is seen that we need only take

$$a = -\frac{1}{16\pi} \tag{7-30}$$

for the two tensors to be completely identical.

Since the tensor T is, on all available evidence, the correct energy-momentum tensor of the electromagnetic field, a second question therefore presents itself. How could we have recognized T as the 'correct' tensor if we had only started with the lagrangian density $\mathfrak{L}$? To this question there is indeed a complete answer, but not within the scope of the Lorentz group. Because it involves quite simple mathematics, we shall now indicate this answer in a purely formal way. But any attempt at understanding its significance involves ideas of general relativity.

The procedure is as follows. We consider the dependence of our lagrangian density on the contravariant metric tensor components $g^{\alpha\beta}$, writing this density as follows

$$\mathfrak{L} = ag^{\lambda\sigma}g^{\mu\tau}B_{\sigma\tau}B_{\lambda\mu}$$

The integration volume element involves the factor $\sqrt{-g}$. If one examines the dependence of the determinant g on the $g^{\alpha\beta}$ one finds [by steps similar to those indicated in the derivation of (5-91)] that

$$\frac{\partial g}{\partial g^{\alpha\beta}} = -gg_{\alpha\beta}$$

Since

$$\partial\mathfrak{L}/a\,\partial g^{\alpha\beta} = (\delta_{\lambda\alpha}\,\delta_{\sigma\beta}\,g^{\mu\tau} + g^{\lambda\sigma}\,\delta_{\mu\alpha}\,\delta_{\tau\beta})B_{\sigma\tau}B_{\lambda\mu} = B_{\alpha\mu}B_{\beta}{}^{\mu} + B_{\lambda\alpha}B^{\lambda}{}_{\beta} = -2B_{\alpha\lambda}B^{\lambda}{}_{\beta}$$

it follows that

$$\frac{\partial(\sqrt{-g}\,\mathfrak{L})}{\partial g^{\alpha\beta}} = -2a(B_{\alpha\lambda}B^{\lambda}{}_{\beta} + \tfrac{1}{4}g_{\alpha\beta}B_{\lambda\mu}B^{\lambda\mu})\sqrt{-g}$$

By Eqs. (7-30) and (7-17), it is thus seen that

$$T_{\alpha\beta} = \frac{2}{\sqrt{-g}}\frac{\partial}{\partial g^{\alpha\beta}}(\sqrt{-g}\,\mathfrak{L}) \tag{7-31}$$

Although the actual introduction of the $g^{\alpha\beta}$ as something akin to field variables cannot be justified from our present point of view, we need not leave the discussion with the finding of the representation (7-31). If we recall the connection between symmetry properties of a finite classical system and associated conservation properties‡—a connection that can be extended to continuous systems as well (cf. discussion of Noether's theorem in Sec. 8-3)—the form of the expression (7-31) suggests the possible existence of a connection between the conservation of the energy momentum of the field and the infinitesimal variation of the action integral associated with the variation of the $g^{\alpha\beta}$.

Let us consider then the group of general infinitesimal transformations of the coordinates. A typical transformation has the form

$$x'^{\alpha} = x^{\alpha} + w^{\alpha}(x), \qquad w^{\alpha} \text{ infinitesimals} \tag{7-32}$$

This transformation induces at every 4-point x the infinitesimal *linear* transformation [see (5-46)] whose matrix is $N = I + Q$, $Q = \|w^{\alpha}{}_{,\beta}\|$. Letting G represent the matrix $\|g^{\alpha\beta}\|$, one finds by (5-37), to infinitesimals of first order

$$G'(\mathsf{x}') = (I + Q)G(\mathsf{x})(I + \tilde{Q}) = G + QG + G\tilde{Q}, \qquad G \equiv G(\mathsf{x})$$

But, to the same order (with obvious and permissible assumptions on the smallness of our quantities)

$$G'(\mathsf{x}') = G'(\mathsf{x}) + G_{,\alpha}w^{\alpha}$$

Hence

$$\delta G \equiv G'(\mathsf{x}) - G(\mathsf{x}) = QG + G\tilde{Q} - G_{,\alpha}w^{\alpha} \tag{7-33}$$

represents the infinitesimal variation induced in $g^{\alpha\beta}$ by the infinitesimal coordinate transformation (7-32). The corresponding variation in the action integral (multiplied by c) is then, by Eq. (7-31)—and since $T_{\alpha\beta} = T_{\beta\alpha}$—

$$\begin{aligned}\delta \int \mathfrak{L} \sqrt{-g}\, d^4x &= \int \frac{\partial}{\partial g^{\alpha\beta}} (\sqrt{-g}\, \mathfrak{L})\, \delta g^{\alpha\beta}\, d^4x \\ &= \int \frac{\sqrt{-g}}{2} T_{\alpha\beta}(w^{\alpha}{}_{,\gamma} g^{\gamma\beta} + g^{\alpha\gamma} w^{\beta}{}_{,\gamma} - g^{\alpha\beta}{}_{,\gamma} w^{\gamma})\, d^4x \\ &= \int (T^{\gamma}_{\alpha} w^{\alpha}{}_{,\gamma} - \tfrac{1}{2} T_{\alpha\beta} g^{\alpha\beta}{}_{,\gamma} w^{\gamma}) \sqrt{-g}\, d^4x, \\ &\qquad\qquad d^4x \equiv dx^0\, dx^1\, dx^2\, dx^3\end{aligned}$$

After integrating by parts and allowing for the vanishing of the hypersurface integrals, this variation can be written

$$-\int \left[\frac{1}{\sqrt{-g}} (\sqrt{-g}\, T^{\lambda}_{\gamma})_{,\lambda} + \tfrac{1}{2} T_{\alpha\beta} g^{\alpha\beta}{}_{,\gamma}\right] w^{\gamma} \sqrt{-g}\, d^4x$$

‡ This connection is generally analyzed in terms of infinitesimal canonical transformations. See, e.g., Goldstein, *op. cit.*, secs. 8-6 and 8-7.

If this integral is to vanish for arbitrary w^γ, the expression inside the brackets must be zero. Hence referring to Eqs. (5-89), (5-103), and (5-88a), we find

$$\begin{aligned} 0 &= T^\lambda_{\gamma,\lambda} + T^\lambda_\gamma \frac{1}{2g} g_{,\lambda} - \tfrac{1}{2} T_{\alpha\beta}(g^{\alpha\sigma}\Gamma^\beta_{\sigma\gamma} + g^{\sigma\beta}\Gamma^\alpha_{\sigma\gamma}) \\ &= T^\lambda_{\gamma,\lambda} + T^\lambda_\gamma \Gamma^\sigma_{\lambda\sigma} - T^\sigma_\beta \Gamma^\beta_{\sigma\gamma} = T^\lambda_{\gamma;\lambda} \end{aligned}$$

which are indeed our conservation equations.

The above derivation is obviously very suggestive, but within our present restrictive theoretical framework its implications cannot be fully explored. On the other hand, the energy-momentum tensor of the electromagnetic field can also be considered within the context of the STR from the point of view of Fock's theorem referred to on page 205. The state functions of our system in Fock's sense are now obviously not the potentials, but the field components, and the question arises if the conditions of Fock's theorem are satisfied by this system. There is little difficulty in convincing ourselves that they are essentially satisfied, provided boundary conditions are stipulated that insure the finiteness of the integrals (6-52) and (6-55). The adjoining of such boundary conditions simply means that our complete physical system cannot be in any strict sense a pure field; and of course fundamentally an electromagnetic field is always associated with electric charges—its sources, although regions of space-time exist completely free of charges but filled with electromagnetic radiation. The application of Fock's theorem must be considered therefore in connection with such complete systems (see [4], sec. 33). However, we shall not pursue this question further, but return to our general discussion of the variational method.

When we wish to include in the variational formulation of the electromagnetic field the system of charges with which it is coupled, we have two possible approaches in the nonquantum theory. One approach is the purely phenomenological one of Maxwell's theory of electrodynamics in material media as developed relativistically by Minkowski and others, which is discussed in Sec. 7-3. The second approach is more ambitious. It had its inception in the days when the "theory of the electron" was tantamount to our present "theory of elementary particles." One considers the charged medium as made up of "electrons," i.e., of irreducible charged particles, and on this basis investigates the interaction of each with the electromagnetic field, both external (due to charges not included in our system) and internal (due to the charges in the system).. In ordinary situations when the Maxwell-Minkowski phenomenological theory applies, this second approach, when coupled with an appropriate statistical analysis, leads to essentially the same results. But in general, quite aside from the question of the domain of applicability of such theory, essential difficulties arise when one wishes to push it to its logical conclusions. We shall not now be concerned with these questions, of which some are discussed in Sec. 7-5 and in Appendix

7A, but confine ourselves to indicating how it is possible to set up an action integral for the combined system of field and point charges, which leads to the ordinary Maxwell-Lorentz equations in 'empty' space.

The form of the particle-action integral suitable for our purpose is suggested by the relevant discussion in Sec. 4-3. For a single particle of charge e and proper mass m this integral can be written in general coordinates as follows

$$\begin{aligned} I_p &= -mc\int ds + C\int A_\alpha \dot{x}^\alpha\, ds \\ ds^2 &= g_{\alpha\beta}(\mathsf{x})\, dx^\alpha\, dx^\beta, \qquad \dot{x} \equiv \frac{dx}{ds} \end{aligned} \tag{7-34}$$

where the integrals are taken along the space-time trajectory ("world line") of the particle. We shall determine the constant C and at the same time check the correctness of the action integral (7-34). The vanishing of its variation when the x^α vary subject to the standard conditions, should give us the Lorentz equations of motion of the particle under the action of a given electromagnetic field of potential A. This variation can be computed, for instance, by the method that was applied to the particle Lagrangian (4-73), the parameter condition (4-74) now having of course, by (7-34), the form $g_{\alpha\beta}\dot{x}^\alpha\dot{x}^\beta = 1$. Corresponding to (4-75), the Euler equations are now,

$$\begin{aligned} 0 &= -\frac{mc}{2}\left[\frac{d}{ds}\frac{\partial}{\partial \dot{x}^\alpha}(g_{\beta\gamma}\dot{x}^\beta\dot{x}^\gamma) - g_{\beta\gamma,\alpha}\dot{x}^\beta\dot{x}^\gamma\right] + C\left(\frac{dA_\alpha}{ds} - A_{\beta,\alpha}\dot{x}^\beta\right) \\ &= -mc[g_{\alpha\beta}\ddot{x}^\beta + (g_{\alpha\beta,\gamma} - \tfrac{1}{2}g_{\beta\gamma,\alpha})\dot{x}^\beta\dot{x}^\gamma] + C(A_{\alpha,\beta} - A_{\beta,\alpha})\dot{x}^\beta \end{aligned}$$

Using Eqs. (5-83), (5-85), and (7-8*a*), and multiplying-summing by $g^{\alpha\lambda}$, they assume the form

$$mc(\ddot{x}^\lambda + \Gamma^\lambda_{\beta\gamma}\dot{x}^\beta\dot{x}^\gamma) = CB^\lambda{}_\beta\dot{x}^\beta \tag{7-35}$$

If the coordinates are specialized to be lorentzian, and one compares this expression with Eqs. (7-10) and (4-4) [with suitable identifications and bearing in mind Eqs. (7-5) and the last of Eqs. (7-34)], one finds

$$C = -\frac{e}{c} \tag{7-36}$$

Referring to the definition (5-86), it is seen that the expression in parentheses in Eq. (7-35) is the total covariant derivative $\dot{x}^\lambda{}_{;\gamma}\dot{x}^\gamma \equiv D\dot{x}^\lambda/Ds$. That equation can thus be written

$$m\frac{D\dot{x}^\lambda}{Ds} = \frac{e}{c^2}B_\mu{}^\lambda\dot{x}^\mu, \qquad \dot{x} \equiv \frac{dx}{ds} \tag{7-37}$$

It is the relativistic Lorentz equation of motion of a 'point' charge in completely general coordinates. In lorentzian coordinates this equation reduces, as it should, to Eq. (4-81), upon proper identification of A_α in the latter equation.

In the case of a system of many charged particles (e_A, m_A), $A = 1, 2, \ldots$ the corresponding action integral can be taken as the sum

$$I_p = \sum_A I_p(A) \tag{7-38}$$

In order to obtain the coupling of the field to the charges, one must consider the variation of the combined action [see Eqs. (7-26), (7-24), and (7-30)]

$$I = I_p + I_f, \qquad I_f = -\frac{1}{16\pi c}\int B_{\alpha\beta}B^{\alpha\beta}\sqrt{-g}\,d^4x \tag{7-39}$$

when one varies the A_α, the factor $1/c$ being included, it will be recalled, in order that the integral have the physical dimensions of action. It is now necessary to convert the part of I_p involving the field variables, call it I'_p, into a space-time integral. It is clear that with strict *point* charges one has to introduce singularities.‡ We shall therefore suppose that each of our charged particles has a very small but nonvanishing extension so that its world line is actually a very narrow world tube. By evaluating the element of charge $e\,ds$ in an inertial rest system at a given event $\mathbf{x}$ of that tube, one can define the proper charge density $\rho(\mathbf{x})$ by the equation

$$e\,ds = \rho\sqrt{-g}\,d^4x \tag{7-40}$$

whose cryptic notation is clear from the context. Letting further ρ equal zero everywhere in $\mathfrak{M}$ outside of the world tubes, then by Eqs. (7-38), (7-34), and (7-36), we can write

$$I'_p = -\frac{1}{c^2}\int \rho U^\alpha A_\alpha\sqrt{-g}\,d^4x \tag{7-41}$$

When we introduce (7-41) into Eq. (7-39), we find the part of the total action I involving $\mathbf{A}(\mathbf{x})$ expressed as a multiple integral whose variation for changes in A_α is readily calculated. The result is immediate in the case of I'_p. In finding δI_f, we need only note that

$$\delta(B_{\alpha\beta}B^{\alpha\beta}) = \delta(g^{\lambda\alpha}g^{\mu\beta}B_{\alpha\beta}B_{\lambda\mu}) = 2B^{\alpha\beta}\,\delta B_{\alpha\beta} = 4B^{\alpha\beta}\,\delta A_{\alpha,\beta}$$

so that after the usual steps, we get

$$\delta I_f = \frac{1}{4\pi c}\int \frac{1}{\sqrt{-g}}(\sqrt{-g}\,B^{\alpha\beta})_{,\beta}\,\delta A_\alpha\sqrt{-g}\,d^4x$$

Since B is skew symmetric, we can apply Eq. (5-98) and, combining our results, obtain, as a consequence of the vanishing of δI for arbitrary varia-

‡ Of the nature of the (loosely) so-called "Dirac delta functions." See relevant discussion in Sec. 7-4.

tion of the δA_α, the equations

$$B^{\alpha\beta}{}_{;\beta} = \frac{4\pi}{c}\,\rho U^\alpha \tag{7-42}$$

i.e., the Maxwell-Lorentz set (7-4) On the other hand, variation with respect to the positional variables of a given particle of our system leads to an equation of motion of the form (7-37) for that particle, the interaction with all the other particles of the system arising through the coupling of the field B and its sources as given in (7-42). The limitations inherent in the present treatment are discussed in Sec. 7-5.‡

7-3 RELATIVISTIC FORMULATION OF ELECTRODYNAMICS IN CONTINUOUS MATERIAL MEDIA

The relativistic treatment of electromagnetic phenomena in polarizable and magnetizable continuous media has, so far, been largely of historical interest. Problems in this field, as we know, led to the development of STR, and these problems continued to engage the interest of the early investigators. In the past perhaps the most interesting application of the relativistic treatment consisted in providing a completely consistent and simple explanation of "unipolar induction"—a phenomenon recognized since Faraday's researches. Possible future application of the theory may lie in the currently developing fields of plasma physics and magnetofluidmechanics. In any case this topic provides another important illustration of the power of relativistic methods.

It is possible to derive the electromagnetic equations in material media by a suitable macroscopic space-time averaging over the underlying microscopic Lorentz equations along the lines developed by Lorentz in his pre-relativistic 'electron theory.' This method is described in [7], sec. 34, with references to the original investigations, and it is also considered briefly in the sequel. A direct phenomenological approach was initiated by Minkowski.§ It is based on Maxwell's well-founded phenomenological equations, which hold for media at rest in the observer's inertial frame, and its starting point is a judicious rewriting of these equations in an explicitly covariant form. With the aid of the tensor formalism this is a fairly straightforward task, as we now proceed to show. At the same time it must be borne in mind that now, even more obviously than in the case of the Maxwell-Lorentz equations discussed in Sec. 7-1, the mere covariant appearance of our equations is no guarantee that they are right, without sufficient empirical evidence coupled with adequate operational definitions.

‡ The variational treatment of the electromagnetic field was considered by Larmor, *op. cit.*, chap. 6, and treated relativistically by Poincaré (*op. cit.—Rendiconti*).

§ H. Minkowski, *Nachr. Ges. Wiss. Göttingen*, 1908, p. 53 ff; *Math. Annalen*, **68**: 472 (1910). See also, A. Einstein and J. Laub, *Ann. Physik*, **26**: 532, 541 (1908); and a correction in *Ann. Physik*, **28**: 445 (1909).

The Maxwell equations, it will be recalled, have the following form in gaussian units

$$\text{rot } \mathbf{E} + \frac{1}{c}\frac{\partial \mathbf{B}}{\partial t} = 0, \qquad \text{div } \mathbf{B} = 0 \tag{7-43}$$

$$\text{div } \mathbf{D} = 4\pi\rho, \qquad \text{rot } \mathbf{H} - \frac{1}{c}\frac{\partial \mathbf{D}}{\partial t} = \frac{4\pi}{c}\mathbf{i} \tag{7-44}$$

$$\mathbf{D} = \epsilon\mathbf{E}, \qquad \mathbf{H} = \frac{1}{\mu}\mathbf{B}, \qquad \mathbf{i} = \sigma\mathbf{E} \tag{7-45}$$

it being assumed that the medium is isotropic but not necessarily homogeneous, and that $\mathbf{i}$ represents the conduction current density. With the definition of the field tensor B in terms of the vectors $\mathbf{E}$, $\mathbf{B}$, as given in Sec. 7-1, we already have in (7-1) the covariant expression of Eqs. (7-43). Moreover, if we introduce the antisymmetric 4-tensor H that is defined in terms of $\mathbf{D}$ and $\mathbf{H}$ in exactly the same way as B is defined in terms of $\mathbf{E}$ and $\mathbf{B}$, i.e., by the equation

$$\|H_{\alpha\beta}\| = \begin{bmatrix} 0 & -D^j \\ D^i & H_{ij} \end{bmatrix}, \qquad D^1 = D_x, \ . \ . \ . \ , H_{12} = H_z, \ . \ . \ . \tag{7-46}$$

it is clear, on comparing Eqs. (7-44) and (2-2), and recalling (7-4), that Eqs. (7-44) can be combined into the tensor equation

$$\text{Div } H = \frac{4\pi}{c}\mathsf{i}, \qquad \mathsf{i} = (c\rho, \mathbf{i}) \tag{7-47}$$

By the first of Eqs. (7-47) it follows that the 4-current density i satisfies a conservation equation such as (7-14).

Note that we have introduced a change in notation in (7-47): we are now letting ρ stand for charge density relative to an arbitrary inertial frame. The charge density referred to the local rest frame will now be distinguished, as will other *rest quantities*, by being *primed*. This new convention, as well as the replacement of the previous S^* by the new symbol S' to denote local rest frames, will be more convenient in the present discussion.

As to the covariant formulation of the constitutive equations (7-45), it may be assumed that the structural parameters ϵ, μ, and σ can be treated as 4-scalars, given by the relations (7-45) in the local rest systems. But we still need to know how to express the constitutive equations in a relativistically covariant manner. Since it is not immediately apparent how the first two vector relations in (7-45) can be combined into one covariant expression (but see Prob. 7-13), what we need is a unique method of forming 4-vectors that yield in S' the field vectors occurring in (7-45). Fortunately, this is easily accomplished. Let us begin with the vector $\mathbf{E}$. It is associated with the tensor B, and, moreover, the only 4-vector available for composition with this tensor is the 4-velocity U of S' relative to the inertial frame under consideration; and indeed, the essentially unique 4-vector combination $B_{\beta\alpha}W^{\beta}$ ($\mathsf{W} \equiv \mathsf{U}/c$) has in S' the nonvanishing components

$$B'^{i}_{\beta}W'^{\beta} = B'^{i}_{0}W'^{0} = B'^{i}_{0} = E'^{i}, \qquad E^{1} = E_{x}, \ . \ . \ . \tag{7-48}$$

Similarly, by (7-46), $H'^{\alpha}_{\beta}W'^{\beta} = (0, D'_x, D'_y, D'_z)$. The other two field vectors can be handled in the same way if we introduce the duals of our relativistic field tensors. In fact, returning to *lorentzian coordinates*,

$$\|B^{*}_{\alpha\beta}\| = \begin{bmatrix} 0 & B^{23} & B^{31} & B^{12} \\ \cdot & 0 & B^{03} & -B^{02} \\ \cdot & \cdot & 0 & B^{01} \\ \cdot & \cdot & \cdot & 0 \end{bmatrix}, \qquad B^{*}_{\alpha\beta} = -B^{*}_{\beta\alpha} \tag{7-49}$$

(see Prob. 5-12), and a similar relation holds for $H^{*}_{\alpha\beta}$. It follows that, except for a change in sign, we have for **B** and **H** the same relationship in terms of B^{*} and H^{*} as is given in (7-48) for **E** and B. The covariant transcription of the first two relations in (7-45) is thus simply

$$(H_{\beta\alpha} - \epsilon B_{\beta\alpha})W^{\beta} = 0, \qquad (B^{*}_{\beta\alpha} - \mu H^{*}_{\beta\alpha})W^{\beta} = 0 \tag{7-50}$$

The treatment of the last relation in (7-45) is a little more involved. We must bear in mind that Ohm's law applies only to conduction currents, and that in an inertial frame S moving relative to S' the total current density **i** as measured in S will in general involve a part arising from the *convection* of charges relative to S. We have therefore two problems: the proper covariant formulation of Ohm's law for general continuous conducting media, and the proper definition of the conduction current density **j** in an arbitrary inertial frame S. The first problem is handled very easily; the second problem requires a little care—the literature on the subject is not always too clear.

To find the relativistic extension of Ohm's law, we can start with the expression of this law in a local rest frame S' of our continuous system, namely

$$\mathbf{j}' = \sigma\mathbf{E}' \tag{7-51}$$

and since we already have in (7-48) the covariant transcription of $\mathbf{E}'$, we need only determine the same for $\mathbf{j}'$. To this end we observe that if we assume the existence of a 4-vector *conduction* part j of the 4-current density i, it must have in S' the form $j'^{\mu} = (0,\mathbf{j}')$, so that

$$(\mathsf{j},\mathsf{U}) = 0 \tag{7-52}$$

and by the expression (7-47) for i, we have then in S'

$$i'^{\mu} - j'^{\mu} = i'^{\mu}{}_{\text{conv}} \equiv c'^{\mu} = (c\rho',\mathbf{0}) \tag{7-53}$$

Recalling the definition (6-71) of the projection tensor $\mathcal{P}$, it is then easy to see that with the above assumption, we have in an arbitrary inertial frame S,

$$\begin{aligned} j^\mu &= \mathcal{P}^\mu_{\ \nu} i^\nu & W^\mu &= \gamma\beta^\mu \\ c^\mu &= W^\mu W_\nu i^\nu & \gamma &\equiv \gamma_u \\ & & \beta^\mu &= \frac{u^\mu}{c} \end{aligned} \tag{7-54}$$

where c is the convection 4-current density corresponding to (7-53). A trivial partial check is that Eq. (7-52) is satisfied. We can of course simply rederive Eqs. (7-54) by transforming, say, c'^μ given in (7-53) to the frame S. By (3-29a), we have generally,

$$c\rho = \gamma(c\rho' + \boldsymbol{\beta}\cdot\mathbf{i}'), \qquad \mathbf{i} = \mathbf{i}' + \left(\gamma c\rho' + \frac{\gamma-1}{\beta^2}\boldsymbol{\beta}\cdot\mathbf{i}'\right)\boldsymbol{\beta} \tag{7-55}$$

Hence

$$\rho_{\text{conv}} = \gamma\rho', \qquad \mathbf{c} = \gamma c\rho'\boldsymbol{\beta} = \rho'\mathbf{U} = \rho_{\text{conv}}\mathbf{u} \tag{7-56}$$

and since

$$\mathbf{i} = \mathbf{j} + \mathbf{c} \tag{7-57}$$

we have by (7-47) and (7-55),

$$\rho_{\text{cond}} = \frac{\gamma}{c}\boldsymbol{\beta}\cdot\mathbf{j}', \qquad \mathbf{j} = \mathbf{j}' + \frac{\gamma-1}{\beta^2}(\boldsymbol{\beta}\cdot\mathbf{j}')\boldsymbol{\beta} \tag{7-58}$$

The equivalence of Eqs. (7-56), (7-58) and (7-54) is seen immediately when we note that j and c given in (7-54) satisfy (7-57); and that by (7-52) and (7-57), $(\mathsf{i},\mathsf{W}) = (\mathsf{c},\mathsf{W}) = c_0' = c\rho'$, so that $\mathsf{c} = (\mathsf{W},\mathsf{i})\mathsf{W} = \rho'\mathsf{U}$, in agreement with (7-56).

Combining our results we have the desired relativistic extension of (7-51):

$$\mathcal{P}^\mu_{\ \nu} i^\nu = \sigma B_\nu^{\ \mu} W^\nu \tag{7-59}$$

But now we come to our second problem: does the decomposition (7-54) correspond to our conventional ideas about conduction and convection currents? It is simpler here to consider the latter. A moment's reflection will convince us that we cannot accept the expression (7-56) for $\mathbf{c}$ uncritically. It would give us $\mathbf{c} = 0$ when $\rho' = 0$, but by (7-55) this would generally not mean that $\rho = 0$ (this fact is connected in an interesting way with the relativity of simultaneity, as first pointed out by v. Laue—see Prob. 7-14). It is surely nearer to what we generally understand by convection current density to consider it as represented in an arbitrary inertial frame by the expression

$$\mathbf{c} = \rho\mathbf{u} \tag{7-60}$$

But then also the conduction current density will differ from the expression given in (7-58), i.e., from the spatial part of the left-hand side of (7-59).

At the same time it is easy to see directly that the vector (7-60) cannot in general be extended to a 4-vector [see (7-55)], and this also follows from the fact that the covariant extension (7-54) of the corresponding quantities in S' is unique.

We seem to be confronted thus with a certain dilemma. Its resolution, though, is quite simple. To begin with, our objection to $\mathbf{c}$ given in (7-56), and hence to the expression (7-58) for the conduction current, can be substantiated by turning to the statistical treatment of conduction. It leads not to the expression (7-58) for $\mathbf{j}$, but to the expression

$$\mathbf{j} = \mathbf{i} - \rho\mathbf{u} \tag{7-61}$$

(see [7], sec. 34; and discussion given on page 246). On the other hand, as we have seen, the covariant expression (7-59) represents essentially a unique extension of Ohm's law. There remains therefore only one conclusion: the covariant splitting of $\mathfrak{i}$ as given in (7-54) has only mathematical significance and does not correspond to our physical notions of conduction and convection currents; and indeed, when we pause to consider carefully the laboratory significance of these quantities, their essentially noncovariant character is apparent.

Our minor dilemma is thus completely resolved by the recognition that we can well accept Eq. (7-59) as the relativistic expression of Ohm's law without it being necessary to commit ourselves to the definitions (7-56) and (7-58). Instead, we need only rearrange the terms in the spatial part of (7-59) so that we have the expression (7-61) for $\mathbf{j}$ on the left. It must then follow necessarily that the right-hand side will consist of σ times an expression in the field vectors that reduces to $\mathbf{E}'$ in the rest frame at the given event. This is easily verified. Direct evaluation of the spatial components in (7-59) gives the following relation (that is also contained in preceding results):

$$(\mathbf{j}) = \sigma\gamma\mathbf{E}^*, \qquad \mathbf{E}^* \equiv \mathbf{E} + (\boldsymbol{\beta} \times \mathbf{B}) \tag{7-62}$$

using now the symbol $(\mathbf{j})$ to denote $\mathbf{j}$ given in (7-58). But by Eqs. (7-57), (7-56), (7-60), and (7-55),

$$(\mathbf{j}) - \mathbf{j} = \mathbf{i} - \gamma\rho'\mathbf{u} - (\mathbf{i} - \rho\mathbf{u}) = (\rho - \gamma\rho')\mathbf{u} = (\boldsymbol{\beta} \cdot \mathbf{j}')\mathbf{W} = \gamma\beta^2\mathbf{j}'_{\parallel} \tag{7-63}$$

while by the result (iv) in Prob. 5-12 (where the symbols are explained),

$$\mathbf{E}'_{\parallel} = \mathbf{E}_{\parallel}, \qquad \mathbf{E}'_{\perp} = \gamma\mathbf{E}^*_{\perp} \tag{7-64}$$

Hence, combining Eqs. (7-62), (7-63), (7-64), and (7-51), we obtain the anticipated result:

$$\mathbf{j} = \sigma\gamma(\mathbf{E}^* - \beta^2\mathbf{E}_{\parallel}) \tag{7-65}$$

It will be observed that the relative difference in the values of $\mathbf{j}$ and $(\mathbf{j})$ given in Eqs. (7-65) and (7-62) is only of the order of β^2 (according, incidentally, with its kinematic origin). Practically, we could therefore hardly expect it to be of much significance. But as an illustration of the need of exercising circumspection in applying 4-tensor expressions to physical situations, the preceding discussion is instructive. This observation also suggests that for a better appreciation of Minkowski's phenomenological theory we should reexamine it in terms of conventional vector notation, the mathematical language in which both the physicist and the engineer are more at home.

The three-dimensional language itself must, of course, also be employed with care. Thus, if we wish to deal with the ordinary vector form of the Maxwell-Minkowski field equations, we are assured by the discussion at the beginning of this section that Eqs. (7-43) and (7-44) can already be taken to hold in an arbitrary inertial frame S. But what of the operational significance of the symbols entering in these equations when the portion of the medium under consideration is moving with respect to S? This question obviously calls for careful examination, into which we need not enter here fully, however. It will suffice to illustrate our point with reference to the classical operational definition of the field $\mathbf{E}$ in the interior of a material medium.

It will be recalled that in the usual phenomenological definition of $\mathbf{E}$ when the medium is *stationary* in S, one imagines a 'macroscopically infinitesimal' cavity made in the medium about the point $\mathbf{x}$ under consideration at the given time t, with its principal dimension along the direction of the field vector, and one considers $\mathbf{E}(\mathbf{x},t)$ as given in terms of the force $\mathbf{F}$ that would be experienced by a *test charge* placed at $\mathbf{x}$ at the time t:

$$\mathbf{E} = \frac{1}{e}\mathbf{F} \tag{7-66}$$

where e is the charge of the test particle. We can proceed in similar fashion when $\mathbf{u} \neq 0$ at $(\mathbf{x},t)$ [i.e., when there is gross body motion of the medium at $(\mathbf{x},t)$], if we allow the cavity and the test particle to partake of the motion of the medium. It can be concluded then that in the general case the definition (7-66) must be extended as follows:

$$\mathbf{E}^* = \frac{1}{e}\mathbf{F} \tag{7-67}$$

where $\mathbf{E}^*$ is given in (7-62), and $\mathbf{F}$ stands here for the ordinary, not the minkowskian force, i.e., for $\mathbf{f}$ given in (4-7). In fact, with the field vectors $\mathbf{E}$ and $\mathbf{B}$ having their usual definitions in terms of forces on a test charge and current element that are stationary in S and located in vacuum, the force $\mathbf{F}$ (as would in principle be measured in S) can be computed from Eq. (7-10) that holds in the vacuum constituting our cavity. We need only observe that by the tacitly assumed smallness of our test particle, and by the relative slowness in the variation of the quantities describing our material medium and the macroscopic electromagnetic field (i.e., the average of the underlying microparticle fields)—an ever present tacit assumption underlying the possibility of a consistent phenomenological treatment of the electrodynamics of continuous media—we obtain upon integrating (7-10) over the test particle, using (7-5) and (4-7),

$$F^\alpha = \frac{e}{c} B_\beta{}^\alpha u^\beta = \frac{e}{c} (B_{j0}u^j, B_{i\beta}u^\beta) = \frac{e}{c} (\mathbf{E} \cdot \mathbf{u},\ cE^i + [\mathbf{u} \times \mathbf{B}]^i) \tag{7-68}$$

(with B now referring to the macroscopic field). The spatial part of (7-68) is thus $\mathbf{F} = e(\mathbf{E} + [\boldsymbol{\beta} \times \mathbf{B}])$, in agreement with Eq. (7-67).

It can also be shown by similar reasoning on the basis of the measurement-significance of the field vectors for stationary media, that for moving media it is

$$\mathbf{D}^* = \mathbf{D} + (\boldsymbol{\beta} \times \mathbf{H}), \qquad \mathbf{B}^* = \mathbf{B} - (\boldsymbol{\beta} \times \mathbf{E}), \qquad \mathbf{H}^* = \mathbf{H} - (\boldsymbol{\beta} \times \mathbf{D}) \tag{7-69}$$

rather than the respective quantities **D**, **B**, **H** that possess more immediate physical significance (Prob. 7-15).

This conclusion illuminates also the covariant results (7-50), which can now be written more meaningfully as

$$\mathbf{D}^* = \epsilon \mathbf{E}^*, \qquad \mathbf{H}^* = \frac{1}{\mu} \mathbf{B}^* \tag{7-70}$$

The relation (7-65) can also be expressed in terms of $\mathbf{E}^*$ only, since obviously $\mathbf{E}_\parallel = \mathbf{E}^*_\parallel$; though, unlike the relations (7-70), it does not strictly resemble the corresponding classical relation for reasons that were indicated earlier. These considerations suggest also that it should be of interest to transform the field equations (7-43) and (7-44) so that they involve starred field vectors. It would not be profitable to start with the tensor equations (7-1) and (7-47). It is true that the starred field vectors are proportional to the spatial parts of 4-vectors; this is seen for $\mathbf{E}^*$ in Eq. (7-68) and, with the aid of Eqs. (7-46), (7-49) and a corresponding equation for the tensor H^*, it is readily found that

$$\begin{gathered} H_\beta{}^\alpha W^\beta = \gamma(\mathbf{D}^* \cdot \boldsymbol{\beta}, \mathbf{D}^*), \qquad B^{*\alpha}_\beta W^\beta = -\gamma(\mathbf{B}^* \cdot \boldsymbol{\beta}, \mathbf{B}^*) \\ H^{*\alpha}_\beta W^\beta = -\gamma(\mathbf{H}^* \cdot \boldsymbol{\beta}, \mathbf{H}^*) \end{gathered} \tag{7-71}$$

remembering the definitions (7-69).‡ [This brings to mind the useful decomposition of the equations of motion of a perfect fluid along the direction of the unit 4-vector $\mathbb{W}$ and perpendicularly (in $\mathfrak{M}$) to it (Sec. 6-5).] However, when one considers the significance of each of the equations in

‡ There is in (7-71) an unfortunate double use of the asterisk. However, the asterisk is generally used to designate duals of tensors, while the notation (7-69) and (7-62) is also well established.

the set (7-43) and (7-44) as well as the strict operational significance of all the starred field vectors, it can be concluded that a useful form of the field equations is obtained by proceeding noncovariantly, leaving the pair of equations (with obvious related physical significance)

$$\operatorname{div} \mathbf{B} = 0, \qquad \operatorname{div} \mathbf{D} = 4\pi\rho \tag{7-72}$$

intact, while introducing the vector pair $\mathbf{E}^*$, $\mathbf{H}^*$ (also significantly related in terms of operational definitions) into the remaining equations. Using the time derivative operator D/Dt defined in (i) of Prob. 2-1 [explicitly, $D/Dt = \partial/\partial t + \mathbf{u} \cdot \operatorname{div} - \operatorname{rot}\,(\mathbf{u} \times \quad)$], as well as Eqs. (7-72), these equations can then be written in the very suggestive form

$$\operatorname{rot} \mathbf{E}^* = -\frac{1}{c}\frac{D}{Dt}\mathbf{B}, \qquad \operatorname{rot} \mathbf{H}^* = \frac{1}{c}\left(\frac{D}{Dt}\mathbf{D} + 4\pi\mathbf{j}\right) \tag{7-73}$$

where $\mathbf{j}$ is the conduction current density defined in Eq. (7-61).

The first of Eqs. (7-73) is a useful succinct expression of Faraday's induction law in the Maxwell-Minkowski theory, holding in any given inertial frame. The second of Eqs. (7-73) affords further support for the choice (7-61) for the conduction part of the current density $\mathbf{i}$.

These equations are also convenient for comparison of the present theory with the corresponding results in Hertz' theory (see Prob. 2-1), and in the prerelativistic theory of Lorentz. A concise discussion of these questions with an analysis of the principal pertinent experimental tests is to be found in [7], sec. 36, and in [5], secs. 2, 3, and 17.

Under the restrictive assumptions we have made on the material media, their macroscopic electromagnetic behavior is within proper limits (relating in general to the rapidity in the space-time variation of the material and field quantities) fully represented by the Maxwell-Minkowski equations and suitable boundary conditions (see Prob. 7-16). In many instances greater insight into the physical situations encountered in such problems is gained by considering them as gross manifestations of underlying atomic electromagnetic processes. In particular, by Lorentz' method of averaging applied to stationary media, one arrives at the vectors of electric polarization and of magnetic polarization (magnetization). The phenomenological field vectors $\mathbf{D}$ and $\mathbf{H}$ are then defined quite generally in terms of these polarization vectors $\mathbf{P}^{(e)}$, $\mathbf{P}^{(m)}$ by the equations

$$\mathbf{D} = \mathbf{E} + 4\pi\mathbf{P}^{(e)}, \qquad \mathbf{H} = \mathbf{B} - 4\pi\mathbf{P}^{(m)} \tag{7-74}$$

Moreover, by taking proper account of the polarizability properties of the individual atoms or molecules constituting the medium, we can in principle, deduce the dependence of the polarization vectors, and hence also of the fields $\mathbf{D}$ and $\mathbf{H}$, on external fields and on the mechanical and thermodynamic states of the medium. In any thorough discussion of relativistic phenomenological electrodynamics we would thus also want to investigate the relativistic extension of the 'electron theory' method of Lorentz. Such an investigation is, however, outside the scope of this presentation. We must content ourselves here with a brief outline of this topic, referring the interested reader for details to the literature on the subject.‡

Before we turn to the relativistic generalization of Lorentz' method, let us note that, purely phenomenologically, the polarization vectors considered as spatial densities of the corresponding dipole moment strengths, and the relations (7-74), were already considered by Maxwell. The corresponding relativistic extension is, moreover, in the light of preceding discussion, quite immediate. Assuming that Eqs. (7-74) hold, when properly interpreted, in every inertial frame, their covariant expression is

$$H_{\alpha\beta} = B_{\alpha\beta} + 4\pi P_{\alpha\beta} \tag{7-75}$$

with the introduction of the antisymmetric "polarization 4-tensor"

$$P = \{\mathbf{P}^{(e)}; -\mathbf{P}^{(m)}\} \tag{7-76}$$

[using an understandable symbolic representation of antisymmetric second-rank tensors, in which, e.g., Eq. (7-46) would be written: $H = \{\mathbf{D};\mathbf{H}\}$]. For many simple applications, which include all that have been of purely historical interest, this is all we require. An explanation of unipolar induction is an interesting example that we shall take up presently.

The relativistic extension of the aforementioned statistical theory of Lorentz results quite simply by starting with the fully relativistic Maxwell-Lorentz equations (7-1) and (7-4), and replacing Lorentz' spatial averages by space-time averages. Thus, for any quantity $Q(\mathsf{x})$ associated with our physical system we define its mean value

$$\bar{Q}(\mathsf{x}) = \frac{1}{\delta V} \int_{\delta V} Q(\mathsf{x} + \mathsf{y})\, d^4y \tag{7-77}$$

where the space-time region δV (its 4-volume being also denoted by the symbol δV) encloses the event x, and is macroscopically vanishingly small, but microscopically sufficiently large to include a vast number of the atomic particles and of space-time periods in the oscillations of these particles and of their fields. Two important mathematical conclusions follow at once from this definition. Since we are employing lorentzian coordinates,

‡ We have already referred to [7], sec. 34, which contains references to the original work of Born and of Dällenbach. A discussion of his method in connection with light propagation in material media is presented by Lorentz in chap. 4 of his "Theory of Electrons." A very clear and critical exposition of the classical theory of Lorentz with a discussion of many important applications, is contained in L. Rosenfeld, "Theory of Electrons," North-Holland Publishing Company, Amsterdam, 1951. A treatment based on general statistical mechanics considerations is given in P. Mazur and B. R. A. Nijboer, *Physica*, **19**: 971 (1953). Refinements in the relativistic theory are indicated in a recent note by S. R. De Groot and J. Vlieger, *Physics Letters*, **10**: 294 (1964).

Eq. (7-77) applies when Q stands for any tensor quantity, and $\bar{Q}$ is then of course a tensor of the same type. The other conclusion is merely the result of differentiating both sides of Eq. (7-77), which gives

$$\bar{Q}_{,\nu} \equiv \frac{\partial \bar{Q}}{\partial x^{\nu}} = \overline{Q_{,\nu}} \tag{7-78}$$

[It should be noted however that a strict discussion of our averaging process must involve a proof or an explicit assumption of the fact, which we have tacitly assumed, that the mean values (7-77) are independent of the precise form and size of δV, provided the stated conditions are satisfied; and in fact, these conditions as well need to be specified with greater precision and explicitness than we have done here.]

The application of formula (7-78) to Eqs. (7-1) and (7-4) yields the equations

$$B_{(\alpha\beta,\gamma)} = 0, \qquad B^{\alpha\beta}{}_{,\beta} = \frac{4\pi}{c}\,\bar{\mathfrak{s}}^{\alpha} \equiv \frac{4\pi}{c}\,S^{\alpha} \tag{7-79}$$

We are retaining here the same symbols for the mean values of the 'lorentzian' field components (as we shall not have occasion to employ the two field tensors in the same discussion), but have introduced the new symbol S for $\bar{\mathfrak{s}}$. Comparison of (7-43) with the first set in (7-79) shows that the 'Maxwell' field tensor B can be identified with our mean value of the corresponding 'Lorentz' tensor; and in particular we have Lorentz' result:

$$\bar{\mathbf{E}}_{(\mathrm{Lor})} = \mathbf{E}_{(\mathrm{Max})}, \qquad \bar{\mathbf{B}}_{(\mathrm{Lor})} = \mathbf{B}_{(\mathrm{Max})}$$

The phenomenological identification that can be made in the second set of Eqs. (7-79) is not as obvious; it represents, in fact, the crux of our statistical problem. We consider it here only very briefly.

But first let us pause for a moment to inquire into the possible present applicational interest of the relativistic theory under discussion. The polarization vectors and Maxwell's phenomenological electrodynamic theory have relevance primarily for states of matter under temperatures such that atomic bindings are operative. Few practical situations can be envisaged in which these conditions hold and that involve bulk velocities that are not negligible relative to the velocity of light. In more obvious relativistic situations, such as may occur in a plasma under extremely high temperatures, the state of matter is likely to be that of a fully ionized gas, for which the ordinary macroscopic polarization tensor would not arise. In turning to a consideration of the structure of the smoothed-out density S, we disregard therefore the possible practical aspects of our topic, and proceed with the example of an ordinary polarizable, magnetizable, and conducting substance in mind.

To begin with, it is easy to see (and we leave it to the reader to work out the details) that for any macroscopically continuous medium consisting of charged particles—i.e., of electrons and ions—whatever its internal state and its state of bulk motion relative to a given inertial frame S, there is a part $\mathsf{c} = \rho\mathsf{u}$ of S, the convection 4-current density [with the same meaning of the symbols as in Eq. (7-60)], that corresponds to the bulk motion of the charges relative to S; and a part j, the conduction 4-current density, that corresponds to the motion of the nonbound charges relative to the medium. These two currents combine to give the total free (or "true") 4-current density i that occurs in the Maxwell-Lorentz equation (7-47).

In the case of a polarizable medium, a strict treatment of the bound charges is rather intricate and requires considerable care. The transition from the classical Lorentz analysis to the fully relativistic treatment is, however, fairly direct. Assuming a knowledge of the former (references to the literature are given in the footnote on page 244), one easily arrives at the identification

$$P^{\alpha\beta}(\mathsf{x}) = \frac{1}{c}\,\overline{\{\rho(\mathsf{x})x^{[\beta}U^{\alpha]}\}}_{\text{pol}} \qquad \rho_{\text{pol}} \equiv \rho_{\text{polarization}}, \text{ etc.} \tag{7-80}$$

with understandable notation [including (7-77), and $\mathsf{U} = d\mathsf{x}/d\tau$]; and this expression can be rewritten in terms of sums over the discrete polarization charges, as in the classical theory. It is moreover not difficult to show (Prob. 7-17) that under normal conditions one can derive expressions for the vectors $\mathbf{P}^{(e)}$, $\mathbf{P}^{(m)}$ associated with P [see Eq. (7-76)] that resemble the familiar classical expressions:

$$\begin{aligned} \mathbf{P}^{(e)} &= (P_{10}, P_{20}, P_{30}) = (P^{01}, P^{02}, P^{03}) = \overline{\{\gamma\rho\mathbf{x}\}}_{\text{pol}} \\ \mathbf{P}^{(m)} &= -(P_{23}, P_{31}, P_{12}) = (P^{32}, P^{13}, P^{21}) = \frac{1}{2c}\,\overline{\{\rho\mathbf{x}\times\mathbf{U}\}}_{\text{pol}} \end{aligned} \tag{7-81}$$

With this brief indication we conclude our sketch of the relativistic extension of Lorentz' statistical method. As noted previously, this extension appears at present to have but limited applicational interest.

Returning to our general discussion, let us now consider the relativistic explanation of unipolar induction. As pointed out earlier, the purely phenomenological theory suffices for this task. All that is essentially needed is the transformation law of the polarization tensor P, which, by Eqs. (7-76) and (iv) of Prob. 5-12, is given by the following equations

$$\begin{aligned} \mathbf{P}_{\|} &= \mathbf{P}'_{\|}, & \mathbf{P}_{\perp} &= \gamma[\mathbf{P}'_{\perp} + (\boldsymbol{\beta}\times\mathbf{M}')] \\ \mathbf{M}_{\|} &= \mathbf{M}'_{\|}, & \mathbf{M}_{\perp} &= \gamma[\mathbf{M}'_{\perp} - (\boldsymbol{\beta}\times\mathbf{P}')] \end{aligned} \tag{7-82}$$

where we have replaced $\mathbf{P}^{(e)}$, $\mathbf{P}^{(m)}$ by the more convenient and frequently used symbols $\mathbf{P}$, $\mathbf{M}$. The last term in the second of these equations holds the key to an understanding of the process of unipolar induction. It shows that a magnetized body would become electrically polarized when set in motion, and it is the voltage that can be thus produced by the motion (rotation, in practice) of a magnet that is said to be due to unipolar induction.‡

The transformation equations (7-82), or the corresponding transformation equations of the macroscopic field tensors, together with appropriate boundary conditions, provide also convincing and straightforward explanations of all other 'moving body' electromagnetic experiments that have been performed around the dawn and early part of this century under the impetus of the ether problem, Lorentz' electron theory, and the theory of relativity. Earlier in this section and in Chap. 2 we have referred to the literature where the analysis of these experiments is discussed. Here we wish only to call attention to the noteworthy fact that in some of these experiments essential relativistic corrections appear already to *first* order in β. This is apparent, for instance, in the case of unipolar induction, since it is not the factor γ but the vector product $\boldsymbol{\beta} \times \mathbf{M}'$ that is characteristic for this process. Another observation is also in place. Although the statistical theory previously mentioned is not essential for the analysis of the macroscopic processes represented by the experiments in question, it can be of interest when we wish to have a better understanding of these processes. Thus, in considering unipolar induction we may want to inquire as to the basic reason for the difficulties experienced by earlier investigators in attempting to explain this process in nonrelativistic terms, contrasted with the ease with which it is explained relativistically. Even a very elementary schematic consideration of the underlying atomic picture affords an adequate indication of the correct answer, as we now proceed to show.

To begin with, let us note first that, in contrast to the second of Eqs. (7-82), the last equation (with $\gamma = 1$) can be understood on the basis of classical theory. It can of course be justified with the aid of the phenomenological equations; but it can also be seen to follow from Lorentz' statistical theory when it is observed that a moving atomic electric dipole is effectively equivalent to an amperian magnetic dipole. Thus, if the former dipole has the moment $\mathbf{p} = e\mathbf{d}$, we can normally suppose that the velocity in question $\mathbf{u} \approx \Delta\mathbf{s}/\Delta t$ with $|\Delta\mathbf{s}| \gg |\mathbf{d}|$, so that the associated magnetic moment can be taken effectively as $e\mathbf{d} \times \Delta\mathbf{s}/c\,\Delta t = \mathbf{p} \times \boldsymbol{\beta}$ (remembering that we are using gaussian units). On the other hand, no such explanation of the last term in the second of Eqs. (7-82) seems possible on purely nonrelativistic ideas; but it becomes quite simple if we invoke the relativity of simultaneity. It suffices to imagine for this purpose an elementary amperian current with vanishing charge density when it is at rest in our frame S, and apply the first of Eqs. (7-55); it is then found that if $\mathbf{m}'$ is the magnetic moment asso-

‡ See e.g., Whittaker, *op. cit.*, vol. 2, pp. 245, 246, and the references given there. For a specific mathematical discussion see A. Sommerfeld, "Electrodynamics, Lectures on Theoretical Physics," vol. 3, prob. IV. 1, pp. 333, 359–363, Academic Press, Inc., New York, 1952 (translated by E. G. Ramberg). The Maxwell-Minkowski theory is discussed in secs. 34 and 35 of this interesting book.

ciated with the stationary current, there arises an electric moment

$$\mathbf{p} = \boldsymbol{\beta} \times \mathbf{m}' \tag{7-83}$$

when the current circuit moves with velocity $\mathbf{u} = c\boldsymbol{\beta}$ with respect to S (Prob. 7-17).

The result under discussion follows directly from Eqs. (7-81) and (7-83). Suppose that $\mathbf{M}' = \Sigma\mathbf{m}'$, where the summation is taken for all the elementary currents in a unit volume of the stationary body that is assumed magnetized but not polarized; then, by (7-83) and the relativistic contraction of volume

$$\mathbf{P} = \gamma\Sigma(\boldsymbol{\beta} \times \Sigma\mathbf{m}') = \gamma\boldsymbol{\beta} \times \Sigma\mathbf{m}' = \gamma\boldsymbol{\beta} \times \mathbf{M}' \tag{7-84}$$

On the other hand, since we are assuming that $\mathbf{P}' = 0$, the second of Eqs. (7-82) coincides with (7-84). It has thus been made quite evident that the relativistic kinematic relations enter in an essential way in the explanation of unipolar induction.

There is one feature of unipolar induction, as it is produced practically, that needs to be looked into: the fact that the motion of the magnetized body is not uniform but rotational. Does this fact matter at all in principle? And does it matter practically only if the angular velocity is great enough? These questions are part of the general problem concerning the permissible range of variation in the gross velocity field $\mathbf{u}(\mathsf{x})$ of a medium, if the phenomenological electrodynamic theory discussed in this section is to be applicable to it, or at least approximately applicable. Intuitively, it can be expected that the answer to each of the above questions is in the affirmative: the atomic electromagnetic processes that underlie the macroscopic phenomena of interest cannot be wholly independent of the gross accelerations; but unless the latter are sufficiently great their overall effect should be small and, particularly in the practical realization of unipolar induction, the accelerations associated with the attainable angular velocities can certainly be expected to be relatively insignificant. More precisely, we can note that on the one hand, as first pointed out by Einstein and Laub (*op. cit.* on page 236), if our medium consists of parts (no matter how numerous) that are mutually separated by vacuum and that move each uniformly but with individual velocities, then from the superposition principle arising from the linearity of the electromagnetic equations it follows that the Maxwell-Minkowski theory applies rigorously to this medium; while on the other hand, in any medium for which the velocity field $\mathbf{u}$ varies sufficiently rapidly, electromagnetic radiation effects can be expected to come into play, modifying the simple results of the Maxwell-Minkowski theory. The above intuitive conclusion thus appears justified: our phenomenological theory is approximately valid even if $\mathbf{u}$ is not constant, and it must break down if the velocity field experiences sufficiently steep gradients. Beyond this purely qualitative conclusion very little is yet known on this question. Its investigation is likely to be associated with future studies in the macroscopic theory of relativistic plasma.

The subject of ultra hot plasma, as noted before, is one of the small number of new fields of possible significant application of STR. It is still largely in its infancy; and it is quite complicated, since the subject is involved even without any relativistic corrections, compounding as it does the difficulties of fluid dynamics and of electrodynamics. Significant relativistic extensions of present theoretical studies involving the macroscopic continuous-medium approach in this field can therefore be expected only under the challenge of practical problems that may arise in the future. However, even the mere setting up of the equations of the relativistic continuum theory is as yet far from being a trivial problem. Much of the discussion in this section has a bearing on this problem. Together with the discussion of relativistic fluid dynamics and thermodynamics given in Chap. 6, a general basis is provided, at least in part, for extending the nonrelativistic equations of macroscopic plasma theory so as to incorporate relativistic corrections exactly or, as may frequently be warranted, only to first order in β.‡

In this connection let us note again that strict relativistic corrections are likely to be important only for temperatures under which any material medium would be in a state of total or near total ionization, and consequently the considerable complications associated with the polarization tensor P would not arise. It is, in fact, only in the less likely circumstance that occasion existed for treating relativistically a plasma under usual terrestrial conditions that substantial complications would present themselves. Thus, the constitutive equations (7-50) would have to be generalized to allow for anisotropy. Formally this can be easily accomplished by defining the polarization tensor P with the aid of a susceptibility tensor of the fourth rank [see Eq. (7-89)]. But dealing properly with the functional dependence of this tensor and the associated thermodynamic relations would be less easy.

Related complications would also appear in any careful analysis of the energy-momentum tensor of the macroscopic electrodynamic field. This analysis is actually not too simple or completely unequivocal even in the case of the ordinary Maxwell theory of stationary media.§ In the relativistic treatment for moving media the expression that should be used for this

‡ Among specific papers on this subject are the following: B. Zumino, *Phys. Rev.*, **108**: 1116 (1957); E. G. Harris, *Phys. Rev.*, **108**: 1357 (1957); C. L. Tang and J. Meixner, *Phys. Fluids*, **4**: 148 (1961). See also pertinent discussion in J. J. Brandstatter, "An Introduction to Waves, Rays, and Radiation in Plasma Media," McGraw-Hill Book Company, Inc., New York, 1963.

§ See, e.g., [9], sec. 54(d); Panofsky and Phillips, *op. cit.*, chap. 10. A very clear discussion is also contained in R. Becker, "Electromagnetic Fields and Interactions" (edited by F. Sauter), vol. 1, chap. DI, Blaisdell Publishing Company, New York, 1964. This book is a translation of the latest revision of the well-known and very readable "Abraham-Becker" two volumes on electrodynamics, with part E devoted to STR.

energy-momentum tensor has been a topic of disagreement since the appearance of Minkowski's publication on the subject, and has apparently been resolved only recently.‡ We shall however not concern ourselves here with the full details of the subject. As pointed out above, a complete relativistic treatment of all the complicated phenomena possible in polarizable and magnetizable material media may have little more than academic interest.

In approaching the problem of setting up in the Maxwell-Minkowski theory the energy-momentum tensor of the electromagnetic field in continuous material media, we must recognize from the start that this problem is different from that which we considered in Sec. 7-1 in dealing with the Maxwell-Lorentz theory. Owing to the purely phenomenological character of the Maxwell-Minkowski theory we can hardly expect to arrive at the correct expression in terms of an a priori invariantive analysis based on the properties of the field tensors, or in terms of any general argument, such as that presented by Fock's theorem mentioned in Sec. 7-2; it must also be doubtful if we can, in all strictness, speak of the "correct" expression for this tensor that characterizes the field forming part of an interacting complex system of 'matter' and field, considered macroscopically. In fact, in arriving, as we shall presently, at Minkowski's expression for the tensor in question, perhaps the only thing that can be claimed for it with complete certainty is that this expression is by far the most convenient of those that have been proposed; but then it should be borne in mind that the pragmatic criterion of convenience has its place in the fashioning of physical theory.

In the light of the above remarks, it cannot particularly matter what method of deriving the Minkowski tensor we pursue. It is perhaps simplest to follow Minkowski's general procedure of starting in each case with the classical expressions for stationary media, and finding their proper covariant transcription. In the present case, the classical Maxwell expressions (under suitable restrictions on the states of the media) are as follows

$$\begin{aligned} h &= \frac{1}{8\pi}(\mathbf{E}\cdot\mathbf{D} + \mathbf{B}\cdot\mathbf{H}), \qquad & \mathbf{S} &= \frac{c}{4\pi}(\mathbf{E}\times\mathbf{H}) \\ \mathbf{g} &= \frac{1}{4\pi c}(\mathbf{D}\times\mathbf{B}), \qquad & S^{ij} &= h\,\delta_{ij} - \frac{1}{4\pi}(E^iD^j + H^iB^j) \end{aligned} \tag{7-85}$$

where the symbols h and $\mathbf{g}$ have the same meaning as in Eq. (6-30), while $\mathbf{S}$ and S^{ij} correspond to $\mathbf{J}$ and P^{ij}. When we compare these equations with Eqs. (7-19), and recall the relationship of the latter to Eq. (7-17), bearing in mind that the tensor we are seeking must reduce to the tensor (7-17) when the polarization tensor P vanishes, we are led to Minkowski's energy-momen-

‡ A discussion of the rival proposals of Minkowski and of Abraham is contained in [7], sec. 35. Evidence in favor of Minkowski's proposal is presented in [5], sec. 19d, and in [6], sec. 76.

tum tensor

$$S^{\alpha\beta} = \frac{1}{4\pi}\left(B^{\alpha\mu}H_{\mu}{}^{\beta} + \frac{1}{4}\,g^{\alpha\beta}B_{\lambda\mu}H^{\lambda\mu}\right) \tag{7-86}$$

Its acceptance is tantamount to assuming the validity of Eqs. (7-85) in every inertial frame.

As a first important test of the soundness of the choice (7-86), let us compute the 4-force density that this tensor yields in accordance with the relation (6-60). This can be done expeditiously by referring to the steps in the derivation of (7-16) on page 226, which allow us now to write by analogy,

$$\frac{4\pi}{c}\,B_{\beta\alpha}i^{\beta} = B_{\beta\alpha}H^{\beta\gamma}{}_{,\gamma} = (B_{\beta\alpha}H^{\beta\gamma})_{,\gamma} - \tfrac{1}{2}B_{\beta\gamma,\alpha}H^{\beta\gamma}$$

$$= \cdots - \tfrac{1}{4}(B_{\beta\gamma}H^{\beta\gamma})_{,\alpha} - \tfrac{1}{4}(B_{\beta\gamma,\alpha}H^{\beta\gamma} - B_{\beta\gamma}H^{\beta\gamma}{}_{,\alpha})$$

Thus,

$$-S_{\alpha}{}^{\beta}{}_{,\beta} = \frac{1}{c}\,B_{\beta\alpha}i^{\beta} + Z_{\alpha} = f_{\alpha} \tag{7-87}$$

[where the use of the same symbol for force density as in (7-10) need cause no confusion] with

$$Z_{\alpha} = \frac{1}{16\pi}\,(B_{\lambda\mu,\alpha}H^{\lambda\mu} - B_{\lambda\mu}H^{\lambda\mu}{}_{,\alpha}) = \frac{1}{4}\,(B_{\lambda\mu,\alpha}P^{\lambda\mu} - B_{\lambda\mu}P^{\lambda\mu}{}_{,\alpha}) \tag{7-88}$$

using (7-75). We see that the 4-force density $\mathfrak{f}$ arising from the action of the electromagnetic field consists of two parts: a part that is completely analogous to the Lorentz force (7-10), and the part Z whose presence depends on the existence of polarization and magnetization in the medium as represented by the tensor (7-76).

It is the latter force density that generally leads to interpretational complications, with which we shall, however, not concern ourselves. A convincing analysis of this question, granted the availability in general of a precise operational definition of the force in question (acting at interior points of the material medium) would have to be based on a proper averaging of the actions of the underlying charges, involving the Lorentz force formula (7-10). On the other hand, the force field Z vanishes in the simplest (and, normally, important) case of homogeneous and isotropic media; i.e., when

$$P^{\lambda\mu} = \chi^{\lambda\mu}{}_{\alpha\beta}B^{\alpha\beta} \tag{7-89}$$

with the "susceptibility tensor" χ given by

$$\chi^{\lambda\mu}{}_{\alpha\beta} = \chi^{(\lambda\mu)}\,\delta^{\lambda\mu}_{\alpha\beta}, \qquad \text{no summation}$$

$$\chi^{(\lambda\mu)} = \chi^{(\mu\lambda)} = \begin{cases} \tfrac{1}{2}\chi_{\mathrm{e}} \\ -\tfrac{1}{2}\chi_{\mathrm{m}} \end{cases} \quad \text{for } \lambda, \mu = \begin{cases} 0, i \\ i, j \end{cases} \tag{7-90}$$

where the δ symbols are defined in Eq. (5-60), and χ_{e}, χ_{m} are the electric and magnetic susceptibilities. But even with vanishing Z, we can see that our

4-force density (7-87) does not generally satisfy Eq. (7-15). The quantity $\mathsf{f} \cdot \mathsf{U}$ obviously represents a covariant expression of the ohmic heat-production rate by the field B [see the related Eqs. (4-63) and (6-84)]. In the local rest frame S' it yields indeed, when $\mathsf{Z} = 0$, the familiar expression $\mathbf{E}' \cdot \mathbf{j}'$, as is immediately verified.

The chief criticism leveled at Minkowski's tensor (7-86) is that it is not symmetric. We have seen the significance of this symmetry, and in the case of the Maxwell-Lorentz theory, it has indeed been our concern to insure this property for the energy-momentum tensor. However, in the present case we are not dealing with a *complete* system (see Sec. 6-3): the phenomenological Maxwell-Minkowski field must be supplemented by the 'matter' field, as already intimated earlier.

7-4 ELECTROMAGNETIC FIELD OF A CHARGED PARTICLE OF GIVEN MOTION

In the preceding sections of this chapter we have been concerned with the relativistically covariant formulation of the general equations of electrodynamics and, insofar as any reference was made to material systems, the discussion has been essentially phenomenological. We shall now direct our attention to problems involving charged microparticles, such as electrons. Both the motion of such particles in external macroscopic electromagnetic fields as well as the radiation production by such particles when 'macroscopically' accelerated can, in many practical situations, be adequately treated in terms of the *classical* (i.e., nonquantum) equations of STR.

The problems of the former type will not be considered here (except for a few general questions involving arbitrary external fields, that are considered in Sec. 7-5 and in Appendix 7A). They are treated extensively in modern textbooks on electrodynamics;‡ in the relativistic domain, they find important application in the fields of particle accelerators and of high-temperature plasma physics.§

The radiation fields produced by charged particles that are accelerated over macroscopic spatial regions to relativistic speeds, in general admit of very accurate determination by purely classical means. The radiation production by electrons whirled around in the most powerful man-made particle accelerators or in cosmic magnetic fields, falls in this category.¶

‡ E.g., Panofsky and Phillips, *op. cit.;* J. D. Jackson, "Classical Electrodynamics," John Wiley & Sons, Inc., New York, 1962.

§ The latter application can be practically important even if the bulk motion of the plasma requires no relativistic treatment, but when, say, the tail of the maxwellian distribution of a component of the plasma involves an appreciable part in the relativistic region. See, e.g., S. Gartenhaus, "Elements of Plasma Physics," Holt, Rinehart and Winston, New York, 1964; B. Lehnert, "Dynamics of Charged Particles," North-Holland Publishing Company, Amsterdam, 1964.

¶ See, e.g., J. Schwinger, *Phys. Rev.*, **75:** 1912 (1949); *Proc. Nat. Acad. Sci. U.S.A.*, **40:** 132 (1954); L. I. Schiff, *Am. J. Phys.*, **20:** 474 (1952).

The latter application also does not concern us here. Our aim here is to consider, without entering into any details, classical treatments of the interaction between charged particles, principally in order to illustrate further the relevance and power of relativistic methods in this subject. The process of electromagnetic field production and of radiation by an elementary charged particle is an important step in any general study of such interaction, and it is with this application in mind that the following discussion is chiefly concerned.

Except for touching briefly in the next section on the attempts that have been made to treat an extended charged particle relativistically, we shall confine our discussion to *point* charges, without being concerned for the present with the question as to precisely what we are to understand by the latter term. Considered simply as an abstract model, the meaning is clear enough, and the application in this section of the Maxwell-Lorentz theory is unambiguous. We shall in fact derive the field associated with such a particle both by treating it from the start as a *discrete* concentration of charge, and also by finding the appropriate limit of a continuous distribution of charge. We shall begin with the latter method, the deduction of the field of an arbitrary continuous distribution of electric charge having, of course, independent interest. Our discussion will center mainly on the Fourier integrals method because of its wide applicability. For the same reason we also include a few explanatory remarks of a purely mathematical nature relating to the 'delta function' method. This section will conclude with a brief discussion of the covariant treatment of the radiation field.‡

The general problem of electromagnetic field production by a given continuous space-time distribution of charges can be reduced, as we know, to the solution of the *inhomogeneous wave equation*

$$\Box \mathsf{A}(\mathsf{x}) \equiv \left(\frac{1}{c^2}\frac{\partial^2}{\partial t^2} - \nabla^2\right)\mathsf{A}(\mathsf{x}) = \frac{4\pi}{c}\,\mathsf{s}(\mathsf{x}) \tag{7-91}$$

together with suitable initial and boundary conditions, where the 4-potential A is subject to the Lorentz condition

$$\operatorname{Div} \mathsf{A} = 0 \tag{7-92}$$

and the 4-current density s is given in (7-5). For our immediate purpose we need consider only the general boundary condition that expresses the operation of the *law of causality* in electrodynamics as it affects the coupling of charges and field. It is desirable to have an explicit statement of this condition, and because of its importance we present it for the sake of con-

‡ For a comprehensive discussion of electromagnetic field production and radiation problems, see, e.g., pertinent chapters in Panofsky and Phillips, *op. cit.;* J. D. Jackson, *op. cit.;* F. Rohrlich, "Classical Charged Particles," Addison-Wesley Publishing Company, Inc., Reading, Mass., 1965.

venience, but certainly not with all logical strictness, as an additional principle within the general scheme of STR. A possible formulation is as follows:

D With every electric-charge 4-current element inside an infinitesimal space-time region about a given event E there is associated, in empty space, an electromagnetic field that is distributed over the *future* branch of the light cone having E for its vertex; or, in ordinary language, if an element of charge exists within an infinitesimal spatial region about the point P for an infinitesimal duration about the instant t, then in empty space the associated electromagnetic field spreads out from P, beginning at the time t, in a spherical wave centered at P, and propagating with the speed of light.

The field equations can be treated conveniently using Fourier integrals. It can be usually assumed that the functions $s^\nu(\mathsf{x})$ have Fourier transforms

$$\tilde{s}^\nu(\mathsf{k}) = \frac{1}{(2\pi)^2}\int e^{i\mathsf{k}\cdot\mathsf{x}} s^\nu(\mathsf{x})\, d^4x, \qquad \mathsf{k}\cdot\mathsf{k} \equiv k^\nu k_\nu \tag{7-93}$$

that yield the convergent representation‡

$$s^\nu(\mathsf{x}) = \frac{1}{(2\pi)^2}\int e^{-i\mathsf{k}\cdot\mathsf{x}} \tilde{s}^\nu(\mathsf{k})\, d^4k \tag{7-93a}$$

The solution can be obtained then in general as follows.

Assuming merely formally the Fourier transform relations for A, it follows from (7-91) that

$$\tilde{\mathsf{A}}(\mathsf{k}) = -\frac{4\pi}{c}\frac{\tilde{\mathsf{s}}(\mathsf{k})}{\mathsf{k}\cdot\mathsf{k}} \tag{7-94}$$

and then by (7-93) (again purely formally),

$$\begin{aligned}\mathsf{A}(\mathsf{x}) &= \frac{-1}{\pi c}\int d^4k\, e^{-i\mathsf{k}\cdot\mathsf{x}}\frac{\tilde{\mathsf{s}}(\mathsf{k})}{\mathsf{k}\cdot\mathsf{k}} = \frac{-1}{4\pi^3 c}\int\frac{d^4k}{\mathsf{k}\cdot\mathsf{k}}\int d^4y\, e^{-i\mathsf{k}\cdot(\mathsf{x}-\mathsf{y})}\mathsf{s}(\mathsf{y}) \\ &= \frac{-1}{4\pi^3 c}\int d^4y\, \mathsf{s}(\mathsf{y})\int\frac{d^4k}{\mathsf{k}\cdot\mathsf{k}}e^{-i\mathsf{k}\cdot(\mathsf{x}-\mathsf{y})} \equiv \int d^4y\, \mathsf{s}(\mathsf{y})G(\mathsf{x}-\mathsf{y})\end{aligned} \tag{7-95}$$

This formal result accords with the linearity of our field equations and the consequent linear dependence of A on s; but as it stands it is evidently mathematically meaningless. It can be made perfectly sound, though, by proper extensions and redefinitions of the symbols that leave the linearity property intact. Because the physical literature is not always too clear on this subject, and because the formalism in question is widely useful and will

‡ For the theory of Fourier integral transformations see, e.g., E. C. Titchmarsh, "Introduction to the Theory of Fourier Integrals," 2d ed., Oxford University Press, Fair Lawn, N.J., 1948; A. H. Zemanian, "Distribution Theory and Transform Analysis," chap. 7, McGraw-Hill Book Company, Inc., New York, 1965.

be important to us in later connections, it may not be amiss to take the time at this point to consider this mathematical aspect of our problem with a little care.

Let us at first, in continuation of our purely formal development, substitute the last expression in (7-95) in Eq. (7-91), obtaining the relation

$$\mathsf{s}(\mathsf{x}) = \frac{c}{4\pi} \int \Box_x G(\mathsf{x} - \mathsf{y})\mathsf{s}(\mathsf{y})\, d^4y \tag{7-96}$$

If this result made any strict mathematical sense, it would be necessary for a function $\delta(x)$ to exist such that the integral identity

$$\int_{-\infty}^{\infty} \delta(x)f(x)\, dx = f(0) \tag{7-97}$$

is satisfied for every function f that is continuous at $x = 0$, which is impossible.‡ On the other hand, the relation (7-97) can be reformulated into a rigorous linear functional mapping $\mathfrak{D}[f(x)] = f(0)$ having the explicit representation

$$\lim_{n\to\infty} \int_{-\infty}^{\infty} \delta_n(x)f(x)\, dx = f(0) \tag{7-98}$$

where $\{\delta_n(x)\}$ is any function sequence such that

$$\lim_{n\to\infty} \int_a^b \delta_n(x)\, dx = \begin{cases} 0 \\ 1 \end{cases} \quad \text{if the point } x = 0 \text{ is } \begin{matrix}\text{outside} \\ \text{inside}\end{matrix}\ (a,b) \tag{7-98a}$$

In the physical literature the relation (7-98) is generally written simply as (7-97), and one speaks of the "Dirac δ function"; in the mathematical literature, since the work of Laurent Schwartz, one considers the above $\mathfrak{D}$ as belonging to a particular class of *functionals* (i.e., mappings of functions into numbers) called "distributions," whose theory has been extensively developed in the past two decades.§

We shall not require the advanced analytic machinery of the theory of distributions; but on the other hand, we shall refrain from calling δ a "function" and replace the integral sign in an expression such as (7-97) by the symbol $⨍$ as a reminder that such an expression is only a symbolic representation of the corresponding strict relation (7-98). In this sense Eq. (7-96) is valid provided $\int$ is replaced by $⨍$, and provided¶

$$\begin{gathered} \Box G(\mathsf{x}) = \frac{4\pi}{c}\,\delta(\mathsf{x}) \\ \delta(\mathsf{x}) \equiv \delta^{(4)}(\mathsf{x}) \equiv \delta(x^0)\,\delta(x^1)\,\delta(x^2)\,\delta(x^3) \end{gathered} \tag{7-99}$$

‡ By our requirement, $\delta(x)$ must obviously vanish if $x \neq 0$, and consequently the integral in (7-97) could only have the value zero.

§ See, e.g., Zemanian, *op. cit.*, and the references given there.

¶ We have in the above discussion made tacit use of the fact that (7-98) implies the more general relation, $⨍\delta(x - y)f(y)\, dy = f(x)$ at continuity points x of f; this follows at once when one introduces the new integration variable $u = x - y$ and applies the former relation to $f(x - u)$ considered as a function of the variable u.

Then also the last relation in (7-95) holds in a similar sense, i.e.,

$$\mathsf{A}(\mathsf{x}) = \int G(\mathsf{x} - \mathsf{y})\mathsf{s}(\mathsf{y})\, d^4y \tag{7-100}$$

where G is a symbol that plays here a similar role to that played by the symbol δ in (7-97) (in other words, it is associated with a distribution in the sense of L. Schwartz). It is—apart from boundary conditions—defined by Eq. (7-99), which we now recognize as having an associated symbolic meaning: it can be represented rigorously by an infinite sequence of equations, $\Box G_n(\mathsf{x}) = 4\pi\, \delta_n(\mathsf{x})/c$, where the sequence $\{G_n\}$ bears to the symbol G the same relationship as obtains between $\{\delta_n\}$ and the symbol δ.

The symbolic quantity G is commonly known as "the Green's function" for a given problem.‡ In our case, comparison of Eqs. (7-95) and (7-100) suggests examining the relation

$$G(\mathsf{x}) = \frac{-1}{4\pi^3 c} \int \frac{1}{\mathsf{k}\cdot\mathsf{k}}\, e^{-i\mathsf{k}\cdot\mathsf{x}}\, d^4k \tag{7-101}$$

where the divergent integral is suitably interpreted. In order to see the possible sense of this symbolic relation, consider the following one-dimensional Fourier-theorem formula—where necessary regularity conditions are assumed, insuring the existence of the integrals and permitting the indicated interchange of orders of integration

$$f(x) = \frac{1}{2\pi}\int_{-\infty}^{\infty} dk\, e^{-ikx} \int_{-\infty}^{\infty} dy\, e^{iky} f(y) = \frac{1}{2\pi}\lim_{n\to\infty}\int_{-n}^{n} dk\, e^{-ikx}\int_{-\infty}^{\infty} dy\, e^{iky} f(y)$$

$$= \frac{1}{2\pi}\lim_{n\to\infty}\int_{-\infty}^{\infty} dy\, f(y)\int_{-n}^{n} e^{-ik(x-y)}\, dk = \frac{1}{\pi}\lim_{n\to\infty}\int_{-\infty}^{\infty} dy\, f(y)\,\frac{\sin n(x-y)}{x-y}$$

We see here in what sense one can write, as is frequently done,

$$\delta(x) = \frac{1}{2\pi}\int_{-\infty}^{\infty} e^{\pm ikx}\, dk \tag{7-102}$$

[We also have here, incidentally, an example of a sequence $\delta_n(x)$, namely, $1/\pi\, (\sin nx)/x$.] A similar interpretation can be shown to apply to the relation (7-101); but here, in addition, we must also take proper care of the poles in the integrand arising from the zeros of $\mathsf{k}\cdot\mathsf{k}$. In the Green's function method of solution as conventionally presented, one starts with the formal steps (7-100), (7-99), (7-102), and (7-101), in some such order, and then proceeds to specify a particular way of evaluating the integral in (7-101) so that the resulting solution (7-100) satisfies the boundary condition D. We have indicated a rigorous basis for the former steps. The method fre-

‡ This is not the happiest choice of terms; in addition to the use of the word "function" in conflict with the accepted sense of the word in mathematical analysis, the combination of the article and the apostrophe in the designation is a grammatical barbarism. But this usage has apparently universal acceptance. (However, see Rohrlich, *op. cit.*, p. 78.)

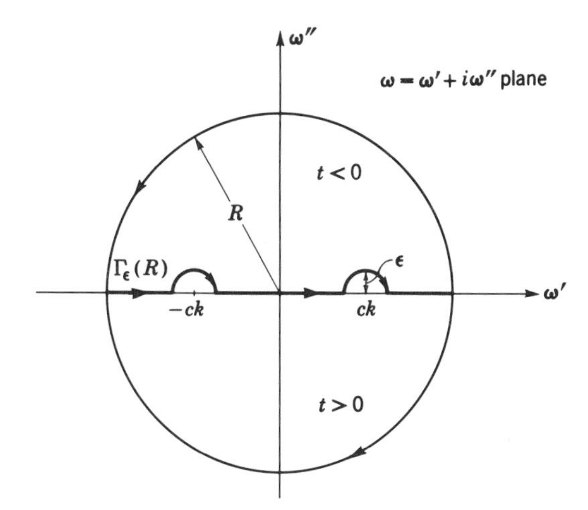

Fig. 7-1 The integration contours for Eq. (7-103).

quently employed in the latter step, which is intrinsically rigorous and finds important application in other similar connections, can be treated conveniently with the symbolic shorthand method as it admits a rigorous recasting along lines precisely similar to those indicated in the above discussion.‡

The method in question involves introducing complex integration with respect to one suitably chosen variable of integration in (7-101) so as to avoid the poles of the integrand, and then going to the limit as this integration contour tends to the corresponding original path of integration. Since $\mathsf{k} \cdot \mathsf{k} = (k^0)^2 - \mathbf{k}^2$, the simplest choice of variable is either k^0 or $|\mathbf{k}|$, and the former choice is the usual one. The integral§ in (7-101) can then be replaced by

$$\lim_{\epsilon \to 0} \int d^3k \, e^{i\mathsf{k}\cdot\mathsf{x}} Q_\epsilon(t,k)$$

$$Q_\epsilon(t,k) = c \int_{\Gamma_\epsilon} \frac{e^{-i\omega t}}{\omega^2 - c^2k^2} \, d\omega \qquad \begin{aligned} \omega &= ck^0 \\ k &\equiv |\mathbf{k}| \end{aligned} \tag{7-103}$$

where Γ_ϵ is a suitably chosen contour in the complex ω plane. Now, as far as satisfying the relation (7-99) is concerned, the particular choice of the contour of integration is immaterial, since upon applying the operator $\square$ inside the integral, the poles disappear and the contour can be continuously deformed to the real ω axis, and the result (7-102) applied. This freedom in the choice of Γ_ϵ can be used to have G satisfy the causality condition D. By taking Γ_ϵ as shown in Fig. 7-1, and noting that for $t < 0$ and $t > 0$ the integrals of $e^{-i\omega t}/(\omega^2 - c^2k^2) = e^{\omega'' t}e^{-i\omega' t}/(. \, . \, .)$ over the upper and lower

‡ Henceforth such possibility will be tacitly understood when we use the symbolic method and symbolic language.

§ This integral is of course improper both because of the poles in the integrand as well as in respect to its δ-like character.

semicircles respectively (Fig. 7-1) tend to zero as their radii go to infinity, we find, by an immediate application of Cauchy's theorem of residues, that

$$Q_\epsilon(t,k) = \begin{cases} 0 & \text{for } t < 0 \\ \dfrac{i\pi}{k}\left(e^{ickt} - e^{-ickt}\right) & \text{for } t > 0 \end{cases}$$

Substituting in (7-103), and thence in (7-101), we find that $G \equiv 0$ for $t < 0$, while for $t > 0$ we have, upon introduction of polar coordinates in the integral over $\mathbf{k}$, and integration over the angles,

$$\begin{aligned} G(\mathsf{x}) &= \frac{-1}{2\pi c r}\int_0^\infty k\,dk\,(e^{ikr} - e^{-ikr})\,\frac{1}{k}\,(e^{ickt} - e^{-ickt}) \\ &= \frac{-1}{2\pi c r}\int_{-\infty}^\infty dk\,(e^{ik(r+ct)} - e^{ik(r-ct)}), \qquad r = |\mathbf{x}| \end{aligned}$$

Thus, by (7-102),

$$G(\mathsf{x}) = \frac{1}{cr}\,\delta(r - ct), \qquad t > 0 \tag{7-104}$$

and the incorporation of condition D is evident when we substitute this expression into (7-100). Since in accordance with D we must take $x^0 > y^0$, the desired solution is

$$\begin{aligned} \mathsf{A}(\mathsf{x}) &= \frac{1}{c}⨍ \mathsf{s}(\mathsf{y})\,\frac{\delta[R - (x^0 - y^0)]}{R}\,d^4y \\ &= \frac{1}{c}\int \frac{\mathsf{s}(x^0 - R,\mathbf{y})}{R}\,d^3y, \qquad R \equiv |\mathbf{x} - \mathbf{y}| \end{aligned} \tag{7-105}$$

In the last expression we recognize the well-known *retarded potential* solution.‡

That the Lorentz condition (7-92) is also satisfied by our solution, can be proven by noting that with a change of integration variables from y^ν to $u^\nu = x^\nu - y^\nu$, Eq. (7-100) can be written as

$$\mathsf{A}(\mathsf{x}) = ⨍\mathsf{s}(\mathsf{x} - \mathsf{u})G(\mathsf{u})\,d^4u$$

Since differentiation under the symbolic integral sign can be here justified (recalling the significance of this symbol), (7-92) is seen to be a consequence of the charge conservation formula (7-14).

‡ The final result is—as it must be—expressed in perfectly orthodox fashion. Moreover, there are methods of solution that employ only explicitly orthodox steps throughout—which is, of course, also not surprising. For such a method, due to Kirchhoff, see, e.g., Lorentz, *op. cit.*, pp. 233–238. For other methods of solution of both homogeneous and the inhomogeneous wave equations and for sundry boundary conditions see, e.g., Panofsky and Phillips, *op. cit.*; and the references given there. For an interesting explicitly covariant method due to Sommerfeld, see Prob. 7-20.

The result (7-105) is, of course, relativistically covariant, but this fact is not in immediate evidence in the integral expression. For some applications it is desirable to have a manifestly covariant expression. A quick way of obtaining it in terms of our symbolic method is by using the following formula obeyed by δ symbols, that has frequent application:

$$\delta[g(x)] = \sum_k \frac{\delta(x - x_k)}{|g'(x_k)|}, \qquad \{x_k\} = \text{set of zeros of } g\text{, assumed all simple [so that } g'(x_k) \neq 0] \tag{7-106}$$

The proof of this formula is obtained by noting that the only nonvanishing contribution from $\delta[g(x)]$ comes from intervals on the x axis that contain x_k, and that we can choose a set of nonoverlapping intervals $\{I_k\}$ such that g is monotonic on each I_k, and I_k contains in its interior the sole zero x_k; so that with the new integration variable $u = g(x)$ [and $x = G(u)$ on I_k],

$$\int f(x)\, \delta[g(x)]\, dx = \sum_k \int_{g(I_k)} f[G(u)]\, \delta(u) \frac{du}{|g'[G(u)]|} = \sum_k \frac{f(x_k)}{|g'(x_k)|} \tag{7-106a}$$

Now, applying (7-106), we see that for $x^0 > 0$

$$\frac{1}{2r}\,\delta(x^0 - r) = \frac{1}{2r}\,[\delta(x^0 - r) + \delta(x^0 + r)] = \delta(\mathsf{x}^2) \tag{7-107}$$

since $\delta(x^0 + r) = 0$ when $x^0 > 0$, and $(x^0 - r)(x^0 + r) = \mathsf{x}^2$. Upon introducing also the obviously covariant quantity (under *orthochronous* Lorentz transformations—the transformations under which the statement $\mathfrak{D}$ is invariant),

$$\theta(\mathsf{x}) = \begin{cases} 1 & \text{for } x^0 > 0 \\ 0 & \text{for } x^0 < 0 \end{cases} \tag{7-108}$$

comparison of (7-104) and (7-107) shows that

$$G(\mathsf{x}) = \frac{2}{c}\,\theta(\mathsf{x})\,\delta(\mathsf{x}^2) \tag{7-109}$$

When this is combined with (7-100) we obtain the desired result

$$\mathsf{A}(\mathsf{x}) = \frac{2}{c}\int \theta(\mathsf{x} - \mathsf{y})\,\delta[(\mathsf{x} - \mathsf{y})^2]\mathsf{s}(\mathsf{y})\, d^4y \tag{7-110}$$

One can now find the general expression for the electromagnetic field (7-8a) given by our solution $\mathsf{A}(\mathsf{x})$, and for the energy and momentum densities residing in this field as represented by the tensor (7-17). We shall not pursue this general subject further, however, referring the interested reader to the previously suggested references; but turn to the topic of our immediate concern, namely, the electromagnetic field production by an arbitrarily moving charged particle.

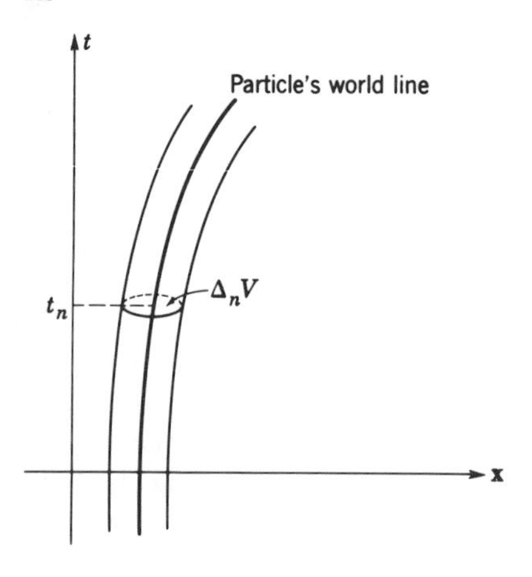

Fig. 7-2 Schematic representation of particle's world line and infinitesimal world tube, in connection with Eq. (7-112). The symbol $\Delta_n V$ is used to represent both the spatial region and its volume.

As stated earlier, we shall confine our discussion to particles that are point structures in the strict mathematical sense. The charge *density* of such a particle is clearly an improper concept, whose relationship to the proper density is similar to that existing between the Dirac 'function' and a proper function. With this understanding, we can think of the particle throughout its history, defined by the world line L given by

$$\mathsf{x} = \mathsf{z}(\tau) \qquad \text{or equivalently} \qquad \mathbf{x} = \mathbf{Z}(t) \tag{7-111}$$

as represented by a sequence of charged space-time filaments L_n enclosing L, whose spatial cross sections have infinitesimal spans (recall a similar treatment in connection with particle action integrals in Sec. 7-2); so that if e is the value of the discrete charge of the particle, we have, in understandable notation [see Fig. 7-2 and Eq. (7-5)],

$$\begin{aligned} \rho_n(u)\,\Delta_n V &= \rho_n\,\Delta_n V^* = e \\ \rho_n(u)\mathbf{u}\,\Delta_n V &= \rho_n\,\Delta_n V^*\mathbf{u} = e\mathbf{u}, \qquad \mathbf{u} = \frac{d\mathbf{Z}}{dt} \end{aligned} \tag{7-112}$$

$$\text{or,} \quad \mathsf{s}_n(\mathsf{x}) = \rho_n(u)\mathsf{u}(t) = \begin{cases} \dfrac{e}{\Delta_n V}\,\mathsf{u}(t) & \text{inside} \\ 0 & \text{outside} \end{cases} \text{ the spatial region } \Delta_n V$$

Thus, remembering the defining process for the δ symbol,‡ we can write

$$\mathsf{s}(\mathsf{x}) = e\,\delta^{(3)}[\mathbf{x} - \mathbf{Z}(t)]\mathsf{u}(t), \qquad \delta^3(\mathbf{x}) \equiv \delta(x)\,\delta(y)\,\delta(z) \tag{7-113}$$

The 4-vector property of the right-hand side of this equation is not

‡ The extension of the definition (7-98) to many-dimensional integration domains is obvious, and the verification of the extended condition (7-98a) for sequences such as we have in the present case, is immediate.

immediately apparent.‡ We can obtain a manifestly covariant expression in terms of a slight broadening of the above limiting procedure, by associating with L_n a subdivision $\{\tau_n^{(k)}\}$ of the proper time parameter τ of L, which becomes infinitely fine as $n \to \infty$, and which includes an interval $\Delta\tau_n$ about the value τ under consideration (which therefore $\to 0$ as $n \to \infty$), during which we suppose the charge density associated with L_n is nonvanishing about the event $\mathsf{z}(\tau)$ [that is, we imagine that there is associated with the particle for each value τ of its history an infinitesimal space-time region about $\mathsf{z}(\tau)$ of nonvanishing charge density]. We have then—in understandable notation that is partly of a purely symbolic character of the type we have been employing, using (7-112) and remembering that $\mathsf{U} = d\mathsf{z}/d\tau = \gamma_u \mathsf{u}$—that $\mathsf{s}(\mathsf{x})$ is associated with the sequence

$$ec \left\{ \frac{\mathsf{U}_n}{\Delta_n V^* c \, \Delta\tau_n} \Delta\tau_n \right\} \equiv ec \left\{ \sum_k \frac{\mathsf{U}_n}{\Delta_n V^* c \, \Delta\tau_n^{(k)}} \Delta\tau_n^{(k)} \right\}$$

in other words, that we can write in terms of our symbolic formalism, and with $\delta(\mathsf{x})$ as defined in (7-99),

$$\mathsf{s}(\mathsf{x}) = ec \int_{-\infty}^{\infty} \mathsf{U}(\tau) \, \delta[\mathsf{x} - \mathsf{z}(\tau)] \, d\tau \tag{7-114}$$

[see the footnote in connection with (7-113)].

A partial check on the consistency of our symbolic results, (7-113) and (7-114), can be obtained by deducing the former result from the latter. This can be achieved by applying an extension of the formula (7-106) when the integrand $f(x)$ in (7-106a) is itself a δ symbol.§ Since for given $\mathbf{x}$ the function $x^0 - z^0(\tau)$ has the unique zero, $\tau = \tau(x^0)$, and since

$$\left| \frac{dz^0}{d\tau} \right|_{\tau = \tau(x^0)} = c\gamma_{u(t)}$$

it follows that

$$\begin{aligned} \int_{-\infty}^{\infty} \mathsf{U}(\tau) \, \delta[\mathsf{x} - \mathsf{z}(\tau)] \, d\tau &= \int_{-\infty}^{\infty} \mathsf{U}(\tau) \, \delta[x^0 - z^0(\tau)] \, \delta^{(3)}[\mathbf{x} - \mathbf{z}(\tau)] \, d\tau \\ &= \frac{1}{c} \frac{\mathsf{U}(\tau(x^0))}{\gamma_u} \delta^{(3)}[\mathbf{x} - \mathbf{z}(\tau(x^0))] \\ &= \frac{1}{c} \mathsf{u}(t) \, \delta[\mathbf{x} - \mathbf{Z}(t)], \qquad \delta(\mathbf{x}) \equiv \delta^{(3)}(\mathbf{x}) \end{aligned}$$

and hence (7-114) is indeed equivalent to (7-113).

‡ For a direct proof of the relativistic covariance of this symbolic expression as applied to a system of charged particles, see B. Podolsky, *Phys. Rev.*, **72**: 624 (1947).

§ Bearing in mind the definition of δ symbols, it can be appreciated that products of these symbols must be handled with great care if they are not to lead to meaningless results.

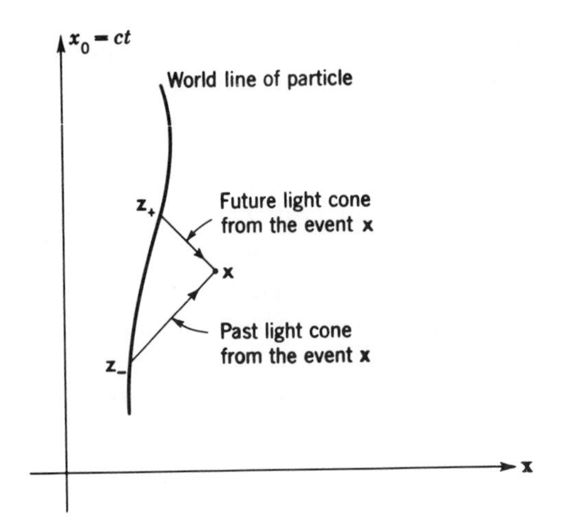

Fig. 7-3 Schematic diagram representing the construction of the "retarded" and the "advanced" 4-points $z_- \equiv z_-(x)$, and $z_+ \equiv z_+(x)$ [as given respectively by Eq. (7-120) and the same equation with $R^0_- < 0$].

The 4-potential A for a charged particle of assigned world line (7-111), can be obtained now most simply from the general formula (7-105) with s given by Eq. (7-113). The immediate result

$$\mathsf{A}(x) = \frac{e}{c} \int \frac{\delta[\mathbf{y} - \mathbf{Z}(t - R/c)]}{R} \, \mathsf{u}\left(t - \frac{R}{c}\right) d^3y \tag{7-115}$$

can be reduced to a conventional form by applying a direct extension of formula (7-106) to multiple integrals. In our case, when only one simple zero of the integrand is involved (and other obvious conditions are satisfied), the three-dimensional extension takes the form

$$\int \delta[\mathbf{F}(\mathbf{y})]G(\mathbf{y})\, d^3y = G(a) \left| \frac{\partial(F)}{\partial(y)} \right|^{-1}_{\mathbf{y}=\mathbf{a}} \qquad \mathbf{F}(\mathbf{a}) = 0 \tag{7-116}$$

which can be proved by steps similar to those used in the proof of (7-106), starting with the change of integration variables, $\mathbf{y} \to \mathbf{F}(\mathbf{y})$.

In our case the zero, $\mathbf{a} = \mathbf{z}_-(x)$, which depends on the field event x, is given by the equation

$$\mathbf{a} - \mathbf{Z}\left(t - \frac{|\mathbf{x} - \mathbf{a}|}{c}\right) = 0 \tag{7-117}$$

and thus determines the event of intersection of the world line of the particle with the past light cone through x (see Fig. 7-3, where, for future use, the corresponding construction for the *advanced* potential is also included), the uniqueness of this intersection 4-point being easily established. Moreover, the Jacobian occurring in formula (7-116) is, in the present case (using understandable abbreviated notation),‡

$$\left[\det \left\| \delta_{ij} - \frac{\dot{Z}^i(x^j - y^j)}{cR} \right\| \right]_{\mathbf{y}=\mathbf{z}_-} = 1 - \frac{\dot{\mathbf{Z}}(t_-) \cdot \mathbf{R}_-}{c|\mathbf{x} - \mathbf{z}_-|}, \qquad \dot{\mathbf{Z}} \equiv \frac{d\mathbf{Z}}{dt}$$

$$\text{where} \quad t_- \equiv t_-(\mathsf{x}) = t - \frac{1}{c}|\mathbf{x} - \mathbf{z}_-|, \qquad \mathbf{z}_- \equiv \mathbf{z}_-(\mathsf{x}) \tag{7-117a}$$

$$\mathbf{R}_- \equiv \mathbf{R}_-(\mathsf{x}) = \mathbf{x} - \mathbf{z}_-$$

Therefore, substituting in (7-116) applied to (7-115), we obtain the explicit form of our solution:

$$\mathsf{A}(\mathsf{x}) = \frac{e}{c}\frac{\mathsf{u}(t_-)}{R_- - (1/c)\mathbf{u}(t_-) \cdot \mathbf{R}_-}, \qquad |\mathbf{R}_-| \equiv R_- \tag{7-118}$$

where the quantities are defined in (7-117a) and in the last equation in (7-112). This is the well-known Liénard-Wiechert solution (1898, 1900), in which, of course, it was originally supposed that the velocities are taken with respect to the lorentzian stationary electromagnetic ether.

In order to bring the expression (7-118) into a manifestly covariant form, we need only observe that by (7-117) and (7-117a) we have

$$R_- = x^0 - ct_- \equiv R^0{}_- \tag{7-117b}$$

so that, $cR_- - \mathbf{u}(t_-) \cdot \mathbf{R}_- = \mathsf{u}(t_-) \cdot \mathsf{R}_-$, and (7-118) can be written:

$$\mathsf{A}(\mathsf{x}) = \frac{e\mathsf{u}(t_-)}{\mathsf{u}(t_-) \cdot \mathsf{R}_-} = \frac{e\mathsf{U}(\tau_-)}{\mathsf{U}(\tau_-) \cdot \mathsf{R}_-} \tag{7-119}$$

where $\tau_- = \tau(t_-)$.

We now turn to the other possible approach, treating the charged particle directly as a discrete point charge and thus finding the solution (7-119) without the intervention of the general solution (7-105) for continuous charge distributions. This approach is obviously the simpler mathematically, and also from a strictly physical point of view it makes at least as much sense to consider the discrete charges as primary and continuous charge distributions as statistical aggregates of such charges§ as to take the reverse position. In any case, the derivation of the solution (7-119) on this approach can be effected very simply and suggestively.

Of the many possible direct methods of solution we present one similar to that used previously in other connections, and which has obvious heuristic interest: we attempt to deduce the solution we are seeking from a small number of basic conditions that impose themselves naturally. In the present case these can be taken as follows. (1) Our solution $\mathsf{A}(\mathsf{x})$ must be covariant under the group $\mathfrak{L}$ as well as under the space-time translations.

‡ The expansion of the determinant is easily found, since generally $\det \|\delta_{ij} - a_ib_j\| = 1 - a_ib_i$, as one verifies immediately.

§ As briefly touched upon in Sec. 7-3.

(2) It must agree with the requirement D. (3) When referred to the rest frame of the particle $S^*(\tau_-)$ [remembering that $\tau_- \equiv \tau_-(\mathsf{x}) = \tau(t_-)$, t_- given in (7-117a)], the component $A^0(\mathsf{x})$ is identical with the Coulomb potential of a stationary point charge (whose numerical value is taken to be e), and $\mathbf{A}(\mathsf{x}) = 0$.

In arriving at our deduction from these assumptions, we shall not need to make explicit use of the field equations, the pertinent implications of these equations being contained in our conditions. By applying both conditions (1) and (2), a first conclusion that can be arrived at from an examination of all the possibilities available to us for constructing a 4-vector is that the general form that our solution can take is

$$\mathsf{A}(\mathsf{x}) = a\mathsf{R}_- + b\mathsf{U}(\tau_-) + c\dot{\mathsf{U}}(\tau_-) + d\ddot{\mathsf{U}}(\tau_-) + \cdots, \qquad \dot{\mathsf{U}} \equiv \frac{d\mathsf{U}}{d\tau}$$

where τ_- is defined under (3), (7-111) being the equation of the given world line of our particle, and $a, b, c, \ldots$ are 4-scalars that can depend on R_-, $\mathsf{U}(\tau_-)$, $\dot{\mathsf{U}}(\tau_-)$, and the higher derivatives. Applying next our assumption (3), it follows directly that in the frame $S^*(\tau_-)$ all the quantities a, c, etc. vanish, and that $b = e/\mathsf{U}^*_- \cdot \mathsf{R}^*_-$. The latter result holds in view of (7-117b) and the relations $U^{*0}_- = c$, $\mathbf{U}^*_- = 0$, and because with our notational conventions the ordinary scalar potential is given by A^0 [see (7-7)]. Finally, since $a, b, \ldots$ are relativistic scalars, the above results hold in every inertial frame, and we arrive at the solution (7-119).

It may be noted that the conclusion concerning the vanishing of a, c, etc. could be obtained without invoking the assumption (3), if we only make use of the *linearity* of our field equations, which implies that their solutions depend always linearly upon their sources, and observe that in the present case the source is represented by a (singular) quantity that is proportional to U.

The solution (7-119), which we have obtained under the specified conditions, is unique—except of course for transformations of the special gauge group (7-21) with the arbitrary 4-scalar χ satisfying the homogeneous wave equation. The associated electromagnetic field given by Eqs. (7-8a) represents, therefore, a unique solution of our problem. It is easily derived if we bear in mind that $\tau_- = \tau_-(\mathsf{x})$, and that this function is according to (7-117a) and (7-117b) given by

$$\begin{matrix} \mathsf{R}^2_- = 0 \\ R^0_- > 0 \end{matrix} \qquad \mathsf{R}_- \equiv \mathsf{R}_-(\mathsf{x}) = \mathsf{x} - \mathsf{z}(\tau_-) \tag{7-120}$$

so that (dropping now the minus sign subscript—which is henceforth to be understood from the context, when not explicitly shown),

$$0 = \frac{\partial \mathsf{R}^2}{\partial x^\mu} = 2R_\nu \left[\delta^\nu_\mu - U^\nu(\tau) \frac{\partial \tau}{\partial x^\mu} \right]$$

i.e.,

$$\frac{\partial \tau}{\partial x^\mu} = \frac{1}{c}\hat{R}_\mu, \qquad \hat{\mathsf{R}} = \frac{\mathsf{R}}{R_\parallel}, \qquad R_\parallel = \frac{1}{c}\mathsf{R}\cdot\mathsf{U}(\tau) \tag{7-121}$$

(with $\tau = \tau_-$, etc.). Since $d\mathsf{R}/d\tau = -\mathsf{U}$, and $\mathsf{U}^2 = c^2$, Eqs. (7-8a), (7-119), and (7-121) lead directly to the desired result:

$$B_{\mu\nu}(\mathsf{x}) = \frac{2e}{c}\left\{\frac{1}{R_\parallel^{\,2}}U_{[\mu}\hat{R}_{\nu]} + \frac{1}{cR_\parallel}(\dot{U}_{[\mu}\hat{R}_{\nu]} - \Omega U_{[\mu}\hat{R}_{\nu]})\right\}$$
$$\Omega \equiv \frac{1}{c}\dot{\mathsf{U}}\cdot\hat{\mathsf{R}}, \qquad \dot{\mathsf{U}} \equiv \frac{d\mathsf{U}}{d\tau} \tag{7-122}$$

(the braces serving to remind us that the quantities inside them are to be evaluated for $\tau = \tau_-$).

As a first simple check of our general formula we consider the special case $U^\mu = (c,0,0,0)$ for all τ, i.e., the case of a point charge stationary in our reference frame. We find at once remembering Eq. (7-117b):

$$B_{i0}(\mathsf{x}) \equiv E^i(\mathsf{x}) = -\frac{e}{R^3}R_i = \frac{e}{R^3}R^i, \qquad H_{ij}(\mathsf{x}) = 0 \tag{7-123}$$

i.e., the familiar Coulomb field of a stationary charge.

If, more generally, the charge moves with uniform velocity relative to our frame (which we are assuming of course to be inertial), so that U is arbitrary but constant, (7-122) leads again immediately to the special result

$$B_{\mu\nu}(\mathsf{x}) = \frac{2e}{c}\left\{\frac{1}{R_\parallel^2}U_{[\mu}\hat{R}_{\nu]}\right\} \tag{7-124}$$

When $u \ll c$, the space-space components of the tensor (7-124) should reproduce the well-known classical expression for the magnetic field of a uniformly moving charge (related to the law of Biot and Savart). Indeed,

$$B^k(\mathsf{x}) = \epsilon^{kij}B_{ij} = \epsilon^{kij}\frac{e}{cR^3}(u_iR_j - u_jR_i) = \frac{e}{c}\frac{1}{R^3}(\mathbf{u}\times\mathbf{R})^k$$

with the approximation,

$$\mathsf{U}\cdot\mathsf{R}_- = c\left(R_-^0 - \mathbf{u}\cdot\frac{\mathbf{R}_-}{c}\right) \approx cR_-^0 = cR_- \approx cR(x^0) \equiv cR$$

in understandable notation.

When $\dot{\mathsf{U}} \neq 0$, the acceleration of the particle is nonvanishing in any given inertial frame and, as we know from classical electrodynamics, there must be radiation of electromagnetic energy by the accelerated charge. Our concluding task in this section is to find a covariant description of this radiation.

The first step, obviously, is to combine Eqs. (7-122) and (7-17), retaining the leading terms as far as behavior at spatial infinity is concerned. Because we shall be interested also in the behavior of the field of a point charge in its vicinity, we compute first the complete energy-momentum tensor of the field (7-122).

To this end let us rewrite (7-122) as

$$B_{\mu\nu}(\mathsf{x}) = B^{(s)}_{\mu\nu}(\mathsf{x}) + B^{(r)}_{\mu\nu}(\mathsf{x}) \tag{7-125}$$

where the 'quasi-static' part $B^{(s)}$ is given by (7-124), and $B^{(r)}$ is the 'radiation' part, i.e.,

$$B^{(r)}_{\mu\nu}(\mathsf{x}) = \frac{2e}{c^2}\left\{\frac{1}{R_{\|}}(\dot{U}_{[\mu}\hat{R}_{\nu]} - \Omega U_{[\mu}\hat{R}_{\nu]})\right\} \equiv \frac{2e}{c^2}\left\{\frac{1}{R_{\|}} Z_{[\mu}\hat{R}_{\nu]}\right\}$$
$$\mathsf{Z} \equiv \dot{\mathsf{U}} - \Omega\mathsf{U} \tag{7-126}$$

Writing the energy-momentum tensor (7-17) in understandable notation as

$$T_{\alpha\beta}(\mathsf{x}) \equiv T_{\alpha\beta} = T^{(s)}_{\alpha\beta} + T^{(sr)}_{\alpha\beta} + T^{(r)}_{\alpha\beta} \tag{7-127}$$

and noting the identities (for $\tau = \tau_-$)

$$B^{(r)}_{\alpha\sigma}\hat{R}^{\sigma} = 0, \qquad B^{(s)}_{\alpha\sigma}\hat{R}^{\sigma} = -\frac{e}{R_{\|}^2}\hat{R}_{\alpha}, \qquad B^{(s)}_{\lambda\mu}B^{(r)\lambda\mu} = 0$$
$$B^{(r)}_{\lambda\mu}B^{(r)\lambda\mu} = 0, \qquad B^{(s)}_{\lambda\mu}B^{(s)\lambda\mu} = -\frac{2e^2}{R_{\|}^4} \tag{7-128}$$

that are easily verified (as $\hat{\mathsf{R}} \cdot \mathsf{U} = c$, $\mathsf{R} \cdot \mathsf{R} = 0$, $\mathsf{R} \cdot \mathsf{Z} = 0$), the terms in (7-127) are found in a few simple steps, and reduce to

$$T^{(s)}_{\alpha\beta} = \frac{e^2}{4\pi}\left\{\frac{1}{R_{\|}^4}\left[\frac{2}{c}U_{(\alpha}\hat{R}_{\beta)} - \hat{R}_{\alpha}\hat{R}_{\beta} - \frac{1}{2}g_{\alpha\beta}\right]\right\} \tag{7-129}$$

$$T^{(sr)}_{\alpha\beta} = \frac{e^2}{2\pi c}\left\{\frac{1}{R_{\|}^3}\left[\Omega\hat{R}_{\alpha}\hat{R}_{\beta} + \frac{1}{c}Z_{(\alpha}R_{\beta)}\right]\right\} \tag{7-130}$$

$$T^{(r)}_{\alpha\beta} = -\frac{e^2}{4\pi c^4}\left\{\frac{1}{R_{\|}^2}\mathsf{Z}^2\hat{R}_{\alpha}\hat{R}_{\beta}\right\}$$
$$= -\frac{e^2}{4\pi c^4}\left\{\frac{1}{R_{\|}^2}(\dot{\mathsf{U}}^2 + c^2\Omega^2)\hat{R}_{\alpha}\hat{R}_{\beta}\right\} \tag{7-131}$$

By way of algebraic check of (7-129), and for comparison with familiar results, let us transcribe these equations into ordinary vector notation, and compare the results with those obtained directly from (7-124), i.e.,

$$\mathbf{E} = \frac{e}{c}\left\{\frac{1}{R_{\|}^2}(U^0\hat{\mathbf{R}} - \hat{R}\mathbf{U})\right\}$$
$$\mathbf{B} = \frac{e}{c}\left\{\frac{1}{R_{\|}^2}\mathbf{U} \times \hat{\mathbf{R}}\right\} \qquad \hat{R} \equiv |\hat{\mathbf{R}}| \tag{7-132}$$

With a few obvious reductions involving (7-121) and the identity $\mathsf{U}^2 = c^2$, we find

$$\begin{aligned} \mathbf{S} &= \frac{c}{4\pi}(\mathbf{E} \times \mathbf{B}) = \frac{e^2}{4\pi}\left\{\frac{1}{R_\parallel^4}[\hat{R}\mathbf{U} + (U^0 - c\hat{R})\hat{\mathbf{R}}]\right\} \\ h &= \frac{1}{8\pi}(\mathbf{E}^2 + \mathbf{B}^2) = \frac{e^2}{8\pi}\left\{\frac{1}{R_\parallel^4}\left(4\frac{U^0}{c}\hat{R} - 2\hat{R}^2 - 1\right)\right\} \end{aligned} \tag{7-133}$$

The direct use of Eqs. (7-129) and (7-19) is seen to yield indeed the same results. In the rest frame of the charge, $R_\parallel = R$, $U^0 = c$, and $\hat{R} = 1$, so that we obtain the familiar results for a stationary charge: $\mathbf{S} = 0$, $h = e^2/8\pi R^4$.

The two expressions (7-130) and (7-131) both involve the acceleration 4-vector $\dot{\mathsf{U}}$ of the particle, but their properties differ significantly. An immediately obvious difference is their rate of falling at spatial infinity, which was of course the basis of the splitting shown in (7-127). In order to see this precisely, and also for the purpose of bringing out an even more crucial difference in the physical implications of $T_{\alpha\beta}^{(sr)}(\mathsf{x})$ and $T_{\alpha\beta}^{(r)}(\mathsf{x})$, let us evaluate these tensors in the rest frame $S^*(\mathsf{x}) \equiv S^*$ of the charge at the time $t = t_-(\mathsf{x})$.

To simplify our writing, we shall presently *omit the asterisk superscript* from our symbols, the fact that the corresponding quantities have to be evaluated in S^* being then understood from the context. Since in S^* we have, in addition to the relations noted earlier, also the following relations

$$\Omega = -\frac{1}{c}\dot{\mathbf{u}} \cdot \hat{\mathbf{R}}, \qquad Z_0 = -c\Omega, \qquad \mathbf{Z} = \dot{\mathbf{u}} \tag{7-134}$$

(for in S^* it follows from the identities $\mathsf{U} \cdot \dot{\mathsf{U}} = 0$ and $\dot{\gamma}_u = \gamma_u^3 u\dot{u}/c^2$, that $\dot{U}^0 = 0$ and $\dot{\mathbf{U}} = \dot{\mathbf{u}}$), we find that Eqs. (7-130) and (7-131) assume the following form:

$$\begin{aligned} T_{00}{}^{(sr)} &= 0, \qquad T_{0i}{}^{(sr)} = \frac{e^2}{4\pi c}\left\{\frac{1}{R^3}\left(\Omega\hat{R}_i + \frac{1}{c}\dot{u}_i\right)\right\} \\ T_{ij}{}^{(sr)} &= \frac{e^2}{2\pi c}\left\{\frac{1}{R^3}\left(\Omega\hat{R}_i\hat{R}_j + \frac{1}{c}\dot{u}_{(i}\hat{R}_{j)}\right)\right\} \end{aligned} \tag{7-135}$$

[A partial check of the algebra is provided by the vanishing of $T^{(sr)}{}_\mu{}^\mu$, for the traces of all three tensors (7-129), (7-130), and (7-131) are zero—as is readily checked (see Prob. 7-10).]

$$T_{\alpha\beta}{}^{(r)} = \frac{e^2}{4\pi c^4}\left\{\frac{1}{R^2}[\dot{\mathbf{u}}^2 - (\dot{\mathbf{u}} \cdot \hat{\mathbf{R}})^2]\hat{R}_\alpha\hat{R}_\beta\right\} \tag{7-136}$$

We can compare, for instance, the squares of the Poynting vectors, $S^i = -cT_{0i}$, for which we find a ratio $(\mathbf{S}^{(sr)})^2/(\mathbf{S}^{(r)})^2$ that is of the order of

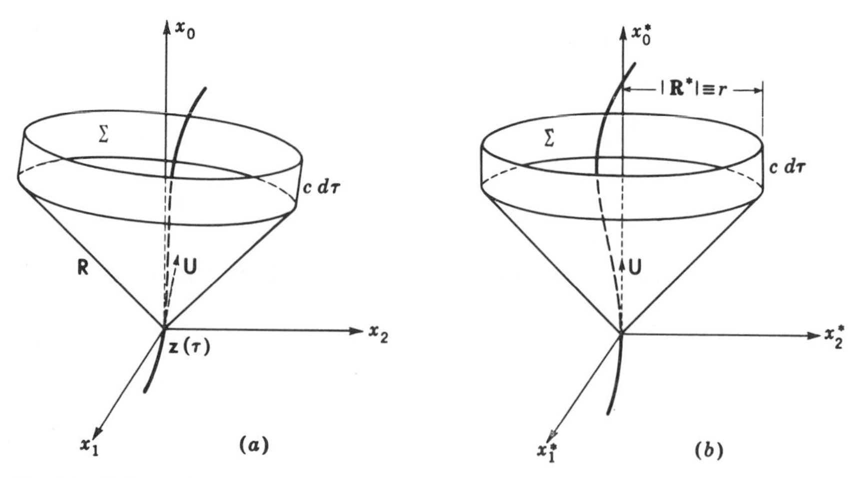

Fig. 7-4 Schematic representation of the integration region Σ occurring in the integral in (7-137), in (*a*) an arbitrary inertial frame, and in (*b*) the rest frame of the particle at its proper time τ.

magnitude $c^4/R^2\dot{\mathbf{u}}^2$. This shows clearly the different behavior of the two Poynting vectors for points that are near and for points that are far from the source in the frame S^*; and a similar conclusion can be seen to follow for an arbitrary inertial frame by applying the corresponding Lorentz transformation, with only the sense of 'near' and 'far' depending on this frame—this dependence disappearing in the latter case when we go to the limit of infinite spatial separation between source and field point.

The important physical quantity to consider in this connection is of course the total rate of radiation of electromagnetic energy across a closed spatial surface surrounding the charge. Considering the rate of decrease of the tensors (7-129), (7-130) and (7-131) at spatial infinity in any given inertial reference frame, it is clear that upon letting this closed spatial surface recede to infinity, only the contribution from (7-131) survives. On the other hand, both the energy flux Λ^0 and the momentum flux Λ^i associated with the latter tensor, are independent of the particular choice of this surface, subject to the above conditions. The quantities Λ^0, Λ^i behave moreover as the components of a 4-vector Λ^μ.

Both properties can be proved conveniently if we choose the closed surface as a sphere σ about the particle in the rest frame S^* of the particle at given instant τ of the particle's proper time, and lying on the forward light cone from the corresponding event. If this sphere is translated along the time axis in S^* an infinitesimal distance $c\,d\tau$ in the positive direction, we obtain a three-dimensional band Σ parallel to $\mathsf{U}(\tau)$ and of height $c\,d\tau$, as shown schematically in Fig. 7-4. Since the 3-surface Σ is covariantly defined (and since we are using lorentzian, and hence *flat*, coordinate frames), the quantities

$$-\frac{d}{d\tau}\int_\Sigma T_\nu^{(r)\mu}\,dS^\nu \tag{7-137}$$

are manifestly the components of a 4-vector, and the asserted covariant property will be established when we show that Λ^μ are given by (7-137). By showing further that these quantities are independent of the radius $r \equiv |\mathbf{R}^*|$ of the sphere σ, it can then be readily concluded that the second property holds as well.

That the quantities (7-137) can be identified with Λ^μ in S^* is seen at once by referring to (7-19) and noting that in S^*, $dS^0 = 0$, and

$$d\mathbf{S} = c\,d\tau\,d\sigma\,\hat{\mathbf{R}}, \qquad d\sigma \equiv \text{surface element on the sphere } \sigma \tag{7-138}$$

so that for $\mu = 0$ and $\mu = i$ respectively, Eqs. (7-137) are seen to give the time rates of flow of energy and of momentum outward through σ—remembering the significance of the quantities in (7-19). In view of the proved covariance of the quantities (7-137), it now follows that they can be identified with Λ^μ in every inertial frame.

In order to evaluate Eqs. (7-137) we need to determine the 4-vector $dS^\nu = c\,d\tau\,d\sigma\,N^\nu$. $d\sigma$ is already given in (7-138); and it is obvious that N, the unit 4-vector normal to the element of 3-surface under consideration, is spacelike, orthogonal to $\mathsf{U} \equiv \mathsf{U}(\tau)$, and lies in the plane formed by the vectors R (to the 4-point under consideration) and U (that is, $\mathsf{N}^2 = -1$, $\mathsf{N}\cdot\mathsf{U} = 0$, $\mathsf{N} = a\hat{\mathsf{R}} + b\mathsf{U}$), so that with proper choice of the positive sense along N [see (6-71)]

$$\mathsf{N} = \hat{\mathsf{R}} - \frac{1}{c}\mathsf{U} \tag{7-139}$$

By Eqs. (7-131) and (7-137) we have, therefore, upon combining our results and remembering the definitions in (7-121),‡

$$\Lambda^\mu = \frac{e^2}{4\pi c^3}\int \frac{L}{R_\parallel^{\,2}}\left(\frac{U^\mu}{c} + N^\mu\right)d\sigma \qquad \begin{aligned} L &\equiv -[\dot{\mathsf{U}}^2 + (\dot{\mathsf{U}}\cdot\hat{\mathsf{R}})^2] \\ \mathsf{U} &\equiv \mathsf{U}(\tau), \text{ etc.}\end{aligned} \tag{7-140}$$

where we have substituted for $\hat{R}^\mu$ by using (7-139). It is not difficult to show that the term involving N in (7-140) gives a zero integral, while the 4-scalar $\int d\sigma\, L/R_\parallel^{\,2}$ evaluated in S^* [see (7-136)] using spherical coordinates yields the result $2\pi\dot{\mathbf{u}}^2\int_0^\pi \sin^3\theta\,d\theta = 8\pi\dot{\mathbf{u}}^2/3 = -8\pi\dot{\mathsf{U}}^2/3$. Substituting in

‡ We do not require now the braces used in (7-131) and signifying that quantities have to be evaluated at the retarded time $\tau = \tau_-(\mathsf{x})$, since now τ is fixed and $\mathsf{R} \equiv \mathsf{x} - \mathsf{z}(\tau)$, where x is a 4-point of our integration region.

(7-140), we have thus the desired result

$$\Lambda^{\mu} = -\frac{2e^2}{3c^4}\dot{\mathsf{U}}^2 U^{\mu} \tag{7-141}$$

which is seen indeed to be independent of anything but kinematic quantities belonging to the particle at the instant under consideration.

The result (7-141) can also be obtained by first evaluating all our quantities in S^*, finding that $\Lambda^{\mu} = -2e^2\dot{\mathsf{U}}^2/3c^3 \equiv \Lambda, 0, 0, 0$, and then transforming to the given frame, using Eqs. (6-40), with the result $\Lambda^{\mu} = \Lambda U^{\mu}/c$, i.e., (7-141). With this method the vanishing of the term involving N in (7-140) is in ready evidence ($\mathbf{N} = \hat{\mathbf{R}}$ in S^*).

The general result (7-141), although of obvious theoretical interest, has the practical inconvenience of involving a time rate taken with respect to the time scale in S^* and not with respect to the time scale in our frame S. This inconvenience is removed in the case of the radiation of energy by taking, in place of the component Λ^0 of the 4-vector (7-141), the corresponding quantity for the ordinary time rate dE_{rad}/dt of the total outward flux of radiation energy E_{rad} as measured in S. Since $d\tau = dt/\gamma_u$,

$$\frac{dE_{\text{rad}}}{dt} = -\frac{2}{3}\frac{e^2}{c^3}\dot{\mathsf{U}}^2 \tag{7-142}$$

and we have a direct covariant and practically useful generalization of Larmor's well-known classical formula (remembering that only the contribution to the energy flux arising from $T^{(r)}$ survives in the limit of going to spatial infinity).

There are many interesting problems and results connected with the radiation field of a charged particle for which covariant methods, including the Fourier integral approach sketched out earlier in this section, are useful tools. Their consideration belongs however in specialized books on electrodynamics, to which we have already given a few useful references. It will suffice to conclude this section with a few immediate observations.

In our discussion of the radiation properties associated with the tensor (7-131), we tacitly assumed the nonnegativeness of the quantity $-(\dot{\mathsf{U}}^2 + c^2\Omega^2)$, which also implies the nonnegativeness of the energy density of the pure radiation field—an obviously important result. This property can be seen directly by evaluating the above covariant quantity in $S^*(\mathsf{x})$, with the result given inside the brackets in (7-136). The latter expression also shows that the quantity in question vanishes when $\dot{\mathbf{U}}$ is parallel to $\hat{\mathbf{R}}$ in S^*, and that it assumes its maximum value when $\dot{\mathsf{U}} \cdot \hat{\mathsf{R}} = 0$. It is not difficult to determine likewise the general angular distribution of the radiation when referred to the frame S^*.

An important property of the field (7-126) is described by the first and fourth relations in (7-128) and the companion relation [where the asterisk now designates the *dual*—see (7-49)]

$$B^{(r)*}{}_{\mu\nu}\hat{R}^{\nu} = 0 \tag{7-143}$$

the latter holding, as is immediately verified, not only for the radiation field, but also for the field (7-124), and hence for the total field (7-122) as well. When expressed in ordinary vector notation, we see by Eqs. (7-18) and (7-49) that the two relations (7-128) and Eq. (7-143) assume respectively the familiar form

$$\mathbf{E} = \mathbf{B} \times \mathbf{R}_1, \ \mathbf{E}^2 = \mathbf{B}^2, \ \mathbf{B} = \mathbf{R}_1 \times \mathbf{E} \qquad \begin{matrix} \mathbf{R}_1 \propto \mathbf{R}_- \\ \mathbf{R}_1^2 = 1 \end{matrix} \tag{7-144}$$

Their significance is, of course, well known. What we have shown is that they retain the same 3-vector form in every inertial frame.

7-5 THE GENERAL CLASSICAL PROBLEM OF THE MOTION OF CHARGED PARTICLES IN A GIVEN ELECTROMAGNETIC FIELD

Much of the preceding part of this book has been—as any book on relativity theory necessarily must be—a tribute to the creative genius of Einstein, along with due recognition of the important contributions to the subject of other leading physicists. In this section on the interaction of charged particles, and in the next chapter on relativistic quantum mechanics, we touch on fields in which the leading developments are due to many outstanding theorists, but it is especially Dirac whose name is associated in a primary capacity with both of these fields. Since it is outside the scope of this book to discuss fully the classical theory of the interaction of charged particles,‡ we now limit our presentation mainly to a discussion of Dirac's stimulating (and, incidentally, very readable) paper on this subject.§

Before we present Dirac's theory, we shall examine briefly what the nature of the problem is, and what essential role is played by the relativistic principles.

The determination of the motion of a system of charged elementary particles interacting mutually and with an external field has been a central problem that has engaged the attention of early workers in STR (M. Born, M. v. Laue, A. Sommerfeld, and others), and it played, of course, an important role in the intensive prerelativistic investigations of Abraham and of Lorentz. Since the advent of quantum mechanics, and particularly of quantum electrodynamics, the purely classical problem of such motion, when special restrictions are not introduced, can no longer be taken to be as fundamental as it naturally appeared to be in those earlier days. Never-

‡ Such discussion and pertinent references can be found in Rohrlich, *op. cit.;* A. O. Barut, "Electrodynamics and Classical Theory of Fields and Particles," The Macmillan Company, New York, 1964.

§ P. A. M. Dirac, *Proc. Roy. Soc. London,* **A167**: 148 (1938).

theless, a solution of this problem entirely in terms of classical relativistic ideas, which in some well-defined sense can be considered as satisfactory, cannot but present at least heuristic interest;‡ and a number of investigators have in more recent times attacked this problem with interesting, though not obviously conclusive, results.

What one may consider here a conclusive result is, in fact, in itself a moot question.§ Because quantum effects are disregarded, while no restriction is imposed on the possible motion of the particles, the resulting theoretical model can generally have at best only indirect contact with experience, and the criteria of its soundness are therefore not completely rigid. Nevertheless, the obvious requirements, such as agreement with the relativistic principles and with well-established classical (i.e., nonquantum) theory in the domain of validity of the latter, narrow down considerably the possible choice of such models. Moreover, an immediate simplification results from the recognition that, with our current ideas concerning the coupling between charges and electromagnetic field, once a formulation of the one-body problem is adopted, the formulation of the many-body problem presents no further essential difficulties. (The actual solution of the resulting equations is, of course, another matter.)

The starting point for the formulation of the one-body problem is naturally the Lorentz force equation (7-10), which, as we know, is perfectly adequate in many practical situations, and which has entered into all our previous considerations involving the interaction between charges and field, including our discussion of the variational principle of electrodynamics in Sec. 7-2. The *general* equation of motion in question should therefore reduce, under appropriate conditions, to the approximate form

$$m\ddot{x}_\alpha = \frac{e}{c} B_{\beta\alpha}(\mathsf{x}) U^\beta, \qquad \dot{x} \equiv \frac{dx}{d\tau} \tag{7-145}$$

where m and e are the rest mass and charge of the particle, and the tensor field B describes the external electromagnetic field.

That Eq. (7-145) itself cannot be generally valid is apparent as soon as we ask for the meaning of the field B. We have referred to it as the *external* field—the field due to the charges distinct from the charge on our particle. But what of the field associated with the particle itself, its "self-field," B_{self}? Has it no effect on its motion? This has obviously been the tacit assumption we have made in applying Eq. (7-10). This assumption is harmless enough in applications of a purely phenomenological character

‡ See e.g., Rohrlich, *op. cit.*

§ We are concerned here only with the classical theory of charged particles that are devoid of any structure giving rise to an internal angular momentum, or to an electric or magnetic multipole moment. We have given in Chap. 4 a few references to recent investigations that are concerned with such structure. This problem is also discussed in Rohrlich, *op. cit.*, sec. 7.5; Barut, *op. cit.*, chap. 2, sec. 4, and references, pp. 83–84.

under usual conditions, where the 4-current (7-5) can be treated as continuously distributed, so that the 'particle' to which the Lorentz formula is applied can be mentally identified with an infinitesimal element of charge in the sense of continuous medium theory, whose field is therefore also of infinitesimal strength. On the other hand, suppose that our continuous charge distribution is subject to accelerations of such magnitude that the resulting radiation of electromagnetic energy cannot be neglected. Then, inasmuch as this energy and associated momentum completely disappear from the original system, it is clear that we must get into conflict with overall conservation of energy and momentum if we do not modify our dynamical equations to allow for a compensation of the energy-momentum loss due to radiation.

In the case of our charged particle, when no restriction is imposed on its acceleration the last-mentioned circumstance must of course be dealt with. But in addition, whatever our model of the particle, whether we think of it as a point or as a small extended structure, since its total charge is finite it is obvious that B_{self} as a whole can no longer be neglected in principle under any circumstances. We have already seen in Sec. 7-4 how to evaluate the rate of energy-momentum loss due to radiation, and it is thus possible to determine the resulting reactive 4-force on the particle. It is less obvious how to determine the reaction arising from the nonradiated fields, i.e., from the contribution to the energy-momentum tensor of the field B_{self} corresponding to the parts (7-129) and (7-130). It is this determination, in fact, that presents the principal difficulty of our problem.

This difficulty is essentially one of principle, and as such it is present even in the simplest case of rest or of uniform motion in the given inertial frame. For it is clear that in order to increase the particle's velocity, the applied force must supply not only the resulting increment $\Delta\mathbf{p}_{\text{mech}}$ of mechanical momentum, but also the resulting increment $\Delta\mathbf{p}_{\text{elm}}$ in the total momentum of the Coulomb field carried along by the particle, as would be computed from (7-129). But the factor $R_{\parallel}^{-4}$ in that expression (corresponding to the familiar inverse fourth power of the distance in the square of a Coulomb field due to a point charge) gives rise to an infinite value upon integration. We are therefore faced with three alternatives: (1) endowing the particle with a finite extension, so that B_{self} remains finite throughout, (2) modifying the field equations in the vicinity of the particle so as to render the total energy and momentum of the Coulomb field finite, or (3) providing a mechanism for the cancellation of the infinite results, while preserving the Maxwell-Lorentz equations.

Alternative (1) is certainly the less drastic of the three, and it has been investigated very extensively, especially by Abraham and by Lorentz at the turn of the century. This approach appeals to our vague intuitive notion that a charge must fill some volume; and it is made plausible by the existence of a simple expression of the dimensions of a length, formed from the fundamental constants e, m, c of the theory (m being the rest mass of the particle—the 'electron'), namely $e^2/mc^2 \equiv a_0$, this length (the "classical radius" of the electron—strictly, to within a factor ≈ 1) appearing in the magical formula

$$mc^2 = E_{\text{Coul}} \approx \frac{e^2}{a_0} \tag{7-146}$$

as well as in other important connections. In (7-146), E_{Coul} stands for the total electromagnetic field energy of a spherical charge distribution of radius a_0 in the rest frame of the particle (that is assumed to exist—in prerelativistic days one spoke, of course, simply of a stationary rigid distribution of charge): the rest mass m of the particle is thus identified wholly with the mass equivalent of its field energy! This was a most intriguing idea that fired the imagination of the earlier investigators. We cannot stop here to discuss this fascinating but largely historical topic. It appears in any case at the present time that the alternative (1) leads to many difficulties and complications. One difficulty existed from the start, namely, the need to provide a mechanism for stabilizing the extended distribution of charge against the mutual electrostatic repulsion of its parts. Within STR we have the additional complication of having to deal in a covariant manner both with this stabilizing mechanism and with the kinematic behavior of the charge distribution. Although Poincaré already dealt with these problems in his *Rendiconti* article, and many ingenious investigations have been published in recent times, a generally accepted theory of the extended electron does not appear to be available.‡

Alternative (2) has been the subject of a very interesting investigation by M. Born and L. Infeld.§ A major drawback of this theory is the nonlinear character of the field equations, which makes it difficult to draw crucial conclusions. Needless to add, the very question as to what should be taken as crucial conclusions in such a classical theory is not entirely obvious. Attempts at 'quantizing' the Born-Infeld theory have met with little success.

‡ A phenomenological covariant treatment of an extended and rigid electron model is contained in a recent comprehensive paper by J. S. Nodvik, *Ann. Phys.*, **28:** 225 (1964). Interesting studies have also been made in recent years with a less direct approach involving covariant form factors [i.e., essentially, the replacement of the space-time δ symbols, occurring in relations such as (7-114), by corresponding regular functions]. In a certain sense this corresponds to replacing the infinitesimal space-time region referred to in D (page 254) as the *source* element of the electromagnetic field, by a small but finite 4-region. For a discussion of these theories due to F. Bopp, R. P. Feynman, R. Peierls and H. McManus, and others, and for references, see, e.g., J. Rzewuski, "Field Theory," chap. 3, sec. 8, PWN-Polish Scientific Publishers, Warszawa, 1964. See also the annotated references in Rohrlich, *op. cit.*, p. 208.

§ M. Born, *Proc. Roy. Soc. London,* **A143:** 410 (1934); *Ann. Inst. Henri Poincaré,* **7:** 155 (1937); M. Born and L. Infeld, *Proc. Roy. Soc. London,* **A144:** 425 (1934).

We now come to the last of our three alternatives, and the one that is at the core of Dirac's classical paper of 1938. In this approach we are free of the two major difficulties referred to above. The field equations are, of course, linear throughout; they are, in fact, simply the Maxwell source-free equations in all of space excepting the point singularities associated with the particles, the Maxwell-Lorentz equations with improper sources of the form (7-114) holding at the latter points. We have, moreover, no charge-stability problem: the particle is not divisible into *parts* that act on each other. This idea of an indivisible *quantum* of charge certainly appears to us today in many respects more reasonable than that of a jelly globule of charge. Perhaps the strongest support for the present approach, and thus for Dirac's classical theory of the electron, comes from the fact that a similar approach underlies the empirically highly successful current theory of quantum electrodynamics, where one deals with a *local* (i.e., 4-point) interaction between electrons and electromagnetic field.

The fly in the ointment in using alternative (3) is the questionable procedure involved in the subtraction of infinities. In the case of quantum electrodynamics, the day is saved on a strictly pragmatic basis: the conclusions of the theory work. This success therefore lends respectability also to Dirac's classical theory. There is indeed an additional supporting consideration: the subtraction procedure can be carried out in a covariant manner. (This criterion played in fact an important heuristic role in the developments in quantum electrodynamics of two decades ago.)

In its simplest terms, the subtraction procedure in the classical case, whatever the particular formalism actually employed, is essentially equivalent to the corresponding steps in the following formulation.

Suppose we start, as an intermediate step in our approach, with the lorentzian model of an electron as a particle with a spherically symmetric charge distribution of small radius a in the rest frame S^* of the particle. Then in S^* the total nonradiated energy E_a^* of $B_{\text{self}}^{(a)}$ is easily shown [using Eqs. (7-133) and (7-135) in an asymptotic manner for $a \approx 0$] to be $\approx e^2/a$, with the corresponding total momentum $\mathbf{G}_a^* = 0$. Moreover,

$$G_a^{*\mu} = \frac{1}{c}\int T_{\text{self}}^{*(a)\mu 0}\, d^3x^* = \frac{1}{c}\int_\Sigma T_{\text{self}}^{*(a)\mu\nu}\, d\Sigma_\nu \qquad (7\text{-}147)$$

where T_{self} represents here the nonradiated part of the energy-momentum tensor of the particle, and Σ is the 3-surface $t^* = \text{const}$, the value of the constant being immaterial, since, by our assumptions, the integral (7-147) is independent of that value. This expression is therefore a 4-vector, which can be taken to represent the total nonradiated 4-momentum G_a of $B_{\text{self}}^{(a)}$,‡

‡ It is to be observed that we could not simply identify cG_a^μ with $\int T_{\text{self}}^{(a)\mu 0}\, d^3x$ in an arbitrary inertial frame S, since the relation $T_{\text{self},\nu}^{(a)\mu\nu} = 0$ does not hold in the 4-region occupied by the particle, and consequently the considerations of Sec. 6-3 do not apply (see Prob. 7-27).

and by (6-40) we have in any given frame S (remembering that $\mathbf{G}_a^* = 0$)

$$\mathbf{G}_a = \frac{1}{c^2} E_a^* \mathbf{U} \equiv m_a \mathbf{U}, \qquad \mathbf{U} \equiv \gamma_u \mathbf{u} \tag{7-148}$$

where $\mathbf{u}$ is the velocity of the particle in S.‡

We have thus obtained a consistent result in this intermediate step, as far as covariance under the Lorentz group is concerned, as represented by the relation (7-148). But by taking now the next step of going to the limit $a \to 0$ in order to avoid the problems presented by the extended model of an electron, we are confronted with the infinite limit of $m_a \approx e^2/ac^2$, and an obvious (though highly formal) way out of this dilemma is to postulate, in addition to the rest mass given in (7-148), an intrinsic inertial mass μ_a for the intermediate model such that

$$\lim_{a \to 0} (m_a + \mu_a) = m \tag{7-149}$$

where m is the *observed* rest mass of our particle. A similar formal process in its proper quantum-electrodynamic setting is known as *mass renormalization*. The complete covariance of the method is insured when our limiting process is such that along with (7-148) we also have the corresponding 4-momentum $\mu_a \mathsf{U}$, so that the measured 4-momentum of the particle has the proper form $\lim_{a \to 0} (m_a + \mu_a)\mathsf{U} = m\mathsf{U}$.

If, in addition to mass renormalization that takes care (in a formal way, whose significance needs to be ascertained) of the infinity in the Coulomb field of a point charge, we also arrange in a covariant manner for overall energy and momentum conservation in the presence of electromagnetic radiation, we have the basis for a consistent classical theory of the dynamics of charged elementary particles. The actual problem is, of course, to accomplish both these tasks in an integrated and natural fashion, with the expectation that the resulting theory may have significant, even if not unrestricted, validity. It is towards the solution of this problem that Dirac's paper under discussion is directed.

In this paper, the underlying approach is entirely in the spirit of our alternative (3): the electron is assumed to be a point structure in the strict sense of the word.§ An important tool in Dirac's method is the use of

‡ See the similar result (4-30).

§ In Lorentz' original treatment of the problem (see, e.g., Lorentz, "Theory of Electrons," note 18, p. 252ff; Jackson, *op. cit.*, sec. 17.3) the overall energy and momentum balance between particle and field is allowed for by considering in the intermediate model of extent a, the net force exerted on each infinitesimal part of the charge distribution by all the other parts of this distribution. Thus, even if one takes the limit $a \to 0$, as one must, if one is not to be involved with a troublesome infinite power series in a, one is essentially still dealing with alternative (1). The limit $a \to 0$ is in this case simply a matter of convenience: the results are expected to hold under suitable restrictions for some small but finite a value.

advanced potentials (see Prob. 7-24) along with the conventional retarded potentials, the former potentials having already been used previously by a number of investigators (see references given in Appendix 7A). A guiding idea for this procedure is the expected symmetry in time of the basic electrodynamic equations. Thus Dirac starts with the following expressions for the total field

$$B = B_{\text{ret}} + B_{\text{in}} = B_{\text{adv}} + B_{\text{out}} \tag{7-150}$$

where

$$\Box \mathsf{A}_{\text{in}} = 0, \quad \Box \mathsf{A}_{\text{out}} = 0 \tag{7-151}$$

The tensors B_{ret} and B_{adv} correspond to the retarded and advanced solutions of our inhomogeneous wave equation,‡ i.e., Eq. (7-91) together with Eq. (7-114), while B_{in} and B_{out} represent the *incoming* and the *outgoing source-free* fields. B_{in} is clearly what we have previously called the *external* field, but with the restriction of satisfying (7-151)—a restriction that can be removed if necessary. On the other hand, B_{out} is *defined* by the time-symmetric relation (7-150).

An important corollary of this relation is the following definition of the field of radiation proposed by Dirac:

$$B_{\text{rad}} \equiv B_{\text{out}} - B_{\text{in}} = B_{\text{ret}} - B_{\text{adv}} \tag{7-152}$$

This definition is seen to be consistent with the usual definition of the field of radiation due to a charged particle in the conventional asymptotic region $t \to \infty$, where only B_{ret} can be expected effectively to survive.§ At the same time it is distinguished by its unrestricted applicability: even at a 4-point z on the world line of the particle the expression (7-152) leads to a well-defined and finite result, when one takes the limit $\mathsf{a} \to 0$ (a spacelike) of this expression evaluated at $\mathsf{z} + \mathsf{a}$. Straightforward but somewhat tedious computation gives in fact the simple expression (Prob. 7-28)

$$B_{\text{rad}}^{\mu\nu}(\mathsf{z}) = \frac{4e}{3c^4}\,[U^\mu(\mathsf{z})\ddot{U}^\nu(\mathsf{z}) - U^\nu(\mathsf{z})\ddot{U}^\mu(\mathsf{z})] \tag{7-153}$$

We shall presently see the connection with the force of radiation reaction on the particle.

The inertial contribution of B_{self}, i.e., the renormalization of the mass of the charged particle to take account of its convected Coulomb field, is handled by Dirac with the aid of the energy-momentum conservation laws for the combined system of charged particle and field. His method has the interesting feature of not actually invoking directly the equation of

‡ Using now this more common notation in place of that used in Sec. 7-4.

§ In all strictness, this would not be the case if our particle can be supposed to have accelerated motion for all time. In fact, in computing the force of radiation reaction on the particle we shall see that we have to take $B_{\text{rad}}/2$ in using the relation (7-152). For this reason many investigators define the radiation field in the first place as this quantity $B_{\text{rad}}/2$.

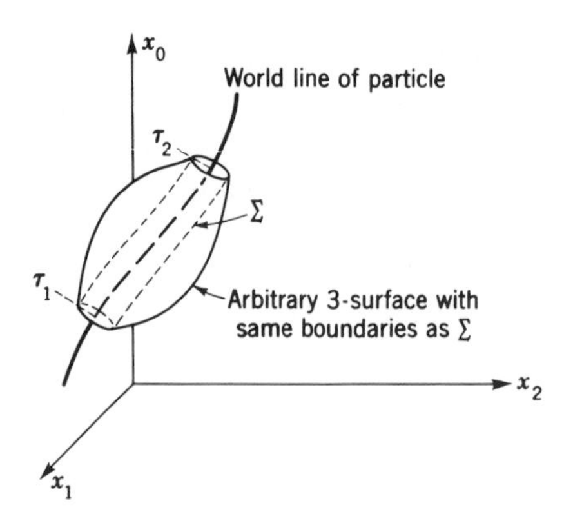

Fig. 7-5 Schematic diagram (with suppression of x_3) to represent the space-time region of integration entering in the discussion relating to Eq. (7-155).

motion of the particle, but deducing instead that equation from his formalism. However, the latter does involve an additional assumption, which, in effect, is essentially equivalent to the equation of motion. Principally for didactic reasons, therefore, rather than for strictly logical reasons, we sketch out, in what follows, Dirac's original approach.

We surround the world line of the particle between its proper times τ_1 and τ_2, by a space-time tube, whose cross section measured in the particle's rest frame is, for every value of τ, a sphere of infinitesimal radius a. In order to evaluate the flux of energy and momentum of the field through the lateral 3-surface Σ of the tube, we separate off from the total field B a part $\breve{B}$ that is regular along the world line, namely

$$\breve{B} = B - \bar{B} = B_{\text{in}} + \tfrac{1}{2}B_{\text{rad}}, \qquad \bar{B} = \tfrac{1}{2}(B_{\text{ret}} + B_{\text{adv}}) \tag{7-154}$$

while the terms in (7-17) involving the singular part $\bar{B}$ give rise to an expansion in negative and positive powers of a; and as in the derivation of (7-153), a quite straightforward but rather lengthy calculation yields the result

$$\int_\Sigma T^{\mu\nu}\, d\Sigma_\nu = \int_{\tau_1}^{\tau_2} \left(\frac{e^2}{2ac}\,\dot{U}^\mu + e\breve{B}^{\mu\nu}U_\nu\right) d\tau + 0(a) \tag{7-155}$$

The crucial point now is the conclusion that the line integral depends only on its endpoints—a conclusion based on energy-momentum conservation considerations, and on the fact that the integral over the 3-surface Σ is independent of its form, as can be seen by applying Gauss' theorem to the integral of the vanishing quantity $T^{\mu\nu}{}_{,\nu}$ in the 4-region between Σ and a similar 3-surface of arbitrary shape having the same boundaries as Σ at τ_1 and τ_2 (see Fig. 7-5). Since τ_1 and τ_2 have been chosen arbitrarily, it follows then from (7-155) that asymptotically ($a \to 0$)

$$\frac{e^2}{2ac}\,\dot{U}^\mu + e\breve{B}^{\mu\nu}U_\nu = \dot{C}^\mu_a \tag{7-156}$$

where C_a^μ is some 4-vector. This vector is not completely arbitrary since, by (7-156), it must satisfy the identity $\mathsf{U} \cdot \dot{\mathsf{C}}_a = 0$. We could also invoke the law of conservation of total angular momentum in attempting to find additional conditions. However, it is not possible to avoid introducing an essentially new assumption in order to fix C_a. It is an attractive feature of Dirac's theory that the required assumption has the virtue of simplicity. It is, in fact, in a sense the simplest we can make, namely

$$\mathsf{C}_a = ck_a\mathsf{U}, \qquad k_a = \text{4-scalar} \tag{7-157}$$

We have then, indeed, combining (7-156) and (7-157), and taking the limit $a \to 0$, an equation of motion for the particle of the usual type

$$m\dot{U}^\mu = \frac{e}{c}\breve{B}^{\nu\mu}U_\nu \tag{7-158}$$

where

$$m = \lim_{a\to 0}\left(\frac{e^2}{2ac^2} - k_a\right) \tag{7-159}$$

The process of mass renormalization described previously is in explicit evidence in Eq. (7-159), which is seen to be essentially equivalent to Eq. (7-149). The inertial effect associated with the energy and momentum of the quasi-static part of B_{self} is thus accounted for (in a definite and covariant, even if only formal, manner). At the same time, the dynamic effect of the reaction upon the particle of the energy-momentum of B_{self} that escapes as radiation is deducible directly from our general equation of motion (7-158). In fact, this equation can be rewritten, using (7-154), as

$$m\dot{U}^\mu - F^\mu_{\text{rad}} = F^\mu_{\text{in}}, \qquad F^\mu_{\text{in}} = \frac{e}{c}B^{\nu\mu}_{\text{in}}U_\nu \tag{7-160}$$

where the self 4-force F^μ_{rad} of radiation reaction is found by (7-153) to have the form

$$F^\mu_{\text{rad}} = \frac{e}{2c}B^{\nu\mu}_{\text{rad}}U_\nu = \frac{2e^2}{3c^3}\left(\ddot{U}^\mu + \frac{1}{c^2}\dot{\mathsf{U}}^2U^\mu\right) \tag{7-161}$$

(using also the identity $\mathsf{U} \cdot \ddot{\mathsf{U}} = -\dot{\mathsf{U}}^2$, following from the differentiation of the familiar identity $\mathsf{U} \cdot \dot{\mathsf{U}} = 0$). This is precisely the form that is obtained when one extends relativistically, as was first done by v. Laue, the corresponding nonrelativistic result found by the early workers in this field, using a number of alternative approaches (see Prob. 7-26).

In the light of the preceding discussion, it can be understood in what sense it is possible, at least in an exploratory manner, to assume, as Dirac did in his original paper, that Eq. (7-160) represents the *exact* classical equation for the motion of an electron in a given external field.‡ As we have

‡ It is not difficult to verify that the result (7-160) is obtained also in the more general case when the external field consists in addition to B_{in}, whose sources are at infinity, also of a part associated with sources at a finite distance.

already observed more than once, precisely what one is to understand by an exact and fully general classical equation of motion of a charged particle is not completely obvious. Dirac's equation can be considered, however, as exact at least as far as concerns its accounting for the interaction between the motion of the particle and its emission of radiation. In Sec. 7-4 we have computed this radiation by assuming the motion of the particle as given; which is obviously only an approximate procedure, since this motion is itself affected by the very process of emission of the electromagnetic radiation. Equation (7-160) accounts fully for this interplay, as must of course be true of any equation of this nature. Dirac's theory recommends itself by the naturalness with which this is accomplished.

Having brought under brief review the positive features of Dirac's theory, let us now examine also very briefly its more questionable elements. We have already called attention to the problematic nature of the "subtraction of infinities" formalism that underlies the renormalization procedure. Whether this type of formalism (both in the classical theory as well as in its quantum-mechanical counterpart) is actually an indication of an inadequacy in our theoretical structure, whose removal will require some radical modifications in or additions to our basic assumptions, is a question whose answer is not yet in sight. In the meantime cautious optimism regarding the essential soundness, if not full comprehensibility, of the renormalization formalism, generated by the practical successes of quantum electrodynamics where this type of formalism plays an important role, appears to be a prevailing attitude.

Another problem, but one that is not quite as baffling, is presented by the occurrence in Dirac's theory of advanced potentials. What can be the precise physical significance of such a potential? It is obviously in disagreement with our principle D (page 254), if it is used on a par with the retarded potentials employed in Sec. 7-4. This is not, however, strictly the case in Dirac's theory. The advanced fields occur here, as we have seen, only as intermediate steps in deriving the general equation of motion. This equation itself contains only the resulting kinematic quantities of the particle as given in Eq. (7-161).

These terms in our equation of motion (7-160) do, however, introduce a new problem: the equation is not of the newtonian type; it contains time derivatives of the acceleration, and consequently the initial conditions required for determining uniquely a given solution are also not of the newtonian type. In addition to the conventional initial position and velocity specifications, further suitable specifications are required, and these must be chosen so as to guarantee not merely a unique solution, but one that is physically acceptable, because Eq. (7-160) admits also of many solutions that are physically absurd.‡ Now, it turns out, as we shall presently show

‡ Detailed discussion of this question and further references are contained, e.g., in Erber, *op. cit.*; Rohrlich, *op. cit.*, chap. 6; G. N. Plass, *Rev. Mod. Phys.*, **33**: 37 (1961).

by a simple example, that when this is done, one has solutions that show peculiar causal behavior within time intervals of the order of magnitude

$$\tau_0 = \frac{2}{3}\frac{a_0}{c} = \frac{2e^2}{3mc^3} \tag{7-162}$$

In this fashion, the finite "radius" a_0 of the particle makes a certain back-door appearance, despite our initial assumption that the particle has zero extension: Dirac's theory is thus in principle not as simple as it starts out to be, even if, in practice, the time interval (7-162) is only 6×10^{-24} sec for the ordinary electron, and much smaller still for any other known charged particle.

All the strange features of Dirac's theory can already be seen in the simplest case of accelerated motion along a given straight line relative to a given inertial frame. With an external force that is electromagnetic (as would generally be the case), we assume that the magnetic force can be neglected. As far as concerns the present considerations, we may just as well also make the mathematically simplifying assumption that our initial velocity and the resulting accelerations are such that we can use the non-relativistic approximation to Eq. (7-160). Using (7-161) and (7-162), this is found to have the form

$$\frac{du}{dt} - \tau_0 \frac{d^2u}{dt^2} = \frac{1}{m} f \equiv g, \qquad u = \frac{dx}{dt} \tag{7-163}$$

If we also assume that f is known as a function of the time, then the general solution of (7-163) can be written:

$$x(t) = x(0) + u(0)t + \int_0^t dt'' \int_0^{t''} a(t')\, dt', \qquad a(t) \equiv \frac{du}{dt}$$

$$a(t) = e^{t/\tau_0}\left[a(0) - \frac{1}{\tau_0}\int_0^t e^{-t'/\tau_0} g(t')\, dt'\right] \tag{7-164}$$

Assuming further that the force f vanishes eventually, we can introduce the physically reasonable condition that for $t \to \infty$ the particle's motion is uniform; in other words, we can invoke Newton's first law asymptotically. Moreover, if this condition is not imposed, then we see by (7-164) that even if $f \equiv 0$, we can have a solution [when $a(0) \neq 0$] that increases exponentially as $t \to \infty$. This so-called "runaway" solution is obviously devoid of any physical sense. On the other hand, again by Eq. (7-164), it is seen that the imposition of the above condition requires that

$$a(0) = \frac{1}{\tau_0}\int_0^\infty e^{-t'/\tau_0} g(t')\, dt' \tag{7-165}$$

The peculiar causal behavior alluded to previously is seen clearly in Eq. (7-165). Unless the external force happens to be essentially constant within the time interval in which the exponential factor in the integrand in (7-165) does not effectively annihilate the other factor g, the acceleration $a(0)$ will not be proportional to $f(0)$; and in general, this acceleration at the instant $t = 0$ will be affected by the values of f at the *future* instants within an interval of the order of magnitude of τ_0 (whose smallness should, however, be borne in mind); this acausal behavior holds, in general, for any t under consideration, since a shift of the origin of time by t will give us a representation of $a(t)$ by the same expression (7-165) with $g(t')$ replaced by $g(t' + t)$ [as is also seen directly by substituting (7-165) in (7-164)].

Although we have based our last discussion on a nonrelativistic approximation, it does not mean that the principles of STR have here no bearing. The derivation of F_{rad}, which is the part in our equation of motion (7-160) responsible for the anomalous dynamic behavior, rested in an essential way on the use of the retarded and the advanced solutions of our inhomogeneous wave equation. Thus the nonconventional terms in Dirac's equation of motion arise in his derivation strictly within the sphere of relativistic considerations. Their extreme peripheral implications on the other hand, if taken seriously, appear to lead us indeed beyond the relativistic principles and into the realm of speculation. It does not at present appear very likely that this phase of Dirac's theory is fraught with special significance. In any case, such significance, if it existed, would have to be revealed by an extension of conventional relativity theory, which, as we have presented it here in agreement with established notions, makes no break with newtonian theory as far as the physicist's conventional principle of causality is concerned.

We have stated earlier that once the equation of motion for a single charged particle is established, there is no difficulty in formulating the corresponding many-body problem. Indeed, suppose we take Eq. (7-160) with F_{in} replaced by the more general F_{ext}, as the equation of motion of the ath particle (using the appropriate subscripts a, b, . . . where needed), with (in understandable notation)

$$F^{\mu}_{(a)\text{ext}}\ (\mathsf{z}_a) = \sum_{b \neq a} F^{\mu}_{(b)\text{ret}}\ (\mathsf{z}_a) + F^{\mu}_{\text{in}}\ (\mathsf{z}_a) \tag{7-166}$$

where generally $F^{\mu}(\mathsf{z}_a) \equiv \dfrac{e_a}{c} B^{\nu\mu}(\mathsf{z}_a) U_{(a)\nu}$; then the resulting set of equations is the one proposed by Dirac for the motion of a system of charged particles in the presence of the external field B_{in}. The consistency of this definition, not only with our general ideas about the role of a field in mediating the interaction between its sources, but also with Dirac's original approach in the one-body problem, is shown by the fact that the equation of motion of the ath particle can also be written in precisely the form (7-158), namely,

$$\begin{aligned} m_a \dot{U}_a{}^{\mu} &= \frac{e_a}{c} \breve{B}^{\nu\mu}_{(a)} U_{(a)\nu}, \qquad \text{no summation for } a \\ \breve{B}_{(a)} &= B - \bar{B}_{(a)}, \qquad \bar{B}_{(a)} = \tfrac{1}{2}[B_{(a)\text{ret}} + B_{(a)\text{adv}}] \end{aligned} \tag{7-167}$$

Moreover, when B_{out} is defined as in (7-150) but with $B_{\text{ret(adv)}}$ replaced by $\sum_a B_{(a)\text{ret(adv)}}$, we find that

$$\breve{B}_{(a)} = \tfrac{1}{2}(B_{\text{in}} + B_{\text{out}}) + \tfrac{1}{2} \sum_{b \neq a} (B_{(b)\text{ret}} + B_{(b)\text{adv}}) \qquad (7\text{-}168)$$

We shall consider these relations, in which the symmetric use of retarded and advanced potentials is an outstanding feature, in Appendix 7A, where this symmetric treatment is an integral part of the adopted point of view.

In conclusion let us note that just as Dirac's work was inspired by a number of preceding investigations in which the component ideas have been explored, including, as already pointed out, the use of retarded potentials, so his investigation in its turn has inspired many interesting investigations over a period of time extending to our own. In the references we have given are contained further references to these investigations.‡

APPENDIX 7A RELATIVISTIC ACTION-AT-A-DISTANCE THEORIES

We have seen in Sec. 7-5 that a major problem in the classical theory of the motion of an elementary charged particle, which is assumed to have no extension, is presented by the infinities arising from the self-field of the particle. The resolution of this problem by the renormalization procedure—as in Dirac's approach surveyed in the last section—may leave us with the uncomfortable feeling that we are dealing with a sleight-of-hand method that cannot be completely trusted, whatever its immediate success. Be that as it may, it is perfectly obvious that a theory of motion of the point electron§ that completely eliminates the divergence difficulties without any subtraction

‡ Let us note in particular an illuminating paper by R. Haag, *Z. Naturforsch.*, **10**a: 752 (1955). This paper contains a careful analysis of the operational meaning of the various electromagnetic fields that are being considered in Dirac's theory, and of the asymptotic conditions both for $t \to -\infty$ and for $t \to +\infty$ required to make this meaning precise, consistently with the condition that needs to be imposed in order to single out the physically sensible solutions. We should also note current investigations of F. Rohrlich relating to the 4-force given in (7-161). It will be observed that the balancing of the radiated energy-momentum represented in (7-141), is already effected by the second term in (7-161), and also that because of the presence of the first term it is possible to have a nonvanishing self-force without radiation and radiation together with a vanishing self-force (as is true for *uniformly accelerated* motion—see Prob. 7-22). Rohrlich has pointed out that some misunderstanding on these questions can be found in the literature.

§ Reverting now to the older generic use of the term to designate an elementary charged particle. It should be noted however that if we take the strictly classical theory as having some degree of validity in the elementary particle domain, our present considerations are best restricted to ordinary electrons and muons since, on our present ideas, the strongly interacting charged particles can hardly be considered as point structures.

schemes would be of considerable interest. It appears possible to develop such a theory if one gives up the presently universally accepted idea of an electromagnetic field and replaces it by the older view of *action at a distance*—not indeed the newtonian idea of instantaneous action at a distance, which, as we know, is inconsistent with STR, but action at a distance with a lapse of time such that principle B (page 38) is satisfied (where the notion of the "speed of light" itself must of course be interpreted in terms of the ideas of action at a distance).

The idea of relativistic action at a distance is already implicit in Poincaré's treatment of gravitation, as discussed by him in the last part of his *Rendiconti* article of 1906 (see Appendix 7B).‡ Little appears to have been done with this idea until it was later reintroduced by a few investigators in the treatment of charged-particle interactions.§

The manner in which the action-at-a-distance approach eliminates the divergence difficulties due to the self-force of a charged point particle is very simple: the self-force itself is eliminated. Electromagnetic action on this view takes place only between different electrons—no electron exerts any electromagnetic action on itself. This utterly effortless way out of our difficulty may appear at first sight as highly felicitous, but on second thought we may well be overtaken by a serious misgiving. We have called attention more than once to the role of the field (mediating the interaction between its sources) in making it possible for the mechanical principle of action and reaction to operate in the combined system in a relativistically covariant manner. If the electromagnetic field is abolished, how can we insure the general validity of the principle of action and reaction? In other words, how can we guarantee that the basic mechanical conservation laws are respected?

If we attempt to develop our theory by expressing the action between two electrons solely in terms of quantities that correspond to the retarded potentials consistently with the causality assumption D (page 254), it is not at all clear how we can take care of the above question. It appears necessary to also draw upon the corresponding "advanced" quantities, and in fact the consideration of symmetry in time (with respect to past and future), which we have already encountered in Dirac's theory, now becomes of primary importance. The most convenient way in which to treat these questions

‡ The idea of retarded propagation of action had already been considered half a century earlier in the electrodynamic investigations of Gauss, Riemann, and others. See R. Reif and A. Sommerfeld, "Encyclopädie der Mathematischen Wissenschaft," vol. 5, pt. 2, sec. 12, 1902.

§ While the germ of the idea can be discerned in a number of such investigations in the twenties, especially in those of J. Frenkel, explicit and direct use as a guiding principle, as expressed in terms of a stationary action formulation, is made in the papers by H. Tetrode, *Z. Physik*, **10**: 317 (1922), and A. D. Fokker, *Z. Physik*, **58**: 386 (1929). The latter paper in particular contains a concise discussion of the rationale in the choice of the action integral (7A-5) for a system of charged particles. A much earlier similar investigation by K. Schwarzschild [*Gött. Nachr.*, **128**: 132 (1903)] had been generally overlooked.

is by starting with an action-principle formulation, to whose discussion we now turn.

Let us first recall the relevant discussion in Secs. 4-3 and 7-2. The results developed there lead to the following action integral for a system of charged particles:

$$I = -\sum_a \int d\tau_a \left(c^2 m_a + \frac{e_a}{c} A_\mu(a)\dot{z}_a{}^\mu\right) - \frac{1}{16\pi c}\int B^{\mu\nu}B_{\mu\nu}\, d^4x \qquad \text{(7A-1)}$$

where the meaning of the symbols and the identity of the independent dynamical variables for the particles and for the field are clear from the context. Both the field equations and the equations of motion of the particles are obtained as the Euler-Lagrange equations for the stationary value of (7A-1), as was shown in Sec. 7-2. Although the formulation there was in terms of a combined four-dimensional action integral, on the assumption of continuous 4-current densities of the particles, it is readily verified that by the application of the δ-formalism method explained in the first part of Sec. 7-4 the results obtained for the continuous case can be transcribed formally into the corresponding results for point particles for which the 4-current densities are given by the symbolic representation (7-114). In the same way it can also be shown that the conservation relations discussed in Sec. 6-3 have a suitable formal transcription in the case of discrete charges. These formal results, however, with the standard retarded solutions of the field equations, present two basic difficulties that were considered in Sec. 7-5: infinite self-forces are present, and the forces of radiation reaction (the so-called *radiation damping* forces) are not properly accounted for.

The first difficulty is, as noted earlier, immediately removed by the assumption of covariant action at a distance. In attempting to find the corresponding action integral by a suitable modification of (7A-1) (which, as we know, has extensive practical validity), the last term in (7A-1) must, indeed, be discarded, since the field as an autonomous dynamical entity is no longer taken to exist; while in the second term, by our assumption of the absence of self-action, we would expect that

$$A_\mu(a) = \sum_{b \neq a} A_\mu{}^{(b)}(a) \qquad \text{(7A-2)}$$

where $A_\mu{}^{(b)}(a)$ is associated with the action upon particle a due to particle b, and—in agreement with experience—should be taken as the retarded Liénard-Wiechert potential 4-vector arising from the charge b and evaluated at the position of the charge a—the use of potentials as auxiliary quantities being, of course, perfectly consistent with the method of action at a distance.

We shall disregard, for the time being, the aforementioned second difficulty and turn our attention to the question of the mechanical conservation relations, and in particular to the principle of action and reaction. It is clear that a necessary condition for this principle to be obeyed by our system

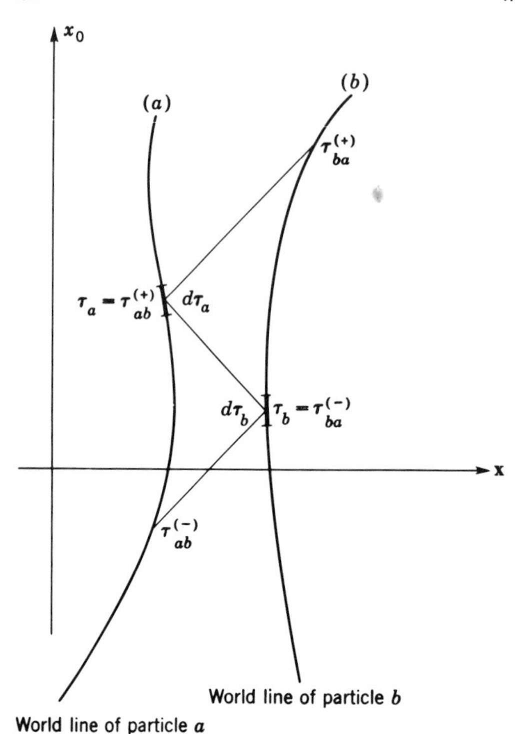

Fig. 7-6 Construction of the 'retarded' and 'advanced' proper times $\tau^{(-)}$, $\tau^{(+)}$ between two particle world lines (a) and (b), associated with two correlated proper times τ_a, τ_b. The zigzag lines lie on light cones. If we wished to attach arrows to these lines to indicate directions in time, each would have to carry two oppositely directed arrows, reflecting the symmetry in time with respect to past and future that is involved in our construction of the action integral.

of charges is that the action integral be a symmetric functional with respect to an interchange of the particles. The second term in (7A-1) must therefore be such a symmetric function, and this will obviously not be the case if we take it as given and substitute from (7A-2). In fact, the result can be written, using (7-119), as

$$-\sum_a \sum_{b \neq a} \frac{e_a e_b}{c} \int d\tau_a \frac{\mathsf{U}_a(\tau_a) \cdot \mathsf{U}_b(\tau_{ba}^{(-)})}{\mathsf{U}_b(\tau_{ba}^{(-)}) \cdot [\mathsf{z}_a(\tau_a) - \mathsf{z}_b(\tau_{ba}^{(-)})]} \tag{7A-3}$$

where τ_{ba} (see Fig. 7-6) is actually a function of τ_a, representing the retarded proper time of particle b relative to the 4-point $\mathsf{z}_a(\tau_a)$—the value of τ_b such that (7-120) is satisfied with $\mathsf{x} = \mathsf{z}_a(\tau_a)$, $\mathsf{z} = \mathsf{z}_b$, and $\tau_- = \tau_{ba}^{(-)}$; and the other symbols are in accordance with our previous usage. It is apparent that the expression (7A-3) is not symmetric under an interchange of a and b. On the other hand, as observed by Fokker (*op. cit.*), interchanging a and b in a term in the sum (7A-3) leads to a term that relates to the action of particle a upon particle b, provided this action is taken to be not of the ordinary retarded but of the advanced type (see Fig. 7-3 with special attention to the direction arrows on the light-cone lines). Such a term will be included in

(7A-1) provided A_μ is given by [see (7-154)]

$$\bar{\mathsf{A}} = \tfrac{1}{2}(\mathsf{A}_{\text{ret}} + \mathsf{A}_{\text{adv}}) \tag{7A-4}$$

In fact, the corresponding term in (7A-3) is proportional to (see Fig. 7-6 for explanation of notation)

$$\frac{\mathsf{U}_b(\tau_b) \cdot \mathsf{U}_a(\tau_{ab}^{(+)})}{\mathsf{U}_a(\tau_{ab}^{(+)}) \cdot [\mathsf{z}_b(\tau_b) - \mathsf{z}_a(\tau_{ab}^{(+)})]}$$

and, by differentiating the expression $\mathsf{R}^2 \equiv (\mathsf{z}_a - \mathsf{z}_b)^2 = 0$ (using understandable abbreviations), we see that $\mathsf{R} \cdot d\mathsf{z}_a = \mathsf{R} \cdot d\mathsf{z}_b$, so that we can replace in the denominator of the above expression U_a by U_b. The factor $\frac{1}{2}$ in (7A-4) is obviously necessary for agreement with established results; in particular, for two charges stationary in a given inertial frame we get the standard result (involving the potential energy term e_1e_2/r), since $\mathsf{A}_{\text{ret}} = \mathsf{A}_{\text{adv}}$ in that case.

The Fokker action integral we have now arrived at, which is given by (7A-1) when the last term is discarded and we substitute the expression (7A-4) for the A in the second term, can be put in a convenient compact form by using Dirac's symbolic expression for retarded and advanced potentials; namely, the representation given in Eq. (i) of Prob. 7-19 for the former, and the same representation—but with the symbolic integration taken between the limits τ_0 and $+\infty$—for the latter [for which the proof is entirely similar to the proof of the representation (i)]. For, combining these two representations, we have

$$\bar{\mathsf{A}}(\mathsf{x}) = e \int\!\!\!\!-_{-\infty}^{\infty} \mathsf{U}(\tau)\, \delta[(\mathsf{R}(\tau)^2]\, d\tau, \qquad \mathsf{R}(\tau) \equiv \mathsf{x} - \mathsf{z}(\tau)$$

and hence the Fokker action integral can be written

$$\begin{aligned} I = &-c^2 \sum_a m_a \int d\tau_a \\ &- \frac{1}{c} \sum_{a \neq b}\sum e_a e_b \int\!\!\!\!- d\tau_a \int\!\!\!\!- d\tau_b\, \delta[(\mathsf{z}_a(\tau_a) - \mathsf{z}_b(\tau_b))^2] \mathsf{U}_a(\tau_a) \cdot \mathsf{U}_b(\tau_b) \end{aligned} \tag{7A-5}$$

This expression, which has some calculational advantages, shows the symmetry under discussion very clearly.

The sense in which we can take the principle of action and reaction to hold for a system of charged particles whose motion is governed by the action integral (7A-5), and the role played by the symmetry with respect to past and future, can now be understood. It is also now clear why advanced potentials are, as stated earlier, an essential ingredient in the present formulation.

The actual derivation, starting with the action integral (7A-5), of the conservation laws for our system of elementary charges can be accomplished with the familiar methods touched upon in Sec. 4-3, with due attention to the special structure of the interaction term.‡

The Euler-Lagrange equations associated with our action integral can be found immediately when we recall the original expression (7A-1) for I with the changes indicated above. With the notation given in (7-154) we find then:

$$m_a \dot{U}_a^{\ \mu} = \frac{e_a}{c} \bar{B}^{\nu\mu} U_\nu, \qquad \text{no summation for } a \tag{7A-6}$$

We are now confronted squarely with the difficulty referred to earlier relating to electromagnetic radiation. How can we account for radiation damping when all the interactions available are as given in (7A-6)? In addition, we also have the perplexing presence of advanced action on a par with retarded action in the expression for the basic elementary force between the charges given in (7A-6). If our theory is to have any claim at being treated as fundamental in any significant sense one must get around these two difficulties, especially the first one, for which there can be no appeal to merely peripheral exceptions (recall the discussion concerning preacceleration in Dirac's theory). For this reason an ingenious attempt by Wheeler and Feynman of circumventing the radiation difficulty is of considerable interest.§

This attempt is based in part on an idea found in Tetrode's paper (*op. cit.*) regarding the role of absorbers in the electromagnetic radiation process, and in part on an observation contained at the end of Dirac's paper discussed in Sec. 7-5, to the effect that his equations of motion for a system of charges can be obtained from Fokker's action principle, provided we have (in the notation explained on pages 282–283)

$$B_{\text{in}} + B_{\text{out}} = 0 \tag{7A-7}$$

If $B_{\text{in}} = 0$, which would be the case in the approach under present discussion, then by results presented in Sec. 7-5, (7A-7) implies that we have the identity in $\mathbf{x}$:

$$\sum_a B_{(a)\text{ret}} = \sum_a B_{(a)\text{adv}} \tag{7A-8}$$

In their interesting analysis, Wheeler and Feynman show how condition (7A-8) can be taken to be satisfied if it is assumed that there are enough *absorbers* in the universe to serve as sinks for all the actions that emanate from any given elementary charged particle. This is clearly not a particularly simple concept, and it involves us, moreover, in considerations out-

‡ We leave this derivation as a worthwhile exercise for the interested reader. The following references can be consulted: J. A. Wheeler and R. P. Feynman, *Rev. Mod. Phys.*, **21:** 425 (1949); Rohrlich, *op. cit.*, secs. 7-1 and 7-2.

§ J. A. Wheeler and R. P. Feynman, *Rev. Mod. Phys.*, **17:** 157 (1945).

side the conventional domain of electrodynamics proper, remotely reminiscent of Mach's principle in mechanics. This is not the place, however, to enter into any critical discussion of this subject.‡

In conclusion, it needs to be emphasized, if it has not been sufficiently clear by now, that relegating the present strictly physical topic to an appendix is not a result of any judgment upon its relative merit. This topic was placed in an appendix for the same reason that the subject of special relativistic treatments of gravitation is presented in the following appendix: simply because, even to a greater extent than in the preceding sections, the discussion is now being limited to a very restricted survey of the subject in order to keep the length of the present chapter within sensible limits in keeping with the character of this book.

APPENDIX 7B THEORIES OF GRAVITATION WITHIN THE FRAMEWORK OF SPECIAL RELATIVITY

Throughout our discussion of STR we have disregarded gravitational phenomena on the ground that they are outside the scope of this theory. Is this view fully justified? On first thought it is doubtless surprising. The classical theory of gravitation is in general already remarkably successful, and Newton's inverse square law is mathematically similar to Coulomb's law. Since the electrostatic force admits the Lorentz force in Minkowski's form as its relativistic extension, could we not have a similar relativistic extension of Newton's law? The answer is that of course we could, and in fact Poincaré, in his *Rendiconti* article, and later Minkowski ([2], p. 90), considered just such a generalization,§ only it did not work. It is obviously not sufficient for such a generalization to agree with the principles of STR, and to reproduce the newtonian results: it must also go beyond them where discrepancies remain to be explained. Now the confrontation of the newtonian theory with astronomical observations is not a total triumph; there exist a few very minute but sensible discrepancies, of which the best known and most widely discussed is a classically unaccounted part in the advance of the perihelion of Mercury of some 43″ per century. The Poincaré-

‡ The interested reader is urged to read the stimulating and very readable original paper of Wheeler and Feynman. Critical discussion of this theory is contained in A. Landé, *Phys. Rev.*, **80**: 283 (1950); P. Havas, *Phys. Rev.*, **86**: 974 (1952). Further general discussion on the classical covariant treatment of the motion of charged elementary particles is to be found in Rzewuski, *op. cit.*, chap. 3, sec. 7; P. G. Bergmann, The Special Theory of Relativity, secs. 33–37, in S. Flügge (ed.), "Encyclopedia of Physics," vol. 4, Springer-Verlag, Berlin, 1962.

§ Poincaré did not precisely start in this fashion, but his result was to the same effect. See Prob. 7-29.

Minkowski theory yields only one-sixth of this value (see solution to Prob. 4-10*b*). What renders this disagreement decisive is the knowledge (since 1916) that the above discrepancy can be fully accounted for within a consistent generalization of Newton's theory, namely, Einstein's theory of gravitation.‡

The Poincaré-Minkowski hypothesis is faced with other difficulties, for example, the theoretical difficulty—already recognized in a similar connection by Maxwell§—springing from the embarrassing fact that the associated field-energy density is not positive definite (as can be easily seen by recalling that the corresponding positive sign in the case of the electrostatic field is due to the fact that like charges *repel* each other). Actually neither Poincaré nor Minkowski pursued the subject far enough to study critically the properties of gravitational interaction, and they did not even raise the far-reaching question of the connection between gravitation and inertia. Providing a satisfactory treatment of the latter question is now generally recognized (largely from the lessons taught us by Einstein) as an essential requirement of a comprehensive theory of gravitation. It is this criterion primarily that, as we shall see, renders it unlikely that such a theory can be successfully formulated within the scope of STR.

It would appear that only within the general scheme of Einstein's theory of gravitation is an acceptable resolution to be found to the subtle questions that are connected with the realization that gravitation plays, in essential respects, a unique role among all known primary interactions. A critical examination, of even the most cursory character, of the special relativistic theories of gravitation is hence hardly feasible without some comparisons with Einstein's theory. If the latter theory were without its difficulties, one could, if one were so inclined, simply dismiss the special relativistic attempts as unnecessary. But this is, at present, also hardly the case. Some acquaintanceship with at least the broad lines of Einstein's general theory of relativity is therefore essential for any meaningful, even if very rapid, discussion of our topic. However, only the barest sketch of the elements of this theory can be attempted here; for details and for a proper introduction to its guiding principles, methods, results, and problems, the reader must be referred to the literature on the subject.¶

The central idea in Einstein's approach in its simplest terms is the identification of gravitational action with geometric structure in space-time. Specifically, this structure is defined by a *riemannian metric* in space-time

‡ See, e.g., R. Adler, M. Bazin, and M. Schiffer, "Introduction to General Relativity," chap. 6, McGraw-Hill Book Company, Inc., New York, 1965; M. G. Adam, *Proc. Roy. Soc. London*, **A270:** 297 (1962).

§ J. C. Maxwell, "Scientific Papers," vol. 1, p. 570, Cambridge University Press, London, 1890. See M. Abraham, *Jahrb. Radioakt. Elektronik*, **11:** 470 (1914).

¶ A very readable and thorough introduction is contained in Adler, Bazin, and Schiffer, *op. cit.* A concise and lucid introduction to the basic physical ideas is also to be found, among others, in [3], [7], and in appropriate parts of [1].

as given in Eq. (5-43), i.e., by the line element (squared)

$$ds^2 = g_{\alpha\beta}(x)\, dx^\alpha\, dx^\beta \tag{7B-1}$$

in our case. The crucial point is that in general this metric is *not flat:* in general, no rectangular coordinates y exist even in a small *finite* space-time region, yielding the expression (5-41):

$$ds^2 = (dy^0)^2 - dy^i dy^i \equiv h_{\alpha\beta}\, dy^\alpha\, dy^\beta \tag{7B-2}$$

only in an infinitesimal region about any given event P is the metric always minkowskian: *locally* lorentzian coordinates can be introduced about P so that (7B-2) holds at P. This purely geometric assumption in Einstein's theory acquires fundamental kinematic and dynamic content from the added physical assumptions concerning the dependence of the metric tensor $g_{\alpha\beta}(x)$ of (7B-1) upon material distributions, and the character of 'free' motions in regions of 'curved' space-time.

The latter assumption is a simple and, in an important sense that we shall soon recognize, natural starting point for the theory that can be stated as follows. The world line (i.e., space-time trajectory) of every particle (of positive or zero rest mass) that is subject to no outside influence of any sort except what we call gravitational, is always a *geodesic* of the space-time manifold.‡ Its equation is thus of the form (recalling the relevant discussion in Sec. 5-5):

$$0 = \left(\frac{dx^\alpha}{ds}\right)_{;\beta} \frac{dx^\beta}{ds} = \frac{d^2x^\alpha}{ds^2} + \Gamma^\alpha_{\beta\gamma} \frac{dx^\beta}{ds}\frac{dx^\gamma}{ds} \tag{7B-3}$$

The law expressed by this equation embodies a number of far-reaching implications that bear on the intimate connection between inertia and gravitation. In a space-time region in which $\mathfrak{M}$ geometry holds (or holds approximately,) the Γ symbols vanish (or practically vanish) in lorentzian coordinates, and Eq. (7B-3) reduces to an expression of Newton's first law and the definition of inertial frames that has been at the base of our discussion of STR; on the other hand, if we have a minkowskian (or, near-minkowskian) region but use non-lorentzian 'accelerated' coordinate systems, then the Γ will make their appearance: the so-called inertial forces, such as the familiar

‡ For the equations of geodesics in flat spaces, see Probs. 1-2 and 3-13. The reader can easily verify that in the case of flat spaces, (7B-3) is the equation of geodesics in general coordinates. The geometric significance of this equation in the case of general riemannian spaces is associated with the geometric meaning of covariant derivatives in such spaces. See, e.g., Adler, Bazin, and Schiffer, *op. cit.*, sec. 2.3. It should be noted also that the parameter s in (7B-3) is as given in (7B-1) along the world line, when the latter is not null; for a *null geodesic* the letter s in (7B-3) must be taken to represent some other suitable evolution parameter, since ds vanishes along such a world line. See the relevant discussion in the aforementioned reference.

centrifugal and coriolis forces, would come into play.‡ The form invariance of Eq. (7B-3) under *general* coordinate transformations, its conformity—in other words—with Einstein's principle of *general covariance* (of "general relativity"), reflects the relativity that attaches to any division into inertial and gravitational forces, while its explicit independence of any inertial parameters characterizing the particle under consideration is an expression of the empirically well-established proportionality of inertial and gravitational masses.

The two principles of "general relativity" and of "equivalence" encountered in the above rapid discussion of the geodesic equation of 'free' motion, are the two pillars upon which Einstein erected his dazzling theoretical structure. The guiding idea is surprisingly simple. The influence of gravitation on physical phenomena can often be deduced from a knowledge of their behavior in minkowskian regions when the corresponding equations are suitably transcribed in general covariant form with due attention to effects of intrinsic nonconstancy of the metric tensor. Equation (7B-3) itself is a case in point. Free motion in a minkowskian vacuum and in lorentzian coordinates is given by the first term of this equation, and the second 'dynamic' term appears when one introduces general coordinates. An important illustration of Einstein's prescription is provided by the case of electrodynamics. Many of the results developed in this chapter, when expressed in general coordinates (note in particular Sec. 7-2), retain their validity in the presence of gravitational fields, but in some instances one must bear in mind that in non-minkowskian regions the Riemann *curvature tensor* (see Prob. 5-18) is not zero and the difference in the result obtained from that which one finds in the minkowskian case represents the effect of gravitation on the electrodynamic process under consideration. As an example, consider the result (i) in Prob. 7-5, which clearly shows the coupling that is thus introduced between the A and g fields (see, e.g., [1], chap. 6).

We have yet to consider the other side of the coin: the setting up, with the aid of suitably chosen physical assumptions, of the equations that determine the 'gravitational' field $g_{\alpha\beta}(x)$. But this is an intricate business into which we cannot enter here even in outline. We must content ourselves with writing down Einstein's field equations, for which fortunately we already have at least the immediately needed mathematical machinery. With the contracted symmetric tensor $R_{\alpha\beta}$ of the Riemann curvature tensor, as defined

‡ With the implication that the latter forces are essentially of the same nature as 'ordinary' gravitational forces, this is a concise statement of Einstein's famous "principle of equivalence," which he introduced early in his intensive gravitational investigations {see *Jahrb. Radioakt. Elektronik*, **4**:411 (1907) sec. V; and [2], paper 4}. In its original form it states essentially that all physical phenomena proceed in the same way in a homogeneous gravitational field giving rise to the acceleration **g** of free fall relative to an inertial frame S, or in a gravitational-free region that has the acceleration $-\mathbf{g}$ relative to S. It thus constitutes a significant generalization of the fact known since Galileo's and Newton's investigations, that all bodies accelerate equally in a given gravitational field.

in Eq. (i), Prob. 7-5, these equations read

$$G_{\alpha\beta} \equiv R_{\alpha\beta} - \tfrac{1}{2}g_{\alpha\beta}R = \kappa T_{\alpha\beta}, \qquad R \equiv R^{\alpha}_{\alpha} \tag{7B-4}$$

where T is the symmetric energy-momentum tensor of everything in the region under consideration that gives rise to an energy and momentum or energy-flow distribution (with added appropriate boundary conditions in the case of limited regions), and κ is the coupling constant for the interaction thus represented (the interaction between the gravitational field and 'matter'—in conventional jargon). It is apparent that these field equations are covariant under the group of general transformations of space-time coordinates, in agreement with Einstein's principle of general relativity. If they reproduce in the classical limit the newtonian gravitational equations, while at the same time yielding results demanded by observation that could not be accounted for by the newtonian theory, and also predict new and subsequently confirmed results, then clearly these equations constitute a fruitful relativistic generalization of the newtonian theory.

That Einstein's theory goes over into the newtonian theory for sufficiently weak stationary gravitational fields and sufficiently small material velocities can be established as follows. We can take the expression (6-36) for our material energy-momentum tensor, and, in view of our assumptions the only surviving component is $T_{00} = c^2\rho^* = c^2\rho$, the ordinary mass density (in energy units) in our nonrelativistic approximation. Equation (7B-4) can be rewritten (since $G^{\alpha}_{\alpha} = -R$) as

$$R_{\alpha\beta} = \kappa(T_{\alpha\beta} - \tfrac{1}{2}g_{\alpha\beta}T^{\gamma}_{\gamma}) \tag{7B-5}$$

so that the right-hand side for $\alpha = \beta = 0$ is, in our classical limit, equal to $\kappa c^2\rho/2$. Since [see (iv), Prob. 5-18 and (i), Prob. 7-5]

$$R_{\alpha\beta} = 2(\Gamma^{\mu}{}_{\alpha[\mu,\beta]} + \Gamma^{\lambda}{}_{\alpha[\mu}\Gamma^{\mu}_{\beta]\lambda}) \tag{7B-6}$$

an examination of the various terms in these equations [remembering the formulas (5-83) and (5-85)] shows that by virtue of our restrictive assumptions, in the 10 equations (7B-5) also on the left only the 00 term survives and that, of the many terms in R_{00}, we need to keep only the term $g_{00,\mu}{}^{\mu}/2 = g_{00,i}{}^{i}/2 = \nabla^2 g_{00}/2$ (for details see, e.g., Adler, Bazin, and Schiffer, *op. cit.*, sec. 9.5). Thus, if we set

$$g_{\alpha\beta} = h_{\alpha\beta} + \phi_{\alpha\beta}, \qquad h_{\alpha\beta} \text{ as in (7B-2)} \tag{7B-7}$$

the result is that, in the classical approximation under consideration, all $\phi_{\alpha\beta} \approx 0$ excepting $\phi_{00} \equiv \phi$, which satisfies the equation

$$\nabla^2\phi = -\kappa c^2\rho \tag{7B-8}$$

We now make the corresponding substitution and restrictions in the equations of motion (7B-3) for a test particle (of nonvanishing rest mass) and find (as $dx^i/ds \approx 0$, $ds \approx cdt$, $\Gamma^i_{00} \approx -g^{i\alpha}\phi_{,\alpha}/2 \approx \delta^{i\alpha}\phi_{,\alpha}/2$)

$$\frac{d^2x^i}{dt^2} = -\frac{c^2}{2}\frac{\partial\phi}{\partial x^i} \tag{7B-9}$$

With the substitution $c^2\phi/2 = \psi$, $\kappa = -8\pi G/c^4$, Eqs. (7B-8) and (7B-9) are seen to assume, indeed, the familiar form of the classical Poisson equation for the gravitational potential ψ and of the associated classical equations of material particle motion.

The first triumph of Einstein's theory came when it was applied to the outstanding problem of Mercury's perihelion precession. By considering the free field equations, i.e., (7B-5) with $T_{\alpha\beta} = 0$, and looking for solutions associated with a point singularity that are spherically symmetric (in suitable coordinates) about the singularity, K. Schwarzschild succeeded in obtaining, in the same year (1916) in which Einstein published his fundamental paper on gravitation ([2], paper 7 is an English translation), a rigorous solution representing a static field about a given stationary mass (with the boundary conditions $g_{\alpha\beta} \rightarrow h_{\alpha\beta}$ at spatial infinity). The 'Schwarzschild line element' in the original and commonly used coordinates is given by the expression

$$\begin{gathered} ds^2 = A(r)c^2\,dt^2 - \frac{1}{A(r)}\,dr^2 - r^2(d\theta^2 + \sin^2\theta\,d\phi^2) \\ A(r) = 1 - \frac{2GM}{c^2r} \end{gathered} \tag{7B-10}$$

where the integration constant M can be identified with the mass of the source particle. This leads to an advance of perihelion for planetary orbits in the field of M, of magnitude (see Adler, Bazin, and Schiffer, *op. cit.*, chap. 6)

$$6\pi\frac{G^2M^2}{c^2J^2} \text{ per revolution,} \qquad J = r^2\frac{d\phi}{dt} \tag{7B-11}$$

When the values of the constants corresponding to the orbit of Mercury are substituted in the equation, one finds the observed result of 43″ per century (in round numbers).

The predictions of the theory concerned the interaction of light and gravitation. The so-called "gravitational red shift" was already deduced in an approximate way by Einstein with the aid of the equivalence principle, in his article of 1907 referred to earlier (see [2], VI). The deduction also involves the use of the principle C of STR (see page 63), which, together with the principle of equivalence, form an important bridge between the special and general theories of relativity as far as concerns the purely *metric* role of the fundamental tensor $g_{\alpha\beta}$. In the case of temporal intervals, they lead—with the aid of the first-order Doppler formula—to the conclusion that in a static homogeneous gravitational field approximately describable by the classical potential ψ, the frequency ν of a given spectral line changes with ψ according to the approximate formula

$$\frac{\Delta\nu}{\nu} = -\frac{\Delta\psi}{c^2} \tag{7B-12}$$

it being assumed, of course, that $\Delta\psi/c^2$ is sufficiently small. The rate of running of a 'standard clock' must therefore also depend on the gravitational field {see [2], p. 106; [7], sec. 53(β)}. This, incidentally, is only one special and approximate result that is included among the general metric conclusions that follow from the twin assumption of Einstein's general theory, namely, that in addition to the role of the $g_{\alpha\beta}$ as potentials, the line element defined in (7B-1) gives the measures of local intervals in terms of standard clocks and rods—a central feature of this theory into whose analysis we cannot enter here, but which must be borne in mind in our later discussion.

The result (7B-12) can be obtained as a precisely defined approximation of a rigorous result deducible from the Schwarzschild solution (7B-10). It can therefore be applied to the spectral shift in the radiation coming from the surface of the sun: $-\Delta\nu/\nu \approx GM/c^2R \approx 2 \times 10^{-6}$. Although, owing to many complicating observational factors, the confirmation of this particular result has not been entirely conclusive (at least as far as the older measurements are concerned), formula (7B-12) has in recent years received brilliant verification by means of terrestrial measurements employing the Mössbauer effect.‡

The gravitational red-shift phenomenon, as we have seen, is not so much a test of the general theory of relativity as of the principle of equivalence. It is sometimes argued that one can also sidestep the equivalence principle by invoking the light-quantum hypothesis, which gives $h\nu/c^2$ for the mass of a photon of frequency ν; so that by conservation of energy it follows that $\Delta(h\nu + h\nu\psi/c^2) = 0$, or $\Delta[\nu(1 + \psi/c^2)] = 0$, which gives (with $\psi/c^2 \ll 1$) the formula (7B-12). However, such reasoning involves a tacit assumption that there is associated with all types of energy not only an inertial mass but, in a similar way, also a *gravitational* mass. This does not follow by itself from the principles of STR, but can be deduced from these principles with the aid of the principle of equivalence.§

The other prediction of the general theory, the deflection of light rays when passing through a strong gravitational field, can be obtained from the Schwarzschild solution by specializing the space-time trajectories to be null,

‡ See Adler, Bazin, and Schiffer, *op. cit.*, pp. 129–130, and the references on experimental tests of the red shift given on p. 131.

§ See [2], VI, sec. 2. It is, incidentally, a little curious that Einstein in this paper does not remark that his result (1a), $\Delta E/E = -\Delta\psi/c^2$ (in our notation), also gives an immediate derivation of the red-shift formula when one substitutes the relation $E = h\nu$, embodying his light-quantum hypothesis.

i.e., taking (7B-10) with $ds = 0$. One finds (Adler, Bazin, and Schiffer, *op. cit.*, sec. 6.4) for the angle α between the asymptotes of such a trajectory, the value

$$\alpha = \frac{4GM}{c^2 r} \tag{7B-13}$$

For starlight passing the sun's limb one gets therefore, $\alpha \approx 1.75''$. The observation of this prediction is also fraught with formidable technical difficulties, and a conclusive result is apparently not yet at hand despite determined efforts by astronomers through all the favorable solar eclipses since 1919.‡

Having summarized very briefly a few of the ideas and results of GTR (the general theory of relativity), we return to our discussion of special relativistic theories of gravitation. In the light of preceding observations the following questions now invite our attention.

1. Since the appearance of the Poincaré and Minkowski formulation within STR that failed to meet essential tests, have other such theories of gravitation been developed that can be considered as coming close to satisfying all presently recognized essential requirements of such a theory?
2. If the answer to question (1) is in the negative, can we nevertheless say that in principle such a theory is possible?
3. In view of the outstanding accomplishments of GTR to date, is there sufficient justification for searching for new paths towards a comprehensive theory of gravitation?
4. What is the present outlook in this field?

Only the briefest discussion of these questions can be presented here, and the reader who wishes to pursue this topic in depth must be directed to the literature on the subject, to which selected references are included here.

The answer that can be given to question (1) obviously depends on what one considers the necessary conditions for a satisfactory relativistic theory of gravitation. An obvious *sine qua non* condition is the meeting of all practically accessible empirical tests. This condition is perhaps at present already fulfilled by the theories that were initiated by Whitehead and by Birkhoff.§ A brief outline of the latter theory will be presented in

‡ See the references given earlier for the other tests. For an older prediction of gravitational light deflection on the basis of the newtonian theory—that gives half the value (7B-13)—see the references in Whittaker, *op. cit.*, vol. 2, p. 180.

§ A. N. Whitehead, "The Principles of Relativity," Cambridge University Press, London, 1922; J. L. Synge, *Proc. Roy. Soc. London*, **A211**: 303 (1952); A. Schild, *Proc. Roy. Soc. London*, **A235**: 202 (1956); A. Schild, Conservative Gravitational Theories of Whitehead's

the sequel; for Whitehead's theory and its generalizations the interested reader can consult the references just given. This theory, like that of Poincaré, involves a relativistic action-at-a-distance rather than field-theoretic approach, and it is similar to Birkhoff's theory in having a symmetric second-rand tensor in $\mathfrak{M}$ represent the gravitational potentials.

If one is inclined to limit oneself only to empirical tests, and if one supposes that such tests as are presently available do not in fact discriminate between Einstein's and, say, Birkhoff's theories, it is clear that further progress in this field can only come from the devising of additional crucial tests. Because of the exceedingly small strength of gravitational coupling such tests are difficult to find and their execution presents an enormous challenge. Nevertheless, at least two such tests have been recently proposed, a gyroscope experiment by Schiff‡ and a radar echo experiment by Shapiro,§ and very delicate preparations are already under way for the implementation of the former proposal.¶

These proposed tests are all based on deductions from GTR, and already from this fact alone the present superiority of the latter theory is evident. It is, however, likely that the decisive touchstone will crystallize from more purely conceptual considerations. We have already called attention very briefly to the complex of ideas connected with the intimate relationship between inertia and gravitation; the entire range of questions relating to the intriguing but difficult problem of the origin and intrinsic significance of the family of inertial reference frames, presents a challenge that in part inspired Einstein's work, in part is met by it, and in part is still wide open. The

---

Type, in "Recent Developments in General Relativity," Pergamon Press/PWN Polish Scientific Publishers, Warszawa, 1962.

G. D. Birkhoff, *Proc. Nat. Acad. Sci., U.S.A.* **29:** 231 (1943); A. Barajas, G. D. Birkhoff, C. Graef, and M. S. Vallarta, *Phys. Rev.*, **66:** 138 (1944); A. Barajas, *Proc. Nat. Acad. Sci., U.S.A.* **30:** 54 (1944); M. Moshinsky, *Phys. Rev.*, **80:** 514 (1950).

See, in this connection, the survey of gravitational theories in G. J. Whitrow and G. E. Morduch, *Nature*, **188:** 790 (1960).

‡ L. I. Schiff, Proposed Gyroscope Experiment to Test General Relativity Theory, in "Proceedings on Theory of Gravitation," Gauthier-Villars, Paris/PWN-Polish Scientific Publishers, Warszawa, 1964; and the references to earlier work. V. I. Pustovoit and A. V. Bautin, *Soviet Phys. JETP*, **19:** 937 (1964). The latter paper contains calculations of the precession of a gyroscope according to Einstein's and according to special relativistic theories of gravitation including that of Birkhoff, and it is found that the results discriminate sensibly between these theories.

§ I. I. Shapiro, *Phys. Rev. Letters*, **13:** 789 (1964). The proposal is to measure time delays between the sending and returning of radar pulses reflected back from one of the inner planets at periods when the pulses will pass sufficiently close to the sun for the cumulative general relativistic gravitational potential effect on the speed of light to lead to detectable results [note the expression for the speed of light obtained from (7B-10) by setting $ds = 0$].

¶ Other possible tests of an astronomical character are discussed in the paper by Whitrow and Morduch referred to earlier.

associated general problem connected with Mach's principle (referred to in this book on previous occasions) and the related cosmological problem, which we must leave out of our present discussion entirely,‡ cannot be excluded from any thorough consideration of gravitational theory. It appears in fact that the basic questions concerning the kinematic and dynamic definitions and relations that underlie the structure of physics, of which some were touched upon in very simplest terms in Chap. 1, are essentially connected with the broad subject of gravitation.

Thus, a reasonable answer to question (4) is that forseeable progress in this difficult subject can be expected to come from a continuation of efforts towards further crucial tests, and towards an understanding of the above fundamental questions within the general framework of GTR. Present evidence does not seem to point to any promising lines of attack on those questions solely in terms of the principles of STR. In fact, recent interesting attempts that have the latter principles as their starting point appear to lead, nevertheless, to the very ideas in Einstein's approach that gave rise to GTR.§ It can thus be expected that questions (1) and (2) will have to be answered in the negative, as already remarked earlier in our discussion.

As to question (3), it is clear that if GTR, whose high aesthetic value is generally appreciated, were already free from all substantial difficulties, there would scarcely exist any strong reasons for other attempts. But, as already noted previously, this is not the case. We cannot enter here into a technical discussion of this question, and must limit ourselves to two immediate observations. One obvious source of difficulties is the complicated *nonlinearity* of the exact field equations (7B-4), as is evident from Eq. (7B-6), remembering the definitions of the Christoffel symbols Γ. Incidentally, an important motivation in more recent times for seeking a generalization of newtonian gravitation within STR has been the desire to find *exact linear* equations for this field that could be quantized by methods similar to those employed for the electromagnetic field. However—as can be gathered, for instance, from the last-quoted references—in some of the attempts to introduce the desired linearity a nonlinearity enters by the back door, which can be explained roughly by the circumstance, peculiar to the gravitational field, that its sources include a contribution from the energy and energy-flow distributions due to itself, which—in principle—cannot be disregarded in an exact theory, and which can in fact be important in special cosmological situations.

Of the specific attempts to formulate a special relativistic theory of

‡ For an extensive introduction to these subjects, see Adler, Bazin, and Schiffer, *op. cit.*, chaps. 11 and 12, and the references given there; also the pertinent parts in [3], [7], [9], and in H. Y. Chiu and W. F. Hoffmann (eds.), "Gravitation and Relativity," W. A. Benjamin, Inc., New York, 1964.

§ See, e.g., W. E. Thirring, *Ann. Phys.*, **16:** 96 (1961) and included references; R. H. Kraichnan, *Phys. Rev.*, **98:** 1118 (1955).

gravitation we choose two, namely those of G. Nordström and of G. D. Birkhoff, that should suffice to illustrate some of the points brought out in the preceding discussion. Nordström's and Birkhoff's theories moreover supplement the Poincaré-Minkowski theory mentioned earlier, in that the representation of the gravitational potentials in the former theories is respectively in terms of a scalar and a symmetric second-rank tensor in $\mathfrak{M}$, contrasted with the 4-vector representation of these potentials in the latter theory. These three types of 4-tensor representations are, in an obvious sense, the simplest that present themselves for the treatment of the gravitational field.

Nordström's theory‡ is now essentially only of historic interest, since it fails to agree with crucial observational data; and it was in fact abandoned even by its author with the appearance of Einstein's gravitational theory of 1915. It has nevertheless considerable heuristic interest, for it incorporates in its simplest terms important characteristic features of gravitational interaction; and it has thus given rise to a good deal of useful discussion.§

There is not much point in our embarking here on a full discussion of Nordström's work—the reader who is interested in such a discussion can find a clear and detailed account in his original articles, which can be quickly mastered by transcribing his long formulas into the compact and transparent tensor notation we have learned. Our present purpose will be adequately served by merely noting some of the principal ideas in Nordström's theory that have, at present, at least didactic interest.

The initial idea—of using a 4-scalar for the gravitational potential—hardly requires any discussion: it is clearly the simplest relativistic generalization of the newtonian potential. Likewise the choice of the field equation

$$\Box\psi = -gs \tag{7B-14}$$

for this potential imposes itself naturally by the requirement of reducing to the Poisson equation in the newtonian limit. Less obvious is the identification of the *source* 4-scalar s. In his first paper Nordström identified s with the material rest density ρ^*, in the notation of Chap. 6. This evidently leads to the correct newtonian limit [see the corresponding discussion for GTR connected with Eq. (7B-8)]; however, if one wishes to incorporate the essential ideas of the correspondence principle (referred to earlier in connec-

‡ G. Nordström, *Ann. Physik*, **42:** 533 (1913); **43:** 1101 (1914). An earlier version is contained in the paper referred to on page 196.

§ This discussion has even been revived in our time. See, e.g., M. Wellner and G. Sandri, *Am. J. Phys.*, **32:** 36 (1964). This contains references to older discussions, to which should be added M. Abraham, *op. cit.* (on page 290); A. Einstein and A. D. Fokker, *Ann. Physik*, **44:** 321 (1914); and a more recent interesting discussion by O. Bergmann, *Am. J. Phys.*, **24:** 38 (1956). A recent speculative attempt to adjoin Nordström's field to Einstein's gravitational field is discussed in R. H. Dicke's article, The Many Faces of Mach, in Chiu and Hoffmann, *op. cit.*

tion with Einstein's theory), it can be concluded on the basis of considerations such as were developed in Chap. 6 that the assumption $s = \rho^*$ is too restrictive, and that the source function must be described in terms of the energy-momentum tensor $T^{\mu\nu}$ ($P^{\mu\nu}$ in the notation of Chap. 6) of the system of sources considered as a continuous medium. This conclusion leads to a unique result: the only 4-scalar that can be constructed from the tensor T is the contraction T^{μ}_{μ} (the "Laue scalar"); thus

$$s = \frac{1}{c^2} T^{\mu}_{\mu} \tag{7B-15}$$

At first sight the physical significance of this expression is not too clear [except for the simple case represented by (6-36), when it is just ρ^*]; but in the case of the practically important systems of the type studied by v. Laue ("complete and static"), referred to in Prob. 6-13, for which $S^{*ij} = 0$ [see (ii) of Prob. 6-13], it is readily verified that the space integral of (7B-15) yields the corresponding total rest mass. Nevertheless, in the necessity of posing (7B-15) we have a serious theoretical limitation of the theory, since plainly not all material systems that need to be considered are of the special Laue type, and in particular the expression (7B-15) vanishes for electromagnetic fields (see Prob. 7-10), ruling out any direct coupling between the gravitational and the latter fields.

Turning to the merits of Nordström's theory on the purely theoretical side, we note three important consequences—omitting the full details of the requisite analysis. The energy of the gravitational field in this theory, unlike what we noted to be the case for the 4-vector theory, is always positive. In fact, considering—to simplify matters—the first version with $s = \rho^*$, and combining the expression for the gravitational 4-force density

$$f_{\mu} = g\rho^*\psi_{,\mu} \tag{7B-16}$$

on the one hand with Eq. (7B-14) and on the other with the proper expression (6-60) for the change in the energy-momentum tensor of the *field*, it is immediately verified that the latter can be taken to have the form (Prob. 7-30)

$$\Theta_{\mu\nu} = \psi_{,\mu}\psi_{,\nu} - \tfrac{1}{2}\psi_{,\lambda}\psi^{,\lambda}g_{\mu\nu} \tag{7B-17}$$

and hence $\Theta_{00} = [\psi_{,0}{}^2 + (\nabla\psi)^2]/2$.

Another interesting and suggestive consequence of Nordström's equations is that inertial mass is a function of the potential ψ. This can be seen in the case of a discrete mass m by reference to Eqs. (4-60), (4-62) with $F_{\alpha} = gm\psi_{,\alpha}$ [see Eq. (7B-16)], which yield the equation $gm\dot{\psi} = c^2\dot{m}$, so that $m = m_0 \exp(g\psi/c^2)$. The connection of a dependence of inertial mass upon gravitational potential with Mach's principle is apparent (see the references given in the last footnote).

Finally, by referring to the part of the lagrangian density representing the interaction between the gravitational field and its sources that has the form (4-55), (4-56), and recalling the remarks made earlier, relative to the metric role played by the differential form (7B-1) in GTR, it can be seen that Nordström's theory is similar to Einstein's in implying a dependence upon the gravitational field of the measures of spatial and temporal intervals. Yet the underlying metric of space-time is minkowskian!

Birkhoff's theory in its original formulation, unlike Nordström's, was not based on any searching analysis of the peculiar properties of gravitation and of its relationship to inertia, and coming, moreover, after GTR had been established, it has had in general very limited appeal; on the other hand, as noted earlier, it is not—or at least it does not at present appear to be—in any conflict with empirical evidence, while having the simplicity of a linear theory in the flat space $\mathfrak{M}$. Its basic structure, granted the tensor character of the potentials, is in fact mathematically of the simplest. The field equations have the obvious form

$$\Box\psi_{\mu\nu} = -\kappa T_{\mu\nu}$$

with boundary conditions on the potentials ψ at spatial infinity similar to those for the newtonian potential. The equations of motion for a particle are

$$\ddot{x}^\lambda = (\psi_\mu{}^\lambda{}_{,\nu} - \psi_{\mu\nu}{}^{,\lambda})\dot{x}^\mu\dot{x}^\nu, \qquad \dot{x} \equiv \frac{dx}{d\tau}$$

and they follow readily from the natural requirement (dictated in part by the newtonian limiting case) that they be linear in the first derivatives of the ψ and quadratic in the $\dot{x}$ and allow for the proportionality of gravitational and inertial masses as well as for the invariance of the proper mass (and conform of course with the identity $\dot{\mathbf{x}} \cdot \ddot{\mathbf{x}} = 0$).

In Birkhoff's original formulation much stress is laid on a special perfect gas form for the tensor T, whose justification appears questionable, and which would impose a drastic restriction on the theory if it were essential. The subsequent developments of the theory by a number of investigators have consisted principally in finding approximate solutions for the stationary one-body problem that agree to the same approximation with the two crucial results (7B-11) and (7B-13) of GTR, and to the refining of the general theoretical structure, such as setting up an action integral and a consistent set of conservation equations.‡

Problems

7-1 (*a*) Recall the significance of charge conservation in Maxwell's electrodynamic theory. Does the relativistic Maxwell-Lorentz theory introduce

‡ See, e.g., in addition to the pertinent references given earlier, A. A. Borgardt, *Soviet Phys. JETP*, **34:** 1632 (1958); A. Capella, *Compt. Rend.*, **258:** 87, (1964). Critical discussion is contained in H. Weyl, *Proc. Nat. Acad. Sci., U.S.A.*, **30:** 205 (1944); *Am. J. Math.*, **66:** 591 (1944); M. Wyman, *Math. Rev.*, **5:** 218 (1944).

any new features? Does charge conservation imply the invariance of charge under Lorentz transformations, and conversely? In this connection compare the conservation equations (7-14) and (6-18) taken with Eqs. (6-19) and (6-20). (See Prob. 6-8.) (*b*) Under what conditions can we be sure that the integral $\int_\Sigma s^\mu \, d\Sigma_\mu$, where Σ is a spacelike 3-surface extending to spatial infinity in all directions, is a 4-scalar independent of the particular choice of Σ? What is the physical significance of this integral? (*c*) Deduce the law (7-14) of charge conservation from the gauge invariance of the Maxwell-Lorentz theory in its variational formulation. [Note that in the case of continuous charge distribution, the integral that corresponds to the second term in (7-34) is of the form $\int s^\mu A_\mu \, d^4x$.]

7-2 Suppose that the relativistic covariance of the Maxwell-Lorentz equations is studied in terms of the electromagnetic potentials ϕ, $\mathbf{A}$. One can prove that the quantities A^α given in Eq. (7-7) are the contravariant com ponents of a 4-vector by starting with a consideration of the classical inhomogeneous wave equations satisfied by the potentials:

$$\Box\phi = 4\pi\rho, \qquad \Box\mathbf{A} = \frac{4\pi}{c}\rho\mathbf{u} \qquad \Box \equiv \frac{\partial}{\partial {x_0}^2} - \nabla^2 \tag{i}$$

Outline the steps in such a proof. Does any complication arise from the fact that in setting up Eqs. (i) use is made of the Lorentz condition on the potentials? [It is necessary to justify first the replacement of the right-hand sides of Eqs. (i) by $\left(4\pi\rho, \frac{4\pi}{c}\rho\mathbf{U}\right) = \frac{4\pi}{c}\rho\mathsf{U}$ with ρ interpreted as the rest charge density.]

7-3 Rewrite Eqs. (7-10) in ordinary vector notation, and deduce these equations from Eq. (7-11) that is taken to hold in the instantaneous rest frame of the charged particle under consideration, by applying the necessary relativistic transformation equations also written out in three-dimensional vector notation. Compare your steps with the corresponding steps given in the text.

7-4 Show that in terms of the dual B^* of the field tensor B as defined in (5-69), Eqs. (7-1) can be written

$$B^{*\alpha\beta}{}_{;\beta} = 0 \tag{i}$$

and the energy-momentum tensor (7-17) can be transformed into the symmetrical expression

$$T^{\alpha\beta} = \frac{1}{8\pi}\left(B^{\alpha\mu}B_\mu{}^\beta + B^{*\alpha\mu}B_\mu{}^\beta\right) \tag{ii}$$

7-5 At the end of Sec. 7-1 and in Sec. 7-2 the discussion of the relativistic Maxwell-Lorentz theory is given in general coordinates, partly by way of preparation for the general relativistic extension of this theory. In this extension, however, the metric of space-time is no longer everywhere flat as it is in $\mathfrak{M}$. Hence formula (i) of Prob. 5-18 can no longer in general be applied in the deduction of Eq. (7-23) under the condition (7-22). Show in fact that in place of (7-23) the general result is

$$\Box A_\alpha + R_{\beta\alpha} A^\beta = 0, \qquad R_{\alpha\beta} = R^\mu{}_{\alpha\mu\beta} \tag{i}$$

On the other hand prove that the conservation equation (7-14) follows from Eq. (7-4) also in the general case. [In proving the second result, one requires an extension of the formula (iii) of Prob. 5-18 to second-rank tensors, which can be obtained by applying the formula to the direct product of two vectors. One also uses symmetry properties of the riemannian tensor R, which imply the symmetry of the contracted riemannian tensor $R_{\alpha\beta}$. The latter property was applied in (i). See, e.g., R. Adler, M. Bazin, and M. Schiffer, "Introduction to General Relativity," secs. 5.2 and 5.3, McGraw-Hill Book Company, Inc., New York, 1965.]

7-6 Prove that every absolute relativistic scalar that can be formed from the field tensor B is a function of the independent scalars J and K^2 given in (7-24). Relate this result to Eq. (xii) of Prob. 3-22, recalling (iii), Prob. 5-12. (Note that in addition to B we have the tensor $g_{\alpha\beta}$ and the pseudotensor $E_{\alpha\beta\gamma\delta}$, and only these tensors, available for the construction of the invariants in question.)

7-7 Consider a charged continuous medium in the presence of an external electromagnetic field B. Suppose that we can neglect all interactions within the medium in comparison with the forces on the charges arising from the field. Show that in lorentzian coordinates the equations of motion of the medium can be written

$$\mu^* \frac{dU^\alpha}{d\tau} = -T^{\alpha\beta}{}_{,\beta}$$

where the symbol μ replaces here the symbol ρ as used in Sec. 6-2, and T is the energy-momentum tensor of the field B. Express these equations in ordinary vector notation and in terms of conventional physical quantities, including the densities of charge and of current of the medium.

7-8 Explain, using relativistic arguments, the attraction of two parallel wires carrying electric currents of the same strength and direction. [Compare your conclusions with the discussion of this problem by D. L. Webster, *Am. J. Phys.*, **29**: 841 (1961).]

7-9 (*a*) Although the splitting of the field tensor B into the 3-vectors **E** and **B** is, as we know, a relative concept, there exist nontrivial relations involving these vectors that have absolute significance. Thus prove the relativistic covariance of the characterization of electromagnetic fields (at a given event $\mathbf{x}$ in vacuo—to be understood in what follows) by the conditions (1) $\mathbf{E} \cdot \mathbf{B} = 0$ and (2) $|\mathbf{E}| = |\mathbf{B}|$, or (3) there exist special (*inertial*—to be understood) frames S' for which $\mathbf{B}' = 0$, or (4) there exist special frames S' for which $\mathbf{E}' = 0$. Show that in the last two cases $|\mathbf{E}'|$ and $|\mathbf{B}'|$ respectively are independent of the choice of the special S', while in the first case one obtains for $|\mathbf{E}'|$ $(=|\mathbf{B}'|)$, by varying S', all possible values between 0 and ∞. Prove also that if condition (1) does not hold and $\mathbf{E} \times \mathbf{B} \neq 0$, then there exist special frames S' for which $\mathbf{E}' \times \mathbf{B}' = 0$, the magnitudes of the 3-fields being independent of the S':

$$E'^2 = \tfrac{1}{4}(Q - J), \qquad B'^2 = \tfrac{1}{4}(Q + J) \qquad Q = +\sqrt{J^2 + K^2} \tag{i}$$

with J, K given in (7-24), i.e.,

$$J \equiv B_{\lambda\mu}B^{\lambda\mu} = 2(B^2 - E^2), \qquad K \equiv B^*_{\lambda\mu}B^{\lambda\mu} = 4\mathbf{E} \cdot \mathbf{B} \tag{ii}$$

($E = |\mathbf{E}|$, etc.). Show that the velocities $\mathbf{v}$ of the special S' relative to the given frame S satisfy the equation

$$\mathbf{v} = \frac{1}{h + h'}\left[\mathbf{S} + \frac{1}{4\pi}(\mathbf{v} \cdot \mathbf{EE} + \mathbf{v} \cdot \mathbf{BB})\right], \qquad h \equiv T_{00} \tag{iii}$$

where T_{00} and $\mathbf{S}$ are given in (7-19) ($S^i = cT^{0i}$); and that the smallest value of $\beta = |\mathbf{v}|/c$, common to all S' moving parallel to the Poynting vector $\mathbf{S}$, is given by

$$\beta^2 = \frac{h - h'}{h + h'} \tag{iv}$$

Show further that when $J \neq 0$ and we let $K \to 0$, we obtain the corresponding results for the two cases represented by the conditions (1), (3) and (1), (4).

Prove these results by applying the transformation equations (with the usual meaning of the symbols)

$$\begin{aligned} \mathbf{E}' &= \gamma[\mathbf{E} + (\boldsymbol{\beta} \times \mathbf{B})] + \frac{1 - \gamma}{\beta^2}\,\boldsymbol{\beta} \cdot \mathbf{E}\boldsymbol{\beta} \\ \mathbf{B}' &= \gamma[\mathbf{B} - (\boldsymbol{\beta} \times \mathbf{E})] + \frac{1 - \gamma}{\beta^2}\,\boldsymbol{\beta} \cdot \mathbf{B}\boldsymbol{\beta} \end{aligned} \tag{v}$$

and the resulting relations

$$\boldsymbol{\beta} \cdot \mathbf{E}' = \boldsymbol{\beta} \cdot \mathbf{E}, \qquad \boldsymbol{\beta} \cdot \mathbf{B}' = \boldsymbol{\beta} \cdot \mathbf{B} \tag{vi}$$

Check these equations. (*b*) Compare the above results with the solution of the eigenvalue problem for the tensor B. In particular, show that the four eigenvalues λ of this tensor can be written in general (in obvious notation) as

$$\lambda_{\pm(\pm)} = \pm\tfrac{1}{2}\sqrt{(\pm)Q - J} \qquad \text{(vii)}$$

so that a field satisfying (1), (2) (known understandably as a "plane-wave," or "null" electromagnetic field) is characterized by the vanishing of all its eigenvalues, and the fields satisfying (1), (3) or (1), (4) are characterized by having two vanishing eigenvalues and two real or two purely imaginary eigenvalues respectively; while in the general case $K \neq 0$, we have

$$\lambda_{\pm(+)} = \pm|\mathbf{E}'|, \qquad \lambda_{\pm(-)} = \pm i|\mathbf{B}'| \qquad \text{(viii)}$$

[in the notation employed in (*a*)]. Deduce the result (viii) directly from the solution of the eigenvalue problem. (See relevant results in Prob. 3-22d.) (*c*) The quantity K in (ii) is only a pseudoscalar under the full Lorentz group. Are any of the considerations in this problem limited only to the restricted group $\mathfrak{L}$?

7-10 Compare the energy-momentum tensors T for free electromagnetic fields and for simple continuous material media considered in Chap. 6. Show that the traces of the former always vanish, while those of the latter are in general $\neq 0$, and, in particular, that they are >0 for the simplest media consisting of so-called incoherent matter. More specifically show that unlike what we found (in Sec. 6-6) to be true in general for material media, the eigenvalues μ of T for the electromagnetic fields are at least doubly degenerate, with

$$\mu = \pm\frac{1}{16\pi}Q \qquad \text{(i)}$$

where Q is defined in (i), Prob. 7-9 (so that for null fields they are all zero). On the other hand, prove that except for null fields, when it equals c, the quantity

$$u = \left|\frac{\mathbf{S}}{h}\right|, \qquad \mathbf{S},\, h \text{ as defined in Prob. 7-9} \qquad \text{(ii)}$$

is $<c$ for the electromagnetic fields as it is [with $\mathbf{S} \equiv c\mathbf{g}$ of Eq. (6-30)] for usual material media. In what respect is this similarity of limited scope? (Consider pertinent results in Prob. 7-9 bearing on this question.)

7-11 (*a*) Show that in terms of the tensor densities as given in Eqs. (5-100), we can write Eqs. (7-4) and (7-14) in general coordinates respectively as follows:

$$\mathfrak{B}^{\mu\nu}{}_{,\nu} = \mathfrak{s}^{\mu}, \qquad \mathfrak{s}^{\mu}{}_{,\mu} = 0 \qquad \text{(i)}$$

where $\qquad \mathfrak{B}^{\mu\nu} = \sqrt{-g}\,B^{\mu\nu}, \qquad \mathfrak{s}^{\mu} = \sqrt{-g}\,s^{\mu}$

(*b*) Find the Maxwell-Lorentz field equations and the equations of motion of a charged particle in a given electromagnetic field for spatial cylindrical and for spatial spherical coordinates using (i) and by conventional vector methods. (*c*) Apply the first of Eqs. (i) to a reference frame S' that is rotating with constant angular velocity w relative to a given inertial frame S. Take the x^3 axes in S and in S' along the axis of rotation. Find the resulting equations in terms of the field vectors $\mathbf{E}'$ as defined in (7-2), and $\mathbf{B}' = (B'_{23}, B'_{31}, B'_{12})$. Compare your result with what one would obtain if S' were also an inertial frame. Do you see any resemblance with the discussion in Sec. 3-5 relating to the clock paradox? [See L. I. Schiff, *Proc. Nat. Acad. Sci., U.S.A.*, **25**: 391 (1939); D. L. Webster, *Am. J. Phys.*, **31**: 590 (1963), eqs. (21) and (22). In comparing your result with those given in these references note the difference in the units employed.]

7-12 In arriving at the result (7-42) by the variation of the action (7-39), we have varied the covariant components A_α of the potential vector A. What would be the result if we vary instead the contravariant components A^α?

7-13 Verify that Eqs. (7-50) can be combined into the single covariant equation

$$\mu H_{\alpha\beta} = B_{\alpha\beta} + 2(1 - \epsilon\mu) W_{[\alpha} B_{\beta]\gamma} W^\gamma$$

7-14 Consider a wire carrying a steady current, so that in the rest system of the wire the charge density is everywhere zero. (*a*) Show that if the wire moves relative to an inertial frame S, then, as measured in S, the charge density is generally $\neq 0$. By examining what is meant by the measurement of charge density in a given reference system, show that the relevant part of (7-55) can be explained as arising from the relativity of simultaneity. (*b*) Show that even in the rest system of the wire the electric field outside the wire can be different from zero. In particular find the electric field at the point P when the wire has the shape of a circular loop of radius R, P being equidistant from the points of the loop (neglecting the thickness of the wire) and having the distance D from the center of the loop. Give the result to second order in terms of the average conduction electron speed w. [Take the positive charges as stationary in the wire. Apply the relativistic transformation to the Coulomb force to deduce the force on a test charge arising from the moving charges. The result to second order is $|\mathbf{E}| = \pi IwRD/c^2(R^2 + D^2)^{3/2}$, where I is the current. See W. G. V. Rosser, *Am. J. Phys.*, **30**: 509 (1962) for details on this problem.]

7-15 Justify the statement made in the text in connection with Eqs. (7-69) by a consideration of the forces acting inside suitable cavities in the medium on appropriate electric and magnetic probes as determined in the inertial frame under consideration.

7-16 Show that the boundary conditions, under normal conditions, on the interface between two media that are consistent with the Maxwell-Minkowski theory, are given by the continuity of the tangential components of $\mathbf{E}^*$, $\mathbf{H}^*$ and of the normal component of $\mathbf{B}$, it being assumed that the bulk local medium velocity $\mathbf{u}$ is continuous across the interface. [Use (7-73). Note: For the analysis in the case that $\mathbf{u}$ is not continuous across the interface and a connection of this analysis with unipolar induction see Sommerfeld, *op. cit.* (Optics), p. 287 ff.]

7-17 (*a*) Prove (7-81). (*b*) Prove Eq. (7-83) under the conditions given in the text.

7-18 (*a*) Find a covariant integral formulation of the Maxwell-Lorentz theory. What theoretical advantages, if any, does such a formulation have? Are we restricted to lorentzian coordinates? (See in this connection Prob. 5-17.)

7-19 (*a*) Show that the δ symbol given in (7-99) can be treated as a relativistically covariant quantity. (*b*) Prove that the retarded potential 4-vector (7-119) can be written (Dirac):

$$\mathsf{A}(\mathsf{x}) = 2e \int_{-\infty}^{\tau_0} \mathsf{U}(\tau)\, \delta[\mathsf{R}(\tau) \cdot \mathsf{R}(\tau)]\, d\tau \tag{i}$$

where $\mathsf{R}(\tau) \equiv \mathsf{x} - \mathsf{z}(\tau)$, (7-111) representing the world line of the charged particle, and $\tau_- < \tau_0 < \tau_+$ (see Fig. 7-3). Check that the physical dimensions of both sides of (i) agree.

7-20 The relativistic generalization of Poisson's equation is represented of course by the inhomogeneous wave equation

$$\Box \psi = 4\pi s \tag{i}$$

Sommerfeld's covariant method of solving Eq. (7-91) (see, e.g., A. Sommerfeld, "Electrodynamics," sec. 29, Academic Press, Inc., New York, 1952) consists in working out a complete analogy to the classical method of solving Poisson's equation with the aid of Green's lemma, by an ingenious application of the method of analytic continuation. One starts with Eq. (i) written in the coordinates $(\mathbf{x}, x_4 = ix_0) \equiv x_\alpha$ $(\alpha = 1, 2, 3, 4)$ (reverting here to the convention regarding Greek indices used in Chap. 3—see footnote on page 223),

$$\psi_{,\alpha\alpha}(x) = -4\pi s(x), \qquad x \equiv (x_1, x_2, x_3, x_4) \tag{ii}$$

assuming that all x_α are *real*. A solution of (ii) is obtained, as stated, by a direct generalization of familiar results. One considers the extension of Green's lemma,

$$\int_V (\psi\phi_{,\alpha\alpha} - \phi\psi_{,\alpha\alpha})\, dV = \oint_S (\psi\phi_{,\alpha} - \phi\psi_{,\alpha})\, dS_\alpha \tag{iii}$$

where V is a region in four-dimensional euclidean space and S is its three-dimensional boundary, with ψ a solution of (ii), and

$$\phi = R^{-2}, \qquad R^2 = (y_\alpha - x_\alpha)(y_\alpha - x_\alpha) \tag{iv}$$

y_α, x_α denoting the integration and field-point coordinates, respectively. Since

$$\phi_{,\alpha\alpha} = 0, \qquad R \neq 0 \tag{v}$$

taking S to consist of two 3-spheres about x whose radii are allowed to tend to 0 and ∞ leads as in the corresponding three-dimensional case to the result

$$\psi(x) = \frac{1}{\pi}\int \frac{s(y)}{R^2}\, d^4y \tag{vi}$$

This expression remains a solution of Eq. (ii) when x_4 is now allowed to range over the complex plane, under proper analytic behavior of the source function s; moreover, for $x_4 = ix_0$, x_0 real (while the x_k and y_k are kept real), the only poles of the integrand in (vi) (assuming s itself regular) lie on the imaginary y_4 axis:

$$y_0^{(\mp)} = x_0 \mp r \qquad \begin{aligned} y_0 &= -iy_4 \\ r &= |\mathbf{y} - \mathbf{x}| \end{aligned} \tag{vii}$$

Thus the path of integration with respect to y_4 can be deformed from the real axis as it is in (vi) to a contour surrounding one or the other of the poles (vii), obtaining respectively, by a simple evaluation of the corresponding residue, the "retarded" and "advanced" solutions of (i):

$$\psi_{\binom{\text{ret}}{\text{adv}}}(\mathbf{x}) = \int \frac{s(y_0^{(\mp)},\mathbf{y})}{r}\, d^3y \tag{viii}$$

(*a*) Verify the outlined steps leading to (viii). (*b*) By using formula (vi) as applied to (7-91) check that (7-92) is satisfied and deduce the associated electromagnetic field. Compare your results with those found in Sec. 7-4.

7-21 It is possible for the radiation emitted by a charged particle to propagate with a velocity less than the velocity of the particle when the latter moves in a continuous medium. Moreover, the radiation is then limited to a conical wake. {This constitutes an optical analog of the acoustic shock wave, or Mach wave, created by a body moving through an elastic medium with supersonic velocity. The electromagnetic radiation thus produced is known as *Cerenkov radiation* (after the physicist who first observed it in 1934); it has found important application in the design of spectrometers for fast charged particles (Cerenkov counters). For the theory of Cerenkov radiation see, e.g., Schiff, *op. cit.*, p. 267 ff.; Jackson, *op. cit.*, sec. 14.9; Sommerfeld, *op. cit.* (Optics), sec. 47 [for a correction see

H. Motz and L. I. Schiff, *Am. J. Phys.*, **21**: 258 (1953)].} As one possible starting point for the study of this radiation, consider the 4-potential $\mathsf{A}(x)$ that can be obtained by a suitable modification of Dirac's formula (i) given in Prob. 7-19 [Cf. N. L. Balazs, *Am. J. Phys.*, **24**: 185 (1956).]

7-22 (*a*) Find the field of a uniformly moving charged particle (in empty space) by conventional vector methods, and then compare your results with those obtained in the text using 4-tensor methods. (*b*) Consider the field of a uniformly accelerated charge (see Probs. 3-17 and 4-2). In what sense is this an idealized problem? Does this electron emit radiation according to the general result found in Sec. 7-4? Does your conclusion conflict with that arrived at by Pauli, namely, that there is no radiation in this case? Explain. (Cf. Rohrlich, *op. cit.*, sec. 5-3.)

7-23 Suppose that we have an electromagnetic field in a 4-region free of charges and that the conditions given in Sec. 6-3 for a 'bounded' system are satisfied. What conclusions can you draw concerning the character of the 4-momentum given by Eq. (6-52)? Illustrate your answer with familiar examples.

7-24 Consider the "advanced" potentials of a point charge [corresponding to the change of the boundary condition D on page 254 by the time inversion transformation (3-49), i.e., by the replacement of the diverging field wave by one converging upon the charge]. Show that they can be obtained by the appropriate changes in the contours in Fig. 7-1, leading to corresponding changes, such as the replacement of $r - ct$ by $r + ct$ in (7-104), and the replacement of R_-^2 by R_+^2 in (7-120), where $\mathsf{R}_+^2 = 0$, $R_+^0 < 0$

$$\mathsf{R}_+ \equiv \mathsf{R}_+(\mathsf{x}) = \mathsf{x} - \mathsf{z}(\tau_+)$$

(see Fig. 7-3). Find also the corresponding change in (i) of Prob. 7-19.

7-25 Using the Fourier integral representation

$$A^\nu(\mathsf{x}) = \frac{1}{(2\pi)^2} \int e^{-i\mathsf{k}\cdot\mathsf{x}} \tilde{A}^\nu(\mathsf{k})\, d^4k \tag{i}$$

for the 4-potentials of a free electromagnetic field that is 'bounded' in the sense defined in Sec. 6-3 (and thus represents what is usually termed an electromagnetic wave packet), verify for this medium directly the general theorem proved in Sec. 6-3 concerning the 4-vector character and constancy in time of the integrals such as (6-52) representing the total energy and momentum of the field. [Note that by the equations satisfied by $A^\nu(\mathsf{x})$ we have the symbolic equation $\tilde{A}^\nu(\mathsf{k}) = A^\nu(\mathbf{k})\, \delta(\mathsf{k} \cdot \mathsf{k})$, and that $\tilde{A}^\nu(-\mathsf{k}) =$ complex conjugate of $\tilde{A}^\nu(\mathsf{k})$, and $\mathsf{k} \cdot \tilde{\mathsf{A}}(\mathsf{k}) = 0$. Recall the symbolic identity (7-106).]

7-26 (*a*) A derivation of the relativistic generalization (7-142) of Larmor's classical formula for the time rate of radiation of an accelerated charged particle, was obtained by Laue [*Ann. Physik*, **28**: 436 (1909)] on the assumption that the latter formula—that is, $dE/dt = -2e^2(d\mathbf{u}/dt)^2/3c^3$—holds in the particle's rest frame, and then applying the appropriate transformations from the rest frame to the inertial frame under consideration. Verify this derivation. (*b*) In the same paper Laue also deduced by the same method the following expression for the force of radiation reaction,

$$\mathbf{F} = \frac{2}{3}\frac{e^2}{c^3}\gamma^2\left\{\ddot{\mathbf{u}} + \left(\frac{\gamma}{c}\right)^2\left[3(\mathbf{u}\cdot\dot{\mathbf{u}})\dot{\mathbf{u}} + \left((\mathbf{u}\cdot\ddot{\mathbf{u}}) + 3\left(\frac{\gamma}{c}\right)^2(\mathbf{u}\cdot\dot{\mathbf{u}})^2\right)\mathbf{u}\right]\right\} \tag{i}$$

$$\gamma \equiv \gamma_u$$

taking for this force in the rest frame the expression $2e^2(d^2\mathbf{u}/dt^2)/3c^3$, a result that has been obtained by Lorentz and others by a number of approximate methods (see, e.g., T. Erber, *op. cit.*, and the references given there). Check this deduction and compare the result with the 4-force (7-161). (Note that $\mathsf{F}\cdot\mathsf{U} = 0$.)

7-27 Consider a particle moving with uniform velocity in the inertial frame S, and suppose that it carries a charge that is spherically distributed in its rest frame. Compute the total energy E and the total momentum $\mathbf{G}$ of its electromagnetic field in S, using the proper kinematic and charge-density transformations (checking that the total charge in S is the same as in the rest frame), but using the standard integral expressions for E and $\mathbf{G}$ involving integration of the energy density of the field and of the Poynting vector over all of ordinary space in S. Show that the result is

$$\mathbf{G} = \frac{4}{3}\frac{E}{c^2}\mathbf{U} \tag{i}$$

Explain the difference between this curious relation and the corresponding well-defined result found in Sec. 7.5. [The attempts at an explanation of the factor $\frac{4}{3}$ in (i) has had an interesting history. See, e.g., F. Rohrlich, *Am. J. Phys.*, **28**: 639 (1960). See also in this connection [5], Secs. 20g, 20h, and Prob. 6-13.]

7-28 Prove the results of Dirac's theory, such as Eqs. (7-153) and (7-155), which were used in Sec. 7.5 without derivation. (See Barut, *op. cit.*, pp. 188, 189.)

7-29 The relativistic theory of gravitation which Poincaré develops in the concluding part of his Rendiconti article, though in certain respects incomplete, is interesting not only because it is the first important attempt to frame a relativistic theory of gravitation, but also because it involves two anticipations: Minkowski's 4-tensor analysis, and the action-at-a-distance approach in electrodynamics (see Appendix 7A). Poincaré starts essentially with some such postulates as the following. (1) All forces transform alike under the Lorentz group. (2) Propagation of gravitational action proceeds with speed c, with the law of causality holding in the sense of D (page 254). (3) The law of force does not involve any time derivatives of the velocities. (4) The gravitational 4-force on a particle is orthogonal to its 4-velocity. (5) For sufficiently small velocities of two interacting mass particles we obtain the newtonian theory as an approximation. Poincaré arrives at a result that can be put in the following form:

$$\frac{d\mathsf{U}_2}{d\tau_2} = Gm_1c^3 \frac{1}{(\mathsf{R} \cdot \mathsf{U}_1)^3} \left[\mathsf{R} - \frac{(\mathsf{R} \cdot \mathsf{U}_2)\mathsf{U}_1}{\mathsf{U}_1 \cdot \mathsf{U}_2} \right] \tag{i}$$

Here the subscripts 1, 2 refer respectively to the 'source' particle and to the particle being acted on. The notation is otherwise similar to that employed in Sec. 7-4 with the omission of the minus subscripts. Check if (i) does indeed follow from the above postulates. Do we also require the postulate of the proportionality of inertial and gravitational masses? Supposing that we employed the field concept and proceeded by complete analogy with the electromagnetic case, would we arrive at the result (i) under suitable restrictions? In what respects does the law (i) appear not to be fully satisfactory, quite apart from any empirical test?

7-30 Prove (7B-17). Compare with pertinent results in Prob. 6-22.

8

Relativity and Quantum Mechanics

In most cases where STR must be applied because we are dealing with small masses and large velocities, quantum effects are also important. Thus it happens that the most significant and the most interesting recent applications of STR lie in the field of quantum mechanics. The present theories of quantized fields and of 'elementary particles' rest on relativistic as well as quantum-mechanical principles. The development of these theories is, however, still very far from being completed. They are moreover both conceptually and mathematically quite intricate and involve topics in advanced quantum mechanics that lie outside the prerequisites assumed in this text. In considering in this concluding chapter the interaction between relativistic and quantum-mechanical ideas, the present and, in some respects, perhaps the most exciting stage in this interaction must therefore unfortunately be left out of our general discussion. Only a brief note pointing out a few central questions together with pertinent references is included (Sec. 8-4) that may be helpful to the reader who is interested in embarking on a study of this broad area of current fundamental research in which both STR and quantum mechanics are indispensable.

Relativity and quantum physics have had many points of contact at various stages in the latter's history. The full story would form a fascinating chapter in the history of theoretical physics, and is yet to be told. A sketch of a few of the highlights is presented in Sec. 8-1.

Of these highlights, the deduction of the relativistic wave equation by Dirac is possibly the most remarkable. An outline of Dirac's original derivation is included in Sec. 8-1, and this equation is again considered as a special case of the general theory of relativistic wave equations. In addition to historical there is at present also some practical theoretical interest in relativistic wave equations for particles of arbitrary spin. An introduction to this topic, without considering the quantization of the associated fields, is presented in Sec. 8-3, following a brief discussion of the theory of spinors in Sec. 8-2.

The theory of spinors is considered in connection with the problem of representations of the Lorentz group, a topic that has independent interest and to which reference was made in Sec. 5-1. A limited introduction to the relevant algebraic theory of group representations is given in Appendix 8A. It includes a brief indication of the Cartan-Weyl theory of the representations of Lie groups, which is presently finding interesting application in the exploratory investigations of dynamical symmetries that govern elementary particle interactions. A successful fusion of these symmetries with the kinematic symmetries engendered by the inhomogeneous Lorentz group has recently been one of the intriguing questions in elementary particle physics, whose current uncertain status is referred to in Sec. 8-4. There is little uncertainty about the fundamental significance in relativistic quantum mechanics of representations of the homogeneous and inhomogeneous Lorentz groups. These are discussed in Appendices 8B and 8C, and applications are indicated in Secs. 8-2, 8-3, and 8-4. These appendices therefore need to be read before the latter sections, which contain many references to the appendices.

Because of the nature of the subject matter presented in this chapter and the very modest scope of the presentation, it was necessary to include here an appreciable number of references to the literature, where topics that are here only mentioned or very lightly touched upon are fully treated. These references were not intended to be in any sense exhaustive, and important omissions may well be present.

8-1 HISTORICAL NOTE

The development of relativistic QM (quantum mechanics) forms one of the most fascinating stories in the history of theoretical physics, a story that is still unfolding. Within the limited scope of this chapter we cannot consider the more recent and in some respects the more interesting phases of this story dealing with relativistic field theory.‡ It must suffice here to point out the earlier prominent peaks in the history of the subject.

The first peak can be discerned, from our present vantage point, at the very birth of quantum physics. Max Planck's quantum hypothesis of 1900, and Einstein's subsequent explicit introduction of the light quantum conjecture, as expressed by the celebrated formula

$$E = h\nu \tag{8-1}$$

constitute, as we now know, a first step in the eventual development of quantum electrodynamics. [For the story of how the search for a workable black-body radiation formula led Planck to the introduction of his momentous hypothesis of the quantum of action, a convenient source is Planck's monograph "The Theory of Heat Radiation" (translated by M. Masius), P. Blakiston's Son and Company, Philadelphia, 1914. Einstein's work on the photoelectric effect (first experimentally discovered by Hertz in 1887) in which the photon hypothesis is introduced (and for which he was later awarded the Nobel Prize) appeared in the same volume of *Ann. Phys.* in which his relativity paper was published.]

The next crucial contribution to this phase of the subject came with Arthur Compton's explanation of his famous x-ray scattering experiments, on the basis of energy and momentum conservation in the collision of a high-frequency photon and a weakly bound atomic electron.§ The classical electrodynamic relation $p = E/c$ between the energy and momentum carried by a plane electromagnetic wave, when combined with (8-1), point to the corresponding quantum relation for the momentum of a photon

$$\mathbf{p} = \frac{h\nu}{c}\mathbf{n} = \frac{h}{\lambda}\mathbf{n} \equiv h\mathbf{q} \tag{8-2}$$

where $\mathbf{n}$ is the unit vector in the direction of propagation of the photon, and the other quantities have their usual meaning. The two formulas (8-1) and (8-2) combine into the single relativistically covariant relation (see Prob. 3-8)

$$\mathsf{p} = h\mathsf{q}, \qquad \mathsf{q} = \frac{\nu}{c}(1, \mathbf{n}) \tag{8-3}$$

‡ The development of quantum field theory is outlined in the respective articles by G. Wentzel, F. Villars, and R. Jost in the Pauli memorial volume, M. Fierz and V. F. Weisskopf (eds.) "Theoretical Physics in the Twentieth Century," Interscience Publishers, New York, 1960; and in Schwinger's preface to J. Schwinger (ed.), "Selected Papers on Quantum Electrodynamics," Dover Publications, Inc., New York, 1958.

§ A. Compton, *Phys. Rev.*, **21:** 207 and 483 (1923); *Phil. Mag.*, **46:** 897 (1923). Also, P. Debye, *Physik. Z.*, **46:** 161 (1923).

and Compton's experiment, in addition to verifying the photon hypothesis, put in striking evidence for the first time the conservation of 4-momentum in a strictly elementary particle interaction.

The first important step in the development of quantum mechanics proper that was to replace the ingenious but makeshift quantum theory of Bohr and of Sommerfeld came about through a conscious application of relativistic ideas. When, in his 1924 doctoral thesis, Louis de Broglie introduced the then daring hypothesis that the relations (8-3) that connect particle and wave properties of electromagnetic radiation apply also to particles of nonvanishing rest mass,‡ he was guided by relativistic kinematic considerations. His starting point was the assumption that the Planck-Einstein formula (8-1) has universal validity, so that for a free particle of rest mass m there is associated a periodicity of frequency ν^* in the particle's rest frame, given by

$$\nu^* = \frac{mc^2}{h} \tag{8-4}$$

The phase function $\nu^* \, \Delta t^*$ of our stationary wave, when evaluated in an arbitrary inertial frame S in which the particle has the velocity v in the x direction, say, reduces by (2-6) to the standard form for the corresponding progressive wave phase function $\nu[\Delta t - (\Delta x/w)]$, with

$$\nu = \gamma_v \nu^*, \qquad w = \frac{c^2}{v} \tag{8-5}$$

Hence, by (8-4), and since $w = \lambda\nu$,

$$\nu = \frac{m(v)c^2}{h}, \qquad q \equiv \frac{1}{\lambda} = \frac{m(v)v}{h} \tag{8-6}$$

The last equation in (8-6), thus obtained, is now seen to agree with the relation (8-2) derived for photons; and in fact, it is readily verified that the two relations in (8-6), when applied to an arbitrary direction of propagation $\mathbf{n}$, can be combined into an equation of the form (8-3) with

$$\mathsf{q} = \frac{\nu}{c}\left(1, \frac{c}{w}\,\mathbf{n}\right) \tag{8-7}$$

that reduces to the corresponding expression in (8-3) as $v \to c$, the general proof of the 4-vector property of q, that is, of the relativistic invariance of $\mathsf{q} \cdot \mathsf{x}$, being implicit in the above argument. {The fact that the phase velocity w in S associated with the moving particle has the value (8-5), which is always $>c$, is of course of no consequence, since no energy propagation is to be associated with it; while, on the other hand, the magnitude of the

‡ De Broglie's thesis has been republished as "Recherches sur la Théorie des Quanta," Masson et Cie, Paris, 1963. His first publications on the subject are in *Nature*, **112:** 540 (1923); *Compt. Rend.*, **177:** 507, 548, 630 (1923).

group velocity, which generally gives the energy-propagation velocity in a wave train, is here given by $d\nu/d(1/\lambda) = dE/dp = [d(E^2 - m^2c^4)^{1/2}/c\,dE]^{-1} = c^2p/E = v$.}

The role of the principles of STR in de Broglie's approach, as far as his main contribution is concerned—the idea of matter waves—was at the time little more than a mental catalyst. These principles, on the other hand, enter significantly into the theoretical investigations of spectroscopic fine structure such as is encountered in particular in atomic hydrogen or ionized helium—a challenging and rewarding problem for much of the first half of this century. An apparent initial success in combining the relativistic and quantum ideas in the treatment of this problem, came when Arnold Sommerfeld applied relativistic mechanics within the older Bohr-Sommerfeld atomic theory to compute the fine structure shifts in hydrogenlike atoms.‡

The Bohr-Sommerfeld integral quantization rules for an electron moving in the centrally symmetric Coulomb field of a stationary point charge Ze,

$$\begin{aligned} \oint p_\phi\,d\phi &\equiv \int_0^{2\pi} m(u)r^2\dot{\phi}\,d\phi = n_\phi h \\ \oint p_r\,dr &\equiv \oint m(u)\dot{r}\,dr = n_r h \end{aligned} \tag{8-8}$$

when combined with the appropriate results of the relativistic Kepler problem (see Sommerfeld, *op. cit.;* also Prob. 4-10), lead to the quantized relativistic energies

$$E_{n_r n_\phi} = mc^2\left\{1 + \left[\frac{\alpha Z}{n_r + (n_\phi{}^2 - \alpha^2 Z^2)^{1/2}}\right]^2\right\}^{-1/2}, \qquad \alpha = \frac{2\pi e^2}{hc} \tag{8-9}$$

where the radial and azimuthal quantum numbers n_r, n_ϕ are defined in (8-8). An expansion in powers of the small dimensionless quantity αZ (for $1/Z$ large compared to the fine structure constant $\alpha \approx \frac{1}{137}$), through terms of the second order, then yields the more serviceable formula

$$\begin{aligned} E_{nn_\phi} &= mc^2 + W_n\left[1 + \frac{\alpha^2 Z^2}{n^2}\left(\frac{n}{n_\phi} - \frac{3}{4}\right)\right] \\ W_n &= -\frac{RhZ^2}{n^2}, \qquad n = n_r + n_\phi \end{aligned} \tag{8-10}$$

where W_n stands for the corresponding nonrelativistic Bohr energy.§

‡ A. Sommerfeld, *Ann. Physik*, **51**: 1 (1916); "Atomic Structure and Spectral Lines," vol. 1, chap. 5, E. P. Dutton and Company, Inc., New York (translated from the fifth German edition by H. L. Brose).

§ The nonrelativistic correction for the motion of the nucleus is allowed for by the familiar procedure of using the appropriated reduced mass of the electron in the Rydberg frequency R. A relativistic correction for the effect of this motion was deduced by C. G. Darwin in his approximate relativistic treatment of the many-body electromagnetic-interaction problem (see the reference to Darwin on page 108).

The relativistic shift given by this formula was checked by F. Paschen for the 4686 Å line of He^+, and the close agreement between calculation and measurement in this case, as well as the agreement obtained for the result (8-9) with x-ray doublet measurements (upon introduction of proper screening constants), rightly appeared as an outstanding triumph of the theory. But this triumph was in part short-lived. In 1925, as a culmination of a series of spectroscopic investigations directed in particular towards the explanation of the alkali and x-ray doublets and the anomalous Zeeman effect, the electron-spin hypothesis of S. Goudsmit and G. E. Uhlenbeck entered the theoretical arena, and the significance of spin-orbit coupling in perturbing the atomic energy levels became apparent; while in the same year and in the following year the new quantum mechanics of Werner Heisenberg and Erwin Schrödinger made its auspicious appearance and indisputably displaced the older theory of Bohr and Sommerfeld. The result (8-9) could no longer be accepted as well-founded,‡ and finding the correct theory of atomic spectroscopic fine structure became an immediate challenge. This challenge was not fully met ("fully"—to the best of our present ability to tell) until about the middle of our century. We shall not undertake here to survey the history of this very exciting and comparatively very recent stage in the development of this subject, nor of the extensive investigations in quantum field theory it has in part stimulated. Instead, we conclude our brief historical note by turning to a remarkable work of P. A. M. Dirac, in which the challenge we spoke of was very largely met, and in a most—at the time—surprising manner. This work may well be considered as representing in many respects the most vivid example of the fruitful interplay of the principles of STR and of QM.

When Dirac published "The Quantum Theory of the Electron" [*Proc. Roy. Soc. London*, **A117:** 610 (1928); **A118:** 351 (1928)], Sommerfeld's approximate formula (8-10) had already been rederived on the basis of the newly gained ideas on quantum mechanics and the electron spin, with Sommerfeld's

‡ Some indication of things not being quite right was actually at hand from the beginning because selection rules given by $\Delta n_\phi = \pm 1$, as demanded by the older theory, did not fully agree with observation. On the other hand, it should be noted that Sommerfeld's theory had played a useful role in the development of theoretical spectroscopy by drawing attention to the importance of taking account of small relativistic corrections when dealing with fine structure, and by pinpointing the significance of the fine-structure constant. The result (8-9) has, moreover, independent interest as giving the correct quasi-classical limit of the strict quantum-mechanical formula for a spinless charged particle (see footnote ‡ on page 320). Let us also note that the full story of the gradual development of the correct ideas and correct methods for treating the problems presented by high-resolution spectroscopy is highly interesting and instructive and finds a certain parallel in the search for the right ideas and formalism to cope with the 'elementary particle spectroscopy' of today. Brief historical surveys of this subject can be found in Sommerfeld, *op. cit.*; Whittaker, *op. cit.*, vol. 2; H. E. White, "Introduction to Atomic Spectroscopy," McGraw-Hill Book Company, Inc., New York, 1934; and in the articles by R. Kronig and B. L. Van der Waerden in the Pauli memorial volume.

quantum number n_ϕ replaced by $j + \frac{1}{2}$ (the "inner" quantum number j, earlier introduced empirically, now recognized as associated with the total angular momentum of the electron); the classical expression of the electron's spin-orbit interaction energy in the nuclear Coulomb field,

$$H_{so} = \frac{Ze^2}{2m^2c^2}\frac{1}{r^3}\mathbf{l}\cdot\mathbf{s} \tag{8-11}$$

had been deduced with the aid of relativistic kinematics by L. H. Thomas,‡ and had in fact been applied in the aforementioned fine-structure calculations; a pure quantum-mechanical (though not relativistically covariant) treatment of the electron spin in terms of 2-component wave functions (two-dimensional spinors) had been successfully introduced by Wolfgang Pauli [Zur Quantenmechanik des magnetischen Elektrons, *Z. Physik*, **43**: 601 (1927)], with the representation

$$s_x = \frac{\hbar}{2}\begin{bmatrix} 0 & 1 \\ 1 & 0 \end{bmatrix}, \qquad s_y = \frac{\hbar}{2}\begin{bmatrix} 0 & -i \\ i & 0 \end{bmatrix}, \qquad s_z = \frac{\hbar}{2}\begin{bmatrix} 1 & 0 \\ 0 & -1 \end{bmatrix} \tag{8-12}$$

($\hbar \equiv h/2\pi$) for the components of the spin vector operator $\mathbf{s}$ that appears in (8-11) (considered as a quantum-mechanical operator equation); and the strict relativistic Schrödinger equation

$$\left[\left(\hbar i\frac{\partial}{\partial x^\mu} - \frac{e}{c}A_\mu\right)\left(\hbar i\frac{\partial}{\partial x_\mu} - \frac{e}{c}A^\mu\right) - m^2c^2\right]\psi = 0 \tag{8-13}$$

for the motion of a charged particle (of charge e and proper mass m) in an external electromagnetic field of 4-potential A—the so-called "Klein-Gordon equation"—had been suggested,§ this equation following directly from the corresponding relativistic classical equation by the substitution

$$p_\nu \rightarrow \hbar i\frac{\partial}{\partial x^\nu} \tag{8-14}$$

that represents the relativistically covariant expression for the identification of the Schrödinger operators for energy and momentum.¶

‡ See pertinent discussion and references in Sec. 3-5; also Jackson, *op. cit.*, sec. 11-5. An analysis of this problem in terms of the skew-symmetric tensor representation of the electric and magnetic dipole moments of a charged particle [see (7-76)] was given by J. Frenkel, Z. *Physik*, **37**: 243 (1926).

§ E. Schrödinger, *Ann. Physik*, **81**: 109 (1926), sec. 6; W. Gordon, *Z. Physik*, **40**: 117 (1926); O. Klein, *Z. Physik*, **41**: 407 (1927); and others. Note that in free space ($\mathsf{A} = 0$), Eq. (8-13) reduces to Eq. (v) of Prob. (6-22) with $\mu = mc/\hbar$.

¶ Equation (8-13) also follows from the Hamilton-Jacobi equation (4-82) (with A standing for $e\mathsf{A}/c$ in the present case—as is readily verified) by the known correspondence between the Hamilton-Jacobi equation in classical mechanics and the Schrödinger equation in QM. Note that we have used the symbol p in (8-14) for the conjugate 4-momentum π of (4-79).

Dirac's immediate objection to the K. G. equation (8-13) was actually not so much because it could not reproduce the fine-structure splitting‡ as because of its being of second order in t, hence entailing as initial conditions the assignment of both ψ and $\partial\psi/\partial t$, which precludes a consistent definition of a conserved positive definite probability density for position. The components of the conserved probability 4-current density j that follow in the usual way from Eq. (8-13), have in fact the form

$$j^{\nu} = \frac{\hbar i}{2m}\left(\psi^* \frac{\partial\psi}{\partial x_{\nu}} - \psi \frac{\partial\psi^*}{\partial x_{\nu}}\right) - \frac{e}{mc}\psi^*\psi A^{\nu} \tag{8-15}$$

so that j^0 can obviously, in general, assume negative as well as positive values. The fact that this 4-current can be properly reinterpreted together with a suitable reinterpretation of the entire formalism, so that the negative probability difficulty disappears, was realized only a few years later.§ But it seems to have been fortunate that Dirac was at the time apparently unaware of this possibility. Thus he started with what he considered to be a necessary demand that his wave equation have the standard form of a Schrödinger time-dependent equation

$$\hbar i \frac{\partial\psi}{\partial t} = H\psi \tag{8-16}$$

where H is the hamiltonian (energy) operator of the system.

Dirac's second objection to the K. G. equation on the ground that it permits negative energy solutions (as one readily verifies) that cannot be simply thrown away as unphysical, as one can do in nonquantum relativistic mechanics, he knew applied as well to his own theory. Again, it was probably fortunate that Dirac had presumably little inkling at the time of the fact that became evident some years later, that if his theory is pushed to its most general logical conclusions, then his underlying interpretation of Eq. (8-16) as a *one-particle* Schrödinger equation becomes in general untenable. He could thus proceed unimpeded by second thoughts with the derivation of his exceptionally far-reaching equation.

We shall discuss this equation in Sec. 8-3 in a more general context. At present we shall summarize Dirac's original reasoning.

The requirement of relativistic invariance led him, in the first place, to the conclusion that Eq. (8-16), being of first order in t, must also be of first order in the x_i, so that in free space the wave equation for the electron must have the form (changing Dirac's original notation slightly)

$$(p_0 + \alpha_k p_k + mc\beta)\psi = 0 \tag{8-17}$$

‡ See, e.g., Schiff, *op. cit.*, sec. 42; H. A. Bethe, "Intermediate Quantum Mechanics," chap. 16, W. A. Benjamin, Inc., New York, 1964. Note, incidentally, that formula (16-22) in the latter book coincides with Sommerfeld's result (8-9) if we identify n_{ϕ} with $l + \frac{1}{2}$.

§ W. Pauli and V. Weisskopf, *Helv. Phys. Acta*, **7:** 709 (1934).

with the identification (8-14), where the operators α_k, β are independent of the p and cannot depend on the x either—in view of the homogeneity of free space—and must therefore commute with both the x and the p as well as operate on a new set of variables ξ in ψ. The further requirement that, in agreement with the correspondence principle (with the corresponding classical result following in the limit of large quantum numbers), the K. G. equation (which is constructed, it will be recalled, upon the classical relation $\mathsf{p}^2 = m^2c^2$) should be deducible from (8-17) upon multiplication by $-p_0 + \alpha_k p_k + mc\beta$, leads straightway to the characteristic relations

$$\begin{aligned} \tfrac{1}{2}(\alpha_i\alpha_j + \alpha_j\alpha_i) &= \delta_{ij} \\ \beta\alpha_i + \alpha_i\beta &= 0 \\ \beta^2 &= 1 \end{aligned} \tag{8-18}$$

To find matrices satisfying these relations,‡ Dirac observed that in addition to the matrices§

$$\begin{bmatrix} \sigma_k & 0 \\ 0 & \sigma_k \end{bmatrix}, \qquad \sigma_1 = \sigma_x, \ . \ . \ . \tag{8-19}$$

they are also satisfied by the 4-rowed matrices

$$\rho_1 = \begin{bmatrix} 0 & \iota \\ \iota & 0 \end{bmatrix}, \rho_3 = \begin{bmatrix} \iota & 0 \\ 0 & -\iota \end{bmatrix} \qquad \iota = \begin{bmatrix} 1 & 0 \\ 0 & 1 \end{bmatrix} \tag{8-20}$$

(omitting Dirac's matrix ρ_2 that will not be used here—see Prob. 8-23*c*), which commute with the σ_k, so that a set of matrices of the desired kind is given by

$$\alpha_k = \rho\sigma_k, \qquad \beta = \rho_3 \qquad \rho \equiv \rho_1 \tag{8-21}$$

He thus obtained for his equation (8-17) the explicit representation

$$(p_0 + \rho\sigma_k p_k + \beta mc)\psi = 0, \qquad \beta \equiv \rho_3 \tag{8-22}$$

where $\psi \equiv \psi(\mathsf{x};\ \xi) \equiv \psi_\xi$ $(\xi = 1, 2, 3, 4)$, and the equation has thus to be considered as a 4-dimensional matrix equation, i.e., as a set of four coupled linear equations:

$$\sum_{\xi'=1}^{4} [p_0\, \delta_{\xi\xi'} + p_k(\rho\sigma_k)_{\xi\xi'} + mc\beta_{\xi\xi'}]\psi_{\xi'} = 0, \qquad \xi = 1, 2, 3, 4 \tag{8-22a}$$

The next crucial step was the proof that these equations are in fact covariant under all Lorentz transformations. Since this covariance is a central theme in Sec. 8-3, we omit here a presentation of Dirac's original proof.

‡ The Pauli matrices given in (8-12), that is, $\sigma_x = 2s_x/\hbar$, etc., satisfy such relations, but it is easily proved that *four* such 2-rowed matrices do not exist.

§ These will also be denoted by σ_k, the dimensionality being understood from the context.

The striking conclusions of the theory came when Eq. (8-22) was converted to the corresponding equation for the electron in a given external field A, by the familiar substitution [in an understandable sense—cf. (4-79)]

$$\mathsf{p} \to \mathsf{p} - \frac{e}{c}\mathsf{A} \tag{8-23}$$

Both the values of the electron's spin and of its magnetic moment, which have had to be fed into the earlier theory, now fell out from the formalism naturally and simply.

For a convenient deduction of the magnetic moment result, it is helpful to introduce Dirac's γ matrices employed by him in the proof of the covariance of his equation (with the only difference that we are here employing a *real* Minkowski metric $g_{0\mu} = \delta_{0\mu}$, $g_{ij} = -\delta_{ij}$)

$$\gamma^\nu = \beta\alpha_\nu \qquad \begin{matrix} \nu = 0, 1, 2, 3 \\ \alpha_0 \equiv I \end{matrix} \tag{8-24}$$

By (8-18) these matrices obey the anticommutation relations

$$\gamma^{(\mu}\gamma^{\nu)} \equiv \tfrac{1}{2}[\gamma^\mu,\gamma^\nu]_+ = g^{\mu\nu}I \equiv g^{\mu\nu} \tag{8-25}$$

Multiplication of Eq. (8-17) on the left by β yields the field free equation

$$(\gamma^\nu p_\nu + mc)\psi = 0 \tag{8-26}$$

and substitution of (8-23) gives the desired equation

$$\left[\gamma^\nu\left(p_\nu - \frac{e}{c}A_\nu\right) + mc\right]\psi = 0 \tag{8-27}$$

The associated second-order differential equation is obtained by multiplication on the left by the operator $\gamma^\mu[p_\mu - (e/c)A_\mu] - mc$. Writing temporarily P_μ for $p_\mu - (e/c)A_\mu$, and decomposing our double-index quantities as in (5-13), we have: $\gamma^\mu P_\mu \gamma^\nu P_\nu = \gamma^{(\mu}\gamma^{\nu)}P_{(\mu}P_{\nu)} + \gamma^{[\mu}\gamma^{\nu]}P_{[\mu}P_{\nu]}$. Since

$$P_{[\mu}P_{\nu]} \equiv \frac{1}{2}[P_\mu,P_\nu] = -\frac{e}{2c}([p_\mu,A_\nu] - [p_\nu,A_\mu])$$

$$= \frac{\hbar e}{2ic}\left(\frac{\partial A_\nu}{\partial x^\mu} - \frac{\partial A_\mu}{\partial x^\nu}\right) = \frac{i\hbar e}{2c}B_{\mu\nu}$$

it follows by (8-25), and putting

$$i\gamma^{[\mu}\gamma^{\nu]} \equiv \frac{i}{2}[\gamma^\mu,\gamma^\nu] = \sigma^{\mu\nu} \tag{8-28}$$

that our second-order equation is

$$\left[\left(p_\mu - \frac{e}{c}A_\mu\right)\left(p^\mu - \frac{e}{c}A^\mu\right) + \frac{\hbar e}{2c}\sigma^{\mu\nu}B_{\mu\nu} - m^2c^2\right]\psi = 0 \tag{8-29}$$

In order to recognize the physical significance of the second term in this equation,‡ let us note that by (7-2), and since $(B_{23}, B_{31}, B_{12}) = \mathbf{B}$, we have

$$\sigma^{\mu\nu}B_{\mu\nu} = 2(\boldsymbol{\pi}\cdot\mathbf{E} + \boldsymbol{\sigma}\cdot\mathbf{B}) \qquad \begin{aligned} \pi^k &= \sigma^{k0} \\ \boldsymbol{\sigma} &= (\sigma^{23}, \sigma^{31}, \sigma^{12}) \end{aligned} \tag{8-30}$$

where the notation in the last of these equations is justified by Eqs. (8-24) and (8-21) and the well-known relations [which are immediately verified for the matrices in (8-12)],§

$$\sigma_k\sigma_r = i\epsilon_{krs}\sigma_s \tag{8-31}$$

which, by (8-28), imply that $\sigma^{kr} = \epsilon_{krs}\sigma_s$. When we compare Eqs. (8-30) and (7-76) we see that the second term in the first equation in (8-30) is proportional to a quantity that has the form of the potential energy due to an elementary magnetic dipole of moment $\boldsymbol{\sigma}$ in an external magnetic field **B**.¶ This suggests considering the nonrelativistic limit of the Hamiltonian H with Dirac's equation taken in the form (8-16). The reduction is accomplished easily upon the substitution‡‡ $p^0 = E/c = (W/c) + mc$, when we find that H contains the term $-e\hbar\boldsymbol{\sigma}\cdot\mathbf{B}/2mc$. It is thus established that the electron's magnetic moment has indeed the empirically predicted magnitude,§§ $|e\hbar/2mc|$.

The spin of the electron manifests itself when we consider A such that $A^0 = A^0(|\mathbf{r}|)$, $\mathbf{A} = 0$ in a given frame S. The total angular-momentum vector operator $\mathbf{j}$ of the electron (the nucleus being considered infinitely heavy) must be a constant of motion in such a spherically symmetric field; i.e., the operators $\mathbf{j}$ and H should commute. An easy calculation shows, however, that the electron's orbital angular-momentum operator $\mathbf{l} = \mathbf{r}\times\mathbf{p}$ does not commute with H, whereas

$$[\mathbf{j},H] = 0, \qquad \mathbf{j} = \mathbf{l} + \frac{h}{2}\boldsymbol{\sigma} \tag{8-32}$$

Since the σ_k satisfy the commutation relations of the components of an angular-momentum vector operator, it can be concluded from (8-32) that

‡ Note that except for this term, Eq. (8-29) is the same as the K. G. equation (8-13). It must therefore be responsible for yielding the new results, if Dirac's equation is indeed capable of doing it.

§ The same relations obviously hold for the matrices (8-19).

¶ Note that the σ_k are hermitian, as indeed they must be, since when (8-22) is put in the form (8-16), H must of course be a hermitian operator. On the other hand, $\pi^k = i\gamma^k\gamma^0 = -i\alpha_k$, that is, they are anti-hermitian, and hence we do not have an analogous immediate interpretation of the first term in (8-30) in terms of an electric dipole moment.

‡‡ See, e.g., Schiff, *op. cit.*, pp. 329–330. An analogous classical result is considered in Prob. 4-14*b*.

§§ A small correction to this value, determined both experimentally and theoretically with great accuracy, represents one of the more recent triumphs of relativistic QM.

the electron has an intrinsic angular momentum represented by the operator $\hbar\boldsymbol{\sigma}/2$, again in full agreement with the empirically confirmed hypothesis of Uhlenbeck and Goudsmit.

Of the other results of Dirac's theory developed in his original papers, we need mention here only his treatment of the probability density of position—the nonnegativeness of this density having been, as we know, one of his primary guiding considerations.‡ Departing again only in nonessential detail from Dirac's original derivation, we premultiply Eq. (8-17) including the substitution (8-23), by $\psi^\dagger$ [the one-rowed matrix that is the hermitian adjoint of the one-columned matrix ψ—see (8-22*a*)], and subtract the hermitian adjoint of that equation postmultiplied by ψ. With the identification (8-14) and the replacement of $p_\nu - (e/c)A_\nu$ by P_ν, noting that

$$\alpha_k^\dagger = \alpha_k, \qquad \beta^\dagger = \beta \tag{8-33}$$

we have the result

$$\begin{aligned} 0 &= \psi^\dagger(\alpha_\nu P_\nu + mc\beta)\psi - [(\alpha_\nu P_\nu + mc\beta)\psi]^\dagger\psi \\ &= \psi^\dagger\alpha_\nu P_\nu\psi - (P_\nu^*\psi^\dagger)\alpha_\nu\psi = \psi^\dagger\alpha_\nu p_\nu\psi + (p_\nu\psi^\dagger)\alpha_\nu\psi \\ &= \hbar i\partial(\psi^\dagger\alpha_\nu\psi)/\partial x^\nu \end{aligned}$$

which suggests that we can take for the conserved probability 4-current, the expression

$$j^\nu = c\psi^\dagger\alpha_\nu\psi = c\psi^\dagger\beta\gamma^\nu\psi \tag{8-34}$$

Its suitability is established in the first instance by showing that it yields the correct nonrelativistic limits for the position probability density and probability-current density, and that it has the transformation properties of a 4-vector (which was proved by Dirac in the second of the quoted articles). That (8-34) gives indeed the desired positive definiteness of the position probability density follows directly, remembering that $\alpha_0 = 1$, so that $j^0/c = \psi^\dagger\psi = \sum_{\zeta=1}^{4} |\psi_\zeta|^2$. Also these results follow immediately from general theory concerning relativistic wave equations discussed in Sec. 8-3.

8-2 SPINORS

Dirac's wave equation of the electron has been the source of many fruitful developments in relativistic QM. The need to understand the transformation properties of the components of Dirac's wave function led early to

‡ For the calculation of the energy levels of hydrogenlike atoms—which leads to a formula of the identical form as Sommerfeld's Eq. (8-9) but with n_ϕ replaced by $j + \frac{1}{2}$ [first completely worked out by W. Gordon, *Z. Physik*, **48:** 11 (1928); C. G. Darwin, *Proc. Roy. Soc. London*, **A118:** 654 (1928)]—see, e.g., Schiff, *op. cit.*, sec. 44; Bethe, *op. cit.*, pp. 214–219. These references also contain a discussion of the expansion of the Dirac Hamiltonian through terms of second order, including a term that corresponds to a first correction to the relativistic mass, and a spin-orbit coupling term of the form (8-11).

the development of the theory of spinors;‡ the example provided by Dirac's equation in yielding intrinsic properties of an elementary particle inspired a long series of investigations aiming at extending this result to all elementary particles, whether known or yet to be discovered;§ and the attendant questions concerning relativistic invariance stimulated intensive investigations of Lorentz group representations, including the fundamental work of Wigner on the representations of the inhomogeneous Lorentz group.

The mathematical and physical significance of spinors requires only a few words of explanation, when we bear in mind the significance of tensors discussed in Chap. 5 and the pertinent results on group representations considered in Appendix 8B. If we consider the definition of tensors in terms of group representations as indicated in Sec. 5-1, and remove the restrictions on the *single-valuedness* of the representations and on the *reality* of the components, we arrive at a definition of spinors of various ranks.

Physical quantities of the character of spinors had already appeared before Dirac's work in Pauli's theory of the spinning electron. The two components $\psi_\alpha(\mathbf{x},t)$, $\psi_\beta(\mathbf{x},t)$ of Pauli's wave function behave, for fixed values of $\mathbf{x},t$, as a vector in the space of the representation $\mathfrak{D}_{1/2}$ of the rotation group $\mathfrak{R}$ (using the notation explained in Appendix 8A). Such a vector $u^A (A = 1, 2)$ may be called an "$\mathfrak{R}$ spinor" (or a "Pauli spinor"). An $\mathfrak{R}$ spinor w of rank r is accordingly a quantity having the components $w^{AB\cdots}$ with r indices, which transform under $\mathfrak{R}$ as the ordered products $u^A v^B \cdots$ of r ordinary spinors (i.e., spinors of rank one); in other words, w is a vector in the representation space associated with $\mathfrak{D}_{1/2}^{[r]}$ (in the notation explained in Sec. 5-1). Such spinor wave functions of rank r are associated with systems of r Pauli particles.

The extension to spinors of the idea of covariance and contravariance (associated, it will be recalled, with the algebraic idea of "contragredience," as given by the relationship between the representations $\breve{\mathfrak{G}}$ and $\mathfrak{G}$, explained in Sec. 5-1) is also immediate. In the present case the standard representation, i.e., $\mathfrak{D}_{1/2}$, is unitary, so that every matrix T of this representation satisfies the relation

$$\breve{T} \equiv \tilde{T}^{-1} = T^* \tag{8-35}$$

Thus, if we call u^A, which transform according to T, the contravariant components of the spinor u, then $(u^A)^*$ can serve as its covariant components, in agreement with the form invariance of $|u^1|^2 + |u^2|^2$.

In the case of the Lorentz group $\mathfrak{L}$, the standard representation group

‡ The formal theory of spinors was initiated by B. L. van der Waerden (see v. der Waerden's historical article in the Pauli memorial volume cited on page 315). The essential ingredients of this theory are implicitly contained in Weyl's "Theory of Groups and Quantum Mechanics," whose first edition appeared in 1928.

§ Among the earliest papers on this subject are E. Majorana, *Nuovo Cimento,* **9:** 335 (1932); P. A. M. Dirac, *Proc. Roy. Soc. London,* **A155:** 447 (1936); A. Proca, *J. Phys. Radium,* **7:** 347 (1936).

is, as we know (Appendix 8B), the complex unimodular group C_2, and our spinors of the first rank are again two-dimensional. The results stated for $\mathfrak{R}$ spinors hold also now, save for the last one, since (8-35) is no longer generally valid. We invoke instead another contragredience relationship that is applicable since it depends only on the unimodularity of the standard representation.

As a result of the unimodularity of the spinor transformation matrices, the expression

$$u^1v^2 - u^2v^1 = C_{AB}u^Av^B, \qquad C = \begin{bmatrix} 0 & 1 \\ -1 & 0 \end{bmatrix} \tag{8-36}$$

is a form invariant, when u^A, v^A are spinors. Covariant components of a spinor u can thus be defined as

$$u_A = C_{AB}u^B \tag{8-37}$$

Since

$$C^{-1} = \tilde{C} \tag{8-38}$$

the inversion of (8-37) is

$$u^A = C_{BA}u_B \tag{8-39}$$

Explicitly, if

$$u \equiv \begin{pmatrix} u^1 \\ u^2 \end{pmatrix} \to u' = Tu, \qquad u_{(c)} \equiv \begin{pmatrix} u_1 \\ u_2 \end{pmatrix} \to u'_{(c)} = T_{(c)}u_{(c)} \tag{8-40}$$

we have, by (8-37) and (8-39), that $u'_{(c)} = Cu' = CTu = CT\tilde{C}u_{(c)}$, so that

$$T_{(c)} = CT\tilde{C} \tag{8-41}$$

and, since det $T = 1$, we have indeed‡

$$CT\tilde{C} = \breve{T} \tag{8-42}$$

By Eqs. (8-41) and (8-38) the mapping $T \to \breve{T}$ of C_2 upon itself is what algebraists term an "inner automorphism"—an "automorphism," i.e., an isomorphic mapping within the group, that is represented by a similarity transformation. The mapping $T \to T^*$ is obviously also an automorphism, though within C_2 it is no longer, as in the case of SU_2, an inner automorphism.§ The significance of the latter automorphism in the analysis of the finite representations of $\mathfrak{L}$ is shown by formula (8B-6). It is thus useful to relate notationally associated spinors that transform according to

‡ We have, for any nonsingular matrix $M = \begin{bmatrix} a & b \\ c & d \end{bmatrix}$, the relation $CM\tilde{C} = \begin{bmatrix} d & -c \\ -b & a \end{bmatrix} = \breve{M}$ det M.

§ This can be seen by applying Schur's lemma to the real unimodular subgroup of C_2, or simply by finding $STS^{-1} = T^* = T$ for $T = \begin{bmatrix} a & 0 \\ 0 & 1/a \end{bmatrix}$ $(a \neq 1)$ and for $T = C$, arriving consecutively at the conclusions $S \propto \begin{bmatrix} \alpha & 0 \\ 0 & 1/\alpha \end{bmatrix}$ and $\alpha = \pm 1$.

T and T^*, and whose components are therefore simply the complex conjugates of each other. It is customary to write $(u^A)^* \equiv u^{\dot{A}}$ and $(u_A)^* \equiv u_{\dot{A}}$. Thus, if $u'^A = T_{AB}u^B$, then $u'^{\dot{A}} = T^*_{\dot{A}\dot{B}}u^{\dot{B}}$. We can immediately verify that lowering and raising of dotted indices can be effected with the matrix C of (8-36) precisely as in the case of undotted indices. It is also obvious in what sense a general spinor can be taken to have indices of four types, with all the rules of tensor algebra discussed in Secs. 5-1 and 5-2 being applicable, provided contraction is allowed only between either the undotted or the dotted indices.‡ It must also be borne in mind that the relative up-down position of the partners in a contraction is generally significant; for example, the expression (8-36) is $u^A v_A = -u_A v^A$.

The close relationship existing between spinors and tensors is apparent from their definition in terms of group representations. An explicit connection between these quantities, resting partly on geometric considerations, served actually as the starting point in the original development of the theory of spinors.§ Such a connection can be deduced from Eqs. (8B-25) and (8B-26). According to these equations and the underlying relationship $q'_x = q_{x'}$, where q'_x is the image of q_x under the mapping induced by the Lorentz transformation $L: x \to x'$, we have

$$q_{W'} \equiv W'^{\nu}\sigma_\nu = (W^\nu\sigma_\nu)' \equiv q'_W = Tq_WT^\dagger \tag{8-43}$$

where we have replaced x, as we may, by an arbitrary 4-vector W. These equations show that $q_W \equiv w$ behaves as a spinor $w^{A\dot{B}}$; and that (taking $W^\nu = \delta^\nu_\mu$) $L^\nu{}_\mu\sigma_\nu = T\sigma_\mu T^\dagger$, or¶

$$\sigma_\lambda = L_\lambda{}^\mu T\sigma_\mu T^\dagger \tag{8-44}$$

‡ The formalism connected with a constant metric tensor, as considered in Sec. 5-3, is also frequently applied to spinors, with C_{AB} and $C^{AB} \equiv C_{BA}$ playing the role of what are termed *metric spinors*. Indeed, it is an immediate conclusion from (8-42) that $\tilde{C} = T\tilde{C}\tilde{T}$ and $C = \breve{T}CT^{-1}$, and these two matrix relations show, upon the introduction of indices, that C^{AB} and C_{AB} transform respectively as *unchanging* (in the terminology introduced in Sec. 5-2) contravariant and covariant spinors. The same result also follows directly by applying for $n = 2$, the general formula for $n \times n$ matrices of which (5-16) is the special case $n = 3$. However, because C is not symmetric, the analogy with the metric tensor breaks down at certain points, and caution is required to avoid errors in sign. One can also use different symbols for the index raiser and the index lowerer. Calling the former, say, D^{AB}, one finds by (8-39) and (8-38), and since $\tilde{C} = -C$, that

$$C^{AB} = D^{AE}D^{BF}C_{EF} = C_{EA}C_{FB}C_{EF} = C_{EA}(-\delta_{EB}) = -C_{BA} = -D^{AB}$$

$$D_{AB} = C_{AE}C_{BF}D^{EF} = C_{AE}C_{BF}C_{FE} = -C_{AB}$$

§ See Van der Waerden, reference on page 325; Weyl, *op. cit.* (Theory of Groups and Quantum Mechanics), pp. 146–149; E. Cartan, Leçons sur la théorie des spineurs, *Actualités Scientifiques et Industrielles*, nos. 643 and 701, Hermann, Paris, 1938; H. A. Kramers, "Quantum Mechanics" (translated by D. ter Haar), secs. 61, 63, Dover Publications, Inc., New York, 1964; [8], chap. 4, secs. 11, 12.

¶ We are using the notation for Lorentz matrices explained in footnote ‡ on page 392, but we are not extending this notation to C_2 matrices [see (8-44*a*)].

so that σ_λ behaves as a mixed *unchanging* tensor-spinor quantity of the first rank as a tensor, and of the same spinor character as w, or explicitly,

$$\sigma'_\lambda{}^{A\dot{B}} = \sigma_\lambda{}^{A\dot{B}} = L_\lambda{}^\mu T_{AE} T^*_{\dot{B}\dot{F}} \sigma_\mu{}^{E\dot{F}} \tag{8-44a}$$

Eq. (8B-25) (with x replaced by W) is thus seen to provide an association with every 4-vector W of a spinor w:

$$w^{A\dot{B}} = W^\nu \sigma_\nu{}^{A\dot{B}} \tag{8-45}$$

where

$$w^{A\dot{B}} = w^{\dot{B}A} \tag{8-46}$$

since the *matrix* w is hermitian (for, obviously, if $w = \|w^{A\dot{B}}\|$, then $\tilde{w} = \|w^{\dot{B}A}\|$ and $w^* = \|w^{A\dot{B}}\|$).

The association $w \rightarrow \mathsf{W}$ given in (8-45) is reversible. Since the Pauli matrices (8A-40) are unitary as well as hermitian and have determinants -1, $C\sigma_k\tilde{C} = -\sigma_k^* = -\tilde{\sigma}_k$ (see footnote ‡, page 326), while $C\sigma_0\tilde{C} = C\tilde{C} = I = \sigma_0$, and hence

$$C\sigma_\nu\tilde{C} = g^{\nu\mu}\tilde{\sigma}_\mu \equiv \tilde{\sigma}^\nu \tag{8-47}$$

i.e., by (8-37),

$$\sigma_{\nu A\dot{B}} = \tilde{\sigma}^{\nu A\dot{B}}, \qquad \sigma_\nu \equiv \|\sigma_\nu{}^{A\dot{B}}\| \tag{8-48}$$

It follows that‡ $\sigma_{\mu A\dot{B}}\sigma_\nu{}^{A\dot{B}} = g^{\mu\lambda}\tilde{\sigma}_\lambda{}^{A\dot{B}}\sigma_\nu{}^{A\dot{B}} = g^{\mu\lambda}$ trace $(\sigma_\lambda\sigma_\nu)$. Since, as is easily verified, trace $(\sigma_\lambda\sigma_\nu) = 2\delta_{\lambda\nu}$, this result can be written as $(g^{\mu\nu} = g_{\mu\nu})$§

$$\sigma_{\mu A\dot{B}}\sigma_\nu{}^{A\dot{B}} = 2g_{\mu\nu} \tag{8-49}$$

When (8-49) is applied to (8-45), we obtain the desired inversion

$$W_\mu = \tfrac{1}{2}\sigma_{\mu A\dot{B}} w_{A\dot{B}} \tag{8-50}$$

The extension of the above results to arbitrary tensors and to spinors satisfying relations that correspond to (8-46) follows immediately from the general definitions of tensors and spinors of arbitrary rank, and from our rules for raising and lowering tensor and spinor indices. It is also obvious how one can transcribe differential tensor operators into corresponding spinor operators so that one can write relativistically invariant wave equations in purely spinor notation.¶

‡ The summations that lead here to the last expression refer solely to matrix operations and for them the dot over the indices is of no consequence.

§ The somewhat clumsy handling of Greek indices can be avoided by writing, say, $\tilde{\sigma}_\nu$ for σ^ν. The derivation of (8-49) is then a bit neater, and this equation can be written in matrix form:

$$\text{trace } (\tilde{\sigma}_\mu\sigma_\nu) = 2g_{\mu\nu} \tag{8-49a}$$

¶ The possibilities of this general spinor formalism were first extensively studied by O. Laporte and G. Uhlenbeck, *Phys. Rev.*, **37:** 1380 (1931). A general survey of the subject is contained in E. M. Corson, "Introduction to Tensor, Spinors, and Relativistic Wave Equations," Blackie & Son, Ltd., Glasgow, 1953. This book contains a fairly comprehensive bibliography on the subject. For more recent references, see, e.g., the

An interesting example of a spinor of higher rank is provided by the spinor associated with the metric tensor $g_{\mu\nu}$. The consistency of Eqs. (8-45) and (8-50) is found to require that

$$\sigma_{\nu A\dot{B}}\sigma^{\nu C\dot{D}} = 2\delta_{AC}\,\delta_{\dot{B}\dot{D}} \tag{8-51}$$

and this is indeed easily checked by direct evaluation, remembering (8-48). If we lower, in (8-51), the indices C, $\dot{D}$, we get $\sigma_{\nu A\dot{B}}\sigma^{\nu}{}_{E\dot{F}} = 2\delta_{AC}\,\delta_{\dot{B}\dot{D}}C_{EC}C_{\dot{F}\dot{D}}$, and hence, by the general formula extending (8-45), we have

$$g_{A\dot{B}E\dot{F}} = g_{\mu\nu}\sigma^{\mu}{}_{A\dot{B}}\sigma^{\nu}{}_{E\dot{F}} = 2C_{EA}C_{\dot{F}\dot{B}} = 2C_{AE}C_{\dot{B}\dot{F}} \tag{8-52}$$

Incidentally, Eq. (8-51) is seen to provide a motivation for treating C_{AB} and $C_{\dot{A}\dot{B}}$ as spinors and for calling them *metric spinors.* Note also that $g_{A\dot{B}C\dot{D}}$ is an *unchanging* spinor just as $g_{\mu\nu}$ is an unchanging tensor under the Lorentz group.

We have based our discussion of spinors on results from the theory of finite representations of $\mathfrak{L}$. It is possible, conversely, to determine with the aid of spinors all the latter representations, and to specify completely all the irreducible ones. This is what Weyl did originally before the term "spinor" was introduced.‡

We already know, and it is an immediate result (see relevant discussion for tensors in Sec. 5-1) that the spinors $u^A v^B \cdots$ (n factors) $\equiv w^{AB\cdots}$ provide a representation of C_2 and hence of $\mathfrak{L}$. This representation of 2^n dimensions is in general reducible.§ It is a remarkable algebraic result that irreducibility is obtained simply by imposing the condition of *total symmetry* (see, e.g., Weyl, *op. cit.*). The associated representation space has then $(n + 1)$ dimensions, since the independent components of $w^{AB\cdots}$ are completely specified by the number of its indices that have the value 1. In the classical algebraic approach to our problem, this representation space is taken to consist of the binary forms (i.e., homogeneous polynomials) of degree n, with the running spinor components u^1, u^2 as the variables x,y. A natural base in this representation space is given by

$$x^m y^{n-m} \equiv e_m, \qquad m = 0, 1, \ldots, n \tag{8-53}$$

For a simple illustration of the efficacy of this method, let us consider the subgroup SU_2 of C_2. The proof that it admits *unitary* irreducible representations is accomplished at one stroke by a normalization of the base (8-53):

---

appendix, Covariant Spinor Formulation of Relativistic Wave Equations under the Homogeneous Lorentz Group, by W. C. Parke and H. Jehle, in W. E. Brittin and A. O. Barut (eds.), "Lectures in Theoretical Physics," The University of Colorado Press, Boulder, 1965.

‡ Weyl, *op. cit.*, chap. 3, secs. 5–8. Weyl uses in this connection the term "tensor" in a general sense to include both spinors and ordinary tensors.

§ Simple instances of such reduction in the case of tensors are given in Prob. 5-1.

$e_m \rightarrow e_{(m)} = e_m[m!(n-m)!]^{-1/2}$ One need only observe that

$$(x^*x + y^*y)^n = n! \sum_{m=0}^{n} e^*_{(m)}e_{(m)}$$

so that with (x,y) (that is, with the spinor u^A) also the $e_{(m)}$ transform according to a unitary transformation. The corresponding representation $\mathfrak{R}_n$ can thus be identified with $\mathfrak{D}_j$, in the notation introduced in Appendix 8A,‡ with $n = 2j$.

For C_2 one obtains in this manner, by dropping the requirement of unitarity, the irreducible representations§ $\mathfrak{D}_j^{(c)}$ and $\mathfrak{D}_j^{(c)*}$. The manifold of all finite-dimensional irreducible representations of C_2 can then be shown to be given by the Kronecker products $\mathfrak{D}_j^{(c)} \times \mathfrak{D}_{j'}^{(c)*}$ $(j,j' = 0, \frac{1}{2}, 1, \ldots)$, a result for which a proof is indicated in Appendix 8B. The general finite irreducible representations $\mathfrak{D}_{jj'}$ of $\mathfrak{L}$ are thus given by the transformations of spinors totally symmetric and of rank $2j$ in undotted, and totally symmetric and of rank $2j'$ in dotted indices, where $2j$ and $2j'$ can have any value $0, 1, 2, \ldots$, and the indices can have either all contravariant or all covariant character. The latter freedom results from the similarity relation (8-41). On the other hand, the full availability of both $\mathfrak{D}_j^{(c)}$ and $\mathfrak{D}_{j'}^{(c)*}$ is connected with the fact referred to previously that complex conjugation does not produce an inner automorphism of C_2.

From results presented in Appendices 8A and 8B we can conclude that the representation $\mathfrak{D}_{jj'}$ of $\mathfrak{L}$ is single-valued or double-valued, according as $j + j'$ is or is not an integer. This result can be seen very simply in the present approach. It suffices to observe that by using base vectors of the representation space of $\mathfrak{D}_{jj'}$ constructed in similar fashion to (8-53), we see directly that the transformation $u^A \rightarrow -u^A$ of C_2 induces the transformation $(-1)^{2j+2j'}I$ in this representation space. Thus, if $j + j'$ is (is not) an integer, the representation is single-(double-) valued because we have $L \rightarrow \pm T \rightarrow (\pm)T_{(jj')}$, in understandable schematic notation.

From our discussion in Sec. 5-1, we know that 4-tensors are associated with single-valued representations of $\mathfrak{L}$. An explicit connection between spinors and tensors has already been indicated. The direct extension of the relations (8-45) or (8-50) associates with every 4-tensor a spinor with the same number of dotted and undotted indices, this number being equal to the rank of the tensor. When this rank is 1, the association (8-45) corresponds to the irreducible four-dimensional representation $\mathfrak{D}_{1/2,1/2}$. In general, the irreducible single-valued representations of $\mathfrak{L}$ are associated with

‡ It is to be noted that we are considering the representation symbols as standing for groups of transformation operations (see pertinent discussion in Appendix 8A), and that in general the associated equivalent matrix representations are connected by arbitrary similarity transformations (8A-8), but in the case of unitary representations it is assumed that the matrix A in (8A-8) is unitary.

§ The meaning of these symbols is explained in Appendix 8B.

tensors of appropriate symmetry (see, e.g., Weyl, *op. cit.*, chap. 5). For example, using previously obtained results it can be shown that $\mathfrak{D}_{11}$ is associated with second-rank traceless symmetric tensors, and $\mathfrak{D}_{10}$, $\mathfrak{D}_{01}$ with second-rank alternating tensors (see Prob. 8-20).

8-3 RELATIVISTIC WAVE EQUATIONS

With the introduction of the elements of the theory of spinors we have an important tool in the study of relativistic wave equations. But before we turn to the analytic considerations, let us examine first very briefly the interpretational aspects of the problem.

We have here two immediate questions. What is the significance of the wave function ψ (whether this is a one-component or many-component quantity) entering the wave equation with which our theory is concerned? How is the relativistic invariance of the theory expressed in terms of measurable quantities constructed by means of the ψ?

The answer to the first question depends on whether we are applying quantum field theory or not. Inasmuch as our concern is with wave equations, we are in any case assuming that ψ represents a field in the sense that it is a function of the space-time variables x. A general quantum-mechanical treatment should, therefore, according to prevailing notions, deal with quantized fields; in other words, the ψ should represent field operators, else such an important case as the electromagnetic field would be excluded from our consideration. However, in many of the early investigations, including those of Dirac and of Wigner, the role of ψ is simply that of a Schrödinger field, i.e., of a wave function for one-particle states, as is of course the case of the original Dirac ψ for the electron. If one talks, in this approach, of wave equations for all possible fields, the interpretation of ψ cannot be uniform: in addition to the one just given it is also purely classical when referring to physical systems such as the electromagnetic field, that have macroscopic significance. It is this limited approach with which we are concerned in this section.

The answer to our second question is now quite simple. It is implicit in discussions contained in preceding chapters, as far as the purely classical fields are concerned (of which the electromagnetic field is possibly the only significant pertinent example), and need not detain us now, although certainly much remains to be said on this subject from an epistemological point of view. In the case of what we have generically called "Schrödinger fields," relativistic invariance—just as any other interpretational result in quantum theory—is formulated in terms of expectation values referring to quantities that can be measured in the laboratory, at least in principle; and the problem is thus again reduced in general to classical invariance considerations.

There is one further pertinent general question that we are simply bypassing because it can get us into deep waters. We refrain from pinpointing the type of entity—the particle—to which our relativistic wave equations apply. Not so many years ago it seemed reasonable enough to talk of "elementary particles." To a particle such as an electron it still appears reasonable to apply this term, but what should we say of the growing family of strongly interacting particles—the so-called hadrons? Yet the term "elementary particle" is convenient and it can do no harm if we leave out any preconceived ideas as to the physical attributes it must embody. Within our present context of leaving out field quantization, we may, in any case, be too drastically limiting the scope of our discussion.

We have then before us the problem of finding the general form of the relativistic wave equation of an elementary particle within the restrictions we have described. There is actually an additional restriction that we may just as well include, since otherwise matters would be even more complicated and also in part more questionable. We shall assume the particle to be 'free,' except for possible interaction with an external electromagnetic field when the particle is charged.‡ Even with these restrictions our general problem is still quite complicated, and we shall forego any attempt to present here a complete summary of known results§ and content ourselves with merely indicating in a general way the nature of these results.

Before we consider the specific analytical questions connected with our general problem, let us first examine briefly some of the consequences of merely requiring the relativistic covariance of our wave functions. This question admits of two alternative approaches. One, followed notably by Wigner, involves the unitary representations of the Poincaré group in the Hilbert space of the wave functions and is, in certain respects, the more fundamental.

The other approach, followed by Dirac, Fierz, and many other investigators, and which is the one we consider in this section, is based on an application (usually tacit) of the same ideas as employed in classical field theory; it is therefore more immediately suitable to the unified treatment of classical and Schrödinger fields with which we are presently concerned. It involves the transformation properties of the wave function (i.e., field) *components* under the homogeneous Lorentz group. Because of the homogeneity of space-time in the absence of external perturbing forces, on our strict special relativistic point of view, it suffices to consider these transformation properties at one arbitrarily chosen space-time point. Thus, as we know, the covariance properties of the electromagnetic field are completely specified by the tensor character under $\mathfrak{L}$ of its components, and the same is true of

‡ The question of interactions in this context is discussed, e.g., in P. Roman, "Theory of Elementary Particles," chap. 2, sec. 4b, North-Holland Publishing Company, Amsterdam, 1960; Rzewuski, *op. cit.* (on page 274), parts of chap. 3.

§ Such a summary is contained in Corson, *op. cit.* For later developments see, e.g., L. L. Foldy, *Phys. Rev.*, **102:** 568 (1956); D. L. Weaver, C. L. Hammer, and R. H. Good, Jr., *Phys. Rev.*, **135:** B241 (1964).

any other purely classical field (though the existence of other classical fields possessing the same type of 'elementary' significance as pertains to the electromagnetic field—the gravitational field being, of course, excluded—appears doubtful). In the case of Schrödinger fields, a further word of explanation is called for.

Our general criterion of relativistic covariance for Schrödinger fields given earlier had reference to quantum-mechanical expectation values, which are in an obvious sense of global character. However, in the present approach what is immediately relevant are obviously the invariance properties of *local* dynamical quantities, and hence, just as in the classical theory, we must deal with densities such as those of energy momentum or of particle or charge current. We can convince ourselves of the necessity of covariance of such quantities, even if their operational validation is not as immediate as that of expectation values. The most suitable analytic starting point in this connection is clearly the lagrangian density of the system under consideration, in terms of which, as we know, the basic densities can be conveniently constructed with their appropriate covariance character guaranteed, provided only the lagrangian density is a 4-scalar (or pseudoscalar).

An essential difference between the Schrödinger and the classical cases in what concerns the transformation properties of the field components is that, in the latter case, and specifically in the case of the electromagnetic field, the field components themselves are measurable, and hence their transformation under $\mathfrak{L}$ must correspond to a single-valued representation; in other words, the wave functions (i.e., the fields) must be 4-tensors. But in the case of Schrödinger fields all the measurable quantities involve the wave functions quadratically (as they are all ultimately reducible to the form of expectation values), and hence double-valued representations of the Lorentz group (which, as we know, involve only an ambiguity in sign) are allowed. Any of the representations $\mathfrak{D}_{jj'}$ can thus be associated with a given Schrödinger field singly or in certain combinations.

With these few observations in mind, let us now consider the general problem of determining the relativistically covariant wave equations, subject to the sundry restrictions we have described.

The general form of these equations can be determined in the first place by invoking the superposition principle of QM, which points to their *linearity;*‡ and by the homogeneity of space-time, which implies the *constancy* of the coefficients. Since we are not restricting the number of components that our wave functions can have, we can also suppose, without essential loss of generality, that the equations constitute a differential system of the first order. Finiteness of the number of components is not logically required—we know that the Lorentz group has infinite-dimensional irreducible representations—but from a physical point of view this restriction appears

‡ Linearity may also be shown to be required by assuming the absence of any self-interactions, and applies therefore to classical as well as Schrödinger fields.

reasonable. Therefore, we can assume also that our differential system is finite. It can thus be written in matrix form as follows:‡

$$A^\nu \frac{\partial \psi}{\partial x^\nu} + B\psi = 0 \tag{8-54}$$

(we shall not deal here with electromagnetic potentials—our new use of the symbol A^ν is thus permissible). Without discussing its implications, we introduce now the simplifying assumption that the matrix B is nonsingular.§ It can then be taken without loss of generality to be proportional to the identity matrix I, and our general equation for free particles assumes the form

$$A^\nu \frac{\partial \psi}{\partial x^\nu} + \kappa\psi = 0 \tag{8-55}$$

It represents a differential system

$$A^\nu_{uv} \frac{\partial \psi_v}{\partial x^\nu} + \kappa\psi_u = 0, \qquad u, v = 1, \ldots, N \tag{8-56}$$

forming a generalization of the Dirac system (8-22*a*) [in the form (8-26)]. This generalization extends, as we shall presently see, to the implicit inclusion of the spin of the particle.¶

The detailed study of Eq. (8-55) admits of a number of approaches. We present a very brief outline of one such approach.‡‡

To begin with, the solutions ψ_u of (8-56) must, as we already know, give rise to a representation $\mathfrak{D}$ of $\mathfrak{L}$. For every L in $\mathfrak{L}$ there must exist an N-rowed matrix $T(L)$ such that, relative to the reference frame S' obtained

‡ The homogeneity of the system is, of course, required by the fact that we are dealing with sourcefree fields: $\psi = 0$ must be a possible solution.

§ The case of unrestricted B is considered by H. J. Bhabha, *Rev. Mod. Phys.*, **21:** 451 (1949).

¶ The general matrix equation we arrive at actually encompasses, as we shall see, the possibility of a multiplicity of spins and of masses, and such theories have been studied extensively by H. J. Bhabha [*op. cit.*, and *Phil. Mag.*, **43:** 33 (1952), as well as earlier papers] and by Harish-Chandra [*Phys. Rev.*, **71:** 793 (1947), and other papers].

‡‡ This is treated fully in I. M. Gelfand, R. A. Minlos, and Z. Ya. Shapiro, "Representations of the Rotation and Lorentz Groups and their Applications," pt. 2, chap. 2, The Macmillan Company, New York, 1963 (translated by G. Cummins and T. Boddington). More condensed versions are contained in Lyubarskii, *op. cit.* (on page 360), chap. 16; and in A. I. Akhiezer and V. B. Berestetzkii, "Quantum Electrodynamics," pp. 385–404, State Publishing of Technical-Theoretical Literature, Moscow, 1953 (in Russian). This approach is based on work by I. M. Gelfand and A. M. Yaglom (references in Lyubarskii, *op. cit.*, p. 379). It is related to the method developed by Bhabha, *op. cit.*, while an alternative treatment is presented by Harish-Chandra, *op. cit.*

from the given one S, by the transformation L, we have

$$\begin{aligned} \psi' &\equiv \psi'(\mathbf{x}') = T\psi(\mathbf{x}) \equiv T\psi \\ & \qquad\qquad\qquad\qquad T \equiv T(L) \\ x' &= Lx \end{aligned} \tag{8-57}$$

That is, $\psi'_u = T_{uv}\psi_v$ ($u, v = 1, \ldots, N$), so that the homomorphism relation $T(L_2L_1) = T(L_2)T(L_1)$ follows.‡

We observe next that the covariance of our theory under $\mathfrak{L}$ is satisfied by requiring that A^ν and κ remain unchanged under the transformations of this group. Two important consequences flow from this when $\kappa \neq 0$. By (8-57) we find that

$$TA^\nu T^{-1} = L_\mu{}^\nu A^\mu \tag{8-58}$$

and since the first term in (8-55) transforms according to the representation $\mathfrak{D} \times \mathfrak{D}_{1/2,1/2}$ (considering that $\partial/\partial x^\mu$ transforms as a 4-vector, i.e., according to $\mathfrak{D}_{1/2,1/2}$—see Prob. 8-20) while the second term transforms according to $\mathfrak{D}$, we can conclude that $\mathfrak{D}$ must be contained in $\mathfrak{D} \times \mathfrak{D}_{1/2,1/2}$. By (8B-31), the latter conclusion means that

with $\mathfrak{D}_{ij}$, $\mathfrak{D}$ must contain also at least one of the 4 representations $\mathfrak{D}_{i\pm 1/2, j\pm 1/2}$ (8-59)

The results (8-58) and (8-59) take us a long way towards solving our problem.

By taking L infinitesimal in (8-58), i.e., by taking $T = I + \frac{1}{2}U_{\mu\nu}\epsilon^{\mu\nu}$ with L as in (8C-14), an easy calculation gives§

$$[A_\lambda, U_{\mu\nu}] = 2g_{\lambda[\mu}A_{\nu]}, \qquad A_\lambda \equiv g_{\lambda\mu}A^\mu \tag{8-60}$$

where $U_{\mu\nu}$ are the generators of $\mathfrak{D}$ (i.e., the base vectors of the corresponding Lie algebra). In particular,

$$A_k = [N_k, A_0], \qquad [A_0, M_k] = 0, \qquad [[A_0, N_3], N_3] = A_0 \tag{8-61}$$

where the M and N are as in (8B-3). The first set of relations (8-61) shows that only A_0 needs to be determined, and by the second set, A_0 commutes with all the elements of the subgroup of $\mathfrak{D}$ corresponding to spatial rotations. The latter conclusion, together with the last relation in (8-61) fixes A_0 to within a few arbitrary parameters. The analysis is straightforward but rather lengthy, and we merely indicate the type of result that has been obtained.

‡ However, bearing in mind the physical significance of the transformations (8-57), is this conclusion fully justified without additional considerations? See related discussion in connection with unitary representations, Wigner, *op. cit.* (*Ann. Math.*).

§ See similar derivation (Prob. 8-14) of (8C-26) using (8C-29), remembering (8C-15).

At first we must describe the base with respect to which our matrices are taken. Suppose that

$$\mathfrak{D} = \sum_a \mathfrak{D}_{i_a j_a} \equiv \sum_a \mathfrak{D}_a \tag{8-62}$$

and that $\mathcal{B}_a$ is the base associated with $\mathfrak{D}_a$, so that our complete base $\mathcal{B} = \Sigma \mathcal{B}_a$. We suppose that $\mathcal{B}_a$ is chosen so that in the restriction of $\mathfrak{L}$ to $\mathfrak{R}$, its vectors constitute the direct sum of standard bases [such as given in (8A-25)] associated with $\mathfrak{D}_l (l \equiv l_a)$ for

$$l = |i - j|, \qquad |i - j| + 1, \qquad . . . , \qquad i + j \tag{8-63}$$

In order to see the connection between this base and that given in the last part of Appendix 8B, we need only observe, remembering (8A-38), that by (8B-31), $\mathfrak{D}_{ij} = \mathfrak{D}_{i0} \times \mathfrak{D}_{0j}$, and that in the restriction to $\mathfrak{R}$, $\mathfrak{D}_{i0}$, and $\mathfrak{D}_{0j}$ are isomorphic to $\mathfrak{D}_i$ and $\mathfrak{D}_j$ respectively. The matrix elements relative to $\mathcal{B}$ are thus labeled by the triplets (a, l, m), where a runs through the set for which the sum in (8-62) is taken, $l \equiv l_a$ has the range (8-63), and

$$m \equiv m_l = -l, \qquad -l + 1, \qquad . . . , \qquad l \tag{8-63a}$$

Now, from the second set of equations (8-61) it follows quite easily with the aid of Schur's lemma, that

$$(A_0)_{alm,a'l'm'} = \delta_{ll'}\, \delta_{mm'} \alpha^l_{aa'} \tag{8-64}$$

The lengthy calculation is needed to determine the $\alpha^l_{aa'}$. The result is of the form (see Gelfand, et al., *op. cit.*, pp. 275–277)

$$\alpha^l_{aa'} = \alpha_{aa'} F_{(aa')}(l_a, i_a, j_a) \tag{8-65}$$

for the nonvanishing α's, where the subscript (aa') in F indicates one of the possible four connections between a and a' that is consistent with (8-59), and $F_{(aa')} = F_{(a'a)}$ (so that effectively there are only two distinct functions F). As the F in (8-65) stand for given expressions, the only remaining indeterminacy is in the constants $\alpha_{aa'}$. This indeterminacy can be narrowed down further by assuming that our theory is also covariant under the wider Lorentz group $\mathfrak{L}^{\uparrow}$. Until the recent discovery of parity nonconservation in weak interactions, such an assumption was accepted without question. It can still be taken to have wide applicability.

The results (8-58) and (8-60) are easily seen to be valid also for $\mathfrak{L}^{\uparrow}$. If we denote by S the operator T corresponding to the spatial inversion P, we find by (8-58) that‡

$$[S, A_0] = 0, \qquad \{S, A_k\} = 0 \qquad \{\ \ \} \equiv [\ \ ]_+ \tag{8-66}$$

‡ The last set in (8-66) follows from the first equation since, by (8B-33) (where, it will be recalled, P stands for the quantity now denoted by S and, similarly, the same symbols N_k are used both for the initial and all other representation Lie algebras) and (8-61), we have $\{S, A_k\} = \{S, [N_k, A_0]\} = [\{S, N_k\}, A_0] + \{[A_0, S], N_k\} = 0$.

By Eqs. (8B-36) and (8B-37) and associated discussion, and using the first of Eqs. (8-66), it is possible, with one exception, to relate $\alpha_{aa'}$ and $\alpha_{\tilde{a}\tilde{a}'}$, where $\tilde{a}$ refers to (j_a, i_a). Thus one finds that

$$\alpha_{aa'} = \alpha_{\tilde{a}\tilde{a}'} \qquad \text{if } i_a \neq j_a \text{ and } i_{a'} \neq j_{a'} \tag{8-67}$$

and very similar relations hold in the other cases.‡

The results relating to (8-55) that we have sketched out concern the mathematical structure of this equation. Let us now consider its possible physical content. We know that intrinsic angular momentum, i.e., *spin*, is a characteristic parameter of elementary particles. How is this parameter contained in our equation? We have mentioned earlier the significance in our scheme of mechanical densities such as energy-momentum and charge current. How are they derivable from our equation and what is the connection between the structure of the matrices A^{ν} and characteristic properties of these quantities? We have so far assumed that the 4-scalar $\kappa \neq 0$. What are the implications of this assumption and of the alternative assumption $\kappa = 0$? Finally, what are the special cases of principal interest to which (8-55) reduces? These are among the questions that now invite our attention.

In order to find the connection between the two universal intrinsic parameters of a free particle§—its rest mass and its spin—and the equation of the form (8-55) with which it is associated, let us consider its state given by the plane wave ψ taken relative to its rest frame, i.e.,

$$\psi = \chi e^{-(i/\hbar)p_0 x^0} \tag{8-68}$$

where χ is independent of x. The function (8-68) will satisfy Eq. (8-55) provided

$$A_0 \chi = z\chi, \qquad z = \frac{\kappa\hbar}{ip_0} = \frac{\kappa\hbar}{imc} \tag{8-69}$$

Hence, in general we may have not one but a number of rest masses m. We might wish to restrict A_0 so as to insure the existence of only one rest mass m in accordance with the common idea that an elementary particle has a unique rest mass. Very significantly, with every eigenvalue z of A_0 there necessarily exists an eigenvalue $-z$. This can be seen very simply by noting that in view of (8-58), det $\|A^{\lambda}p_{\lambda} - zI\| \equiv D(\mathsf{p}) = D(\mathsf{p}')$ under the transformation (8-57) (since $A^{\lambda}p'_{\lambda} = TA^{\lambda}p_{\lambda}T^{-1}$), so that $D(\mathsf{p})$ can depend only on the 4-scalar p^2. Hence in the rest frame of the particle

‡ The exceptional case occurs for $i_a = j_a$ and $i_{a'} = j_{a'}$, when $\alpha_{aa'}$ is either $\neq 0$ and not determined or $= 0$, according as the action of S in the space of $\mathfrak{D}_a$ and $\mathfrak{D}_{a'}$ is of the same type or not. See Gelfand, et al., *op. cit.*, pp. 280–282.

§ We should be reminded that our present discussion rests on the sundry idealizations relating to the interpretation of the propagation equation (8-36), including the idea of *free* particles.

the determinant of the system of equations (8-69) can depend only on p_0^2, which is seen to imply the stated result.‡ We see that if we wish to limit consideration to systems of the conventional unique particle-antiparticle type we must impose upon A_0 the following restriction:

$$A_0 \text{ has one and only one nonvanishing pair of eigenvalues} \tag{8-70}$$

The spin (or spins) of the particle can be found by considering how the components of χ transform under the subgroup $\mathfrak{R}$, bearing in mind that in its rest frame the particle's angular momentum consists only of its spin. Referring to our discussion relating to the base with respect to which the matrix elements (8-64) were expressed, it can be seen that for every value a in (8-62), χ transforms according to the set of $\mathfrak{D}_{l_a}$, where the l_a are given by (8-63), and for each l_a the components are numbered by m given in (8-63a). In general, we are confronted therefore with the possibility of a spectrum of spin values, with only one simplifying feature, stemming from (8-59), that the spins are either all integral or all half-integral. If, as in the case of the mass, and for similar reasons, we consider a particle elementary only if it is associated with a unique spin, then we must introduce a further restriction, this time on the nature of our representation $\mathfrak{D}$. It is at once apparent by reference to (8A-38) that the only choice that can be made in (8-62) consistently with the assumption of unique spin $s(>0)$ is

$$\mathfrak{D} = \mathfrak{D}_{s0} + \mathfrak{D}_{0s} \tag{8-71}$$

Both terms in (8-71) are moreover necessary, according to (8-67), if our theory is to be covariant under $\mathfrak{L}^{\uparrow}$.

Turning now to our second question relating to the physical content of the system (8-56), it will be convenient to establish first the general form of the lagrangian density $\mathfrak{L}$ for which they can be the Euler equations. We can start with the following conditions for $\mathfrak{L}$. $\mathfrak{L}$ must obviously be a 4-scalar; it can be assumed real, as a convenient normalization; and it must involve quadratically the ψ and their first derivatives, in order to lead to (8-56).

The result is expressible in terms of a nonsingular hermitian matrix M, of order N, which has to be chosen so as to satisfy the following relations that involve the matrices T of the representation $\mathfrak{D}$ (giving the transforma-

‡ We have tacitly assumed that A_0 has purely imaginary eigenvalues when the eigenvectors represent proper states (since κ, as a 4-scalar, is a real quantity). This property can be established as follows, when it is assumed that our equation is derivable from an action principle (see later discussion relating to Lagrangians). If χ is an eigenvector of A_0 with eigenvalue α, then by (8-74), $A_0\chi \circ \chi = \alpha^*(\chi \circ \chi) = -\chi \circ A_0\chi = -\alpha(\chi \circ \chi)$. Hence $\alpha^* = -\alpha$ unless $\chi \circ \chi = 0$. But in the latter case we see by Eq. (8-84) that the energy density vanishes identically, so that χ could not be considered as a physically admissible wave function.

tion properties of our wave functions ψ) with respect to a given base, and the matrices A^ν of Eq. (8-55): the expression

$$\psi^\dagger M\psi \equiv \psi_u^* M_{uv}\psi_v \equiv \psi \circ \psi, \qquad M^\dagger = M \tag{8-72}$$

is a form invariant under our basic group, and hence,‡

$$MT^{-1}M^{-1} = T^\dagger \tag{8-73}$$

for all our T; we have the identity

$$A^\nu\psi_1 \circ \psi_2 = -\psi_1 \circ A^\nu\psi_2 \tag{8-74}$$

When and only when such a matrix M can be found is our wave equation (8-55) derivable from a lagrangian density $\mathfrak{L}$, and its general form, except of course for the arbitrariness in a multiplying constant and in a suitable additive divergence, is given by the expression

$$\mathfrak{L} = \frac{1}{2}\left(A^\nu \frac{\partial\psi}{\partial x^\nu} \circ \psi + \psi \circ A^\nu \frac{\partial\psi}{\partial x^\nu}\right) + \kappa\psi \circ \psi \tag{8-75}$$

The sufficiency part of this result is easily proven.§ We have, in fact, for the usual variation as applied to the action integral for fields, and since $\delta(\partial\psi/\partial x^\nu) = \partial(\delta\psi)/\partial x^\nu$, that

$$\begin{aligned}\delta\mathfrak{L} = \mathrm{Re}\left[A^\nu \frac{\partial\psi}{\partial x^\nu} \circ \delta\psi + \frac{\partial}{\partial x^\nu}(A^\nu\,\delta\psi \circ \psi) - \left(A^\nu\,\delta\psi \circ \frac{\partial\psi}{\partial x^\nu}\right)\right] \\ + \kappa(\delta\psi \circ \psi + \psi \circ \delta\psi) = \left(A^\nu \frac{\partial\psi}{\partial x^\nu} + \kappa\psi\right) \circ \delta\psi + \delta\psi \circ \left(A^\nu \frac{\partial\psi}{\partial x^\nu} + \kappa\psi\right) \\ + \frac{\partial}{\partial x^\nu}(\cdot\;\cdot\;\cdot)\end{aligned}$$

where we have used (8-74). The Euler equations arising from the Lagrangian (8-75) are therefore seen to consist of the set (8-56) and of the complex conjugate set [remembering the definition (8-72) and the fact that M is

‡ If $\psi \circ \psi$ is a form invariant, then so is $\psi_1 \circ \psi_2$, as is easily proved when we note that by (8-72) and since $M^\dagger = M$,

$$\psi_1 \circ \psi_2 = (\psi_2 \circ \psi_1)^* \tag{8-73a}$$

Thus, $T\psi_1 \circ T\psi_2 = \psi_1 \circ \psi_2$, that is, $(T\psi_1)^\dagger MT\psi_2 = \psi_1{}^\dagger M\psi_2$ for all our ψ_1,ψ_2, and T, and hence $T^\dagger MT = M$.

§ It is, in fact, only necessary to assume that (8-74) holds for $\nu = 0$, for its validity for $\nu > 0$ can then be deduced. For a proof that the stated conditions are necessary, see, e.g., Bhabha, *op. cit.* (on page 334); Gelfand, et al., *op. cit.;* Lyubarskii, *op. cit.* The more general case (8-54) is considered in the first reference. It should be noted that the symbol (ψ,ψ) used in the last two references corresponds to what is denoted here by $\psi \circ \psi$ (in order to differentiate this product symbol from that commonly employed in QM for the inner product in Hilbert space).

nonsingular]. This Lagrangian is a relativistic invariant by virtue of the covariance property of our $\circ$ product and it is real in view of (8-73a).‡

There are a number of pertinent questions that arise in the present discussion and that must be omitted from our rapid presentation. We cannot consider, for instance, the question of the restrictions, if any, that must be imposed on the matrices A^ν in order that Eq. (8-55) be derivable from a Lagrangian (see Prob. 8-25 for an interesting special case). Let us note only that condition (8-74) is necessarily satisfied for all values of ν if it is satisfied for $\nu = 0$, as we can readily see by using the first of Eqs. (8-61), and considering corresponding infinitesimal T in the expression of covariance for our $\circ$ product.

We have introduced the Lagrangian for our problem chiefly for the purpose of deriving the fundamental field densities. When ψ transforms as a tensor, we can apply immediately the results given in Sec. 6-7 to find the energy-momentum density. We can adapt the procedure employed there for deriving this quantity to the case of ψ transforming in any manner according to the representation (8-62). A more systematic and general method is however available in Emmy Noether's theorem connecting invariance properties of a lagrangian problem with corresponding conservation rules.

According to this theorem, if we are given a lagrangian density $\mathfrak{L}(\psi_a; \partial\psi_a/\partial x^\nu)$ whose integral over an arbitrary x region D is a form invariant under the infinitesimal group

$$\begin{aligned} x^\nu \rightarrow x'^\nu &= x^\nu + \epsilon^\nu(x) \\ \psi_a(x) \rightarrow \psi'_a(x') &= \psi_a(x) + \eta_a(x) \end{aligned} \tag{8-76}$$

(and hence, of course, also under the corresponding integrated continuous group), then for the solutions ψ of the Euler equations we have the identities (using the comma notation for partials)

$$\begin{gathered} Q^\nu{}_{,\nu} = 0, \qquad Q^\nu = -T_\mu{}^\nu \epsilon^\mu + \frac{\partial \mathfrak{L}}{\partial \psi_{a,\nu}} \eta_a \\ T_\mu{}^\nu = \frac{\partial \mathfrak{L}}{\partial \psi_{a,\nu}} \frac{\partial \psi_a}{\partial x^\mu} - \delta^\nu_\mu \mathfrak{L} \end{gathered} \tag{8-77}$$

The proof follows directly upon using relations similar to (7-33), namely,§

$$\begin{aligned} \psi'(x) - \psi(x) \equiv \delta\psi &= \psi'(x) - \psi'(x') + \psi'(x') - \psi(x) \\ &= -\frac{\partial \psi}{\partial x^\mu} \epsilon^\mu + \eta \end{aligned} \tag{8-78}$$

‡ The Lagrangians of the form (8-75) have the peculiarity that they vanish for the solutions of their Euler equations.

§ That quantities are to be taken only to first order in our infinitesimals is to be understood in what follows.

By our assumption, we have, writing $\mathfrak{L}'$ for $\mathfrak{L}(\psi'; \partial\psi'/\partial x'^{\nu})$ and $d\tau$ for $dx^1\, dx^2\, \ldots$, and noting that $d\tau' = (1 + \epsilon^{\nu}{}_{,\nu})\, d\tau$ and $\delta(\psi_{a,\nu}) = (\delta\psi_a)_{,\nu}$:

$$0 = \int_{D'} \mathfrak{L}'\, d\tau' - \int_D \mathfrak{L}\, d\tau = \int_D (\mathfrak{L}' - \mathfrak{L})\, d\tau + \int_D \mathfrak{L}(d\tau' - d\tau)$$

$$= \int_D \left(\frac{\partial \mathfrak{L}}{\partial \psi_a}\, \delta\psi_a + \frac{\partial \mathfrak{L}}{\partial \psi_{a,\nu}}\, \delta\psi_{a,\nu} + \mathfrak{L}\epsilon^{\nu}{}_{,\nu} \right) d\tau$$

$$= \int_D \left\{ \left[\frac{\partial \mathfrak{L}}{\partial \psi_a} - \frac{\partial}{\partial x^{\nu}} \left(\frac{\partial \mathfrak{L}}{\partial \psi_{a,\nu}} \right) \right] \delta\psi_a + \frac{\partial}{\partial x^{\nu}} \left(\frac{\partial \mathfrak{L}}{\partial \psi_{a,\nu}}\, \delta\psi_a + \mathfrak{L}\epsilon^{\nu} \right) \right\} d\tau$$

Since the vanishing of the expression in the brackets yields our Euler equations, and the integration region D is arbitrary, the result (8-77) follows immediately upon substitution for $\delta\psi_a$ from (8-78).

The immediately relevant applications of this theorem are obtained by considering the following three special cases. First, if we take ϵ^{ν} constant, then since our $\mathfrak{L}$ does not depend explicitly on the x, we must have $\eta_a = 0$. Consequently, the infinitesimals ϵ^{ν} being arbitrary, Eq. (8-77) yields the conservation equations

$$T_{\mu}{}^{\nu}{}_{,\nu} = 0, \qquad T_{\mu}{}^{\nu} \text{ given in (8-77)} \tag{8-79}$$

This is simply the energy-momentum conservation result (6-119), the explicit $\mathbf{x}$ independence of $\mathfrak{L}$ signifying the absence of given external forces.

Suppose next that (8-76) corresponds to the transformations given in (8-57) with L in $\mathfrak{L}$, so that $\epsilon^{\mu}(x) = \epsilon^{\mu}{}_{\nu} x^{\nu}$ $(\epsilon_{\nu\mu} = -\epsilon_{\mu\nu})$, and

$$\eta_a(x) = \tfrac{1}{2}\epsilon_{\lambda\mu}(U^{\lambda\mu})_{ab}\psi_b$$

Then, by (8-77), and putting [see (6-116)] $(\partial\mathfrak{L}/\partial\psi_{a,\nu}) = \Pi_a^{\nu}$, we have

$$\begin{aligned} Q^{\nu} &= -T_{\sigma}{}^{\nu}\epsilon^{\sigma}{}_{\tau}x^{\tau} + \tfrac{1}{2}\Pi_a^{\nu}\epsilon_{\lambda\mu}(U^{\lambda\mu})_{ab}\psi_b \\ &= \epsilon_{\lambda\mu}(\tfrac{1}{2}\Pi^{\nu}U^{\lambda\mu}\psi - T_{\sigma}{}^{\nu}g^{\sigma\lambda}\delta_{\tau\mu}x^{\tau}) = \epsilon_{\lambda\mu}(\cdot\;\cdot\;\cdot\; - T^{\lambda\nu}x^{\mu}) \\ &= \tfrac{1}{2}\epsilon_{\lambda\mu}(\Pi^{\nu}U^{\lambda\mu}\psi + x^{\lambda}T^{\mu\nu} - x^{\mu}T^{\lambda\nu}) \end{aligned}$$

where we have introduced matrix notation for quantities in which the indices are suppressed, with Π^{ν} and ψ standing for one-rowed and one-columned matrices respectively. Since the $\epsilon_{\lambda\mu}$ are arbitrary, it follows by the first relation in (8-77) that

$$\begin{aligned} &R^{\lambda\mu\nu}{}_{,\nu} = 0 \\ &R^{\lambda\mu\nu} = 2x^{[\lambda}T^{\mu]\nu} + \Pi^{\nu}U^{\lambda\mu}\psi, \qquad \Pi_a^{\nu} = \frac{\partial\mathfrak{L}}{\partial\psi_{a,\nu}} \end{aligned} \tag{8-80}$$

This result is clearly a generalization of the relativistic angular-momentum tensor relations discussed in Sec. 6-3. The latter represent a relativistic extension of the corresponding classical orbital angular-momentum relations, so that the second term in the expression for the tensor R in (8-80) must be associated with the intrinsic angular momentum, i.e., with the *spin* possessed by the system described by $\mathfrak{L}$. This conclusion is readily checked in the special case of the Dirac equation (Prob. 8-27). An important question in this connection is the symmetry of the tensor of energy-momentum (density) $T_{\mu\nu}$ defined in (8-77). We have discussed the significance of this symmetry in Chap. 6, and we were briefly concerned with this question in Sec. 7-2. In the general case, when the spin part of the tensor R is not zero, the conservation equation (8-80) can hold without the tensor T being symmetric. Instead, we can introduce in this case an associated symmetric tensor according to Belinfante's method, using a suitable tensor Ω, as indicated in Sec. 7-2 [see (7-29) and the discussion following it].‡ We can find this tensor by expanding the conservation equation (8-80), which, upon using (8-79) leads to the equation

$$T^{\mu\lambda} - T^{\lambda\mu} + (\Pi^{\nu} U^{\lambda\mu}\psi)_{,\nu} = 0$$

Hence we can take $2\Omega^{[\mu\lambda]\nu} = \Pi^{\nu} U^{\lambda\mu}\psi$, and since $U^{\mu\nu} = -U^{\nu\mu}$, we have the simple choice

$$\Omega^{\lambda\mu\nu} = \tfrac{1}{2}(\Pi^{\lambda} U^{\mu\nu} - \Pi^{\mu} U^{\nu\lambda} - \Pi^{\nu} U^{\lambda\mu})\psi \tag{8-81}$$

Lastly, suppose that the components ψ_a consist of two sets of mutually conjugate complex quantities $\psi_u, \psi_u{}^*$. The above results remain, of course, valid when rewritten in an obvious way. In addition, we can consider the case, $\epsilon^{\nu} = 0$, $\eta_u = i\alpha\psi_u$, $\eta_u{}^* = -i\alpha\psi_u{}^*$ (α a real constant), corresponding to the assumption that our theory is invariant under the gauge transformations

$$\psi_u \to e^{i\alpha}\psi_u, \qquad \psi_u{}^* \to e^{-i\alpha}\psi_u{}^* \tag{8-82}$$

It follows by (8-77) that $Q^{\nu} = i\alpha(\Pi_u^{\nu}\psi_u - \Pi_u^{\nu *}\psi_u^*)$, and that we have the conservation rule (as α is arbitrary)

$$J^{\nu}_{,\nu} = 0, \qquad J^{\nu} = iq(\Pi_u^{\nu}\psi_u - \Pi_u^{\nu *}\psi_u^*) \tag{8-83}$$

where q is a real parameter associated with our physical system (or particle). In order to see that this parameter can be identified with electric charge, it is necessary to consider the system in the presence of an external electromagnetic field, with our Lagrangian (and thus the equations of motion) extended by means of the prescription (8-23). Because these considerations constitute a digression from our immediate topic, we do not pursue them here, referring the interested reader to Pauli's survey article cited earlier.

All the conservation results we have obtained can be immediately applied to our lagrangian problem (8-75). Thus, bearing in mind that $\mathfrak{L} = 0$ for the solutions ψ of our problem, we find by (8-77),

$$T_{\mu}{}^{\nu} = \Pi^{\nu}\frac{\partial\psi}{\partial x^{\mu}} + \Pi^{\nu *}\frac{\partial\psi^*}{\partial x^{\mu}} = \frac{1}{2}\left(\psi^{\dagger} M A^{\nu}\frac{\partial\psi}{\partial x^{\mu}} + \frac{\partial\psi^{\dagger}}{\partial x^{\mu}} A^{\nu\dagger} M\psi\right)$$

‡ See W. Pauli, *Rev. Mod. Phys.*, **13:** 203 (1941), p. 205.

using matrix notation, or

$$T^{\mu\nu} = \frac{1}{2}\left(\psi \circ A^{\nu}\frac{\partial\psi}{\partial x_{\mu}} + A^{\nu}\frac{\partial\psi}{\partial x_{\mu}} \circ \psi\right) \tag{8-84}$$

Similarly it follows from (8-83) that $J^{\nu} = iq(\psi^{\dagger}MA^{\nu}\psi - \psi^{\dagger}A^{\nu\dagger}M\psi)/2$, which, in view of (8-74), can also be written

$$J^{\nu} = iq(\psi \circ A^{\nu}\psi) \tag{8-85}$$

Our discussion relating to Eq. (8-55) has so far dealt only with the case $\kappa \neq 0$. Let us pause now very briefly to consider the equation

$$A^{\lambda}\frac{\partial\psi}{\partial x^{\lambda}} = 0 \tag{8-86}$$

(for details see the relevant sections in Gelfand, et al., *op. cit.*). To begin with, Eq. (8-58) is no longer valid. The equivalence of Eq. (8-86) in the frames S and S' implies by (8-57), that

$$A^{\nu}\frac{\partial\psi'}{\partial x'^{\nu}} = XA^{\mu}\frac{\partial\psi}{\partial x^{\mu}} = XA^{\mu}T^{-1}L^{\nu}{}_{\mu}\frac{\partial\psi'}{\partial x'^{\nu}},$$

where X is a nonsingular matrix. Hence, instead of (8-58) we have the relation

$$XA^{\nu}T^{-1} = L_{\mu}{}^{\nu}A^{\mu} \tag{8-87}$$

It is obvious that the otherwise arbitrary matrices X must be chosen so as to form a representation of our basic group. It can then be shown that relations involving the A^{ν} such as (8-61), (8-64), and (8-65) retain their validity provided the representations labeled by a and a' now refer to the X and the T respectively. Our results relating to the existence of a lagrangian density also carry over to the present case, except that only condition (8-74) is required, but not condition (8-73).

The most important and best-known field whose equations of propagation can be put in the form (8-86) is, of course, the Maxwell field, into whose discussion we need not enter here.‡ The only other such field presently considered to be associated with known particles is the so-called Weyl (or 2-component neutrino) field (see Prob. 8-28). Both fields are associated with massless particles. This is not fortuitous. We need only assume that (8-86) is derivable from a Lagrangian to be able to conclude that the physically acceptable solutions of (8-86) are all associated with vanishing masses. In fact, suppose that, on the contrary, the particle associated with our equation has a nonvanishing rest mass, and consider its state described

‡ We should note however that our assertion is only true of the original Maxwell equations in free space (see Gelfand, et al., *op. cit.*, pp. 312–314). If we wish to include the potential 4-vector, treating the Maxwell field in terms of 10 components, as is the case of the Proca field (referred to later), we must resort to the more general form (8-54).

by a plane wave (8-68) in its rest frame. By Eq. (8-86) we have then $p_0 A_0 \chi = 0$, and either $p_0 = 0$, or $A_0 \chi = 0$, and hence by (8-84) the energy density $T_{00} = 0$. In either case we arrive at a contradiction.

Our general outline of results connected with Eqs. (8-55) and (8-86) is now completed. The starting point has been a set of reasonable and simple assumptions consistent with STR. But has our underlying aim been attained? Are all such equations associated with 'elementary particles,' and are the equations of all such free particles of the matrix form (8-55) or (8-86)? The answer to both parts of this question appears at present to be in the negative. The usefulness of equations that lead to multiple particle masses and particle spins is questionable.‡ On the other hand, the graviton (if it exists) is assumed to have spin 2, and among the short-lived hadrons that have been recently discovered occur half-integral spins $>\frac{1}{2}$, but as we shall presently see, their equations of free motion are of the Dirac-Fierz-Pauli (DFP) type that cannot generally be subsumed under the form (8-55). It is only if we choose (for no compelling reason that we can advance at present) to suitably restrict the meaning of the term "elementary particle" that we can arrive at the same unique results both with the equations of the type (8-55) and with those of the DFP type. The corresponding particles, which we shall temporarily call "special," have unique masses and unique spins ≤ 1.§

Let us first consider how we can arrive at the special particles with our present approach. We have already seen that in order to obtain a unique particle spin we are led to the form (8-71) of our representation $\mathfrak{D}$ when $s > 0$ and when we require covariance under $\mathfrak{L}^{\uparrow}$. The smallest such value of s yields Dirac's equation. Can this special case be singled out among all the others in a significant way? An affirmative answer is provided by a remarkable theorem that involves the not-too-restrictive assumption that

$$A_0 \textit{ is diagonalizable} \tag{8-88}$$

This theorem states that *of all equations* (8-55) *that are covariant under* $\mathfrak{L}^{\uparrow}$ *for which* (8-88) *holds only Dirac's equation has the property that* J_0 *is positive definite.*¶ We shall only sketch out the proof of this theorem (for details see, e.g., Akhiezer and Berestetzkii, *op. cit.*; Gelfand, et al., *op. cit.*). By (8-88)

‡ They are, in part, related to so-called nonlocal theories of particle interactions, which have so far remained in the purely speculative stage. See, e.g., A. Pais and G. E. Uhlenbeck, *Phys. Rev.*, **79:** 145 (1950).

§ It is possible to argue, of course, that in some nontrivial sense the particles of this category do form a distinguished group, and then the theory under discussion assumes in this respect added interest.

¶ The immediate importance, of this property, when referring to Schrödinger fields, for which J_0 is proportional to probability density, is quite obvious. Its full significance appears, however, only when one considers quantized fields. Similar remarks hold about the property of positive definiteness of the energy density, which enters in the theorem that is mentioned next.

the eigenvectors of J_0 form a complete set, i.e., a base in our ψ space. Hence if $J_0 \geq 0$ for the solutions of our equation, this relation is also true over the entire ψ space. Then, using Eqs. (8-64) and (8-73), one arrives by a few simple steps at the result (8-71) with $s = \frac{1}{2}$. The conclusion that the associated equation coincides with Dirac's equation can be obtained by applying Eqs. (8-64), (8-65), (8-59), (8-67) and (8-74) as shown in the above references, and arriving at a set of A^ν that are equivalent to the matrices γ^ν in Eq. (8-26). That the representation (8-71) with $s = \frac{1}{2}$ corresponds to Dirac's equation can also be recognized more simply by considering its direct spinor representation, which we shall present shortly.

What about spin 0, which is possessed by pions and should belong to our special class? The linkage relation (8-59) shows that we cannot have $\mathfrak{D} = \mathfrak{D}_{00}$ but must have at least $\mathfrak{D} = \mathfrak{D}_{00} + \mathfrak{D}_{1/2,1/2}$. Both spins 0 and 1 come then into play. However, it can be shown that the wave functions associated with spin 1 are physically unacceptable in the same sense as encountered previously. We have now again a selection theorem similar to the one given above. *Under the assumption* (8-88), *the energy density* T_{00} *is positive definite for solutions of* (8-55) *only when either*

$$\mathfrak{D} = \mathfrak{D}_{00} + \mathfrak{D}_{1/2,1/2} \tag{8-89}$$

or

$$\mathfrak{D} = \mathfrak{D}_{1/2,1/2} + \mathfrak{D}_{10} + \mathfrak{D}_{01} \tag{8-90}$$

(see Gelfand, et al., *op. cit.*). In the last case, the associated spins are seen to be again 0 and 1, but now it can be shown that the value 0 for the spin is ruled out by the physical inadmissibility of the corresponding wave functions. The particles covered by this case are thus of spin 1. The Maxwell field, when quantized, has associated with it, as we know, massless particles of spin 1. But we have at present no definite indication of the existence of spin-1 particles with nonvanishing mass that could be included among what we have called the *special* particles (among which we do not include the "resonances"). There exists, however, an important algebraic argument that unites the two representations (8-89) and (8-90).

This argument is based on the idea of an algebra generated by the matrices A^ν (see Prob. 8-23; Roman, *op. cit.*; Corson, *op. cit.*). The algebra generated by the Dirac matrices and specified by the relations (8-25) is the simplest and best known. Next in simplicity is the algebra determined by the Duffin relations‡

$$A^\lambda A^\mu A^\nu + A^\nu A^\mu A^\lambda = -A^\lambda g^{\mu\nu} - A^\nu g^{\mu\lambda} \tag{8-91}$$

which can also be put, as is immediately verified, into the more compact form

$$[A^\lambda,[A^\mu,A^\nu]] = 2g^{\lambda[\nu}A^{\mu]} \tag{8-92}$$

‡ R. J. Duffin, *Phys. Rev.*, **54:** 1114 (1938). Note that the Lorentz metric convention used in this paper differs from that used here.

Now, both Eq. (8-55) corresponding to (8-89) and the one corresponding to (8-90) satisfy these relations and they are, in fact, characterized by them. Moreover, in both cases each component of a solution ψ satisfies a K. G. equation (8-13). This condition, which is, of course, satisfied by the Dirac wave functions, must indeed be characteristic of the special particles since they must have unique masses.‡

For the case (8-89) it is easy to construct the system (8-56) with $N = 5$ [this being the number of independent components corresponding to (8-89)], which is equivalent to the K. G. equation for the free motion of a particle described by a one-component wave function (and hence spinless—see reference § on page 320). In fact, with $\kappa = mc/\hbar$ and vanishing 4-potential, Eq. (8-13) can be written as the system $-g^{\nu\mu}(\partial\psi_\mu/\partial x^\nu) + \kappa\psi = 0$, $\partial\psi/\partial x^\nu + \kappa\psi_\nu = 0$, which is of the form (8-56) with $\psi_u = (\psi_0, \psi_1, \psi_2, \psi_3, \psi_4)$ $(\psi_4 \equiv \psi)$, and $A^\nu_{uv} = \delta_{u\nu}\delta_{v4} - \delta_{u4}g^{v\nu}$. One verifies quite easily that these matrices satisfy Eq. (8-91) [as $(A^\lambda A^\mu A^\nu)_{uv} = -\delta^\lambda_u g^{\mu\nu}\delta_{v4} + \delta_{u4}g^{\lambda\mu}g^{v\nu}$].

One can similarly change into the form (8-56) the K. G. equations for a 4-vector field ψ_ν. Since $\mathfrak{D}_{1/2} \times \mathfrak{D}_{1/2} = \mathfrak{D}_0 + \mathfrak{D}_1$, it follows by the same reasoning as employed at a previous occasion that both spins 0 and 1 are associated with such a field. One additional 4-scalar equation is therefore required to restrict the number of independent components to $2s + 1 = 3$ if spin 0 is to be excluded. Essentially the only 4-scalar available for this purpose is the 4-divergence of ψ_ν, so that the complete set of equations is

$$\frac{\partial^2\psi_\nu}{\partial x^\mu\,\partial x_\mu} + \kappa^2\psi_\nu = 0, \qquad \frac{\partial\psi^\nu}{\partial x^\nu} = 0 \tag{8-93}$$

The corresponding fully equivalent set (8-56) are the Proca equations§

$$\frac{\partial\psi_\mu}{\partial x^\nu} - \frac{\partial\psi_\nu}{\partial x^\mu} + \kappa\psi_{\mu\nu} = 0, \qquad g^{\lambda\mu}\frac{\partial\psi_{\mu\nu}}{\partial x^\lambda} + \kappa\psi_\nu = 0 \tag{8-94}$$

it being assumed that $\kappa \neq 0$. We now have

$$A^\lambda_{uv} = \delta_{u\nu}\delta_{v(\mu\nu)}g^{\lambda\mu} + \delta_{u(\mu\nu)}(\delta_{\lambda\nu}\delta_{v\mu} - \delta_{\lambda\mu}\delta_{v\nu}) \tag{8-95}$$

where, say, $(\mu\nu) = 01, 02, 03, 23, 31, 12$, and $\psi_u = (\psi_\nu;\psi_{(\lambda\mu)})$, in understandable notation. It is again easy but a bit tedious to check that (8-91) are

‡ By continuing the argument involving the determinant $D(\mathsf{p})$, which was indicated on page 337, it can be concluded that in general the components of ψ satisfy equations of higher order. See especially Bhabha, *op. cit.*

§ See reference to A. Proca on page 325. The Proca equations were studied extensively in the thirties, especially by N. Kemmer (see references in Corson, *op. cit.*), under the surmise that nuclear forces were mediated by spin-1 particles. Vector mesons have in recent years appeared among the so-called resonances, i.e., very short-lived hadronic particles.

satisfied.‡ Finally, by a method similar to that used in the case of the first selection theorem that leads to Dirac's equation, it is possible to prove in the present case that Eq. (8-55), associated with the representations (8-89) and (8-90), is precisely the matrix equation determined by the relations (8-91). It is now generally known as the Duffin-Kemmer equation.

The particles we have called special may perhaps form a distinguished class in some significant sense. But unlike what could have been assumed two or three decades ago, we can no longer suppose that particle spins higher than 1 can be excluded from general consideration. Current findings in particle physics are inconsistent with such a view. Since, moreover, we have at present no indication, either experimental or theoretical, that the new short-lived particles do not possess unique masses and spins, we cannot limit ourselves to Eqs. (8-55) and (8-86) and must consider also wave equations of the type first developed by Dirac, and systematized and further developed by Fierz and Pauli. These equations, now usually referred to (as we have already done earlier) as Dirac-Fierz-Pauli or DFP equations, are finding in fact considerable application in recent kinematic particle analyses.

The DFP theory is fully discussed both in the original papers of Fierz and Pauli and in the general surveys to which we have referred.§ We shall therefore limit our remarks to just a few essential points.

The principal characteristic properties of the DFP equations are as follows. In accordance with the fact that they deal with particles (and antiparticles) having a unique proper mass, they include a set that is equivalent to the K. G. equations for each component of the wave function. The covariance of the theory is manifest because the equations have an explicitly covariant structure and because the ψ components represent tensors (or pseudotensors) in the case of integral spins and spinors in the case of half-

‡ In applying formula (8-95), we have to take $\delta_{u(\mu\nu)} = -\delta_{u(\nu\mu)}$. Explicitly we have: $A^0 = \begin{bmatrix} \cdot & a^0 \\ -\tilde{a}^0 & \cdot \end{bmatrix}$, $A^k = \begin{bmatrix} \cdot & a^k \\ \tilde{a}^k & \cdot \end{bmatrix}$, where a^ν are 4×6 matrices and the dots stand for zero rectangular matrices, and

$$a^0 = \begin{bmatrix} \cdot & \cdot & \cdot & \cdot & \cdot & \cdot \\ 1 & \cdot & \cdot & \cdot & \cdot & \cdot \\ \cdot & 1 & \cdot & \cdot & \cdot & \cdot \\ \cdot & \cdot & 1 & \cdot & \cdot & \cdot \end{bmatrix}, \qquad a^1 = \begin{bmatrix} 1 & \cdot & \cdot & \cdot & \cdot & \cdot \\ \cdot & \cdot & \cdot & \cdot & \cdot & \cdot \\ \cdot & \cdot & \cdot & \cdot & \cdot & -1 \\ \cdot & \cdot & \cdot & \cdot & 1 & \cdot \end{bmatrix}$$

$$a^2 = \begin{bmatrix} \cdot & 1 & \cdot & \cdot & \cdot & \cdot \\ \cdot & \cdot & \cdot & \cdot & \cdot & 1 \\ \cdot & \cdot & \cdot & \cdot & \cdot & \cdot \\ \cdot & \cdot & \cdot & -1 & \cdot & \cdot \end{bmatrix}, \qquad a^3 = \begin{bmatrix} \cdot & \cdot & 1 & \cdot & \cdot & \cdot \\ \cdot & \cdot & \cdot & \cdot & -1 & \cdot \\ \cdot & \cdot & \cdot & 1 & \cdot & \cdot \\ \cdot & \cdot & \cdot & \cdot & \cdot & \cdot \end{bmatrix}$$

(the dots now representing zeros).

§ M. Fierz, *Helv. Phys. Acta*, **12:** 3 (1938); M. Fierz and W. Pauli, *Proc. Roy. Soc. London*, **A173:** 211 (1939). See also more recent discussions such as P. A. Moldauer and K. M. Case, *Phys. Rev.*, **102:** 279 (1956); C. Fronsdal, *Nuovo Cimento Suppl.*, **9:** 416 (1958).

integral spins. Lastly, the uniqueness of particle spins is guaranteed by the inclusion of suitable explicitly covariant equations of constraint, the so-called subsidiary conditions, that properly limit the number of independent components of the wave function. It is this last point that leads to substantial complications and—in the case of the presence of external electromagnetic fields, when the equations need to be modified by the prescription (8-23)—the measures introduced to insure consistency with the subsidiary conditions are pretty ponderous. On the other hand, the positive definiteness of the energy density in the case of integral spins and of the probability density of position in the case of half-integral spins, holds without restriction.‡ However, their expressions are not in general unique; only their total integrated values are always unique.

The first of the characteristic properties of the DFP equations, which we have just enumerated, requires no comment. The second property represents, aside from the subsidiary conditions, a direct extension of Dirac's equation when written in spinor form. We therefore turn now to a brief consideration of the latter equation, which as we have noted before, had inspired much of the theory we have outlined in the preceding pages, including the theory of spinors.

Let us recall the significance of the special symbols σ_μ that act as unchanging spinor-tensors in the spinor formalism as shown by Eqs. (8-44) and (8-44a), and the associated symbols $\bar{\sigma}_\mu$, which enter in (8-49a) ($\bar{\sigma}_0 = \sigma_0$, $\bar{\sigma}_i = -\sigma_i$). In addition to the latter relations between these symbols, we find from (8A-41) that

$$\bar{\sigma}_{(\mu}\sigma_{\nu)} = \sigma_{(\mu}\bar{\sigma}_{\nu)} = g_{\mu\nu} \tag{8-96}$$

It follows that

$$\pi\bar{\pi} = \bar{\pi}\pi = \mathsf{p}^2 \qquad \begin{aligned} \pi &\equiv p^\mu\sigma_\mu \\ \bar{\pi} &\equiv p^\mu\bar{\sigma}_\mu \end{aligned} \tag{8-97}$$

Hence if ψ^A and $\phi_{\dot{A}}$ are two spinors connected by the relations (in obvious matrix notation)

$$\pi\phi = \lambda\psi, \qquad \bar{\pi}\psi = \mu\phi \tag{8-98}$$

we obtain the K. G. equation (8-13) (with $\mathsf{A} = 0$) upon applying (8-14) and taking $\lambda\mu = m^2c^2$. The covariance under $\mathfrak{L}$ of Eqs. (8-98) is manifest. If we write these equations explicitly in terms of the appropriate tensor and spinor indices [noting that, by (8-48), and since the $\bar{\sigma}$ are hermitian, $\bar{\sigma}_\nu = \|\sigma^{\nu A\dot{B}}\| = \|\widetilde{\sigma_{\nu A\dot{B}}}\|^\dagger = \|\sigma_{\nu\dot{A}B}\|$]

$$\sigma_\mu{}^{A\dot{B}} p^\mu \phi_{\dot{B}} = \lambda\psi^A, \qquad \sigma_{\nu\dot{A}B}p^\nu\psi^B = \mu\phi_{\dot{A}} \tag{8-99}$$

‡ The two theorems relating to these properties, mentioned earlier, had reference to equations of the form (8-56), which, in general, are not of the DFP type. When they are of that type (for spins >1), it is a case of condition (8-88) not holding. See Gelfand, et al., *op. cit.*, pp. 347–349.

we also see directly, recalling the significance of the position and the dotting of the indices, and the discussion relating to $\mathfrak{L}^{\uparrow}$ in Appendix 8B, that by taking $\lambda = \mu$, Eqs. (8-99) are covariant also under $\mathfrak{L}^{\uparrow}$. We have, in fact, the representations $\mathfrak{D}_{1/2,0}$ and $\mathfrak{D}_{0,1/2}$ for ψ^A and $\phi_{\dot{A}}$, and the joint representation (8-71) with $s = \frac{1}{2}$ that is irreducible under $\mathfrak{L}^{\uparrow}$. Specifically, we have the following reciprocal transformations under the space inversion transformation P:

$$\psi^A \leftrightarrow \phi_{\dot{A}}, \qquad \sigma_\mu{}^{A\dot{B}} \leftrightarrow \sigma_{\mu\dot{A}B} \tag{8-100}$$

The above observations suffice to show that Eqs. (8-98) with

$$\lambda = \mu = \pm mc$$

are equivalent to the Dirac equations for the free motion of an electron, whose relativistic covariance is thus manifest. We can easily exhibit this equivalence directly by introducing the quantities $\Psi_\pm^A = \psi^A \pm \phi_{\dot{A}}$, or $\Psi_\pm = \psi \pm \phi$ in matrix form, into Eqs. (8-98), obtaining with $\mu \equiv \pm mc$: $\mu\Psi_\pm = \pi\phi \pm \bar{\pi}\psi = p^0\phi + p^k\sigma_k\phi \pm (p^0\psi - p^k\sigma_k\psi) = \pm(p^0\Psi_\pm - p^k\sigma_k\Psi_\mp)$; i.e.,

$$(p^0 \mp \mu)\Psi_\pm - p^k\sigma_k\Psi_\mp = 0$$

By introducing the 1×4 matrix $\Psi = \begin{bmatrix} \Psi_+ \\ \Psi_- \end{bmatrix}$ these equations can be combined into one matrix equation

$$\left(p^0 - p^k\begin{bmatrix} 0 & \sigma_k \\ \sigma_k & 0 \end{bmatrix} - \mu\begin{bmatrix} \sigma_0 & 0 \\ 0 & -\sigma_0 \end{bmatrix}\right)\Psi = 0$$

which, by Eqs. (8-21) and (8-20), is seen to coincide indeed with Dirac's equation (8-22) for $\mu = -mc$. The quantity Ψ is known as a "Dirac spinor," or a "bispinor."

The DFP equations have, in the case of half-integral spins, the same form as (8-98) with ϕ and ψ standing for spinors of a given rank that are totally symmetric in the dotted and undotted indices, so that by the argument presented in our concluding remarks on spinors (beginning on page 329) we can see immediately not only the covariance of the equations under $\mathfrak{L}^{\uparrow}$, but also the type of the irreducible representation $\mathfrak{D}$ with which they are associated. The reduction to the K. G. equations for the wave-function components follows also immediately, as indicated above for the Dirac equation.‡

In closing our general discussion of relativistic wave equations, let us note that all the familiar results obtained with Dirac's equation, such as the appearance of a magnetic moment, polarization properties of plane

‡ For the integral spins Fierz also introduces a formalism that represents a certain generalization of that for the Proca equations. For half-integral spins an alternative mixed tensor and Dirac spinor formalism, having certain methodological advantages, has been proposed by W. Rarita and J. Schwinger. See Prob. 8-21.

wave solutions, charge conjugation, and particle-antiparticle relationship can be extended with little difficulty to the general equations. These are discussed in the general references on this subject given earlier. By way of illustration we consider here one such result for Dirac's equation, namely the important relativistically covariant expressions known as *bilinear covariants*, which occur, in particular, in the interaction parts of Lagrangians referring to coupling of a Dirac spinor field with other fields. These are the familiar relativistically covariant (and real) expressions (with $\psi \equiv \Psi$)

$$\begin{gathered}\bar{\psi}(x)\psi(x), \qquad \bar{\psi}(x)\gamma^5\psi(x), \qquad \bar{\psi}(x)\gamma^\nu\psi(x) \\ \bar{\psi}(x)i\gamma^5\gamma^\nu\psi(x), \qquad \bar{\psi}(x)\sigma^{\mu\nu}\psi(x)\end{gathered} \tag{8-101}$$

where $\sigma^{\mu\nu}$ are given in (8-28), $\gamma^5 \equiv \gamma^0\gamma^1\gamma^2\gamma^3$ [see Prob. 8-23 ($\gamma_\nu \equiv g_{\nu\mu}\gamma^\mu$)], and

$$\bar{\psi} = \psi^\dagger\gamma^0 \tag{8-102}$$

in matrix notation is the *adjoint* Dirac spinor. It is easily verified (Prob. 8-26) that γ^0 plays here the role of the matrix M of Eq. (8-72), so that the first expression in (8-101) coincides with $\psi \circ \psi$, which we know is a 4-scalar for the general equation (8-55). The third and last expressions in (8-101) then suggest considering $A^{\nu_1} \cdots A^{\nu_n}\psi \circ \psi$, and by using Eqs. (8-57), (8-58), (8-72), and (8-73) it is indeed readily established that these quantities behave under Lorentz transformations as the contravariant components of a tensor of rank n.‡ By invoking also Eq. (8-74) it can be shown further that $A^\nu\psi \circ \psi$ and $A^{[\mu}A^{\nu]}\psi \circ \psi$ are purely imaginary [in agreement with (8-101) where, according to (8-26), we have $A^\nu = i\gamma^\nu$], $A^{(\mu}A^{\nu)}\psi \circ \psi$ is real, and generally§ $(A^{\nu_1} \cdots A^{\nu_n}\psi \circ \psi)^* = (-1)^n A^{\nu_n} \cdots A^{\nu_1}\psi \circ \psi$. As for the second and fourth expressions in (8-101), it is known that these are pseudotensors (scalar and vector), which follows from the fact that γ^5 commutes with the $\sigma_{\mu\nu}$ and hence with all proper Lorentz-transformation operators and that it anticommutes with the space-inversion operator S (see Prob. 8-26). If Q is a matrix having similar properties in our general case, then it is now an obvious conclusion that the quantities $QA^{\nu_1} \cdots A^{\nu_n}\psi \circ \psi$ represent the components of a pseudotensor under $\mathfrak{L}^\uparrow$.

8-4 A NOTE ON THE POSTULATE OF RELATIVITY IN ELEMENTARY PARTICLE PHYSICS

What is the role played by the principles of STR in current theoretical investigations in elementary particle physics? How successful have these

‡ One can show similarly that $\partial\psi/\partial x^\nu \circ \psi$ is a 4-vector, and $A^\mu\, \partial\psi/\partial x^\nu \circ \psi$ is a tensor (giving, incidentally, an alternative proof that $A^\nu\, \partial\psi/\partial x^\nu \circ \psi$ is a scalar), with obvious generalizations leading to tensors of higher rank.

§ $$\begin{aligned}(A^{\nu_1} \cdots A^{\nu_n}\psi \circ \psi)^* = [\psi^\dagger(A^{\nu_n})^\dagger \cdots (A^{\nu_1})^\dagger M\psi]^\dagger &= \psi^\dagger M A^{\nu_1} \cdots A^{\nu_n}\psi \\ &= (-1)^n\psi^\dagger(A^{\nu_1})^\dagger \cdots (A^{\nu_n})^\dagger M\psi,\end{aligned}$$

since, by (8-74), $MA^\nu M^{-1} = -(A^\nu)^\dagger$.

principles been in this new field, and what appears to be the immediate outlook for their remaining unchallenged as further regions of high-energy reactions are penetrated? These are questions it would be desirable to examine, even if only very briefly and in a general way, in closing our study of the broad subject of special relativity. Unfortunately, the prerequisites for any meaningful discussion of these questions far exceed what is being assumed in this text; and in any case, the central ideas of elementary particle theory are not yet sufficiently crystallized to permit such a discussion within a short space. We must content ourselves with a very brief descriptive note, merely calling attention to some pertinent considerations and pointing out a few helpful references.

The meaning to be attached to the term "elementary particle" should perhaps be cleared up first. We have already observed in Sec. 8-3 that this is an elusive term, and doubts have been frequently expressed as to its admitting of any strict general significance. As far as free particles are concerned, in their immediate kinematic manifestations,‡ Wigner's definition of an elementary particle in terms of irreducible unitary representations of the inhomogeneous Lorentz group, mentioned in Sec. 8-3, is perhaps as reasonable a definition as is needed or can be given at present. In any case what needs to be examined first is the fundamental question whether one can basically divorce the notion of an elementary particle from that of an associated quantized field.

An application to the quantum domain of classical relativistic ideas concerning propagation of action would seem to point to a negative answer to the above question. Yet even classically, there have been, in recent years, as mentioned on a few previous occasions, a number of attempts to formulate so-called action-at-a-distance theories that do away with associated fields. The status of these theories is however uncertain, and in any case, this question has little more than academic interest if quantization is not included. But when it is included, and when we are attempting to deal with experiences in the microworld of a more and more remote character, it clearly becomes unsafe to rely on any a priori reasoning resting on classical ideas, and the possibility must be left open that new and perhaps totally unexpected ideas would be required to synthesize accumulated information.

In the light of these considerations, it is reasonable to suppose that for a considerable time to come all available methods of treating 'elementary' quantum systems will have to be explored to their fullest. In all likelihood a combination of approaches now dealt with more or less separately will be required to encompass the behavior of elementary particles in their multiform manifestations. But the energetic and enthusiastic emphasis of the field concept by some investigators and of the particle concept (as it occurs in the S-matrix treatment) by others doubtless represents a constructive phase

‡ The term "kinematic," it should be noted, is used in elementary particle physics more in the classical sense of *mechanical* (bearing on the *general* newtonian laws).

in the present early stage in the development of the theory, in the sense that analysis must precede synthesis. In both of these approaches the relativistic principles play a dominant role along with the general principles of QM.

The electron and the photon were the first elementary particles to be studied by the combined application of relativistic and quantum-mechanical methods. In order to achieve internal theoretical consistency and highest agreement with experimental results, the full machinery of field quantization based on covariantly formulated perturbation theory has had to be developed. The essential results of this theory and some of the accompanying conceptual imagery can be expected to survive mathematical refinements and the introduction of new methods of treating particles and fields. The theory of the electromagnetic and electron-positron fields is certainly the most successful of current fundamental physical theories, both in its astonishing agreement with experiment and in the wealth of ideas that have come from its development. At the same time, from a strictly logical and purely mathematical point of view, this theory is still poorly understood and is beset with difficulties. For an appreciation of present developments in the theory of elementary particles a thorough acquaintanceship with the methods, results, and remaining logical difficulties of the present theory of the electromagnetic and electron-positron fields is most important. The principles of STR, it should be added, have played a decisive part in the development of this theory. On the other hand, it is in the domain of electrodynamics that the question of the limits of validity of these principles is likely to be put eventually to a crucial experimental test.

The principal developments of quantum field theory are summarized in the articles cited in the footnote on page 315. They cover the most creative period in the development of this subject, beginning with the groundbreaking work of Dirac and culminating in the formulations of Tomonaga, Schwinger, Feynman, and Dyson. The latter incorporate all the basic ideas concerning quantized fields that were developed by Dirac, Heisenberg, Pauli, Weisskopf, and others in the preceding two decades, and exploit with spectacular success, using explicitly relativistically covariant methods, the crucial ideas of mass and charge renormalization.‡ While the latter idea

‡ A very helpful introduction to the subject is contained in the two volumes by J. D. Bjorken and S. D. Drell, "Relativistic Quantum Mechanics," and "Relativistic Quantum Fields," McGraw-Hill Book Company, Inc., New York, 1964 and 1965. Among other lucid texts, which have a more complete coverage of certain topics, and different emphases, are W. E. Thirring, "Principles of Quantum Electrodynamics" Academic Press, Inc., New York, 1958 (translated by J. Bernstein); J. M. Jauch and F. Rohrlich, "The Theory of Photons and Electrons," Addison-Wesley Publishing Company, Inc., Cambridge, Mass., 1955; S. S. Schweber, "An Introduction to Relativistic Quantum Field Theory," Row, Peterson and Company, Evanston, Ill., 1961; Akhiezer and Berestetzkii, *op. cit.* (on page 334), and newer editions; N. N. Bogoliubov and D. V. Shirkov, "Introduction to the Theory of Quantized Fields," Interscience Publishers, Inc., New York, 1959 (translated by G. M. Volkoff).

involves essentially the nonclassical concept of vacuum polarization, mass renormalization has, as we know, a classical analog in the subtraction treatments of the infinite self-energy of a *point* electron (touched upon in Sec. 7-5). It is, in the first instance, in connection with these renormalization processes that the conceptual and mathematical difficulties of quantum electrodynamics appear, and already in the much simpler analogous classical problem we can see the subtlety of these difficulties, and the great challenge presented by their complete elucidation.

Despite these difficulties, and other reservations of a purely logical nature that still surround the subject of quantum electrodynamics, useful concepts and procedures have emerged from its investigation (such as asymptotic states, basic properties of scattering matrices, virtual processes, Feynman diagrams) that have interpenetrated the thinking in the field of particle interactions. Yet basically, its central mathematical structure today stands apart from the rest of elementary particle physics. Quantum field theory does have something useful to say about pion phenomena at lower energies.‡ But in the strictly relativistic energy domain, the conventional field-theoretical formalism of quantum electrodynamics, resting as it does essentially on perturbation methods, is powerless to deal directly in any strict sense with the dynamics of strong interactions.§

In these circumstances two extreme attitudes can be adopted. One can give up completely the notion that quantum field theory must necessarily

‡ See, e.g., E. M. Henley and W. Thirring, "Elementary Quantum Field Theory," McGraw-Hill Book Company, Inc., New York, 1962; G. C. Wick, *Rev. Mod. Phys.*, **27**: 339 (1955); G. Källén, "Elementary Particle Physics," chap. 5, Addison-Wesley Publishing Company, Inc. Reading, Mass., 1964. The methods initiated by G. F. Chew and F. E. Low in connection with the treatment of these low-energy phenomena, based on integral relations whose scope was later enlarged in the theory of dispersion relations, contributed to the subsequent development of the relativistic S-matrix approach to high-energy particle phenomena.

§ Although the coupling constant of the weak interactions for low-energy phenomena of the usual kind such as ordinary β decay is very small so that perturbation methods appear to be particularly suitable, in general, renormalization effects due to strong couplings lead to serious problems, especially in the (still largely unexplored) high relativistic domain. Let us note, in this connection, that in some respects the subject of weak interactions has been in the past and is likely to be in the future among the most exciting and rewarding of the fields of investigation in elementary particle physics. The discoveries of parity violation about a decade ago and of possible CP violation quite recently, are striking examples; and the nature of the mass difference of the electron and the muon, which otherwise act practically like twins (except that they have associated with them their individual neutrinos, as recently discovered), is certainly among the most intriguing of present enigmas in particle physics. The interested reader will find an extensive treatment of the subject of weak interactions in the low-energy domain in Källén, *op. cit.*, part 4; S. Gasiorowicz, "Elementary Particle Physics," part 4, John Wiley & Sons, Inc., New York, 1966. Problems in the high-energy domain are discussed in the article by A. Pais in "Theoretical Physics" (collection of lectures given at the seminar on theoretical physics at Trieste, summer 1962), International Atomic Energy Agency, Vienna, 1963.

be deeply relevant to all of elementary particle physics, and attempt to devise new fundamental approaches; or one can attempt to revamp present quantum field theory so that it can be extended to all elementary interactions.

The first attitude is in some respects the more inviting—provided there are enough promising clues to follow. It has been vigorously championed particularly by Geoffrey Chew.‡ Both the point of view and the essentials of the associated S-matrix method are presented in the first of the cited references, and the idea behind the self-consistency methods dubbed "bootstrap dynamics" is explained in the second of these references. Later developments have included interesting attempts to provide a basis for dynamical symmetries of hadrons (i.e., strongly interacting particles) in terms of bootstrap dynamics.§ Whatever the partial successes of this general ambitious program, whether it represents or is developing into basic theory, or is essentially only clever phenomenology, must be deemed to be still an open question.

The verdict on the essential soundness and fruitfulness of the pure S-matrix approach may come soon or may be long in coming, but it is probable that it represents, in any case, an important as well as an interesting step in the present exploratory and groping stage in the theoretical investigations of hadron dynamics; and among the very interesting questions raised by this program that directly touch on our topic is the place of space-time concepts in a formalism that shuns their use entirely, although it involves the Lorentz group itself in an essential manner (the 4-vector property of energy momentum of a particle is a basic postulate, for one thing). Since the spatial distances involved in hadronic interactions (in the center-of-mass frame of the system) are of the order of magnitude of 10^{-13} cm or less, it is not possible at present to be dogmatic on this question: it could turn out to be among the key questions in future breakthroughs in basic particle physics, or it may be devoid of all physical content.¶

If the full role of the relativistic principles and ideas in the S-matrix approach calls for elucidation, little needs to be said about this role in the field-theoretic approach. On the classical relativistic level we know that the field-theoretical point of view appears to be the most natural and certainly, to date, the most fruitful that can be taken in dealing with interacting systems (that admit a meaningful classical treatment). It is understandable to make the assumption that this state of affairs persists as we go over

‡ G. F. Chew, "S-Matrix Theory of Strong Interactions," W. A. Benjamin, Inc., New York, 1961; G. F. Chew, M. Gell-Mann, and A. H. Rosenfeld, Strongly Interacting Particles, *Scientific American*, February 1964.

§ See, e.g., R. H. Capps, Bootstrap Models and Internal Symmetry, in W. E. Brittin and L. Marshall (eds.), "Lectures in Theoretical Physics," vol. 8B, The University of Colorado Press, Boulder, 1965; R. F. Dashen and S. C. Frautschi, *Phys. Rev.*, **145**: 1287 (1966).

¶ As Chew argues eloquently in his article The Dubious Role of the Space-Time Continuum in Microscopic Physics, *Science Progress*, **51**: 529 (1963).

to the quantum domain.‡ But how far can one go with this assumption in the face of the difficulties mentioned before, and what possible directions can one pursue? The answer to the first part of our question is that for the present not very far; as to possible directions, there have been essentially two.§ Attempts are being made, especially by Schwinger, to boldly extend in a purely formal way the range of application of conventional field theory so as to embrace all elementary interactions. This is an ambitious and interesting program with flexibility to adapt itself to pertinent empirical results.¶ But here, as in the case of the S-matrix approach, the question whether what is being accomplished adds up to basic theory or merely exploratory phenomenology, is no less appropriate.

Whether the eventual answer to the last question turns out to be favorable or not, the importance of present efforts in another direction, that of probing the logical and mathematical foundations of field theory, and in particular of quantum electrodynamics, is quite obvious. These investigations are especially relevant to the subject of our present note, because a precise understanding of the structure of field theory cannot but lead also to a better understanding of the significance of special relativity in the microdomain.

We have here also an extremely challenging and profoundly difficult program, which may require prolonged additional effort for yielding conclusive results. Its primary task can be seen to consist in the finding of the precise physical significance of the mathematical formalism known as quantum electrodynamics—which performs so miraculously in representing

‡ In the words of a leading champion of this point of view, Julian Schwinger (in his 1965 Nobel prize lecture, reprinted in *Phys. Today*, June 1966), "relativistic quantum mechanics—the union of the complementarity principle of Bohr with the relativity principle of Einstein—*is* quantum field theory."

§ There is actually also a third direction, initiated by Heisenberg. The central idea here is that all elementary particles are only the manifestations of excitations of a universal quantized relativistic field described by nonlinear equations (or *equation*, when we consider the field components as combined into one universal spinor, with additional indices corresponding to symmetry groups other than the Lorentz group), so that all the basic couplings with their proper strengths and all the self-energies or masses are determined by self-consistency requirements upon the solutions of this all-embracing equation that involves only one universal constant of the dimensions of a length. This is clearly a most alluring idea. However, no indication appears to exist yet that can be taken to definitely point to the essential correctness of Heisenberg's majestic hypothesis. Its latest implementation (which is very ingenious but which contains problematic assumptions) is described in H. P. Dürr and W. Heisenberg, *Z. Naturforsch.*, **16a**: 726 (1961); *Nuovo Cimento*, **37**: 1447 (1965).

¶ A convenient and comprehensive introduction to these investigations is contained in the notes of Schwinger's lectures at the Brandeis Summer Institute in Theoretical Physics of 1964 entitled Field Theory of Particles (in "Particles and Field Theory," vol. 2, Prentice-Hall, Inc., Englewood, N.J., 1965). See also J. Schwinger, Phenomenological Field Theory, in B. Kursunoglu, A. Perlmutter, and I. Sakmar (eds.), "Symmetry Principles at High Energy," W. H. Freeman and Company, San Francisco, 1965.

a large group of phenomena involving electrodynamic interactions—so as either to establish and explain the exclusiveness of these phenomena, or else develop a mathematically precise reformulation of this formalism that admits of significant extension to other types of interaction whether weak or strong.‡ Because a natural logical tool of investigation involves here the setting up of initial axioms and studying their consequences and inner consistency, the general program is sometimes known narrowly as axiomatic field theory; and because, by the very nature of what one wishes to accomplish, rigorous mathematical methods need to be resorted to, it is possible to get the impression that there is something of a striving in this work for mathematical perfection for its own sake. It hardly needs to be stressed that such an impression would be entirely misleading since, quite obviously, mathematics is used in physical theory only as a tool, and the only legitimate criterion to apply is that it is a useful tool, which means in particular that it leads to no logical inconsistencies or ambiguities; but whether it is rigorous in the accepted mathematical sense is quite unessential, provided only that it is possible at least in principle to render it completely rigorous.§

In addition to the principal approaches to elementary particle theory that we have mentioned, there is also another approach—the group-theoretic. This is strictly not an alternative approach, but a method which is significantly associated with all approaches to particle physics. With the aid of the algebraic and analytic theory of group representations, this method takes account of the symmetry relations that underlie elementary phenomena. Because all accumulated evidence and our deepest intuition (which is, perhaps, essentially the same thing) point to such symmetries as reflecting very fundamental aspects of the structure or framework of

‡ A lucid introduction to the ideas and methods presently employed in this program, especially to those developed by A. S. Wightman, is contained in the monograph by R. F. Streater and A. S. Wightman, "PCT, Spin and Statistics, and All That," W. A. Benjamin, Inc., New York, 1964. Informative annotated bibliographies are included. A convenient collection of important initial papers in this field is contained in L. Klein (ed.), "Dispersion Relations and the Abstract Approach to Field Theory," Gordon and Breach, Science Publishers, Inc., New York, 1961. A readable partial introduction to the subject is also contained in G. Barton, "Introduction to Advanced Field Theory," Interscience Publishers, New York, 1963.

§ On the other hand, the need for mathematical rigor in the investigations in question does lead to mathematical topics of a somewhat higher level of difficulty than is usual in conventional physical theories. Let us add in this connection that, of the topics treated in chap. 2 of the cited monograph by Streater and Wightman, it is only those involving analytic functions in many variables and the analysis of linear operators in Hilbert space that are rather demanding. The topic of distributions, except for its relative novelty, need not present any difficulty, and in fact an obvious and easy extension of the realization of ordinary distributions in terms of the limit-processes sketched out in Sec. 7-4 provides a simple concrete explanation of the abstractly defined formalism. The problems presented by products of distributions are also easily appreciated in terms of this representation.

elementary phenomena, the results of the group-theoretic method have a degree of absoluteness about them that is unique.

The consequences of the set of universal symmetries described by the Lorentz group is of course what much of this book is about. The importance of considering the inhomogeneous Lorentz group in the analysis of the relativistic kinematic behavior of elementary quantum systems has been made clear especially by Eugene Wigner, to whose basic paper of 1939 we have already referred a number of times (in Appendices 8B and 8C).‡

Wigner's method of finding the irreducible representations of $\mathcal{P}$ in the case of the restricted group is outlined in Appendix 8C, where an alternative approach due to Shirokov is also indicated. The physical significance of these representations, whether of the restricted or full Poincaré group, is fully discussed in Wigner's initial and subsequent papers just mentioned. The underlying idea is similar to that employed in Sec. 8-3 in arriving at the transformations (8-57), which yield a representation of the homogeneous Lorentz group. But now we deal specifically with quantum-mechanical systems, and, as mentioned in Sec. 8-3, the association of the state vectors for a given system with the elements of our group $\mathcal{P}$ must be governed by the requirement of invariance of the absolute values of all scalar products formed in the Hilbert space of these state vectors, so that the physical behavior of our isolated elementary system does not violate the principle of relativity and the fact that free space-time is homogeneous. The necessary conclusion that the representations must be unitary is of far-reaching scope. It leads, as can be inferred from results presented in Appendix 8C, to the algebra of hermitian operators, the *generators* (to within a factor of i) of our transformation operators. These generators include, as we know, the basic observables of our quantum-mechanical system. We also have, incidentally, using Wigner's theorem presented on page 379, an interesting confirmation of the fact that the space of state vectors for our systems must necessarily be infinite dimensional.

‡ An extensive recent discussion of this subject with special emphasis on the representations of the full inhomogeneous Lorentz group is presented in Wigner's article Unitary Representations of the Inhomogeneous Lorentz Group Including Reflections, in "Summer Conference on Theoretical Physics" (Istanbul, 1962), Gordon and Breach, Science Publishers, Inc., New York, 1963. A comprehensive discussion of the interpretive considerations connected with space-time symmetries is contained in R. M. F. Houtappel, H. Van Dam, and E. P. Wigner, *Rev. Mod. Phys.*, **37**: 595 (1965). This includes a sketch of Wigner's analysis of the representations of $\mathcal{P}$ (secs. 4.8, 4.9, and 4.10). Another useful and comprehensive exposition of this topic, including a discussion of important applications, is given in A. S. Wightman's article L'invariance dans la mécanique quantique relativiste, in C. DeWitt and R. Omnes (eds.), "Dispersion Relations and Elementary Particles," Hermann, Paris, John Wiley & Sons, Inc., New York, 1960. The antiunitary operators representing the time inversion transformations were first established by Wigner (*Gött. Nachr.*, 1932). In addition to the treatment of the space and time reflections in the representations of the full inhomogeneous group in the above references, see also Yu. M. Shirokov, *Nucl. Phys.*, **15**: 1, 13 (1960).

The conclusions that can be reached in Wigner's approach concerning the possible wave equations that can be satisfied by the state vectors of a given unitary representation of $\mathcal{P}$, as well as the association of particle spins and proper masses in terms of the "little groups" contained in the representations, do not differ essentially from what can be obtained using the approach discussed in Sec. 8-3. It is also possible, as indicated in part in Sec. 8-3, to adjoin the effect of space-time translations so that the results of the latter approach are equivalent to those yielded by Wigner's approach. However, in dealing exclusively with quantum-mechanical systems, Wigner's approach is evidently more direct and more deeply grounded as far as the quantum-mechanical aspects are concerned, and seems most appropriate for dealing with quantized fields. It has, in fact, in part inspired significant field theoretic investigations initiated by R. Haag (see the references given on page 356). On the other hand, this method must be supplemented by considerations of the type presented in Sec. 8-3 when our concern is with density quantities such as the density of position probability or of energy associated with a given elementary system.‡

The group-theoretic aspects of field theory have so far been among the most important as far as general results are concerned. The connection between spin and statistics and the so-called PCT (or CPT, etc.) theorem are the only major practical accomplishments that can as yet be claimed for general field theory. The remarkable connection between spin and statistics, known at first only as a purely empirical hypothesis (and still so considered in many elementary textbooks), was first shown to be deducible from the principles of QM and of STR in the case of free fields in a famous paper of Pauli [*Phys. Rev.*, **58**: 716 (1940)]. Incidentally, the analysis in this interesting and instructive paper as far as group-theoretical results are concerned does not involve essentially more than is presented or indicated in Sec. 8-3 and in the appendices, and only very elementary results of field theory. On the other hand, the later deductions of this result under more general conditions, as well as the more incisive proofs of the PCT theorem (the comprehensive assertion that, under the assumptions for which the spin-statistics connection holds and the usual assumptions of local $\mathcal{L}$-invariant field theory, the invariance under the combined operations of space-time inversion PT and charge conjugation C is universally valid) involve the more advanced

‡ For the deduction of particle wave equations in Wigner's approach, see E. P. Wigner and V. Bargmann, *Proc. Nat. Acad. Sci. U.S.A.*, **34**: 211 (1948). A comparison of the two approaches, is to be found in E. P. Wigner, *Z. Physik*, **124**: 665 (1948). The possibility of defining in a meaningful and covariant manner operators for the position of a particle is discussed in M. H. L. Pryce, *Proc. Roy. Soc. London*, **A195**: 62 (1949); T. D. Newton and E. P. Wigner, *Rev. Mod. Phys.*, **21**: 400 (1949); and in a number of later papers, such as, e.g., C. Fronsdal, *Phys. Rev.*, **113**: 1367 (1959); R. Acharya and E. C. G. Sudarshan, *J. Math. Phys.*, **1**: 532 (1960); A. Sankaranarayanan and R. H. Good, Jr., *Phys. Rev.*, **140**: B509 (1965). A well-known investigation by L. L. Foldy and S. A. Wouthuysen [*Phys. Rev.*, **78**: 29 (1950)], dealing with spin-$\frac{1}{2}$ particles, has also been important in this connection.

techniques of general field theory including considerations using the complex Lorentz group.‡

The aforementioned results are associated primarily with space-time symmetries. Recently, special symmetries associated in particular with the dynamics of hadrons have come into prominence; most importantly the group SU_3, introduced by M. Gell-Mann and by Y. Ne'eman, which has led to the few outstanding very recent predictions in particle physics (Ω^-, Ξ^*).§ Like the simpler and all-important isospin symmetry which is described by the familiar group SU_2, so also the internal (or, dynamic) symmetry associated with the group SU_3 has, in the first instance, no direct connection with the Lorentz group. However, empirically an extension of SU_3 to the group SU_6, for the purpose of representing the combination of the degrees of freedom associated with SU_3 and the ordinary spin degrees of freedom of a particle [suggested by Wigner's introduction of the group SU_4 to describe nuclear supermultiplets as arising from a combination of SU_2 (isospin) and SU_2 (spin)—*Phys. Rev.*, **51**: 106 (1937)] has met with encouraging partial successes. This has raised the very interesting but as yet entirely inconclusive question as to how this integration of the two types of symmetry can be accomplished in a relativistically covariant fashion; i.e., how to combine in a meaningful and useful manner the groups SU_3 and $\mathcal{P}$.¶ This question may or may not turn out to be of the most profound importance to the further development of particle physics, but it has in any case stimulated intensive and interesting investigations of group representations and of the Poincaré group.

In conclusion, let us note that even an enumeration of broad topics that enter in the study of elementary particle theory, of which this section essentially consists, and certainly any examination of these topics, must make it perfectly obvious that the relativistic principles that have played an important role in the past in the exploring of the fundamental physical forces have still an equally important if not greater role to play in the future. Even if limits exist, as is entirely conceivable, beyond which these principles are in default, we have every indication that there is much to be done yet within these limits. What we have learned should remain useful for a long time to come.

‡ See, e.g., Streater and Wightman, *op. cit.*, and the references given there to the original papers.

§ See, e.g., M. Gell-Mann and Y. Ne'eman, "The Eightfold Way," W. A. Benjamin, Inc., New York, 1964. A clear and concise discussion of the subject is given in Gasiorowicz, *op. cit.*, chaps. 16, 17, and 18. A helpful first introduction to this topic, including a description of attempts to generalize the Gell-Mann–Ne'eman theory relativistically, is contained in the short survey article by T. W. Kibble, *Contemporary Physics*, **6**: 436 (1965). The currently investigated dynamical symmetries, unlike the space-time symmetries, are only approximate (one speaks of *broken symmetries*), and the discovery of the possible underlying exact internal symmetries and the mechanism of their perturbation are among the most challenging immediate problems in elementary particle theory.

¶ See, e.g., the comprehensive survey article by A. Pais, *Rev. Mod. Phys.*, **38**: 215 (1966).

APPENDIX 8A GROUP REPRESENTATIONS

The present discussion constitutes a continuation of the outlines presented in Appendixes 1A, 3A, and 5A, and the relevant discussion in Secs. 5-1 and 5-2; and it is equally very limited in scope.‡

We begin with a few definitions and elementary results from the theory of groups.

Given an arbitrary group $G = \{g\}$, a subgroup H of G is "invariant" (or, "normal") when

$$gH = Hg \qquad \text{for all } g \text{ in } G \tag{8A-1}$$

where by $gH(Hg)$ we understand the set of elements obtained by multiplying each element of H on the left (right) by g. The group G itself and the subgroup consisting solely of the unit element of G are trivial examples of invariant subgroups. Nontrivial examples are provided by $\mathfrak{L}$, considered as a subgroup of the *complete* (or *full*) homogeneous Lorentz group $\mathfrak{L}_f$, and by the group $\mathfrak{T}$ of all translations (3A-1) in $\mathfrak{M}$, which forms a normal subgroup of the complete inhomogeneous Lorentz group ("Poincaré group"), $\mathcal{P}$ (see Prob. 8-4).

The sets $gH(Hg)$ are known as the "left (right) cosets" of G relative to the subgroup H (whether invariant or not). For any subgroup H we have the result: if g' is in $H_g \equiv gH$ then $H_{g'} = H_g$, and conversely (with a corresponding result for the right cosets). [If $H \equiv \{h\}$, and $g' = gh$, then $(gh)H = g(hH) = gH$; conversely if $g'H = gH$, that is, $g'h' = gh''$, then $g' = gh''(h')^{-1}$ is in H_g.] Thus the cosets for given H form a unique partition of G. If the subgroup H is invariant, the right and left cosets coincide, and we have in addition the important result,

$$H_{g'}H_{g''} = H_{g'g''} \tag{8A-2}$$

which follows at once from (8A-1): $g'Hg''H = g'g''H^2 = g'g''H$. Consequently, the mapping $g \rightarrow H_g$ is a *homomorphism* of G onto the set of cosets

‡ The classic introductions to the subject of group representations of interest to physicists, are the following: H. Weyl, *op. cit.* (on page 162); E. P. Wigner, "Group Theory," Academic Press, Inc., New York, 1959 (translated by J. J. Griffin from a revision of the German edition first published in 1931); B. L. van der Waerden, "Die gruppentheoretische Methode in der Quantenmechanik," Springer Verlag, Berlin, 1932. An extensive treatment of the Lorentz group is to be found, e.g., in M. A. Naimark, "Linear Representations of the Lorentz Group," The Macmillan Company, New York, 1964 (translated by A. Swinfen and O. J. Marstrand). A generally useful and concise coverage of our subject is contained in G. Ya. Lyubarskii, "The Application of Group Theory in Physics," Pergamon Press, New York, 1960 (translated by S. Dedijer). Of special mathematical interest are the presentations in H. Weyl, "The Classical Groups," Princeton University Press, Princeton, 1939; H. Boerner, "Representations of Groups," North-Holland Publishing Company, Amsterdam, 1963; F. D. Murnaghan, "The Theory of Group Representations," The Johns Hopkins Press, Baltimore, 1938. These books contain extensive bibliographies.

$\{H_g\} \equiv \Gamma$, with all the elements of G belonging to H corresponding to the unit element of Γ. The group Γ thus determined by (8A-2) is known as the "factor group" (or "quotient group") of G relative to H, and one generally writes G/H for Γ. For example,

$$\frac{\mathfrak{L}_f}{\mathfrak{L}} = \{I,P,T,-I\} \tag{8A-3}$$

(where the inversion transformations P,T were denoted by $R^{(x)}$ and $R^{(t)}$ in Prob. 3-21), and

$$\frac{\mathcal{P}}{\mathcal{T}} = \mathfrak{L}_f \tag{8A-4}$$

An important corollary of the above result, which is readily perceived, is that every homomorphism of a group G onto a group G' is equivalent to an isomorphism between G' and G/H, where H is the map in G of the identity of G' (the "kernel" of the homomorphism), and is evidently a normal subgroup of G.

Let us now recall the definition of *linear* representations (or simply, "representations"—as they are more frequently called) of a group $G = \{g\}$. Quite generally, a representation $\mathfrak{R}$ of G is determined by a homomorphism of G onto a group $G_{\mathfrak{R}}$ of linear transformations ("operators") T over a vector space V_n (the "representation space") of dimensionality n that can be finite or infinite (the latter case being considered only in Appendix 8C): to every g of G there corresponds under $\mathfrak{R}$ an element $T(g)$ of $G_{\mathfrak{R}}$, and for every pair g', g'' of G,

$$T(g')T(g'') = T(g'g'') \tag{8A-5}$$

When the correspondence between G and $G_{\mathfrak{R}}$ is also one to one, i.e., when $\mathfrak{R}$ is given by an isomorphism, the representation is said to be "faithful" (or "true"). If a representation $\mathfrak{R}$ is not faithful, it is readily concluded (see the penultimate paragraph) that if H is the kernel of the homomorphism of $\mathfrak{R}$, then $\mathfrak{R}$ constitutes a faithful representation of the factor group G/H. In particular, if G has no nontrivial invariant subgroups—we say then that G is a "simple" group—it follows that every nontrivial representation (i.e., excluding the representation given by $G_{\mathfrak{R}} = \{1\}$) is necessarily faithful.

An important illustration of this case is provided by the three-dimensional rotation group $\mathcal{R}$. By use of the properties of these rotations discussed in Appendix 3A, it can be shown that the only normal subgroup of $\mathcal{R}$ not consisting only of the unit element is $\mathcal{R}$ itself. This group is therefore simple. It is also possible to prove that the group $\mathfrak{L}$ is likewise simple, either by similar reasoning using the corresponding results concerning the transformations of $\mathfrak{L}$ as given in Prob. 3-22, or, alternatively,‡ by proceeding

‡ E. P. Wigner, *Ann. of Math.* **40,** 149 (1939), sec. 4D.

directly, using the simplicity of $\mathcal{R}$ and the general decomposition of a Lorentz transformation given in Sec. 3-4, namely

$$T = R'^{-1}LR \tag{8A-6}$$

(in the notation of Sec. 3-4—so that T here represents a general Lorentz transformation).

A central concept in the theory of group representations is that of reducibility, which was considered briefly in Sec. 5-2. The general definition can be stated as follows. A given representation $\mathfrak{R}$ of a group G is "reducible," or "irreducible," according as the representation space V_n contains or does not contain a proper nonzero subspace V_l' $(0 < l < n$ if n is finite), which is "invariant" under $G_\mathfrak{R}$, where, by the latter statement, we mean that for every T in $G_\mathfrak{R}$ the vector Tv is in V_l' whenever v is in V_l'. If, in addition to containing the invariant subspace V_l', the representation space V_n of $\mathfrak{R}$ contains also another invariant subspace V_m'' $(m = n - l)$ such that V_n is the *direct sum* of V_l' and V_m'',

$$V_n = V_l' + V_m'' \tag{8A-7}$$

[see discussion following (5-13) for the definition of the direct sum of vector spaces], we say that $\mathfrak{R}$ is "completely reducible" (or "decomposable"). The significance of this idea is easy to perceive, and will be in evidence as we proceed with our outline of the subject.

The distinction between reducibility and complete reducibility becomes more palpable when we go over to matrix representations. By this we mean the following. With every representation $\mathfrak{R}$ and a given base $\mathcal{B}$ in V_n there is associated a group of n-rowed matrices $\{M\}$, which is isomorphic with $G_\mathfrak{R}$ (see pertinent discussion in Chap. 5); we have thus a "matrix representation" associated with $\mathfrak{R}$ for every possible base $\mathcal{B}$ in V_n. All these matrix representations are said to be mutually "equivalent," and, explicitly, if a change of base $\mathcal{B} \to \mathcal{B}'$ is effected according to Eq. (5A-3), then the connection between the matrices of the corresponding representations $\mathfrak{R}_\mathcal{B}$, $\mathfrak{R}_{\mathcal{B}'}$ is given by the similarity transformation‡

$$M' = A^{-1}MA \tag{8A-8}$$

[If, in the notation of Appendix 5A, we represent the operator T in $\mathcal{B}$ by the equations $T\mathsf{u}_a = M_{ba}\mathsf{u}_b$, then, by (5A-3),

$$T\mathsf{u}_a' = A_{ba}T\mathsf{u}_b = A_{ba}M_{cb}\mathsf{u}_c = A_{ba}M_{cb}A_{dc}^{-1}\mathsf{u}_d' = (A^{-1}MA)_{da}\mathsf{u}_d']$$

Now, if V_l' is an invariant subspace of V_n, then for a base $\mathcal{B}$ that is *adapted* to V_l', by V_l' containing the first l of the base vectors, every element

‡ The transformation (8A-8) is frequently given with A replaced by A^{-1}, corresponding to an interchange of primed and unprimed base vectors in (5A-3).

M of $\mathfrak{R}_{\mathfrak{B}}$ has the form

$$M = \begin{bmatrix} M' & N \\ 0 & M'' \end{bmatrix} \qquad \begin{aligned} M' &= \text{square matrix of order } l \\ M'' &= \text{square matrix of order } m = n - l \end{aligned} \tag{8A-9}$$

For if we represent every vector v of V_n symbolically by the matrix $\begin{bmatrix} v' \\ v'' \end{bmatrix}$, where v' stands for the set of components of v relative to the base vectors in V'_l, and if we write correspondingly, $M = \begin{bmatrix} M' & N \\ S & M'' \end{bmatrix}$, then

$$Mv = \begin{bmatrix} M'v' + Nv'' \\ Sv' + M''v'' \end{bmatrix}$$

and by our assumption [implying that $(Mv)''$ must be zero with v''] it follows that $S = 0$. Moreover, since, by (8A-9), the product of two matrices M, M_1 has the form

$$\begin{bmatrix} M'M'_1 & M'N_1 + NM_1'' \\ 0 & M''M_1'' \end{bmatrix}$$

we see that not only does the matrix family $\{M'\}$ form a representation of our group G, but that this is true also of the matrix family $\{M''\}$, although in general the rectangular matrix N in (8A-9) need not vanish. On the other hand, if, by a proper choice of $\mathfrak{B}$, N is zero for all the elements of G, then our representation is seen to be completely reducible since then we clearly have (8A-7), where V''_m is an invariant subspace of V_n associated with $\{M''\}$. Conversely, if $\mathfrak{R}$ is completely reducible, as originally defined, with the corresponding decomposition (8A-7), then it is evident that we can find a base $\mathfrak{B}$ that is adapted (in an obvious sense) to V'_l and V''_m, with the matrices of $\mathfrak{R}_{\mathfrak{B}}$ having the form

$$M = \begin{bmatrix} M' & 0 \\ 0 & M'' \end{bmatrix}, \qquad M',\ M'' \text{ as in (8A-9)} \tag{8A-10}$$

In the majority of physical applications we deal with representations that have the important property of being completely reducible if they are reducible. To simplify our discussion we therefore limit our attention here to representations that have this property. For a full discussion of this question we refer the interested reader to the references given earlier. We content ourselves here with illustrating the property in question by simple but useful examples, and with noting without proof two pertinent general theorems.

An immediate example is provided by the transformations of importance in QM, namely, the *unitary* transformations (or operators). The property that the form (8A-9) necessarily implies the form (8A-10) can be proved as follows, using the notation employed earlier:

$$I_n = MM^\dagger = \begin{bmatrix} M' & N \\ 0 & M'' \end{bmatrix} \begin{bmatrix} M'^\dagger & 0 \\ N^\dagger & M''^\dagger \end{bmatrix} = \begin{bmatrix} \cdots & NM''^\dagger \\ \cdots & M''M''^\dagger \end{bmatrix}$$

so that $M''M''^\dagger = I_m$, $NM''^\dagger = 0$; whence, $M''^\dagger M'' = I_m$,

$$0 = NM''^\dagger M'' = N$$

Another immediate example for the complete reducibility property is provided by the important class of groups called "abelian" (every pair of whose elements commute). For these groups this property can be justified with the aid of a remarkably useful and yet very simple algebraic theorem known as *Schur's lemma.* We require here only part of this lemma, which can be stated as follows

If a matrix S commutes with every member of an irreducible matrix representation $\{M\}$ of a given group, then S must be a "scalar" matrix (i.e., a multiple of the identity).

[This result can be proved by noting that if S is not the zero matrix (which is of course also a scalar matrix), and if λ is an eigenvalue of S (necessarily existing) and v an associated eigenvector, then by our commutability assumption, $0 = M(S - \lambda I)v = (S - \lambda I)Mv$, so that Mv is also an eigenvector, for each of our M. Since the space spanned by the set $\{Mv\}$ is invariant under $\{M\}$, it must coincide by our irreducibility assumption with the entire underlying vector space, and hence $S - \lambda I = 0$.] When this result is applied to the matrices of an irreducible representation of an abelian group, it follows that each is a scalar matrix and hence it must be an ordinary number in view of the assumed irreducibility.

The importance in physical applications of groups possessing the complete reducibility property is explained in part by two theorems. One states that this property belongs to every finite group (see, e.g., Boerner, *op. cit.*, pp. 48–49), and hence, in particular, to the permutation groups; the other, the famous *Peter-Weyl theorem,* states (in its general formulation) that for *semisimple* Lie groups, all finite-dimensional reducible representations are completely reducible.‡ A Lie group, it will be recalled, is a continuous group having a finite number of parameters (see Appendix 3A). We have already given the definition of a simple group: it is a group containing no proper invariant subgroups. If this restriction is relaxed to allow invariant subgroups that are not abelian we have the definition of a "semisimple" group (in both cases *discrete* invariant subgroups are allowed).

‡ The original formulation [F. Peter and H. Weyl, *Math. Ann.*, **97:** 737 (1927)] involved also the assumption of compactness (the term is explained in the sequel) of the group, and the finiteness of the dimensionality of the irreducible representations was in consequence a conclusion, not an assumption.

We have already seen that the physically important groups $\mathfrak{R}$ and $\mathfrak{L}$ are in fact simple, and hence the Peter-Weyl theorem applies to them a fortiori.

The restriction to finite-dimensional representations to which the conclusion of the Peter-Weyl theorem applies simplifies considerably the analysis of a given representation $\mathfrak{R}$. After obtaining a decomposition as given in (8A-10), in terms of a given matrix realization $\mathfrak{R}_{\mathfrak{B}}$, representing what is called in an obvious sense, the "direct sum"

$$\mathfrak{R} = \mathfrak{R}' + \mathfrak{R}'' \tag{8A-11}$$

of the component representations associated with the invariant subspaces V'_l, V''_m, we can proceed in a similar manner with further decomposition if either $\mathfrak{R}'$ or $\mathfrak{R}''$ or both are reducible. By the finiteness n of the original representation, this process must terminate after a finite number of steps. The final result is therefore of the form

$$\mathfrak{R} = \mathfrak{R}_1 + \mathfrak{R}_2 + \cdots + \mathfrak{R}_p, \qquad \mathfrak{R}_1, \mathfrak{R}_2, \ldots \text{ irreducible} \tag{8A-12}$$

where p is finite, and some of the components $\mathfrak{R}$ may be mutually isomorphic. Moreover, it can be proved without difficulty that except for the order of the terms, the total decomposition (8A-12) is unique.‡ This is evidently a cardinal result of the theory under survey.

The central task of this theory, the determination and classification of all the irreducible representations of a given group, has engaged the attention of a number of leading algebraists, notably, G. Frobenius, W. Burnside, I. Schur, E. Cartan, and H. Weyl. Many interesting general methods have been devised, into which we cannot however enter here in any systematic fashion even in outline (they are discussed in the references given on page 360). For our immediate objectives it will in any case suffice to turn directly to a study of the representations of the groups $\mathfrak{R}$ and $\mathfrak{L}$ (the latter being considered in Appendices 8B and 8C).

In the case of connected Lie groups such as $\mathfrak{R}$ and $\mathfrak{L}$, which can be totally generated from their infinitesimal elements, the representation problem simplifies considerably, inasmuch as it suffices to confine attention to these elements. In fact, suppose that $\mathfrak{R}$ is a given representation of the set $\bar{G}$ of infinitesimal elements of our group G, then by applying Lie's integration theory (using the result in Prob. 3-19*a* and the theorem on page 74),§ $\mathfrak{R}$ can be extended to a representation of all of G; moreover, if $\mathfrak{R}$ is irreducible when referring to $\bar{G}$, the extension over G must obviously be also irreducible. Conversely, to every irreducible representation of G corresponds an irreducible representation of $\bar{G}$ since, by the above reasoning, it is readily proved

‡ See, e.g., Weyl, *op. cit.*(The Theory of Groups and Quantum Mechanics), chap. 3, sec. 6.

§ This integration, as can be readily verified, is quite simple, involving straightforward exponentiation when, as in the present instances, the underlying transformation group is linear (the theory outlined in Appendix 3A was general). See, e.g., Naimark, *op. cit.*, secs. 4.3 and 7.3.

that every nontrivial proper invariant subspace relative to a representation of $\bar{G}$ must remain an invariant subspace for the extended representation. We can reduce our analysis further by noting that the representation of every element (3A-5) has the form (with Q now denoting a typical generator matrix)

$$M_\epsilon(Q) = I + \epsilon Q, \qquad \epsilon \text{ infinitesimal} \tag{8A-13}$$

and that the structure of the matrix $M_\epsilon(Q)$ is given completely by the structure of the "generator" matrix Q. Thus, it is sufficient to investigate the structure of these generators Q, and it will be helpful to utilize in this connection a convenient and commonly used terminology and to recall pertinent results given in Appendix 3A.

The general transformation equations (3A-3) can be looked upon as representing a given realization of an abstract r-parameter Lie group G—the transformations of $\mathfrak{R}$ form in fact a *representation* (it may be called the "natural representation") of the group of spatial rigid-body rotations. The *generators* (or, "infinitesimal operators," as they are frequently called) Q_u given in (3A-5) form accordingly a realization of what is known as the *Lie algebra* of G (or, "infinitesimal group," in the older literature).

By the term "algebra" one presently understands a mathematical system consisting of a vector space $\{v\}$ over a field F together with a bilinear composition ("multiplication") $v_1 \circ v_2$, which is distributive with respect to vector addition and associative as well as commutative with respect to multiplication by elements of F, but is itself in general neither commutative nor associative [$\alpha(v_1 \circ v_2) = (\alpha v_1) \circ v_2$, but in general, $v_1 \circ (v_2 \circ v_3) \neq (v_1 \circ v_2) \circ v_3$]. The system of ordinary vectors and vector multiplication is an important familiar example of an algebra. An algebra is called a "Lie algebra" if its multiplication satisfies the two conditions

$$\begin{gathered} v_1 \circ v_2 = -v_2 \circ v_1 \\ (v_1 \circ v_2) \circ v_3 + (v_2 \circ v_3) \circ v_1 + (v_3 \circ v_1) \circ v_2 = 0 \end{gathered} \tag{8A-14}$$

(the latter being known as the "Jacobi identity").

The definition of an r-parameter continuous group implies that the vector space spanned by the generators Q_u is r dimensional. The multiplication $Q_u \circ Q_v$ is defined in our realization by the commutator $[Q_u,Q_v]$ (see Prob. 3-19*b*), which we know satisfies the multiplication conditions (8A-14) of a Lie algebra. The essential content of Lie's integration theory (outlined in part in Appendix 3A) is that a Lie group (or a connected part of it including the identity) is essentially determined by a given Lie algebra. When the group (3A-3), with which we start, is *linear*, so that it constitutes a natural representation of the underlying transformation group, we have to deal with the *matrices* of the transformations and with matrix generators [see the discussion leading to Eq. (3A-23)], which define what we may term the "natural Lie algebra." By a *representation* of this algebra $\mathfrak{A}_0$ we understand a homomorphic mapping of its elements onto the elements of a matrix algebra $\mathfrak{A}$, where the "homomorphism" is now understood to have reference to all the operations defining an algebra, and the product in $\mathfrak{A}$ is defined as in $\mathfrak{A}_0$, that is, $\mathfrak{A}$ is also a Lie algebra.

The natural Lie algebra of $\mathcal{R}$ can be defined by the base vectors, consisting of the matrices [see (3A-24)]‡

$$U_1 = \begin{bmatrix} 0 & 0 & 0 \\ 0 & 0 & 1 \\ 0 & -1 & 0 \end{bmatrix}, \quad U_2 = \begin{bmatrix} 0 & 0 & -1 \\ 0 & 0 & 0 \\ 1 & 0 & 0 \end{bmatrix}, \quad U_3 = \begin{bmatrix} 0 & 1 & 0 \\ -1 & 0 & 0 \\ 0 & 0 & 0 \end{bmatrix} \tag{8A-15}$$

and the structure constants, which, according to Eqs. (3A-23) and (3A-24), are given by

$$c_{ijk} = \epsilon_{ijk} \tag{8A-16}$$

Our problem is to find all irreducible representations of this algebra, and in this case we fortunately have a relatively simple procedure for solving this problem completely, owing to a very helpful property of $\mathcal{R}$, namely its *compactness*. What one understands by a Lie group being "compact" perhaps calls for a word of explanation.

By the compactness of a continuous group $G = \{g(a)\}$ we simply mean that the space $\mathcal{S}$ of the group elements g, considered as a topological manifold, is compact. We may usually think of the topology as defined by a specification of the *limit points* of subsets of $\mathcal{S}$ in terms of the limit points of the corresponding subsets in the parameter space $\{a\}$; and compactness can then be defined by the property that every infinite subset of $\mathcal{S}$ has a limit point in $\mathcal{S}$. [By way of illustration, the reader will recall that a subset of a euclidean space is compact if and only if it is bounded and closed (i.e., if it is contained in a finite sphere and it contains all its limit points).]

Compact Lie groups possess the remarkable property of having only *finite-dimensional* irreducible representations (see Peter and Weyl, *op. cit.*). Another important property shared by these groups with finite groups is that every matrix representation of such a group is equivalent to a *unitary* representation.§ We have already noted the happy property of unitary representations of being completely reducible when they are reducible. We now take account of an additional advantage. The unitarity of a group

‡ The matrices (8A-15) are also found in the literature with the opposite signs arising from the definition of the rotations as that of vectors rather than of coordinate axes. Indeed, $U_k = (dR_{\phi \mathbf{e}_k}/d\phi)|_{\phi=0}$, using the notation employed on page 70, and a change in the interpretation of the rotation operation entails a change in the sign of the rotation angle ϕ.

§ For a concise proof for finite groups and for $\mathcal{R}$, see, e.g., Luybarskii, *op. cit.*, secs. 15 and 16. The proof for finite groups involves a summation over all the elements of the group; in the continuous case the corresponding integration is always manageable for compact groups, because of the boundedness of continuous functions defined over a compact space.

representation implies that the corresponding generators are anti-hermitian since, for any matrix Q, if $M^\dagger = M^{-1}$ and $M = e^Q \equiv \exp(Q)$, then $Q^\dagger = -Q$ because $M^\dagger = \exp(Q^\dagger)$ and $M^{-1} = \exp(-Q)$. Thus, if we have a unitary representation of $\mathcal{R}$,‡ with associated generators U_1, U_2, U_3 [using the same symbols as for the 'natural' generators (8A-15)], and we set

$$U_k = iJ_k, \qquad k = 1, 2, 3 \tag{8A-17}$$

then the J_k are *hermitian* matrices, and we can exploit the eigenvalue properties of such matrices in studying such representations.

The method is in fact well known in QM in connection with the study of angular-momentum operators (see, e.g., Schiff, *op. cit.*, sec. 24), for by (8A-16) we see that the J_k satisfy the commutation relations

$$[J_k, J_r] = i\epsilon_{krs} J_s \tag{8A-18}$$

which will be recognized as being precisely of the form satisfied by the components of an angular-momentum vector operator (when $\hbar = 1$). In the language of the quantum-mechanical problem, our task is to find the matrices that represent the three operators J_k for a particular base in Hilbert space.§ This base is built up of the eigenvectors common to one of the J_k, say J_3, and to the operator function (representing the square of the angular momentum)

$$J^2 = J_1{}^2 + J_2{}^2 + J_3{}^2 \tag{8A-19}$$

which commutes with all the J_k by virtue of (8A-18). The method of obtaining the angular-momentum matrices follows from a general theory initiated by Cartan, of which we shall presently give a brief description. Although we may assume that the reader is acquainted with the quantum-mechanical treatment, it may be helpful to review it rapidly at this point.

The first step is to introduce the operators

$$J_\pm = J_1 \pm iJ_2 \tag{8A-20}$$

and to note that, by (8A-18), we have the relations

$$[J_3, J_\pm] = \pm J_\pm \tag{8A-21}$$

and

$$J_\mp J_\pm = J^2 - J_3(J_3 \pm 1) \tag{8A-22}$$

‡ The compactness of $\mathcal{R}$ can be recognized at once by considering, e.g., the parameter space given by the vector $\mathbf{\Omega}$ in (3A-9) with $-\pi \leq \Omega \leq \pi$, and with the identification for each direction of $\mathbf{\Omega}$ of the points corresponding to $\Omega = -\pi$ and $+\pi$ (which clearly yield the same rotation).

§ In the terminology now common in the literature on QM, such a base is known as a "representation"—which must be distinguished from the group-theoretical meaning of this term. Let us note also that the mathematical similarity in the case under discussion, of the two problems, the group-theoretical and the quantum-mechanical, has in the past received scant attention among physicists, because group-theoretical methods were, with a few notable exceptions, not generally appreciated or explicitly recognized as such.

which lead to the following immediate conclusions. If we represent by ψ_{am} the common set of normalized eigenvectors of J^2 and J_3, so that

$$J^2\psi_{am} = a\psi_{am}, \qquad J_3\psi_{am} = m\psi_{am} \tag{8A-23}$$

then by (8A-21), $J_3(J_\pm\psi_{am}) = (m \pm 1)J_\pm\psi_{am}$. Hence

$$J_\pm\psi_{am} = C_{am}\psi_{a,m\pm1} \tag{8A-24}$$

where, by (8A-22) and (8A-23), and since the ψ are assumed normalized, and $J_+ = J_-^\dagger$,

$$\begin{aligned}|C_{am}|^2 = (J_\pm\psi_{am}, J_\pm\psi_{am}) &= (\psi_{am}, J_\mp J_\pm\psi_{am}) \\ &= a - m(m \pm 1)\end{aligned} \tag{8A-25}$$

This equation shows that the eigenvalue set $\{m\}$ must contain, for each fixed a, the appropriate roots of $a - m\,(m \pm 1) = 0$, since otherwise the step-up and step-down processes indicated in (8A-24) could continue indefinitely, which is clearly inconsistent with the expression (8A-25). The largest and smallest of the pertinent roots have the respective values $\mp\frac{1}{2}(1 - \sqrt{1 + 4a}) \equiv \pm j(a) \equiv \pm j\,[j \geq 0$ since, by the first of Eqs. (8A-23), $a \geq 0]$. This result can be written:

$$|m| \leq j, \qquad a \equiv a(j) = j(j + 1) \tag{8A-26}$$

The next important step is to note that, by a repetition of the above reasoning regarding the absolute value of m for fixed a, it can be concluded that the only possible values of m for given a are those that are obtained by unit steps starting with $-j$ and ending with j. This yields directly the crucial conclusion that $2j$ must be a positive integer or zero. Thus the eigenvalue problem (8A-23) is completely solved, and with the definition (8A-26) for $j = j(a)$, we have:

$$\begin{aligned} j &= 0, \tfrac{1}{2}, 1, \ldots \\ m &= -j, -j + 1, \ldots, j - 1, j \end{aligned} \tag{8A-27}$$

The matrix elements of the operators J_k are now also immediately found (with a given choice of the arbitrary phase factors). Indeed, by Eqs. (8A-24), (8A-25), and (8A-26), upon choosing the square root of (8A-25) as $C_{am} = +[j(j + 1) - m(m \pm 1)]^{1/2}$, we have

$$J_\pm\psi_{am} = [j(j + 1) - m(m \pm 1)]^{1/2}\psi_{a,m\pm1}$$

It follows, in view of the orthogonality relations of the Hilbert-space vectors ψ_{am} (as nondegenerate eigenvectors of the hermitian operator J_3), and using now the convenient Dirac bra-ket notation, that

$$\langle jm|J_\pm|j'm'\rangle = [j(j + 1) - mm']^{1/2}\,\delta_{jj'}\,\delta_{m,m'\pm1}$$

Remembering the relations (8A-20), we have thus the desired matrix elements:

$$
\begin{aligned}
\langle jm|J_1|j'm'\rangle &= \tfrac{1}{2}\,[j(j+1) - mm']^{1/2}\,\delta_{jj'}(\delta_{m,m'+1} + \delta_{m,m'-1}) \\
\langle jm|J_2|j'm'\rangle &= -\frac{i}{2}\,[j(j+1) - mm']^{1/2}\,\delta_{jj'}(\delta_{m,m'+1} - \delta_{m,m'-1}) \qquad \text{(8A-28)} \\
\langle jm|J_3|j'm'\rangle &= m\delta_{jj'}\,\delta_{mm'}
\end{aligned}
$$

For instance, the submatrices corresponding to the quantum numbers $j = \frac{1}{2}$ and 1 are (using the same symbols for these matrices as for the corresponding operators):

$$
j = \tfrac{1}{2}: \qquad J_1 = \tfrac{1}{2}\begin{bmatrix} 0 & 1 \\ 1 & 0 \end{bmatrix}, \qquad J_2 = \tfrac{1}{2}\begin{bmatrix} 0 & -i \\ i & 0 \end{bmatrix}, \qquad J_3 = \tfrac{1}{2}\begin{bmatrix} 1 & 0 \\ 0 & -1 \end{bmatrix} \qquad \text{(8A-29)}
$$

$$
j = 1: \qquad J_1 = \frac{1}{\sqrt{2}}\begin{bmatrix} 0 & 1 & 0 \\ 1 & 0 & 1 \\ 0 & 1 & 0 \end{bmatrix},
$$

$$
J_2 = \frac{1}{\sqrt{2}}\begin{bmatrix} 0 & -i & 0 \\ i & 0 & -i \\ 0 & i & 0 \end{bmatrix}, \qquad J_3 = \begin{bmatrix} 1 & 0 & 0 \\ 0 & 0 & 0 \\ 0 & 0 & -1 \end{bmatrix} \qquad \text{(8A-30)}
$$

The physical interpretation of the above results is assumed known and does not in any case concern us at this place. What we wish to show now is that the same mathematical steps lead, as remarked before, to a solution of our representation problem.

First let us note that in forming an expression such as given in (8A-19), we are outside the rules of a Lie algebra; we are exploiting, however, the fact that the elements of our algebra are matrices and hence admit also of ordinary matrix multiplication. The method we have outlined is thus entirely applicable to our group-theoretical problem. That for each value (8A-27) of j, the matrices (8A-28) are the generators (within the factor i) of a representation algebra $\mathfrak{A}_j$ of $\mathfrak{R}$, is an immediate consequence of the fact that by our construction they satisfy the commutation relations (8A-18). It remains only to prove that each $\mathfrak{A}_j$ is irreducible, and that as j runs over the set (8A-27), the corresponding representations $\mathfrak{D}_j$ exhaust essentially all the irreducible representations of $\mathfrak{R}$.

The irreducibility of $\mathfrak{A}_j$ follows readily from an application of the commutation relations (8A-21) similar to that made above. Irreducibility with respect to the set J_+, J_-, J_3 will of course imply the irreducibility relative to our original set U_1, U_2, U_3, connected with the former set by Eqs. (8A-17) and (8A-20). Now, if the representation space S_j of $\mathfrak{D}_j$ contains a subspace S' that is invariant under the J_k, then J_3 must have at least one eigenvector

ϕ inside S',‡ and by operating on ϕ with J_+ and J_-, it follows that S' contains all the vectors $\psi_{-j}, \ . \ . \ . \ , \psi_j$, i.e., that $S' = S_j$.

The fact that within a similarity transformation our present method gives us *all* our irreducible unitary representations can be shown to follow from the above analysis and the general theorem, mentioned earlier, asserting that the compact Lie groups have only finite-dimensional irreducible representations;§ but we need not enter here into the details of the argument.

The preceding method was sketched out in any case mainly because it establishes a link between group-representation theory and a familiar topic in QM, and also because it serves as a simple yet very important example of the general theory of Lie group representations developed by Cartan, Weyl, and others, which is currently gaining interest in connection with symmetry studies directed towards understanding the regularities observed in the high-energy 'spectroscopy' of elementary particles. We shall have occasion (in Sec. 8-4) to refer to this theory and to the applications to elementary particle physics, and we therefore pause briefly now to state some of its principal results, and to point out similarities with the above treatment for $\mathfrak{R}$.¶

The general theory is well developed for semisimple Lie groups, and especially for those semisimple groups that are also compact. These groups have, in fact, been completely classified by Élie Cartan, and this classification has been recently of some interest in connection with the exploratory

‡ Since the operator J_3', to which J_3 reduces when its domain of definition is restricted to S', is also hermitian, and since if ϕ is an eigenvector of J_3'—necessarily existing—it is of course also an eigenvector of J_3.

§ That, in particular, the natural representation given by (8A-15) is equivalent to that given by (8A-30), is easily verified directly (Prob. 8-5).

¶ A concise and thorough survey of the theory of representations of Lie groups, of interest to physicists, due to G. Racah, who has himself made valuable contributions to the subject, has been recently reprinted (from his Princeton 1951 lecture notes entitled "Group Theory and Spectroscopy") in "Ergebnisse der exakten Naturwissenschaften," 37 Band, Springer-Verlag, Berlin, 1965. This volume also contains a reprinting of W. Pauli's CERN report of 1956 entitled "Continuous Groups and Quantum Mechanics," which, in addition to a brief introduction to the theory of representations of Lie algebras, also includes a survey of results on the representations of the homogeneous and inhomogeneous Lorentz groups. A more recent set of lectures by Racah, "Lectures on Lie Groups," which includes a discussion of the representations of the group SU_3 is contained in F. Gürsey, (ed.), "Group Theoretical Concepts and Methods in Elementary Particle Physics," Gordon and Breach, Science Publishers, New York, 1964.

For the mathematically-minded reader the following textbook by an expert in the field can be recommended: N. Jacobson, "Lie Algebras," Interscience Publishers, New York, 1962. This book contains extensive references to the mathematical literature on the subject. Of these references we wish to call the reader's attention especially to the following papers by E. B. Dynkin on semisimple group representations: The Structure of Semisimple Lie Algebras, *Am. Math. Soc. Transl.*, (1), **9** (1950); Maximal Subgroups of the Classical Groups, *Am. Math. Soc. Transl.*, (2), **6** (1957)—particularly, the summary in the Supplement, p. 319 ff.

theoretical investigations in particle physics. We do not discuss here this classification, since such discussion is available in many recent easily accessible survey articles.‡ We shall only note the available algebraic criteria in terms of the structure constants c_{uvw} [see (3A-23)], for the semisimplicity or compactness in question. Such criteria were found by Cartan, who is responsible for laying the complete groundwork for this theory.

Cartan's necessary and sufficient condition for semisimplicity is surprisingly simple: it is just the nonvanishing of the determinant of the symmetric matrix

$$g_{uv} = c_{wux}c_{xvw} \tag{8A-31}$$

If in addition this matrix is negative definite (i.e., if $g_{uv}a_u a_v$ is negative for all nonvanishing vectors a_u), then the semisimple group is compact, this being also a necessary condition.

The actual values of the c_{uvw} depend of course on the arbitrary choice of the base vectors of the Lie algebra; but it is easily verified by reference to the defining equations (3A-21) that, upon writing the structure constants as $c^w{}_{uv}$, they can be thought of as representing the components of a tensor of the covariance and contravariance character indicated by the placement of the indices, with respect to the group of linear transformations over the underlying vector space (see Chap. 5). [With $\{Q_u\}$ serving as a base in the vector space of our algebra, we have, by (3A-21) (the notation being self-explanatory), $[\mathrm{v}_\xi,\mathrm{v}_\eta] \equiv [\xi^u Q_u,\eta^v Q_v] = \xi^u\eta^v[Q_u,Q_v] = \xi^u\eta^v c^w{}_{uv}Q_w = \zeta^w Q_w$, $\zeta^w = c^w{}_{uv}\xi^u\eta^v$, and the tensor property of $c^w{}_{uv}$ follows by the quotient theorem of tensor calculus.] It follows that g_{uv} is a tensor, and the above conditions are thus seen to have absolute validity, as they must. Moreover, since this tensor is symmetric, it has real eigenvalues,§ and these conditions state that a Lie group is semisimple if and only if there are no zero eigenvalues and that it is also compact if and only if the eigenvalues are all negative.

The latter case is exemplified by the Lie algebra for $\mathfrak{R}$, for which

$$g_{ij} = -2\delta_{ij} \tag{8A-32}$$

as follows at once from Eqs. (8A-31) and (8A-16). The structure constants for $\mathfrak{L}$, on the other hand, can be shown to satisfy the condition for semisimplicity, but not for compactness. The fact that the group $\mathfrak{L}$ is not

‡ In addition to the references to Racah's lecture notes given in the preceding footnote, the following survey articles, for example, contain summaries of the Cartan-Weyl theory: A. Salam, The Formalism of Lie Groups, in "Theoretical Physics," International Atomic Energy Agency, Vienna, 1963; G. de Franceschi and L. Maiani, *Fortschr. Physik*, **13**: 279–384 (1965). The latter article contains an extensive bibliography covering both theory and applications to particle physics.

§ We are involved here in the tacit assumption of the *reality* of the structure constants. In general, the underlying number fields of the algebraic structures of present interest in physics are either real or complex. It needs to be stressed that even if the number field is left unspecified, as is usual in physical writing, the distinction can be crucial.

compact is easily seen directly by considering the transformations of the form (2-6) or (3A-29): the parameter spaces are here respectively the semi-open interval $0 \leq \beta < 1$, and the infinite interval $0 \leq \psi < \infty$.

The tensor (8A-31) plays also a useful role in the analysis of the representations of a given Lie algebra. Since for semisimple groups the matrix (8A-31) satisfies the relation (5-25) (with the indices $a, b, \ldots$ taken to have the same range as $u, v, \ldots$, namely, $1, 2, \ldots, r$), we can form the tensor g^{ab} given by (5-26), and for a given representation, we can consider the sum

$$C = g^{ab}Q_aQ_b \tag{8A-33}$$

where the Q_a now denote the generators of our representation serving as base vectors of the associated algebra, and the products Q_aQ_b, as noted previously, are ordinary matrix products. This expression has an important property, first proved by H. Casimir—C is therefore known as a "Casimir operator"—that it commutes with all the generators. [The proof is straightforward:

$$[C,Q_u] = g^{ab}\{Q_a[Q_b,Q_u] + [Q_a,Q_u]Q_b\} = g^{ab}(c^w{}_{bu}Q_aQ_w + c^w{}_{au}Q_wQ_b) \equiv c^{wa}{}_u(Q_aQ_w + Q_wQ_a) = 0$$

because by (8A-31) (that is, $g_{uv} = c^w{}_{ux}c^x{}_{vw}$, in our present notation), and the Jacobi identity (3A-22), the tensor $c^{wa}{}_u$ is antisymmetric in the upper indices.] The quantity (8A-33) is moreover an *invariant* under changes of base. [With $Q_a \equiv \mathbf{e}_a$ we have, by Eqs. (5-33), (5-37), and the last equation in (5-34): $C' = N^a{}_uN^b{}_vg^{uv}M^c{}_aQ_cM^d{}_bQ_d = \delta^c_u\,\delta^d_v g^{uv}Q_cQ_d = C$.]

The commutativity property of the Casimir operator (8A-33) leads, upon application of Schur's lemma (given on page 364), to the significant conclusion that with every irreducible representation $\mathfrak{R}$ of a semisimple group there is associated a unique eigenvalue of this operator, having every vector of the representation space of $\mathfrak{R}$ as its eigenvector. In the case of the group $\mathfrak{R}$, Eqs. (8A-32) and (8A-17) show that $C/2$ coincides with J^2 given in Eq. (8A-19). In this case, as we have seen, the eigenvalues $a(j)$ of J^2 given in Eqs. (8A-26), (8A-27) specify uniquely all the irreducible representations of our group. In general, as is to be expected, the operator C does not suffice to characterize completely the irreducible representations of a group (semisimplicity is henceforth tacitly assumed), but further operators ("generalized Casimir operators") can be frequently found, which, together with C, form a complete set that does suffice for such a characterization.‡ However, the only general approach to the group-representation problem presently available is that presented by the Cartan-Weyl theory.

‡ Casimir's approach, inspired by quantum-mechanical considerations, came after the investigations of Cartan and Weyl. It has been subsequently significantly extended by Racah. See Racah, *op. cit.* ("Group Theory and Spectroscopy"), part 3, sec. 4. See also L. C. Biedenharn, *J. Math. Phys.*, **4:** 436 (1963).

The starting point of this theory is a judicious choice of base in our Lie algebra, comprising two sets. The first set consists of mutually commuting elements $H_1, \ldots, H_\rho$, where ρ is the largest number of such elements in the Lie algebra, a number that is easily verified to be characteristic of the group and not of the chosen base. This number is called the "rank" of the group and it obviously determines the highest dimension of its abelian subgroups. In the case of $\mathfrak{R}$, $\rho = 1$, since no two of its generators commute, and in fact its only abelian subgroups are the one-parameter groups of rotation about a fixed axis. For $\mathfrak{L}$, Eqs. (3A-28) and in particular Eqs. (3A-27*b*), show that $\rho = 2$. Another Lie group of rank 2 of current physical interest is the group SU_3, where by SU_n one understands the group of all n-rowed unitary and unimodular matrices, this being a group of $n^2 - 1$ parameters with $\rho = n - 1$.

The second set of Cartan base vectors, $E_1, \ldots, E_{r-\rho}$ supplementing $H_1, \ldots, H_\rho$, have the following properties. Consider a general representation of our Lie algebra over the infinite-dimensional Hilbert space (with our number field, of course, assumed now to be that of all complex numbers); then the H can be chosen to be hermitian operators, while the E can be arranged in pairs, $E_{\pm 1}, \ldots, E_{\pm\sigma}$, where $\sigma = (r - \rho)/2$, such that $E_a = E^\dagger_{-a}$. [That σ is indeed an integer is a general result holding for semisimple groups (see, e.g., Racah, *op. cit.*, pt. 2, sec. 1).] Furthermore, the commutation relations involving the E have the following simple form (with $x = 1, \ldots, \rho$; $a = 1, \ldots, \sigma$; $A, B = \pm 1, \ldots, \pm\sigma$):

$$[H_x, E_{\pm a}] = \pm r_x(a) E_{\pm a} \tag{8A-34}$$

$$[E_a, E_{-a}] = r_x(a) H_x, \qquad \text{summation over } x \tag{8A-35}$$

$$[E_A, E_B] = \begin{cases} N_{AB} E_{A+B} \\ 0 \end{cases} \quad \text{if } A + B \neq 0 \text{ and } r_x(A) + r_x(B) \begin{array}{c} \text{is} \\ \text{is not} \end{array} \text{ a root} \tag{8A-36}$$

where by the term "root" for given A one understands the number sequence $r_x(A)$, $x = 1, \ldots \rho$, satisfying Eqs. (8A-34), with $r_x(-a) = -r_x(a)$. These are always real and—together with the quantities N_{AB}, which are also real nonvanishing numbers—they represent the structure constants of the group in the Cartan base. The complete set of commutation relations in this base consists of the above relations together with those for the H:

$$[H_x, H_y] = 0, \qquad x, y = 1, \ldots, \rho \tag{8A-37}$$

All the results of the Cartan-Weyl theory flow from these canonical commutation relations. From Eqs. (8A-37) it follows that for any given representation algebra, the hermitian operators $H_1, \ldots, H_\rho$ (using as before the same letters to indicate the generators in the initial and in all representation algebras) have a common set of eigenvectors with associated eigenvalue sets $(h_1, \ldots, h_\rho)$ that determine ρ-dimensional vectors called "weights" (or "weight vectors"). It is in terms of these weight vectors that the irreducible representations are uniquely described. In the previous treatment of $\mathfrak{R}$, the hermitian operator J_3 played the role of the only member H of the commuting Cartan set, and the weight space was one-dimensional with $h \equiv m$. We could have, moreover, classified the irreducible representations by the largest values j within families of weights m that are related to each other according to the prescription in (8A-27); although our procedure was actually simpler because we also made use of the Casimir operator J^2. The corresponding general prescription is similar, but a good deal more complicated (see, e.g., Racah, *op. cit.*, part 3).

Again, our method of constructing the generator matrices of the irreducible representations of $\mathfrak{R}$ involved the relations (8A-21) that are a special case of (8A-34), with the two *roots* ± 1. The commutation relation between J_+ and J_-, i.e., (8A-35), was not involved in our analysis because we made use of J^2 and the relation (8A-22). In the general theory, the system of root vectors enters in the analysis of irreducible representations in a similar but considerably more complicated fashion [see, e.g., Racah, *op. cit.* (Lectures on Lie Groups), p. 24 ff.]; and it also plays an important role in the classification of semisimple groups.

We conclude our rapid and limited summary of results of the Cartan-Weyl theory by mentioning one general theorem that is of particular interest in our application of the theory. This theorem is to the effect that every simple Lie group of rank ρ has ρ *fundamental* irreducible representations that are such that every irreducible representation of the group can be obtained by reduction from their Kronecker products. [The "Kronecker product" of representations is defined in Sec. 5-1.] We shall not stop to consider the precise sense in which the word "fundamental" is to be taken in this theorem, nor the problems connected in general with the reduction of Kronecker products of representations—these questions are interesting and important, but involve ideas that, for the sake of brevity, we have omitted from our discussion (and hence, once again, the interested reader must be referred to the references we have given, especially to those of Racah). In the applications we make of this theorem it is apparent which representations are fundamental, and also the reduction of our Kronecker products presents no special problems.

Thus, in the case of the group $\mathfrak{R}$, we have the well-known Clebsch-Gordan formula, familiar in quantum mechanics in connection with the problem of addition of angular momenta, which can be written symbolically [see (8A-12)]:

$$\mathfrak{D}_j \times \mathfrak{D}_{j'} = \mathfrak{D}_{|j-j'|} + \mathfrak{D}_{|j-j'|+1} + \cdots + \mathfrak{D}_{j+j'} \qquad \text{(8A-38)}$$

where $\mathfrak{D}_j$ is generated from $\mathfrak{A}_j$, determined by the matrices (8A-28) ($j' = j$).‡ It is seen at once that we can obtain all the irreducible representations by taking the successive Kronecker products of $\mathfrak{D}_{1/2}$ with itself, and applying the decomposition formula (8A-38), and that $\mathfrak{D}_{1/2}$ is distinguished by this property among all the irreducible representations of $\mathfrak{R}$. It follows that $\mathfrak{D}_{1/2}$ is the *fundamental* representation of the above theorem, and that the theorem itself affords an immediate and direct proof that the sequence of representations $\mathfrak{D}_j$ (obtained by 'integration' from the $\mathfrak{A}_j$) yield indeed *all* the irreducible representations of $\mathfrak{R}$.

An immediate question that now presents itself concerns the explicit form relative to a suitable base of the fundamental representation of $\mathfrak{R}$. Recalling the connection between representations of a Lie algebra and the corresponding representations of the group, as well as the significance of the generators (8A-29) and of the quantities (8A-17), it follows that in terms of the parameters as given in (3A-9), we have (using now the symbol S to represent the matrices in $\mathfrak{D}_{1/2}$)

$$\begin{aligned} S(\mathbf{\Omega}) &= e^{i\Omega_k J_k} \equiv \exp(i\Omega_k J_k) = \exp\left(i\Omega_k \frac{\sigma_k}{2}\right) \\ &= \cos\frac{\Omega}{2} + in_k\sigma_k \sin\frac{\Omega}{2} \qquad \text{(8A-39)} \\ &= \begin{bmatrix} \cos\frac{\Omega}{2} + in_3 \sin\frac{\Omega}{2} & in_- \sin\frac{\Omega}{2} \\ in_+ \sin\frac{\Omega}{2} & \cos\frac{\Omega}{2} - in_3 \sin\frac{\Omega}{2} \end{bmatrix} \end{aligned}$$

where $n_k = \Omega_k/\Omega$, $\Omega = |\mathbf{\Omega}|$, $n_\pm = n_1 \pm in_2$, and σ_k are the Pauli matrices

$$\sigma_1 = \begin{bmatrix} 0 & 1 \\ 1 & 0 \end{bmatrix}, \qquad \sigma_2 = \begin{bmatrix} 0 & -i \\ i & 0 \end{bmatrix}, \qquad \sigma_3 = \begin{bmatrix} 1 & 0 \\ 0 & -1 \end{bmatrix} \qquad \text{(8A-40)}$$

In the expansion of the exponential one makes use of the anticommutation properties of these matrices,

$$\sigma_{(k}\sigma_{r)} = \delta_{kr} \qquad \text{(8A-41)}$$

which imply that $\Omega_{k_1} \cdots \Omega_{k_n}\sigma_{k_1} \cdots \sigma_{k_n} = \Omega^n$ if n is even, and $= \Omega_k\sigma_k\Omega^{n-1}$ if n is odd.

The matrices (8A-39) are easily verified to be unitary, as we know they must be. In addition

$$\det S = \cos^2\frac{\Omega}{2} + ({n_3}^2 + n_-n_+)\sin^2\frac{\Omega}{2} = 1$$

‡ See, e.g., Lyubarskii, *op. cit.*, sec. 49; or any recent textbook on the applications of group theory to QM, such as M. Tinkham, "Group Theory and Quantum Mechanics," McGraw-Hill Book Company, Inc., New York, 1964; M. Hamermesh, "Group Theory," Addison-Wesley Publishing Company, Inc., Reading, Mass., 1962.

These matrices are thus also unimodular.‡ Moreover, we can convince ourselves easily that every unitary unimodular 2-rowed matrix can be put in the form (8A-39). The totality of these matrices forms therefore the group SU_2 (recall the definition of SU_n given earlier).

An important property of the representation $\mathfrak{D}_{1/2}$ that is in clear evidence in the explicit form (8A-39) is the *two-valuedness* arising from the half-angles: for a fixed direction of $\mathbf{\Omega}$, the rotations given by Ω and $\Omega' = \Omega + 2\pi$ are identical, but for the corresponding matrices (8A-39) we have,

$$S(\mathbf{\Omega}') = \cos\left(\frac{\Omega}{2} + \pi\right) + i \sin\left(\frac{\Omega}{2} + \pi\right) n_k \sigma_k = -S(\mathbf{\Omega})$$

The representation $\mathfrak{D}_{1/2}$ does not accord, therefore, with our original definition of a representation as given by a homomorphism of the given group onto a group of linear operators, and hence by a single-valued correspondence. On the other hand, we have noted the group-theoretical significance of $\mathfrak{D}_{1/2}$, while its quantum-mechanical significance relating to the description of the intrinsic spin of particles is well known. It is to be expected therefore that $\mathfrak{D}_{1/2}$ has an intimate connection with $\mathfrak{R}$, and that the two-valuedness has basic significance. In order to show that this is indeed the case, we must digress again briefly to consider another topological property of our group manifold—its connectivity.

We had already observed at a previous occasion that the group $\mathfrak{L}$ is connected, but that the full Lorentz group $\mathfrak{L}_f$ is not (see Prob. 3-21). The latter is in fact the sum of four disjoint pieces, $\mathfrak{L}$ [which in the notation of (8A-42) would be denoted by $\mathfrak{L}_+^\uparrow$], and

$$P\mathfrak{L} \equiv \mathfrak{L}_-^\uparrow, \qquad T\mathfrak{L} \equiv \mathfrak{L}_-^\downarrow, \qquad PT\mathfrak{L} = -\mathfrak{L} \equiv \mathfrak{L}_+^\downarrow \tag{8A-42}$$

using the product notation as in (8A-1) and the notation for the inversion transformations as given in (8A-3). The separation of these pieces can be seen at once from the fact that going from one piece to another entails a jump in either the value of the determinant (by 2), or in the time-time element of the Lorentz transformation matrix [by at least 2, since we have either (3-51), or $T_{00} \leq -1$], or in both. A similar disconnectedness exists between $\mathfrak{R}$ and $-I\mathfrak{R} \equiv \mathfrak{R}_-$, the two pieces of the three-dimensional orthogonal group.

What we mean by each piece in question being itself *connected* is intuitively perfectly clear. Analytically, this property can be formulated

‡ This result follows immediately from the tracelessness of the matrices (8A-40). We have, in fact, the following formula holding for an arbitrary matrix:

$$\det(\exp A) = \exp(\operatorname{trace} A)$$

A direct proof: $\det(\exp A) = \det[\lim_{n\to\infty} (I + A/n)^n] = \lim [\det(I + A/n)]^n = \lim [1 + \operatorname{trace} A/n + 0(1/n^2)]^n = \lim (1 + \operatorname{trace} A/n)^n$.

by requiring that any two elements g_1, g_2 of our group manifold $\mathfrak{G}$ belonging to this piece can be joined by a continuous curve lying in this piece. If, in addition, it is true that every such curve that is also closed (i.e., $g_1 = g_2$) can be continuously deformed so as to shrink to a point while remaining inside the group manifold piece, the latter is said to be *simply connected;* otherwise, it is *multiply connected.* For example, a sphere or its surface are simply connected, but the surface of a doughnut or the entire doughnut are quite obviously not simply connected. We say that such a manifold is doubly connected because it contains two (but not more than two) families of closed continuous curves such that every member of each family can be continuously deformed into any other member of that family, but it cannot be deformed into a member of the other family, with an obvious general definition of the multiplicity of connectedness. We shall now show that the group manifold for $\mathfrak{R}$ is in fact doubly connected.

In order to prove our assertion we can employ any continuous parameter set because connectivity is a topological property and hence is invariant under homeomorphic transformations (see footnote on page 8). Choosing our parameters as the quantities Ω_i (see footnote on page 368), we see that the parameter space consists of the interior and the surface of a sphere of radius π in $\mathcal{E}_3$, but with the antipodal points on the sphere identified since rotations about a given direction by the angles π or $-\pi$ are indistinguishable. It follows that a continuous curve within our group manifold, which connects such a pair of antipodal points, is *closed*, but it cannot be continuously deformed into a point (if we slide off the 'double point' into the interior of the sphere ever so little, the curve is torn at that point). We can also convince ourselves easily that the family of closed curves of this construction and the family of all other closed curves within our manifold are the only ones that cannot be continuously deformed into each other. The group $\mathfrak{R}$ is therefore doubly connected.

Because of this connectivity property of $\mathfrak{R}$, one can define over its manifold, in addition to continuous single-valued functions, also 2-valued functions that have an everywhere continuous behavior when we do not restrict ourselves to a single branch, as can be verified without difficulty.‡ It has been our tacit assumption that we are dealing with *continuous* group representations; in other words, that the matrix elements of our matrix representations are continuous functions over the group manifold, or, equivalently, that they are continuous over the parameter space of the Lie group under consideration. Consequently in the case of $\mathfrak{R}$ we can have, along

‡ The reader may recall the intervention of multiply connected regions in the solution of partial differential equations of classical physics, such as the electromagnetic equations, with the attendant mathematical and physical considerations. An interesting reference to the multiconnectedness question in this connection, prior to the emergence of topology as a well-developed mathematical subject, is contained in vol. 1 of Maxwell's Treatise (pp. 17-20 in the 3d edition).

with single-valued representations, also two-valued representations. $\mathfrak{D}_{1/2}$, as we have seen, is such a representation, and it can be shown that this is also true of all representations $\mathfrak{D}_{n/2}$ when n is an odd positive integer. The primary significance of $\mathfrak{D}_{1/2}$ is now this: it is a representation (in fact, the 'natural representation,' in the terminology introduced previously) of the smallest group (in a sense that is made precise in the exact theory of this topic) that is *simply connected* and that is homomorphic to $\mathfrak{R}$.‡

In general, a group $\bar{G}$ thus associated with a multiply connected group G is called the "universal covering group" of G, the association being unique, as follows from the exact theory.§ The analytic importance of the covering group derives from the obvious fact that all representations of G are *single-valued* representations of $\bar{G}$.

APPENDIX 8B REPRESENTATIONS OF THE HOMOGENEOUS LORENTZ GROUP

It was noted in Appendix 8A that $\mathfrak{L}$ is not compact. It need not, therefore, have nontrivial *finite* unitary representations, and indeed it does not, as Wigner has proved.¶ For the applications we make in Secs. 8-2, 8-3, and 8-4, we can confine our discussion of the infinite-dimensional representations to the inhomogeneous Lorentz group, and of the finite-dimensional representations to the homogeneous Lorentz group. We consider here the latter, after first outlining Wigner's proof of the nonexistence of nontrivial finite unitary representations of $\mathfrak{L}$.

This proof is based on results given in Prob. 3-22b. Using the same symbols for the matrices in the given representation as for the corresponding Lorentz matrices, we have: $S_\alpha S_{\alpha'} = S_{\alpha+\alpha'}$, $T_\psi S_\alpha T_\psi^{-1} = S_{\sigma\alpha}$. Here $\sigma = e^{-\psi}$, and the parameter ψ takes on all real values, so that σ can assume arbitrary positive integral values n. Hence for each α, $S_\alpha \equiv S$ satisfies the relations $S_{n\alpha} = S^n = T_n S T_n^{-1}$ ($n = 1, 2, \ldots ; T_n \equiv T_{\psi(n;\alpha)}$), which imply, on the assumption that our representation is unitary and finite, that $S = I$, as follows readily from the properties of the eigenvalues of finite unitary matrices. The easily established conclusion that *all* the matrices of our representation must then coincide with the unit matrix, completes our proof.

In the derivation of the finite-dimensional irreducible representations of $\mathfrak{L}$ a number of methods have been employed. Since this group is semisimple (in fact, as indicated in Appendix 8A, it is even simple), an application or adaptation of Cartan's approach as modified by the utilization of Casimir

‡ It is of course 2-1 homomorphic, and $\mathfrak{R}$ is actually isomorphic with the factor group of $\mathfrak{D}_{1/2}$ relative to its invariant subgroup $\{I, -I\}$ (remembering the faithfulness of the representations of the *simple* group $\mathfrak{R}$).

§ See, e.g., Pontrjagin, *op. cit.*, chap. 8; Weyl, *op. cit* (Classical Groups), pp. 258–260.

¶ Wigner, *op. cit.* (on page 361), sec. 4B.

operators (see discussion relating to $\mathfrak{R}$ in Appendix 8A) is one possibility. A treatment somewhat along such lines is presented in Pauli's article referred to on page 371. His analysis covers both the homogeneous and the inhomogeneous Lorentz groups with inclusion of the infinite-dimensional representations. For the homogeneous Lorentz group it is easily verified that the following expressions that form natural generalizations of expression (8A-19) for $\mathfrak{R}$, can be taken as Casimir operators:

$$\tfrac{1}{2}U_{\mu\nu}U^{\mu\nu}, \qquad \tfrac{1}{4}E_{\mu\nu\alpha\beta}U^{\mu\nu}U^{\alpha\beta} \tag{8B-1}$$

where the generators $U^{\mu\nu}$ of our Lie algebra satisfy according to (3A-28) the following commutation relations, when expressed in terms of our *real* Minkowski metric:

$$[U_{\mu\nu},U_{\alpha\beta}] = 2(g_{\nu[\alpha}U_{\beta]\mu} - g_{\mu[\alpha}U_{\beta]\nu}) \tag{8B-2}$$

We shall not pursue here Pauli's method, but turn instead to a more specialized approach, particularly suited to the study of the finite-dimensional representations of $\mathfrak{L}$, which has the added merit of illuminating certain aspects of the structure of this group.

The central idea in this approach is immediately apparent when, following Weyl,‡ we introduce in our Lie algebra the base

$$Q_k^{\pm} = \tfrac{1}{2}(M_k \pm iN_k) \qquad \begin{aligned} M_k &= \tfrac{1}{2}\epsilon_{kij}U_{ij} \\ N_k &= U_{k0} \end{aligned} \tag{8B-3}$$

The new commutation relations,

$$[Q_i^+,Q_j^-] = 0, \qquad [Q_i^{\pm},Q_j^{\pm}] = \epsilon_{jik}Q_k^{\pm} \tag{8B-4}$$

that follow immediately from (8B-2) then show in the first place that every matrix in the representation corresponding to our algebra,§ and in particular in $\mathfrak{L}$ itself, can be written uniquely as the product of two matrices, one belonging to a group $\mathfrak{Q}^+$ and the other to a group $\mathfrak{Q}^-$, each element of $\mathfrak{Q}^+$ commuting with each element of $\mathfrak{Q}^-$; and in the second place, that each of the groups $\mathfrak{Q}^+$, $\mathfrak{Q}^-$ forms a representation of the three-dimensional complex proper orthogonal group $\mathfrak{R}^{(c)}$ (Prob. 8-7*b*).¶ The first conclusion bears on the structure of $\mathfrak{L}$, which we shall presently discuss more fully; the second

‡ The underlying algebraic idea, represented by what Weyl calls the "unitarian trick," is explained in Weyl, *op. cit.* (Classical Groups), chap. 8, sec. 11. This method must be applied with caution, because topological properties such as connectivity and compactness can be drastically modified when transition is made from the field of real numbers to that of complex numbers.

§ It is to be remembered that we have been using the same symbols for the corresponding elements of all Lie algebras of a given group.

¶ This group differs from $\mathfrak{R}$ only in being defined over the field of complex numbers.

conclusion enables us to write down directly all the irreducible finite-dimensional representations of $\mathfrak{L}$.

We require the following group-theoretical result of which the first part can be verified with little difficulty (Prob. 8-8). Suppose that a given group G contains two subgroups G_1, G_2 having only the identity in common, with every element g_1 of G_1 commuting with every element g_2 of G_2, and such that every element g of G can be written (necessarily uniquely) as the product $g = g_1g_2$—one says that G is the "direct product" of G_1 and G_2: $G = G_1 \times G_2$.‡ Then, if $\{M_k\} \equiv \mathfrak{R}_k$ is a representation of $G_k (k = 1, 2)$, it follows that the Kronecker products $M = M_1 \times M_2$ formed from all possible pairs constitute a representation of G (with $M \to g_1g_2$ when $M_k \to g_k$), for which we write (see page 133)

$$\mathfrak{R} \equiv \{M\} = \mathfrak{R}_1 \times \mathfrak{R}_2 \tag{8B-5}$$

Moreover, all the irreducible representations of G (assumed finite, and completely reducible if reducible) can be obtained in this manner by taking for $\mathfrak{R}_1$ and $\mathfrak{R}_2$ in (8B-5) all the irreducible representations of G_1 and G_2.

Applying this theorem to our case, we have the important result that *all the finite irreducible representations of* $\mathfrak{L}$ are given by

$$\mathfrak{D}_{jj'} = \mathfrak{D}_j^{(c)} \times \mathfrak{D}_{j'}^{(c)*}, \qquad j, j' = 0, \tfrac{1}{2}, 1, \ldots \tag{8B-6}$$

where $\mathfrak{D}_j^{(c)}$ are the irreducible representations of $\mathfrak{R}^{(c)}$ and are the analytical extensions of the representations $\mathfrak{D}_j$ discussed in Appendix 8A.§

A more explicit variant of the above method originated with a theory of Einstein and Mayer on what they called "semivectors."¶ It is a highly instructive approach, and we shall consider it in some detail. The complex field consideration is introduced now directly by starting with the complex proper orthogonal group in four dimensions, $\mathfrak{R}_4^{(c)}$. The key idea is again a direct product decomposition. We shall begin indeed by proving the following theorem.

‡ More generally, if $G_1 = \{g_1\}$, $G_2 = \{g_2\}$ are any given groups, one defines their *direct product* $G = G_1 \times G_2$ as the group consisting of the ordered pairs (g_1,g_2), with group composition defined by $(g_1',g_2')(g_1'',g_2'') = (g_1'g_1'', g_2'g_2'')$ (omitting the symbols designating composition in the groups G_1, G_2, G). It is not difficult to prove that the sets $\{(g_1,e_2)\}$, $\{(e_1,g_2)\}$, where e_k is the unit in G_k $(k = 1, 2)$, are isomorphic to G_1, G_2 respectively, and that they form subgroups of G such that $G = \{(g_1,e_2)\} \times \{(e_1,g_2)\}$ according to the definition given above.

§ This statement and the expression (8B-6) itself require elucidation, but clarification will ensue from subsequent discussion.

¶ A. Einstein and W. Mayer, *Sitz. Preuss. Akad.*, **522** (1932). For a discussion of the connection between semivectors and spinors (the latter are considered in Sec. 8-2), see V. Bargmann, *Helv. Phys. Acta*, **7**: 57 (1934), which contains further references to the work of Einstein and Mayer. Our presentation follows expositions in Murnaghan, *op. cit.*, chap. 12, and G. Racah, *Nuovo Cimento, Suppl.*, **142**: 75 (1959).

Every matrix R of $\mathfrak{R}_4^{(c)}$ admits of the representation:

$$R = MN \qquad \text{or} \qquad (-M)(-N) \tag{8B-7}$$

$$\begin{gathered} M = mI + U \\ \tilde{U} = -U, \qquad \hat{U} = U, \qquad m^2 + \tfrac{1}{4}U_{\alpha\beta}U_{\alpha\beta} = 1 \\ N = nI + V \\ \tilde{V} = -V, \qquad \hat{V} = -V, \qquad n^2 + \tfrac{1}{4}V_{\alpha\beta}V_{\alpha\beta} = 1 \end{gathered} \tag{8B-8}$$

where $\hat{U}$ denotes the *dual*‡ of U, and $\alpha, \beta = 1, 2, 3, 4$. The sets $\{M\}$, $\{N\}$ are normal subgroups of $\mathfrak{R}_4^{(c)}$ which have only the abelian normal subgroup $\{I, -I\} \equiv \mathfrak{I}$ in common, and each is a representation of $\mathfrak{R}_3^{(c)} \equiv \mathfrak{R}^{(c)}$. [Because of the two-valuedness in (8B-7) due to the existence of the subgroup $\mathfrak{I}$, the decomposition in (8B-7) is not a strict direct product, but one *modulo* $\mathfrak{I}$—as one may express it briefly.]

Our proof of this theorem will be based on the following four results.

In general, an antisymmetric matrix $A = \|A_{\alpha\beta}\|$ of the fourth order satisfies the relation

$$A\hat{A} = -a_i\alpha_i I \qquad \begin{aligned} a_i &= A_{i4} \\ \alpha_i &= \tfrac{1}{2}\epsilon_{ijk}A_{jk} \end{aligned} \tag{8B-9}$$

as is easily verified by simply multiplying the two matrices

$$A = \begin{bmatrix} 0 & \gamma & -\beta & a \\ -\gamma & 0 & \alpha & b \\ \beta & -\alpha & 0 & c \\ -a & -b & -c & 0 \end{bmatrix}, \qquad \hat{A} = \begin{bmatrix} 0 & c & -b & \alpha \\ -c & 0 & a & \beta \\ b & -a & 0 & \gamma \\ -\alpha & -\beta & -\gamma & 0 \end{bmatrix}$$

where $a = a_1$, $b = a_2$, etc. In particular,

$$[A, \hat{A}] = 0 \tag{8B-9a}$$

Every element S of the initial Lie algebra of $\mathfrak{R}_4^{(c)}$ can be represented by the sum

$$\begin{gathered} S = A + B \\ \tilde{A} = -A, \qquad \hat{A} = A, \qquad \tilde{B} = -B, \qquad \hat{B} = -B \end{gathered} \tag{8B-10}$$

where

$$[A, B] = 0 \tag{8B-10a}$$

Indeed, precisely as for $\mathfrak{R}$, so also for an orthogonal group of any order, and in particular for $\mathfrak{R}_4^{(c)}$, it follows that the generators coincide with the set of antisymmetric matrices. Since $\tilde{S} = -S$, it suffices therefore to take $A = (S + \hat{S})/2$, $B = (S - \hat{S})/2$, the relation (8B-10a) following from (8B-9a).

‡ The asterisk used in the definition (5-69), which we have previously employed for this purpose, is now unsuitable, because its more customary function in QM is to indicate the complex conjugate of a quantity.

The totality $\{A\} \equiv \mathfrak{A}$ of the matrices A given in (8B-10) and the corresponding family $\{B\} \equiv \mathfrak{B}$ form Lie subalgebras, each isomorphic with the initial Lie algebra of $\mathfrak{R}^{(c)}$. This result is established directly by noting that the two sets of matrices

$$A_1 = \tfrac{1}{2}\begin{bmatrix} 0 & \sigma_1 \\ -\sigma_1 & 0 \end{bmatrix}, \qquad A_2 = \tfrac{1}{2}\begin{bmatrix} 0 & -\sigma_3 \\ \sigma_3 & 0 \end{bmatrix}, \qquad A_3 = \tfrac{1}{2}\begin{bmatrix} i\sigma_2 & 0 \\ 0 & i\sigma_2 \end{bmatrix}$$

$$B_1 = \tfrac{1}{2}\begin{bmatrix} 0 & -i\sigma_2 \\ i\sigma_2 & 0 \end{bmatrix}, \qquad B_2 = \tfrac{1}{2}\begin{bmatrix} 0 & -\iota \\ \iota & 0 \end{bmatrix}, \qquad B_3 = \tfrac{1}{2}\begin{bmatrix} i\sigma_2 & 0 \\ 0 & -i\sigma_2 \end{bmatrix} \tag{8B-11}$$

can be taken as bases in $\mathfrak{A}$ and $\mathfrak{B}$ respectively,‡ where the symbols are as in (8-19), (8-20); and that

$$[A_i,A_j] = \epsilon_{jik}A_k, \qquad [B_i,B_j] = \epsilon_{jik}B_k \tag{8B-11a}$$

Lastly, by straightforward expansion we find

$$e^A = (\cos a)I + \frac{\sin a}{a}A, \qquad a = \sqrt{a_ia_i}$$
$$e^B = (\cos b)I + \frac{\sin b}{b}B, \qquad b = \sqrt{b_ib_i} \tag{8B-12}$$

since $a_i = \alpha_i$ and $b_i = -\beta_i$ in the notation used in (8B-9), so that by (8B-9), $A^2 = A\hat{A} = -a_ia_iI$, $B^2 = -B\hat{B} = -b_ib_iI$.

The proof of the theorem is now evident. To the given matrix R there corresponds by Lie's theory an alternating matrix S such that $R = \exp(S)$. Hence by (8B-10) and (8B-12),

$$R = \exp(A + B) = \exp(A) \cdot \exp(B) \equiv MN$$

with M, N satisfying the conditions (8B-8), and $\mathfrak{A}$ and $\mathfrak{B}$ each isomorphic with the Lie algebra of $\mathfrak{R}^{(c)}$. The fourth and last relations in (8B-8) follow from (8B-12): $m^2 + \frac{1}{4}U_{\alpha\beta}U_{\alpha\beta} = \cos^2 a + (\sin^2 a/a^2)a_ia_i = 1$, and similarly for N.

An important corollary of this theorem, of immediate interest to us, is that all the finite-dimensional irreducible representations of $\mathfrak{R}_4^{(c)}$ are given by

$$\mathfrak{D}_{jj'} = \mathfrak{D}_j^{(c)} \times \mathfrak{D}_{j'}^{\prime(c)}, \qquad j, j' = 0, \tfrac{1}{2}, 1, \ldots \tag{8B-13}$$

subject to the two-valuedness, where the symbols are as in (8B-6), and the prime in the last factor in (8B-13) is for the purpose of indicating the *independence* of the parameters of the two representations in the product.

‡ These were chosen simply by taking $(A_j)_{i4} = \delta_{ij}/2$ and $(B_j)_{i4} = -\delta_{ij}/2$, the factors $\frac{1}{2}$ being introduced in order to have the standard form (8B-11a) for the commutation relations.

Recalling our discussion in Appendix 8A relating to the *fundamental* representation SU_2 of $\mathfrak{R}$ and its double role as the covering group of $\mathfrak{R}$ and as the representation from which all the irreducible representations of $\mathfrak{R}$ can be generated by Kronecker-product formation and decomposition, it can be conjectured that similar results obtain in the present case. In confirmation, we show that we have in fact the 2-1 homomorphism

$$C_2 \times C_2' \approx \mathfrak{R}_4^{(c)} \tag{8B-14}$$

where C_2 is the group of two-dimensional complex unimodular matrices (i.e., matrices of determinant 1). Because of the fundamental importance of this result we shall consider its derivation at some length.

One instructive method that is related to a useful procedure arising in the theory of spinors‡ is to define a correspondence between $\mathfrak{R}_4^{(c)}$ and $\{C_2, C_2'\}$ in the following manner. We set up a one-to-one mapping between the points x_α $(\alpha = 1, 2, 3, 4)$ of our four-dimensional complex space and 2-rowed matrices:

$$q_x = \begin{bmatrix} x_3 - ix_4 & x_1 - ix_2 \\ x_1 + ix_2 & -x_3 - ix_4 \end{bmatrix} = x_\alpha \sigma_\alpha, \qquad \sigma_4 = -i\iota \tag{8B-15}$$

where σ_k are the Pauli matrices (8A-40). A transformation

$$q_x \rightarrow q_x' = (\pm\rho) q_x (\pm\tilde{\tau}), \qquad \rho \text{ and } \tau \text{ in } C_2 \tag{8B-16}$$

induces then a transformation $x \rightarrow x' = Rx$ of $\mathfrak{R}_4^{(c)}$ when we take

$$q_x' = q_{x'} \equiv x_\alpha' \sigma_\alpha$$

In fact, the linearity of the transformation in x thus induced by (8B-16) is obvious; the transformation is orthogonal, since

$$x_\alpha' x_\alpha' = -\det q_x' = -\det q_x = x_\alpha x_\alpha$$

(as $\det \rho = \det \tau = 1$); and it is proper (i.e., its determinant $= +1$) because it can be reached continuously from the identity transformation. The origin of the double sign in (8B-16) is also obvious.

In order to establish the converse of this result and thus complete the proof of the homomorphism (8B-14), we follow Murnaghan in associating with $q_x \equiv q^{(x)}$ the 1-column matrix ξ whose elements are given by

$$\xi_\alpha \equiv \xi_{(ab)} = q_{ab}^{(x)} \equiv q_{ab} \qquad \begin{aligned} (ab) &= 2a + b - 2 \\ a, b &= 1, 2 \end{aligned} \tag{8B-17}$$

‡ The theory of spinors itself provides, as indicated in Sec. 8-2, an alternative approach to our representation problem for $\mathfrak{L}$; in fact, one of the earliest approaches.

Then, by (8B-15):

$$\xi = Kx$$

$$K = \begin{bmatrix} 0 & 0 & 1 & -i \\ 1 & -i & 0 & 0 \\ 1 & i & 0 & 0 \\ 0 & 0 & -1 & -i \end{bmatrix}, \qquad K^{-1} = \tfrac{1}{2}\begin{bmatrix} 0 & 1 & 1 & 0 \\ 0 & i & -i & 0 \\ 1 & 0 & 0 & -1 \\ i & 0 & 0 & i \end{bmatrix} \tag{8B-18}$$

and a given element R of $\mathfrak{R}_4^{(c)}$ is represented by the transformation

$$\xi \to \xi' = S\xi, \qquad S = KRK^{-1} \tag{8B-19}$$

The first of these relations can be written by (8B-17) and by using the notation indicated in (8B-17), as

$$q'_{ab} = S_{(ab),(cd)}q_{cd}$$

Comparison of these equations with Eqs. (8B-16), which have the explicit form (dropping the $\pm$ sign)

$$q'_{ab} = \rho_{ac}q_{cd}\tilde{\tau}_{db} = \rho_{ac}\tau_{bd}q_{cd}$$

shows that, except for the double-sign two-valuedness, the matrices ρ, τ associated with the given matrix R are uniquely determined by the equations

$$S_{(ab),(cd)} = \rho_{ac}\tau_{bd} \tag{8B-20}$$

In fact, if the pair ρ', τ' is another solution of (8B-20) for given R and hence for given $S_{(ab),(cd)}$, then $\rho'_{ab} = \lambda\rho_{ab}$, $\tau'_{ab} = \tau_{ab}/\lambda$ and since ρ, τ, ρ', τ' are in C_2, it follows that $\lambda = \pm 1$. The correspondence between the matrix pairs $(\pm\rho, \pm\tau)$ of C_2 and the matrices R of $\mathfrak{R}_4^{(c)}$ is thus proven. That this correspondence is a homomorphism is seen immediately by referring to the form of the mapping (8B-16): if $x' = Rx$, $x'' = R_1x'$, then

$$q''_x = \rho_1 q'_x\tilde{\tau}_1 = \rho_1\rho q_x\tilde{\tau}\tilde{\tau}_1 = (\rho_1\rho)q_x(\widetilde{\tau_1\tau})$$

The homomorphism (8B-14) is thus fully established.

The present approach provides also an alternative proof of the theorem relating to Eqs. (8B-7) and (8B-8). In fact, (8B-20) can be written in matrix form as $S = \rho \times \tau$. But by (5-3), $\rho \times \tau = (\rho \times \iota)(\iota \times \tau)$. Hence, referring to (8B-19), we see that we have (8B-7) with

$$M = K^{-1}(\rho \times \iota)K \qquad N = K^{-1}(\iota \times \tau)K \tag{8B-21}$$

There is little difficulty in showing that the properties (8B-8) are also satisfied (Prob. 8-9). On the other hand, the present result (8B-14) can also be obtained without difficulty with our previous approach, as can be seen for instance by starting with the relations (Prob. 8-9)

$$
\begin{aligned}
KA_sK^{-1} &= \frac{i}{2}\sigma_s \times \iota \\
KB_sK^{-1} &= -\frac{i}{2}\iota \times \tilde{\sigma}_s
\end{aligned}
\qquad s = 1, 2, 3 \tag{8B-22}
$$

where the matrices A and B are defined in (8B-11).

The general result we have obtained for the complex orthogonal group in four-dimensional space‡ leads to corresponding conclusions for a number of its important subgroups (see Racah, *op. cit.*), of which $\mathfrak{L}$ is of course the subgroup of principal interest to us. In this case the general relationship (8B-13) reduces to the previously indicated result (8B-6), and correspondingly, the homomorphism (8B-14) specializes to $C_2 \times C_2^* \approx \mathfrak{L}$; in other words, we have the 2-1 homomorphism

$$C_2 \approx \mathfrak{L} \tag{8B-23}$$

These results can be shown to follow from the corresponding general results by using Racah's method based on an examination of the elements of the product of the matrices M, N of (8B-7), which leads to the determination of the appropriate relations between the elements of M and N for the $\mathfrak{R}_4^{(c)}$ subgroups of interest. In this manner, Racah has shown, for instance, that for the subgroup $\mathfrak{R}^{(c)}$, the result (8B-14) holds with omission of the prime; in other words, that we have the simple homomorphism

$$C_2 \approx \mathfrak{R}^{(c)} \tag{8B-24}$$

Combining this result with the result (8B-23) we have then an alternative and explicit proof of the previously noted isomorphism between $\mathfrak{L}$ and $\mathfrak{R}^{(c)}$.

Because of its connection with the theory of spinors, it is of interest to deduce (8B-23) using the method based on Eqs. (8B-15) and (8B-16). The obvious substitution $x_k = x^k$, $x_4 = ix^0$ (x^ν *real*), and $\sigma_0 = i\sigma_4 = \iota$ brings (8B-15) into the form

$$q_x = x^\nu \sigma_\nu, \qquad \nu = 0, 1, 2, 3 \tag{8B-25}$$

Since the matrix q_x is hermitian, it is clear that in order to have $q'_x = q_{x'}$, we require the restrictions on ρ and τ insuring that q'_x is also hermitian. Dropping the $\pm$ sign in (8B-16), and writing out the condition $q'^{\dagger}_x = q'_x$, we find the relation $wq_x = q_x w^\dagger$, $w = \rho^{-1}\tau^*$, that has to be satisfied for all hermitian q_x. Taking $q_x = \iota$, we have $w = w^\dagger$, and since the family of all hermitian matrices q_x is obviously irreducible, we must have $w = \lambda\iota$.§ But

‡ In one respect our present point of departure has not been general enough. Some recent applications, referred to in Sec. 8-4, involve the *complex Lorentz* group. However, the extension of our present results to that group is immediate. One need only replace (8B-15) by (8B-25) with x^ν complex, while keeping (8B-16).

§ By an obvious extension of the statement of Shur's lemma given on page 364.

det w = det (ρ^{-1}) det $(\tau^*) = 1$, and hence $\lambda = \pm 1$, that is, $\tau = \pm\rho^*$. Thus, for the subgroup $\mathfrak{L}$ the relation (8B-16) assumes the form

$$q_x \to q'_x = (\pm\rho)q_x(\pm\rho^\dagger) \tag{8B-26}$$

and the conclusion (8B-23) follows directly as in the general case.

After this fairly detailed discussion relating to the structure of $\mathfrak{L}$, we can return with fuller appreciation to our initial method [involving introduction of the base (8B-3)], which is practically the most expeditious. As we have seen, it leads quite simply to the fundamental result (8B-6). It is not much more difficult to obtain also an extension to $\mathfrak{L}$ of the result (8A-38) for $\mathfrak{R}$, whose theoretical significance was noted in Appendix 8A, and whose practical quantum-mechanical significance is well known.

Suppose that $\psi^{jj'}_{mm'}$ is a *standard* base for the representation $\mathfrak{D}_{jj'}$, in the sense of being the generalization of the base ψ_{jm} in the case of $\mathfrak{R}$, as defined in Eqs. (8A-23), etc. Thus, if, by analogy to Eq. (8A-20), and using the generators given in (8B-3), we now write

$$\begin{aligned} J_k &= -iQ_k^+ \\ J'_k &= -iQ_k^- \end{aligned} \qquad k = 1, 2, 3 \tag{8B-27}$$

then the J and the J' satisfy the commutation relations (8A-18), and setting

$$J_\pm = J_1 \pm iJ_2, \qquad J'_\pm = J'_1 \pm iJ'_2 \tag{8B-27a}$$

we have by the results in Appendix 8A leading to (8A-28), and remembering the definition of $\psi^{jj'}_{mm'}$,

$$\begin{aligned} J_u\psi^{jj'}_{mm'} &= C^{jm}_u\psi^{jj'}_{m+u,m'} && u = 0, \pm 1 \\ J'_u\psi^{jj'}_{mm'} &= C^{j'm'}_u\psi^{jj'}_{m,m'+u} && \text{no summation over } u \end{aligned} \tag{8B-28}$$

We have replaced here $J_\pm$ and J_3 by $J_{\pm 1}$ and J_0 for the purpose of shortening the formulas, and the C have—by Eqs. (8A-23), (8A-24), and (8A-25)—the following values (with suitable choice of arbitrary phase factors): $C^{jm}_0 = m$, $C^{jm}_{\pm 1} = [j(j+1) - m(m \pm 1)]^{1/2}$. Now, by (8B-6) the elements $\psi^{jj'}_{mm'}$ of our base can be identified with understandable notation and without loss of generality, with the products $\psi_{jm}\psi'^*_{j'm'}$, remembering the significance of corresponding symbols in Appendix 8A. Correspondingly, we can take for the base of a given Kronecker product $\mathfrak{D}_{jj'} \times \mathfrak{D}_{j_1j_1'}$, the products

$$\psi^{jj'j_1j_1'}_{mm'm_1m_1'} = \psi_{jm}\psi'^*_{j'm'}\psi^{(1)}_{j_1m_1}\psi^{(1')*}_{j_1'm_1'} \tag{8B-29}$$

By relations connected with the Clebsch-Gordan expansion (8A-38) for $\mathfrak{R}$, we have‡

$$\psi_{jm}\psi^{(1)}_{j_1m_1} = \sum_{J=|j-j_1|}^{j+j_1} (jmj_1m_1;JM)\Psi_{JM}, \qquad M = m + m_1 \tag{8B-30}$$

‡ See, e.g., Lyubarskii, *op. cit.*, sec. 54, which contains also a derivation of the values and properties of the Clebsch-Gordan coefficients.

with a similar expansion (using similar notation) for the primed quantities. Combining (8B-30) and the similar primed expansion, we obtain for the vectors (8B-29) an analogous expansion involving the $\Psi_{JM},\Psi^*_{J'M'}$ and products of pairs of Clebsch-Gordan coefficients, which can be represented symbolically by an expression analogous to (8A-38), namely,‡

$$\mathfrak{D}_{jj'} \times \mathfrak{D}_{j_1j_1'} = \sum_{\substack{|j-j_1|\leq J\leq j+j_1 \\ |j'-j_1'|\leq J'\leq j'+j_1'}} \mathfrak{D}_{JJ'} \tag{8B-31}$$

An immediate consequence of this expansion is that we can indeed generate all irreducible finite representations of $\mathfrak{L}$ starting with the two *fundamental* representations $\mathfrak{D}_{1/2\,0}$, $\mathfrak{D}_{0\,1/2}$, as we have previously anticipated.

We conclude our discussion of representations of the homogeneous Lorentz group by considering the extension to the group $\mathfrak{L}^\uparrow$ obtained when the space inversion transformation P is adjoined to $\mathfrak{L}$.

Let us first consider briefly the analogous simpler case of the three-dimensional orthogonal group, $\mathfrak{O}$. This group is the direct product $\mathfrak{R} \times \mathfrak{I}$, where $\mathfrak{I} = \{I,-I \equiv P\}$. By a theorem mentioned earlier, it follows that every irreducible representation of $\mathfrak{O}$ coincides with either $\mathfrak{D}_j$ or $-\mathfrak{D}_j \equiv (-I)\mathfrak{D}_j$, since the irreducible representations of the abelian subgroup $\mathfrak{I}$ are the numbers $+1$, -1. Thus, when j is an integer, the resulting two representations $\mathfrak{D}_j^+$, $\mathfrak{D}_j^-$ are distinct and single-valued, while for half-integral j we have only one representation $\mathfrak{D}_j$, since this representation is already double-valued by a difference in sign.

The situation in the case of $\mathfrak{L}^\uparrow$ is more complicated than for $\mathfrak{O}$, because the subgroup $\mathfrak{I}$ of $\mathfrak{L}^\uparrow$ does not commute with the subgroup $\mathfrak{L}$, and hence $\mathfrak{L}^\uparrow$ is not the direct product of $\mathfrak{L}$ and $\mathfrak{I}$.§ In fact, it is easily verified that

$$PL_{v_k}P^{-1} = L_{-v_k}, \qquad k = 1, 2, 3 \tag{8B-32}$$

where L_{v_k} is the special Lorentz transformation along the x^k axis (that is, $v_i = 0$, $i \neq k$).

The effect of the relation (8B-32) on the representations of $\mathfrak{L}^\uparrow$ can be deduced very simply, by observing that for a given representation it leads $\left(\text{through application of the operator } d/dv_k \Big|_{\mathbf{v}=0}\right)$ to the anticommutation relations

$$[P,N_k]_+ = 0 \tag{8B-33}$$

‡ For details of derivation and discussion, see, e.g., Lyubarskii, *op. cit.*, sec. 68.

§ It is the "semidirect product" of these groups—since *every* element of $\mathfrak{L}^\uparrow$ can be represented uniquely as the product of an element of $\mathfrak{L}$ and an element of $\mathfrak{I}$, and since $\mathfrak{L}$ is a normal subgroup of $\mathfrak{L}^\uparrow$. Similarly, the Poincaré group is the semidirect product of its normal subgroup $\mathfrak{L}_f$ and its subgroup of space-time translations, $\mathfrak{T}$. For a definition of the *semidirect product* and motivation, see, e.g., G. W. Mackey, "Group Representations in Hilbert Space," sec. 5, published as an appendix in I. E. Segal, "Mathematical Problems of Relativistic Physics," American Mathematical Society, Providence, 1963.

[remembering the notation introduced in (8B-3), and retaining the letter P in all representations, in accordance with our convention]. When these are combined with the commutation relations

$$[P,M_k] = 0 \tag{8B-34}$$

that follow from the commutability of P with every element of $\mathfrak{R}$, and we use the definition (8B-27), with J_k, J'_k replaced now by J_k^+, J_k^- respectively, we get the relations (as $P^2 = I$)

$$PJ_k^{\pm}P = J_k^{\mp} \tag{8B-35}$$

which determine the behavior of our representations. For if $\mathfrak{D}$ is any given finite irreducible representation of $\mathfrak{L}^{\uparrow}$ it must contain at least one representation $\mathfrak{D}_{jj'}$ of its subgroup $\mathfrak{L}$ with associated representation space $V_{jj'}$ spanned by the standard base $\{\psi_{mm'}^{jj'}\}$. Then, by (8B-28), dropping the superscripts j, j', and letting $P\psi_{mm'} = \phi_{mm'}$, we find, upon applying (8B-35) that

$$\begin{aligned} J_u^{\pm}\phi_{mm'} &= J_u^{\pm}P\psi_{mm'} = PJ_u^{\mp}\psi_{mm'} \\ &= P\begin{cases} C_u^{m'}\psi_{m,m'+u} \\ C_u^{m}\psi_{m+u,m'} \end{cases} = \begin{cases} C_u^{m'}\phi_{m,m'+u} \\ C_u^{m}\phi_{m+u,m'} \end{cases} \qquad u = 0, \pm 1 \end{aligned} \tag{8B-36}$$

Consequently, the vectors $\phi_{mm'}$ transform according to $\mathfrak{D}_{j'j}$, spanning the representation space $V_{j'j}$, and it is apparent that the representation space V of the given irreducible representation of $\mathfrak{L}^{\uparrow}$ is the union of $V_{jj'}$ and $V_{j'j}$, and that we have to consider the following two possibilities.

If $j \neq j'$, then $\mathfrak{D}_{jj'}$ and $\mathfrak{D}_{j'j}$ are distinct irreducible representations of $\mathfrak{L}$, as can be seen from our previous discussion, and the vector spaces $V_{jj'}$ and $V_{j'j}$ have only the zero vector in common, that is, $V = V_{jj'} + V_{j'j}$. The irreducible representation of $\mathfrak{L}^{\uparrow}$ under consideration has therefore the dimensionality $2(2j + 1)(2j' + 1)$.

If $j = j'$, the form of Eqs. (8B-36) suggests introducing the two new bases $\chi_{mm'}^{\pm} = \psi_{mm'} \pm \phi_{mm'}$, and we find the characteristic relations

$$P\chi_{mm'}^{\pm} = \pm\chi_{mm'}^{\pm} \tag{8B-37}$$

These relations show that each of the spaces $V_{\pm}$ spanned by the vector sets $\{\chi_{mm'}^{\pm}\}$ is separately invariant under $\mathfrak{L}^{\uparrow}$, so that we have two distinct representations $\mathfrak{D}_{+}^{j}$ and $\mathfrak{D}_{-}^{j}$, each of dimension $(2j + 1)^2$.

APPENDIX 8C UNITARY REPRESENTATIONS OF THE INHOMOGENEOUS LORENTZ GROUP

The inhomogeneous Lorentz group, in addition to not being compact, is also not semisimple, since it contains the *abelian* invariant subgroup $\mathfrak{T}$. Its treatment presents, however, as we shall see, no unusual difficulties on that score.

It is rather the infinite dimensionality of the unitary representations that introduces essential complications. Every irreducible representation space is now a strict Hilbert space and not a finite-dimensional vector space, and the elements of any given Lie algebra are hermitian operators that need not be bounded or possess only discrete spectra and admit of strict (infinite-dimensional) matrix representations. Because of this transition from ordinary algebraic to operator-analytic considerations, new types of representation-theory structure become possible, and key results such as Schur's lemma, or the standard connection between a Lie algebra and the associated representation group, have to be reexamined. We need not enter here, however, into a discussion of these analytic questions. It suffices for our purpose to know that these questions have been subjected to thorough mathematical study, and that in consequence we can feel secure that the simple-minded steps we shall pursue rest on the solid rock of sophisticated mathematical justification.‡

In content, too, the present discussion is considerably restricted. Only those irreducible representations of the Poincaré group are considered that have immediate obvious physical interest, although the possibility of other representations assuming practical interest in the future certainly cannot be ruled out. An even more serious omission from the physical point of view is the restriction to ordinary single-valued or double-valued representations. In the application of unitary representations of $\mathcal{P}$ to QM one has to deal with "ray representations" (also known as "projective representations"), for which the representation-space vectors admit of arbitrary phase factors. It is far from trivial to show, as Wigner has done,§ that this arbitrariness can be disposed of in such manner that the resulting continuous¶ representations are of the ordinary type. Strictly speaking, this result has to be modified when we deal with the full Poincaré group including time inversions. In the latter case antiunitary operators must also be admitted.‡‡ We here limit our discussion to the *restricted* Poincaré group, the inhomogeneous group corresponding to $\mathcal{L}$ (but we shall retain the symbol $\mathcal{P}$ to denote it).

The methods that have been employed in deriving the irreducible representations in question can be grouped into two classes, one involving

‡ The reader who is interested in the finer mathematical details should consult the article by Mackey quoted in Appendix 8B and the references included therein to his own investigations and to those of J. von Neumann, and of F. Mautner. The book by Naimark referred to in Appendix 8A contains a lucid exposition of the analysis pertaining to the infinite-dimensional representations of the homogeneous Lorentz group.

§ In sec. 5 of his pioneering article of 1939, which has already been quoted several times.

¶ *Continuity* of our representations has been tacitly assumed all along.

‡‡ An operator A defined over a Hilbert space $\{\psi\}$ is "antiunitary," when it is "antilinear," i.e., when $A(\psi + \psi') = A\psi + A\psi'$ and $A(\lambda\psi) = \lambda^* A\psi$, and when $(A\psi,A\psi) = (\psi,\psi)$. These conditions imply that $(A\psi,A\psi') = (\psi',\psi)$. (Consider the norm of $\psi + \psi'$ and of $i\psi + \psi'$.)

an integral and the other a differential approach. The global approach dealing directly with the representations themselves, and the one initiated by Wigner, has obvious mathematical and applicational advantages. But the infinitesimal-operator method has its obvious advantages, too. In fact, when Wigner completed his first investigation on this subject, it was not yet known that the latter approach can be justified in the infinite-dimensional case.‡

What makes the direct (i.e., integral) method of determining the family $\{\mathfrak{R}\}$ of irreducible unitary representations of $\mathcal{P}$ formally fairly easy is the very presence in $\mathcal{P}$ of the invariant abelian subgroup $\mathfrak{T}$. It is, in fact, immediately verified that§

$$T(a)L = LT(L^{-1}a) \qquad \begin{matrix} T(a) \in \mathfrak{T} \\ L \in \mathfrak{L} \end{matrix} \tag{8C-1}$$

[using the customary symbol $\in$ for set inclusion, and denoting by $T(a)$ the translation $\mathsf{x} \to \mathsf{x} + \mathsf{a}$]. Now, because of the abelian property of $\mathfrak{T}$ its irreducible unitary representations are one-dimensional, according to the result given in Appendix 8A, which can be shown to have general validity. It follows that if U_a is the operator representing $T(a)$, and ψ is a vector of such a representation, then $U_a\psi = e^{i\theta(a)}\psi$, with $\theta(a + b) = \theta(a) + \theta(b)$ since $U_aU_b = U_{a+b}$. By the continuity of our representations and since $\theta(0) = 0$, we can conclude that $\theta(a)$ is a linear homogeneous function, which we write as $\theta(a) = -p_\mu a^\mu$, without implying for the moment more than the reality of the p_μ that is required by the unitarity of U_a. Thus, these U_a satisfy the eigenvalue relation¶

$$U_a\psi(p) = e^{-ip_\mu a^\mu}\psi(p) \tag{8C-2}$$

Consequently, if we reduce a given $\mathfrak{R}$ with respect to $\mathfrak{T}$, then the associated representation space $\mathcal{H}(\mathfrak{R}) \equiv \mathcal{H}$ will have as space the vectors $\psi_\zeta(p)$, where ζ is a degeneracy label. The set $\mathcal{P}(\mathfrak{R}) \equiv \mathcal{P}$ of quadruplets p for which $\psi_\zeta(p)$ is in $\mathcal{H}$ can be determined using (8C-1), and with the aid of the vectors $\psi_\zeta(p)$ one can express all the operators U of $\mathfrak{R}$, as shown in the following discussion.

By Eq. (8C-1),

$$U(a)U(L) = U(L)U(L^{-1}a), \qquad U(a) \equiv U_a \tag{8C-3}$$

‡ This was first shown by L. Gårding, *Proc. Nat. Acad. Sci., U.S.A.*, **33**: 331 (1947).

§ Strictly, we are dealing with the transformations $x \to Lx + a$, which can be denoted by (L,a) with the law of combination $(L,a)(L_1,a_1) = (LL_1, La_1 + a)$. We are writing L and $T(a)$ for $(L,0)$ and $(1,a)$ respectively (denoting here by 1 the identity transformations, and also employing now ordinary as well as sans serif letters to denote 4-vectors); in particular, $(L,a) = T(a)L$.

¶ At this point one is first confronted, in a mathematically rigorous treatment, with the necessity of exercising care, in this instance—in the handling of the continuous spectrum, a problem that is ever present in QM, and that enters here obviously in a very essential manner.

Hence, if $p \in \mathcal{P}$ we have, dropping temporarily the index ζ, that‡

$$\begin{aligned} U(a)[U(L)\psi(p)] \equiv U(a)\phi(p) &= U(L)U(L^{-1}a)\psi(p) \\ &= U(L)\exp[-ip_\mu(L^{-1}a)^\mu]\psi(p) \\ &= \exp[\cdot\ \cdot\ \cdot]\phi(p) = \exp[-i(Lp)_\mu a^\mu]\phi(p) \end{aligned} \quad (8C\text{-}4)$$

Since by construction $\phi(p)$ defined in Eq. (8C-4) is in $\mathcal{H}$, this equation shows that $Lp \in \mathcal{P}$ for every L of $\mathfrak{L}$; and since our representation is assumed to be irreducible, it can be concluded that no other p are in $\mathcal{P}$. The last assertion will also be immediately apparent when we have introduced the method of infinitesimal operators, which it will be desirable to do in any case. We shall also see then that the p_μ can be considered as the components of a 4-vector. Thus, for every irreducible unitary representation $\mathfrak{R}$ of $\mathfrak{P}$, the associated set $\mathcal{P}$ coincides with one of the following covariantly characterized classes:§

$$\begin{aligned} &\textbf{I:} && \mathsf{p}^2 = m^2, \ (1)\ p_0 > 0 \text{ or } (2)\ p_0 < 0 \\ &\textbf{II:} && \mathsf{p}^2 = 0, \quad (1)\ p_0 > 0 \text{ or } (2)\ p_0 < 0 \\ &\textbf{III:} && \mathsf{p} = 0 \\ &\textbf{IV:} && \mathsf{p}^2 = -n^2 \end{aligned} \quad (8C\text{-}5)$$

where m and n can assume arbitrary positive values, a unique class corresponding to each such value [together with a choice of (1) or (2) in the case of category I]. Moreover, reintroducing the degeneracy label ζ, and comparing Eqs. (8C-2) and (8C-4), we see that $\phi(p)$ lies in the closed linear manifold spanned by the $\psi_\zeta(Lp)$,¶ so that we can write in general

$$U(L)\psi_\zeta(p) = \sum_{\zeta'} R_{\zeta'\zeta}(L,p)\psi_{\zeta'}(Lp) \quad (8C\text{-}6)$$

In order to determine the functions $R_{\zeta'\zeta}(L,p)$, and thus find the representation $\mathfrak{R}$, Wigner utilizes what he calls the *little groups* of $\mathfrak{P}$. The "little group" $\mathcal{G}(p)$ associated with a given 4-vector p is the subgroup of $\mathfrak{L}$ which leaves p invariant, i.e.,

$$L \in \mathcal{G}(p), \qquad \text{if } L \in \mathfrak{L} \text{ and } Lp = p \quad (8C\text{-}7)$$

‡ In the last step in (8C-4) we apply the identity $(La)_\mu(Lb)^\mu = L_\mu{}^\nu a_\nu L^\mu{}_\sigma b^\sigma = a_\sigma b^\sigma$, using (3-53) in the form

$$L_\mu{}^\nu L^\mu{}_\sigma = \delta^\nu_\sigma \quad \text{(i)}$$

It is to be noted that by thinking of a Lorentz transformation in its active role as a mapping of vectors, the *tensor character* of its matrix elements follows from the quotient theorem of tensor calculus. Thus, (i) is obtained from the defining equations, $g_{\mu\lambda}L^\lambda{}_\rho L^\mu{}_\sigma = g_{\rho\sigma}$ by multiplying-summing both sides by $g^{\rho\nu}$.

§ Covariance is here understood with respect to $\mathfrak{L}$. It should be remembered that we are now designating by the symbol $\mathfrak{P}$ the *restricted* Poincaré group.

¶ Let us note in this connection that a priori we cannot suppose that the set of ζ values is finite, and it can in fact be infinite, even continuously so. A *closed* infinite-dimensional vector space is one which contains all the limits of its vector sequences.

Within an isomorphism there are only four distinct little groups $\mathcal{G}_w$ (w = I, II, III, IV) corresponding to the four categories in (8C-5), with no distinction being made between the divisions (1) and (2) (see Prob. 8-11). The crux of Wigner's idea, based on a general method due to Frobenius, is to reduce the representation problem to the more tractable task of finding the corresponding representations of a suitably chosen associated little group. This is accomplished as follows, by using the isomorphism relation‡

$$U(L')U(L) = U(L'L) \tag{8C-8}$$

and the unitarity of $R_{\zeta\zeta'}(L,p)$ considered as a matrix with respect to the ζ indices.§

Let p_* be a chosen element in our p set $\mathcal{P}$, and let p be an arbitrary element in $\mathcal{P}$, then there exists a Lorentz transformation $L_{(p)}$ such that

$$L_{(p)}p_* = p \tag{8C-9}$$

Hence, if we decompose an arbitrary element L of $\mathfrak{L}$ as follows:

$$L = L_{(p')}L_*L_{(p)}^{-1} \qquad \begin{aligned} L_* &= L_{(p')}^{-1}LL_{(p)} \\ p' &= Lp \end{aligned} \tag{8C-10}$$

then in the first place, by (8C-9), $L_*p_* = L_{(p')}^{-1}Lp = L_{(p')}^{-1}p' = p_*$, i.e.,

$$L_* \in \mathcal{G}(p_*) \tag{8C-10a}$$

for every p in $\mathcal{P}$ and L in $\mathfrak{L}$; and in the second place, since, by (8C-6) and (8C-8),

$$R(L'L,p) = R(L',Lp)R(L,p) \tag{8C-10b}$$

(written in matrix form—possibly in an extended sense), we have by this result and (8C-10a) that (again in matrix form)

$$U(L)\psi(p) = \tilde{\psi}(p')R(L_{(p')},p_*)R(L_*,p_*)R(L_{(p)}^{-1},p) \tag{8C-11}$$

where we have retained the old symbols for the corresponding matrices, with ψ standing for the conventional (possibly infinite) one-column matrix. In view of the unitarity of the matrix R we can choose a base in $\mathcal{H}$ so that

$$R(L_{(p)},p_*) = I, \qquad p \in \mathcal{P} \tag{8C-12}$$

[which by (8C-6) is equivalent to the relation $U(L_{(p)})\psi(p_*) = \psi(p)$], and since, by (8C-10$b$), $R(1,p) = I$ and $R^{-1}(L,p) = R(L^{-1},Lp)$, we have, by

‡ As a matter of convenience we avoid two-valuedness in the induced representations of $\mathfrak{L}$ by supposing (generally tacitly) that this group is replaced by its *universal covering group*, which, by reasoning similar to that indicated in Appendix 8A in connection with $\mathfrak{R}$, and using results presented in Appendix 8B, can be seen to be identifiable (in the sense of isomorphism) with the complex unimodular 2-rowed matrix group C_2. We shall, however, retain the present notation, and continue referring to $\mathfrak{L}$ rather than to C_2.

§ This property is established, and is, in fact, only meaningful when the scalar product in our representation Hilbert space $\mathcal{H}$ has been suitably defined. The present rapid, formal sketch of Wigner's theory omits a number of essential analytical details.

(8C-12) and (8C-9), that $R(L_{(p)}^{-1},p) = I$. Hence, (8C-11) reduces to $U(L)\psi(p) = \tilde{\psi}(p')R(L_*,p_*)$. Reintroducing the indices, and substituting from (8C-10), we have then

$$\begin{aligned} U(L)\psi_\zeta(p) &= \sum_{\zeta'} R_{\zeta'\zeta}(L_{(Lp)}^{-1}LL_{(p)})\psi_{\zeta'}(Lp) \\ R_{\zeta\zeta'}(L) &\equiv R_{\zeta\zeta'}(L,p_*) \end{aligned} \qquad (8C\text{-}13)$$

The determination of our representation $\mathfrak{R}$ has thus been reduced indeed to the corresponding problem for the appropriate little group $\mathcal{G}_w$ ($w = I, \ldots$) [in view of (8C-10a), and since the $\psi_\zeta(t)$ forms a base in $\mathcal{H}$].

Turning now to the concrete task of determining the quantities $R_{\zeta\zeta'}(L)$ defined in (8C-13) for L in $\mathcal{G}_w$ we limit our discussion to the physically most interesting cases $w =$ I and II.‡ The first case admits of an immediate solution. The set $\mathcal{P}$ can now be written more explicitly and with evident meaning, as $\mathcal{P}_m^+$ or $\mathcal{P}_m^-$, and an obvious choice of the 4-vector p_* is $(m,0,0,0)$ and $(-m,0,0,0)$ respectively. In either case, $\mathcal{G}_{\mathrm{I}}$ can be identified with $\mathfrak{R}$, whose irreducible unitary representations $\mathfrak{D}_j (j = 0, \frac{1}{2}, 1, \ldots)$ are well known, and have been in part discussed in Appendix 8A. Every representation $\mathfrak{R}$ in the category I can thus be completely characterized by the symbols $\mathfrak{R}_{m,j}^+$ or $\mathfrak{R}_{m,j}^-$, with the associated ζ indices assuming the values $1, 2, \ldots, 2j + 1$. As to explicit expressions for the $\mathfrak{D}_j$ matrices these are also well known.§ For $j = \frac{1}{2}$ we have found in Appendix 8A the explicit form (8A-39).¶

The identification of the little group $\mathcal{G}_{\mathrm{II}}$ is not as immediate as it is for the other categories. One interesting method for doing this, as originally shown by Wigner, is to use the representation (8B-26) for Lorentz transformations to obtain explicitly the matrices of $\mathcal{G}_{\mathrm{II}}$ (see Prob. 8-12). Another obvious and instructive method involves the infinitesimal approach. Inasmuch as we shall presently turn to a consideration of this approach, we present now such a derivation for the group $\mathcal{G}_{\mathrm{II}}$.

The infinitesimal elements of $\mathcal{G}(p^*)$ are given by‡‡

$$\begin{aligned} L^\mu{}_\nu &= \delta^\mu_\nu + \epsilon^\mu{}_\nu, & \epsilon^\nu{}_\mu &\text{ infinitesimal} \\ \epsilon_{\mu\nu} &= -\epsilon_{\nu\mu}, & \epsilon^\nu{}_\mu p_*{}^\mu &= 0 \end{aligned} \qquad (8C\text{-}14)$$

‡ $\mathcal{G}_{\mathrm{III}}$ is clearly isomorphic to $\mathfrak{L}$. A discussion of the unitary representations of $\mathfrak{L}$ is contained in Naimark, *op. cit.* A summary of results on infinite-dimensional and, in particular, unitary representations of $\mathfrak{L}$ is given in Lyubarskii, *op. cit.*, pp. 291–292. $\mathcal{G}_{\mathrm{IV}}$ is isomorphic to the homogeneous Lorentz group with two underlying spatial dimensions, as is seen by taking $\mathsf{p}^* = (0,0,0,1)$. For its discussion see V. Bargmann, *Ann. Math.*, **48**: 568 (1947).

§ See, e.g., Lyubarskii, *op. cit.*, sec. 47, or Wigner, *op. cit.* (Group Theory), pp. 166–168.

¶ The totality of matrices of this form constitute, as noted before, the group SU_2. This, as we also know, can be taken as the covering group of $\mathfrak{R}$, and it is strictly the group with which the little group $\mathcal{G}_{\mathrm{I}}$ should be identified.

‡‡ Using the notation explained in the footnote on page 392, so that (8C-14) (excluding the last relation) corresponds to (3A-10).

With the choice $p_*^{\,0} = p_*^{\,3} = 1$, $p_*^{1,2} = 0$, the last two relations in (8C-14) imply that $\epsilon_{01} = \epsilon_{13}$, $\epsilon_{02} = \epsilon_{23}$, and $\epsilon_{03} = 0$. Hence,

$$U(L) = I + \frac{i}{2}\,\epsilon_{\mu\nu}J^{\mu\nu} = I + i[\epsilon_{01}(J^{01} + J^{13}) + \epsilon_{02}(J^{02} + J^{23}) + \epsilon_{12}J^{12}]$$

where

$$J_{\mu\nu} = -iU_{\mu\nu} \tag{8C-15}$$

The Lie algebras of $\mathcal{G}_{II}$ have thus the three generators $W_1 \equiv J^{01} + J^{13}$, $W_2 \equiv J^{02} + J^{23}$, and $J \equiv J^{12}$, which, by (8B-2) and (8C-15), are found to satisfy the commutation relations

$$[W_1,W_2] = 0, \qquad [J,W_1] = iW_2, \qquad [J,W_2] = -iW_1 \tag{8C-16}$$

That J is associated with an ordinary spatial rotation about the x^3 axis is already clear from the form of our $\mathbf{p}_*$. The last two relations in (8C-16) are therefore reminiscent of (8A-21); in fact, they can be written

$$[J,W_\pm] = \pm W_\pm, \qquad W_\pm \equiv W_1 \pm iW_2 \tag{8C-17}$$

However, the first relation (8C-16) is equivalent to $[W_+,W_-] = 0$, whereas $[J_+,J_-] = 2J_3$. This is a basic difference and, in fact, it is the group of rigid motions in a euclidean plane $\mathcal{E}_2$ (the two-dimensional "euclidean group") to which $\mathcal{G}_{II}$ is isomorphic, as is readily verified by finding the generators of $\mathcal{E}_2$ and checking that they satisfy commutation relations of the structure (8C-16). Needless to add, we have here only a similarity in the abstract structure of the two groups $\mathcal{E}_2$ and $\mathcal{G}_{II}$, and W_1, W_2 are generators associated with certain types of strict Lorentz transformations,‡ and not of any spatial translations.

In order to find our irreducible Lie-algebra representations we can proceed as we did in Appendix 8A in obtaining the matrices (8A-28). Our present Casimir operator is

$$W^2 = W_+W_- = W_1^{\,2} + W_2^{\,2} \tag{8C-18}$$

and corresponding to (8A-23) we can now write

$$W^2\psi_{wj} = w^2\psi_{wj}, \qquad J\psi_{wj} = j\psi_{wj} \tag{8C-19}$$

and also obtain the relation analogous to (8A-24). The crucial difference comes in with the analog of (8A-25), which, owing to (8C-18), has now the radically different form: $|C_{wj}|^2 = w^2$. We have consequently now no constraint on j arising from this relation and, moreover, the equation analogous to (8A-24) has the simple form (with a proper choice of arbitrary phase)

$$W_\pm\psi_{wj} = w\psi_{w,j\pm1}, \qquad w \geqq 0 \tag{8C-20}$$

‡ These transformations are expressible in terms of the matrices S_α given in Prob. 3-22 (see Prob. 8-12).

We have therefore before us two essentially distinct cases:‡ (1) $w = 0$, and (2) $w > 0$.

In case (1), $W_1 = W_2 = 0$, and we are reduced to a consideration of the unitary representations of the *abelian* group $\mathcal{R}_2$ that are therefore all one-dimensional. It is easily established that these representations§ are of the form $e^{ij\phi}$ (ϕ being the angle of rotation), and hence j must be restricted to one of the following values

$$j = 0, \tfrac{1}{2}, -\tfrac{1}{2}, 1, -1, \ldots \tag{8C-21}$$

because our representations can be at most two-valued (or single-valued, relative to our universal covering group). In case (2), it follows from (8C-20) that our irreducible representations are infinite-dimensional, with w admitting any positive value and j assuming either all positive and negative integral or all positive and negative half-integral values, as we see by the same considerations that led to (8C-21). Case (2) provides thus an example of the possibility for the index ζ to run through an infinity (in fact, a continuous infinity) of values. However, only case (1) appears to have physical significance.

We have seen how the infinitesimal operator approach including Casimir operator considerations is effective in the analysis of the irreducible representations of $\mathcal{E}_2$. It can be expected that this approach would also be of interest in the treatment of the similar but more complex group $\mathcal{P}$. In addition to purely mathematical, there are also physical reasons for this expectation, such as those deriving from the known connection between generators of unitary transformations and conserved dynamical quantities in QM.

As to the Casimir operators in the present case, it is easily checked that the quantities (8B-1) that serve as Casimir operators for $\mathcal{L}$ will not do, and that instead the following expressions constitute an independent set of Casimir operators for $\mathcal{P}$:

$$P_\lambda P^\lambda \equiv M^2, \qquad -S_\lambda S^\lambda \equiv S^2 \tag{8C-22}$$

where [see (i), Prob. 5-20]

$$S^\lambda = \tfrac{1}{2}E^{\lambda\mu\nu\sigma}J_{\mu\nu}P_\sigma = \tfrac{1}{2}E^{\lambda\sigma\mu\nu}P_\sigma J_{\mu\nu} \tag{8C-23}$$

Here $J_{\mu\nu}$ are the *hermitian* generators for $\mathcal{L}$, and the P_μ are similar generators for $\mathcal{T}$. We can easily check these results with the aid of the Lie integrability conditions relating to $\mathcal{P}$. These consist of those relating to $\mathcal{L}$, that

‡ This division is analogous to the separation in little group categories for $\mathcal{P}$. The group $\mathcal{E}_2$, as far as geometric (or kinematic) structure is concerned, is evidently analogous to $\mathcal{P}$, with w^2 corresponding to m^2, and with the divisions (1) and (2) corresponding respectively to the categories III and I, II, IV.

§ Note that we are now referring to the representations of the group itself and not of its Lie algebra.

is, (8B-2), or

$$[J_{\mu\nu},J_{\alpha\beta}] = 2i(g_{\nu[\alpha}J_{\beta]\mu} - g_{\mu[\alpha}J_{\beta]\nu}) \tag{8C-24}$$

[where, for reasons presently to be explained, we are now taking $J_{\mu\nu}$ with opposite sign to that given in (8C-15)]; of the integrability conditions relating to $\mathfrak{T}$,

$$[P_\mu,P_\nu] = 0 \tag{8C-25}$$

which result from the commutativity of this subgroup; and of the commutation relations deriving from the coupling between $\mathfrak{L}$ and $\mathfrak{T}$ within $\mathcal{P}$, namely,

$$[P_\lambda,J_{\mu\nu}] = 2ig_{\lambda[\nu}P_{\mu]} \tag{8C-26}$$

In the derivation of (8C-26) we must go back to the definition (3A-5) of the generators in the initial Lie algebra since, in general, an element of $\mathcal{P}$ is not associated in the usual way with a matrix in our initial representation. Thus, in the initial algebra, our commutation relations are derived as follows [recalling the definition given above (3A-23), and since, obviously, in the notation of (3A-5), the generators $Q_u \equiv Q_\lambda$ for the translations coincide with $\partial/\partial x^\lambda$]:

$$\left[\frac{\partial}{\partial x^\lambda}, (U_{\mu\nu})^\sigma{}_\tau x^\tau \frac{\partial}{\partial x^\sigma}\right] = (U_{\mu\nu})^\sigma{}_\lambda \frac{\partial}{\partial x^\sigma} = 2\delta^\sigma_{[\nu}g_{\mu]\lambda}\frac{\partial}{\partial x^\sigma} = g_{\lambda\mu}\frac{\partial}{\partial x^\nu} - g_{\lambda\nu}\frac{\partial}{\partial x^\mu}$$

[the expression for the matrix elements $(U_{\mu\nu})^\sigma{}_\lambda$ can be derived from (3A-25), or directly—as the reader may wish to verify]. To the differential operators $\partial/\partial x^\lambda$ there correspond, in a given representation Lie algebra, the operators $-iP_\lambda$ [the sign convention agreeing with that in (8-14)]. The generators $iJ_{\mu\nu}$ stand in similar relationship to the differential operators $(U_{\mu\nu})^\sigma{}_\tau x^\tau\, \partial/\partial x^\sigma$. It should be noted that by Eqs. (3A-21) and (3A-23) the correspondence between the initial generators and the associated matrix generators involves a reversal in sign. It is in this sense that we are now taking the generators $J_{\mu\nu}$ (in an arbitrary representation algebra) with opposite sign to that used previously.

Because this question of signs is a bit confusing, it is desirable to confirm our results by an independent derivation. We indicate one that has independent interest. It consists in applying the composition rule for $\mathcal{P}$ transformations‡ to the product

$$U(L,a)U(L_\epsilon,\eta)U^{-1}(L,a) \tag{8C-27}$$

[where $U(L,a)$ is the unitary operator corresponding in a given representation to the transformation (L,a), L_ϵ is the infinitesimal Lorentz transformation given in (8C-14), and η^ν are infinitesimal], and comparing the result

‡ See footnote § on page 391. Note that $(L,a)^{-1} = (L^{-1},-L^{-1}a)$.

with what one gets by substituting

$$U(L_\epsilon,\eta) = I + \frac{i}{2} J_{\mu\nu}\epsilon^{\mu\nu} - iP_\mu\eta^\mu \tag{8C-28}$$

in (8C-27). The resulting relations

$$\begin{aligned} UJ_{\mu\nu}U^{-1} &= L^\alpha{}_\mu L^\beta{}_\nu(J_{\alpha\beta} + 2P_{[\alpha}a_{\beta]}) \\ UP_\mu U^{-1} &= L^\alpha{}_\mu P_\alpha, \end{aligned} \qquad U \equiv U(L,a) \tag{8C-29}$$

yield the commutation relations (8C-24), (8C-25), and (8C-26) when we replace here L and a by L_ϵ and η respectively (Prob. 8-14).

While we have checked that (8C-22) are indeed Casimir operators for $\mathcal{P}$, it may be wondered if they constitute a complete system of such operators. Racah's theory mentioned in Appendix 8A is not applicable now since $\mathcal{P}$ is not semisimple. We have, however, in the present case, a direct method of establishing the completeness of the set (8C-22). It is based on the recognition that every Casimir operator for $\mathcal{L}$ must be a 4-scalar. The last assertion is in a sense a tautology. We say that an operator has a certain tensor character under $\mathcal{L}$ when it satisfies a relation of the type represented in (8C-29) (with $\mathsf{a} = 0$) where J is in this sense an antisymmetric tensor of second rank, and P a 4-vector. An operator O is thus a 4-scalar when $U(L)OU^{-1}(L) = O$ for all L in $\mathcal{L}$, that is, when it is a Casimir operator for $\mathcal{L}$. The proof of the completeness of the operators (8C-22) reduces then to showing that there is no 4-scalar operator that is independent of the latter and that commutes with the P_μ. Now, the 4-scalars‡

$$C_\lambda C^\lambda, \qquad C_\lambda S^\lambda \qquad C_\lambda \equiv J_{\lambda\mu}P^\mu \tag{8C-30}$$

form together with the operators (8C-22) a complete independent Casimir set for the subgroup $\mathcal{L}$, as can be shown (Prob. 8-15) by using the following relations, which are of interest also in other connections, and whose proof is straightforward when one remembers the properties of $E_{\alpha\beta\gamma\delta}$,

$$C_\lambda P^\lambda = 0, \qquad S_\lambda P^\lambda = 0 \tag{8C-31}$$

$$J_{\mu\nu} = \frac{1}{\mathsf{P}^2}(2C_{[\mu}P_{\nu]} + E_{\nu\mu\alpha\beta}S^\alpha P^\beta) \tag{8C-32}$$

$$[P_\mu,S_\nu] = 0, \qquad [S_\mu,S_\nu] = iE_{\mu\nu\alpha\beta}S^\alpha P^\beta \tag{8C-33}$$

$$\begin{aligned} [S_\mu,C_\nu] = iP_\mu S_\nu, \qquad [P_\mu,C_\nu] &= i(P_\mu P_\nu - g_{\mu\nu}\mathsf{P}^2) \\ [C_\mu,C_\nu] &= i\mathsf{P}^2 J_{\mu\nu} \end{aligned} \tag{8C-34}$$

On the other hand, by reference to Eqs. (8C-25) and (8C-26), it is apparent that the operators (8C-30) do not commute with P_μ.

‡ The quantity $C_\lambda S^\lambda$ is actually a pseudoscalar, since S^λ is a pseudovector. In the case of the restricted Lorentz group, the distinction is, of course, inconsequential.

We shall now sketch out briefly a method of obtaining the irreducible unitary representations of $\mathcal{P}$ starting with the Casimir operators (8C-22).‡ As we would expect, this method has points of contact with the Cartan-Casimir-Racah approach for semisimple groups.§ To begin with, an extension of Schur's lemma to our infinite-dimensional case,¶ permits the classification of our representations in terms of the eigenvalue pairs m^2, s^2 of the two operators (8C-22). Moreover, in each representation space we can choose a base by taking the common eigenvectors of a commuting set of operators such as P_μ (of which, of course, only three are independent) and a component of S, say, S_3 [see (8C-33)]. In terms of these vectors $\psi(\mathsf{p},s_3)$, the representation in question can be readily determined, as we indicate in the special case $m > 0$.

Let us note first that consideration of the eigenvalue m^2 leads to the divisions I, II, and IV [Eq. (8C-5)]. The subclasses (1) and (2) in I and II arise in addition because in the case of the *restricted* Poincaré group, with which we are presently concerned, the sign of the eigenvalues of P_0 is an additional invariant.‡‡ Moreover, the 4-vector character of P_μ, shown by the second of the relations (8C-29), has already been noted.

The last-mentioned relations aid us also in the derivation of the representations under consideration. According to these relations, if we know for a given representation of our Lie algebra the results of the operation of the S_ν upon $\psi(\mathsf{p}_*,s_3)$ for a fixed value p_* of p contained in our set $\mathcal{P}$, then we can deduce these results when the S_ν operate upon $\psi(\mathsf{p},s_3)$, where p is an arbitrary value in $\mathcal{P}$. In fact, it can be shown that S_ν satisfy the same relations (8C-29) as P_ν (see Prob. 8-16). Hence, if L is the Lorentz transformation $\mathsf{p}_* \rightarrow \mathsf{p}$, so that, by (8C-29), $U(L)\psi(\mathsf{p}_*,s_3) \equiv U\psi(p_*) = \psi(p)$ [since

$$P^\mu U\psi(p_*) \equiv P^\mu\phi = UL^\mu{}_\lambda P^\lambda\psi(p_*) = UL^\mu{}_\lambda p_*{}^\lambda\psi(p_*) = p^\mu U\psi(p_*) = p^\mu\phi]$$

then

$$S_\nu\psi(p) = S_\nu U\psi(p_*) = UL_\nu{}^\lambda S_\lambda\psi(p_*) \tag{8C-35}$$

As in the little group method, the natural choice for p_* is $\mathsf{p}_* = 0$, and hence $p_0 = m$, limiting our discussion now to category I(1). Our transformation L is then simply given by (6-40), while the representations of S_ν reduce to the representations of the Lie algebras for $\mathcal{R}$ since, by the

‡ For a complete discussion of this method, including the treatment of the full Poincaré group, see Iu. M. Shirokov, *Soviet Phys. JETP*, **6**: 664, 919, 929 (1958); **9**: 620 (1959).

§ Pauli's treatment referred to previously is of the same type.

¶ The proof outlined on page 364 is applicable, since our Casimir operators (8C-22) are hermitian [see (8C-23), in which (8C-26) is applied].

‡‡ The division III (i.e., $\mathsf{p} = 0$), as we have seen earlier, leads to the representations of $\mathcal{L}$. This result can now be seen to follow from the fact that in this special case (8C-25) and (8C-26) are trivial identities, while the quantities (8B-1) can serve as additional Casimir operators.

second relation in (8C-31), $S_0 = 0$ now, and by (8C-33),

$$[\Sigma_k,\Sigma_r] = i\epsilon_{krs}\Sigma_s, \qquad \Sigma_k = \frac{1}{m} S_k \tag{8C-36}$$

We confirm thus fully, remembering (8C-23), the result obtained using Wigner's method (see Prob. 8-16).

In order to have the complete Lie-algebra representations, we still need to find the representations of the operators C_ν defined in (8C-30). Using the commutation relations (8C-34), these can be found explicitly in terms of the operators P, S, and derivatives with respect to the P. Similar expressions for the J are then obtained using (8C-32). For these results we refer the interested reader to the second of Shirokov's papers cited earlier.‡

Problems

8-1 (*a*) Compare the early stages in the history of STR and of QM. What essential similarities and differences can you discover? (*b*) Considering the fundamental principles of STR and of QM, what can be said about their domains of universal validity? (If you are not yet acquainted with general relativity, disregard cosmological considerations; but whether gravitational considerations can be wholly put aside in answering this question is something to think about.)

8-2 In what sense can we say that Dirac's relativistic quantum theory of the electron has been a very important step in the development of what we now call the theory of elementary particles? Specifically, what basic ideas in the latter theory known to you have had their origin in Dirac's theory, whether directly or indirectly?

8-3 Using classical relativistic results, prove that the energy of a photon is proportional to its frequency. (This result is already contained in Einstein's first paper on relativity.) What is the corresponding relation for the 4-momentum of the photon? Suppose that the result of the Compton-effect experiment, giving $\Delta\lambda = C(1 - \cos\theta)$ (see page 116), C independent of the photon's energy, were known before the introduction of Planck's constant of action (an experimentally purely fictitious assumption). Explain how this result would have pointed strongly to the existence of such a universal constant.

8-4 (*a*) Prove the relations (8A-3) and (8A-4). How is the last relation changed when we replace $\mathcal{P}$ by one of its principal subgroups, such as $\mathcal{P}_+^\uparrow$

‡ See footnote ‡ on page 399. Only the final results are given, but there is little difficulty in checking their validity, using results that were obtained here. Note however that Shirokov's notation differs from that presented here.

(the proper orthochronous inhomogeneous Lorentz group)? (*b*) Show that $\mathcal{P}$ is the semidirect product (as defined in footnote § on page 388) of $\mathcal{L}_f$ and $\mathcal{T}$.

8-5 Prove directly the equivalence of the representations determined by the generators (8A-30) and by the generators J_k as given by (8A-15) and (8A-17).

8-6 (*a*) Find the covering group of the two-dimensional rotation group $\mathcal{R}_2$ and determine the connectivity type of the $\mathcal{R}_2$ manifold. (Note that connectivity multiplicity need not be finite.) (*b*) Discuss the connectivity properties of the $\mathcal{L}$ and $\mathcal{L}_f$ manifolds and draw *qualitative* conclusions concerning their covering groups. [Recall Eqs. (8A-42). Note that only when the group manifold is connected is the universal covering group unique.]

8-7 (*a*) Obtain the finite transformations of $\mathcal{L}$ from its generators. [It suffices to apply the method of exponentiation. By using (8A-6), one reduces the problem to the determination of the finite spatial rotations and of the special Lorentz transformations (2-6).] (*b*) Verify Eqs. (8B-4) and the statement following these equations.

8-8 Prove the theorem stated in the text relating to (8B-5). [The first part of this theorem follows in straightforward fashion with the aid of (5-3). The proof of the irreducibility of $\mathfrak{R}$ whenever $\mathfrak{R}_k (k = 1, 2)$ are irreducible can be based on a converse of Schur's lemma given on page 364, to the effect that a matrix representation is irreducible if every matrix that commutes with all the matrices of the representation is necessarily a scalar matrix. With our assumption that all reducible representations are decomposable, the proof of this converse should be fairly obvious. On the other hand, the proof that all the irreducible representations of G are obtained as stated requires a little more of the elementary group-theoretical machinery than was presented in the text, and can be omitted. It is outlined in Wigner, *op. cit.* (Group Theory), pp. 173–174.]

8-9 (*a*) Verify that the matrices (8B-21) satisfy the relations (8B-8). (*b*) Verify the relations (8B-22) and then deduce the homomorphism (8B-14).

8-10 (*a*) Verify at least the first of the following formulas giving an explicit connection between the matrices T of C_2 and the associated matrices L of $\mathcal{L}$:

$$L(T)^{\mu}{}_{\nu} = \tfrac{1}{2}\mathrm{Tr}(\bar{\sigma}^{\mu} T \sigma_{\nu} T^{\dagger}), \qquad \mathrm{Tr} \equiv \text{trace} \tag{i}$$

$$T(L) = \pm L_{\mu\nu}\bar{\sigma}^{\mu}\sigma^{\nu}[L_{\mu\nu}\bar{\sigma}^{\mu}\sigma^{\nu}L_{\lambda\tau}\bar{\sigma}^{\tau}\sigma^{\lambda}]^{-1/2} \tag{ii}$$

where $\bar{\sigma}^{\mu}$ are defined in footnote § on page 328. [To prove (i) recall (8-44) and the relation (8-49*a*). The verification of (ii) is more complicated. One requires (8-44) and (8-51), but also a formula reducing the products of four σ symbols that occur inside the brackets in (ii). See A. J. Macfarlane, *J. Math.*

Phys., **3**:1116 (1962). Note that there are minor differences in the notation employed in this paper and in the text.] (*b*) Show that

$$L(T^\dagger) = \tilde{L} \tag{iii}$$

Thence deduce that every matrix T of C_2 can be written

$$T = UH \qquad \begin{matrix} U \text{ unitary} \\ H \text{ hermitian} \end{matrix} \tag{iv}$$

[In the proof of (iii) one can use the fact that

$$\text{Tr}\,(AB\ .\ .\ .\ F) = \text{Tr}\,(B\ .\ .\ .\ FA)$$

etc., and that $\bar{\sigma}^\mu = \sigma_\mu$. From (iii) it can be seen that $\tilde{L} = L$ implies

$$T^\dagger(L) = \pm T(L)$$

The result (iv) then follows by recalling that $T(L)$ is unitary when L is a spatial rotation, and that according to (8A-6), (3-26), and (3-29), a general matrix of $\mathfrak{L}$ can be written as the product of a matrix of $\mathfrak{R}$ and a symmetric Lorentz matrix. One can also show that H is positive definite. See Macfarlane, *op. cit.*] (*c*) Show that when $T = \begin{bmatrix} \alpha & 0 \\ 0 & 1/\alpha \end{bmatrix}$, α real, then $L(T)$ is the special Lorentz transformation (2-6) (with x_1 replaced by x_3) with $\beta = (1 - \alpha^4)/(1 + \alpha^4)$. Compare this result with Eq. (iii) in Prob. 3-20.

8-11 (*a*) Prove that the set $\mathcal{P}$ defined on page 391 coincides with the set $\{Lp_*\}$, where p_* is an arbitrary element of $\mathcal{P}$ and L runs through all the elements of $\mathfrak{L}$. (*b*) Prove that the little groups $\mathcal{G}(\mathsf{p})$ and $\mathcal{G}(\mathsf{p}')$ are isomorphic when p and p' correspond to the same category I to IV [Eq. (8C-5)].

8-12 (*a*) Show that the matrices T of C_2 that yield the little group $\mathcal{G}_{\text{II}}$ can be written

$$T = \begin{bmatrix} \alpha & \alpha\beta \\ 0 & \alpha^* \end{bmatrix}, \qquad |\alpha| = 1 \tag{i}$$

(Take $p_*^1 = p_*^2 = 0$, $p_*^0 = p_*^3 = 1$.) Verify that the matrices (i) admit the decomposition

$$T = AB \qquad \begin{matrix} A = \begin{bmatrix} \alpha & 0 \\ 0 & \alpha^* \end{bmatrix} \\ B = \begin{bmatrix} 1 & \beta \\ 0 & 1 \end{bmatrix} \end{matrix} \tag{ii}$$

where the matrices $A \equiv A(\alpha)$, $B \equiv B(\beta)$ satisfy the following composition rules:

$$A(\alpha)A(\alpha') = A(\alpha\alpha') \tag{iii}$$

$$B(\beta)B(\beta') = B(\beta + \beta') \tag{iv}$$

$$B(\beta)A(\alpha) = A(\alpha)B[(\alpha^*)^2\beta] \tag{v}$$

Consider the analogy of (iii) to (8C-8), of (iv) to $U(\mathsf{a})U(\mathsf{a}') = U(\mathsf{a} + \mathsf{a}')$ $[U(\mathsf{a}) \equiv U_a$ defined in (8C-2)], and of (v) to (8C-3)—which is seen by taking $\alpha = e^{i\theta/2}$ and $\beta = \xi + i\eta$, and considering β as the planar vector (ξ,η), so that $(\alpha^*)^2\beta = R_\theta^{-1}\beta$, where R_θ is the operation of rotating a planar vector through the angle θ. Deduce from this analogy that the group of matrices (i) is isomorphic to the euclidean group $\mathcal{E}_2$ (of rotations and translation in a plane). [E. P. Wigner, *Ann. of Math.*, **40**: 149(1939) sec. 6D.] (*b*) Show that the Lorentz transformations $L(B)$ for the B given in (ii) are of the type given in (iii) Prob. 3-22. (This can be done in a number of ways. Review some pertinent results in Prob. 3-22.) What type of matrices are $L(A)$? Compare with the corresponding result in Prob. 8-10*c*.

8-13 Prove that the solution of our unitary representation problem for $\mathcal{P}$ for the case $w = 0$ in category II (see page 396) can be obtained by taking the limit $m = 0$ of the corresponding solution for category I. (Bear in mind that the choice of $\mathsf{p}*$ in $\mathcal{P}$ is arbitrary, and that the representations in question are fixed only within a unitary similarity transformation.)

8-14 (*a*) Verify the relations (8C-29) by comparing the two alternative expansions of (8C-27) as indicated in the text, and check Eqs. (8C-24) and (8C-26). (*b*) Prove the second relation in (8C-29) by starting with (8C-3) and using the connection between $\partial U(\mathsf{a})/\partial a^\mu \Big|_{\mathsf{a}=0}$ and P_μ.

8-15 (*a*) Verify the relations (8C-31)–(8C-34). [Note that

$$E^{\sigma\alpha\beta\gamma}E_{\sigma\lambda\mu\nu} = -\delta^{\alpha\beta\gamma}_{\lambda\mu\nu}$$

similarly to the formula (5-60), and taking account of (5-75).] (*b*) Show that the operators (8C-22) and (8C-30) form a complete independent Casimir set for the subgroup $\mathcal{L}$ of $\mathcal{P}$ in the sense that they commute with all the generators $J_{\lambda\mu}$, and that all similar quantities, such as the operators (8B-1), can be expressed in terms of this set.

8-16 (*a*) Prove that the operators S_ν defined in (8C-23) satisfy relations such as (8C-29) for P_ν. Does this result follow from general considerations? (*b*) Show for the case of the category $I(1)$ that Wigner's and Shirokov's methods of solving the unitary representation problem for $\mathcal{P}$ (the restricted group) are equivalent. How would you characterize the method for treating the category II that was indicated in the text?

8-17 (*a*) Check that the quantities (8B-1) are Casimir operators for $\mathcal{L}$. (*b*) Which, if any, of the operators (8B-1) and (8C-22) are of the form (8A-33)?

8-18 (*a*) Show that from the relation (8-45) or (8-50) it follows that

$$W_\mu W^\mu = \tfrac{1}{2}w_{A\dot{B}}w^{A\dot{B}} = \det \|w_{A\dot{B}}\| = \det \|w^{A\dot{B}}\| \qquad \text{(i)}$$

(*b*) Prove that if W is a null vector with $W_0 > 0$, then the associated spinor $w^{A\dot{B}}$ has the form

$$w^{A\dot{B}} = u^A u^{\dot{B}}, \qquad u \text{ determined except for an arbitrary phase factor} \quad \text{(ii)}$$

and that we can write in matrix form

$$W_\mu = \tfrac{1}{2} u^\dagger \sigma_\mu u, \qquad u = \begin{bmatrix} u_1 \\ u_2 \end{bmatrix} \quad \text{(iii)}$$

These relations can be used as a starting point (as they have been so used in the early investigations) in the development of the spinor formalism. [In the derivation of (ii) in addition to (i), it is only necessary to note that by our assumption that $W_0 > 0$ it can be concluded that $W_0 \pm W_3 > 0$. In proving (iii), we must remember the relation (8-46) for σ_μ.]

8-19 Show that the unimodular group C_2 is obtained from the special unitary group SU_2 by converting the three real parameters of the latter group, such as the Ω_k in (8A-39), into complex parameters. What conclusions can one draw from this result concerning the connection between the irreducible representations of $\mathfrak{R}$ and the finite-dimensional irreducible representations of $\mathfrak{L}$? [Using the lemma given in the footnote on page 377, it can be shown that every matrix of C_2 can be written as the exponential of a linear combination of σ_k ($k = 1, 2, 3$) with complex coefficients. Results presented in Appendix 8B and in Sec. 8-2 point to the answer to the last question in the problem.]

8-20 What are the irreducible tensor representations of $\mathfrak{L}$ that correspond to $\mathfrak{D}_{00}$, $\mathfrak{D}_{1/2,1/2}$, $\mathfrak{D}_{11}$, $\mathfrak{D}_{10}$, and $\mathfrak{D}_{01}$? Check your results partially by counting the number of independent tensor components in each case. Compare your conclusions in the last three cases with the results of Prob. 5-1, and in the last two with considerations relating to (8B-8). What modifications are introduced by requiring irreducibility relative to $\mathfrak{L}^\uparrow$? (See Laporte and Uhlenbeck, *op. cit.;* Gelfand, Minlos, and Shapiro, *op. cit.*, pp. 248–251.)

8-21 (*a*) Consider a wave function in spinor form representing a massive particle of spin $n + \frac{1}{2}$, n a positive integer. Show that the function can also be expressed in the mixed spinor-tensor form, $\psi_{\lambda_1 \cdots \lambda_n}$, where the λ_k are tensor indices, and ψ is symmetric in all these indices and is a Dirac bispinor for each fixed set of these indices. Show further that the wave equations of Fierz' type for the free motion of the particle can be written as

$$\begin{aligned} \left(\gamma^\nu \frac{\partial}{\partial x^\nu} + \kappa\right) \psi_{\lambda_1 \cdots \lambda_n} &= 0 \\ \gamma^\nu \psi_{\nu \lambda_2 \cdots \lambda_n} &= 0 \end{aligned} \quad \text{(i)}$$

and that the conditions

$$\frac{\partial}{\partial x_\nu} \psi_{\nu\lambda_2\cdots\lambda_n} = 0, \qquad \psi^\nu{}_{\nu\lambda_3\cdots\lambda_n} = 0 \tag{ii}$$

follow from (i). (*b*) For the case $n = 1$, verify that a possible expression for the lagrangian density is

$$\begin{aligned}\mathfrak{L} = \bar{\psi}^\mu \left(\gamma^\nu \frac{\partial}{\partial x^\nu} + \kappa\right) \psi_\mu - \tfrac{1}{3}\bar{\psi}_\mu \left(\gamma^\mu \frac{\partial}{\partial x_\nu} + \gamma^\nu \frac{\partial}{\partial x_\mu}\right) \psi_\nu \\ + \tfrac{1}{3}\bar{\psi}_\mu\, \gamma^\mu \left(\gamma^\nu \frac{\partial}{\partial x^\nu} - \kappa\right) \gamma^\lambda \psi_\lambda\end{aligned} \tag{iii}$$

using the notation (8-102). Find the energy-momentum tensor density and the particle 4-vector current density using (iii). (*c*) For massless particles show that for $n = 1$ the theory admits the gauge transformation

$$\psi_\mu \to \psi_\mu + \frac{\partial \chi}{\partial x^\mu}, \qquad \gamma^\nu \frac{\partial \chi}{\partial x^\nu} = 0$$

What can be said about the general case? [This approach was introduced by W. Rarita and J. Schwinger, *Phys. Rev.*, **60:** 61 (1941).]

8-22 Consider wave functions associated with $\mathfrak{D}_{n/2,0} + \mathfrak{D}_{0,n/2}$. When $n = 1$ we get the Dirac wave functions for particles of spin $\frac{1}{2}$. How far can you generalize to integral $n > 1$ the familiar results for the latter wave functions? [See D. N. Williams, 'The Dirac Algebra for any Spin,' in Brittin and Barut (eds.), *op. cit.* (see footnote ¶ on page 329).]

8-23 In addition to groups and their representations, another classical algebraic topic finding application in physics is that concerned with the structure of "algebras" (the term is defined on page 366). Among the most important and best known algebras in physics is the algebra determined abstractly by the anticommutation relations (8-25) [or (8-18)], the "Dirac algebra." This is an *associative* algebra over the field of complex numbers, having a *unit* element 1 (also known as a "hypercomplex number system"). (*a*) Show that a base $\{\Gamma_a\}$ in this algebra can be generated from the elements γ_λ satisfying the relations

$$\tfrac{1}{2}\{\gamma_\lambda,\gamma_\mu\} = g_{\lambda\mu}1 \equiv g_{\lambda\mu} \tag{i}$$

by taking

$$\begin{aligned}\{\Gamma_a\} &= \{1; \gamma_\lambda; \gamma_{\lambda\mu}; \gamma_{\lambda\mu\nu}; \gamma_5\}, \qquad a = 1, \ldots, 16 \\ \Gamma_1 &= 1 \\ \gamma_{\lambda\mu} &\equiv i\gamma_\lambda\gamma_\mu, \qquad \lambda < \mu \\ \gamma_{\lambda\mu\nu} &\equiv i\gamma_\lambda\gamma_\mu\gamma_\nu, \qquad \lambda < \mu < \nu \\ \gamma_5 &= \gamma_0\gamma_1\gamma_2\gamma_3\end{aligned} \tag{ii}$$

Assume that you are dealing with a given matrix representation. {Designating the matrices of the representation by the same symbols as for the abstract algebra, we can show that Tr $(\Gamma_a) = 0$ $(a \neq 1)$ [remembering that the trace of a matrix is invariant under a similarity transformation and that

$$\gamma_\lambda \gamma_\mu \gamma_\lambda^{-1} = -\gamma_\mu, \qquad \lambda \neq \mu \tag{iii}$$

by (i); and noting that $\gamma_{\lambda\mu\nu} \propto \gamma_\pi \gamma_5 (\pi \neq \lambda, \mu, \nu)$ and that $\gamma_\lambda \gamma_5 = -\gamma_5 \gamma_\lambda$]; $\Gamma_a^2 = \pm 1$; and $\Gamma_a \Gamma_b \propto \Gamma_c$ ($c \neq 1$ unless $a = b = 1$). From this we can deduce that the set (ii) is linearly independent. It is then clear that the resulting system is closed under all the operations of an algebra and that $\{\Gamma_a\}$ forms a base in this algebra.} Proceeding from the above results it is possible to prove that an *irreducible* matrix representation of the Dirac algebra is of order 4 (i.e., the matrices are of order 4), and that any two sets of 4×4 matrices satisfying (8-25) (we shall call such a set a "Dirac matrix set") are connected by a similarity transformation, which is, moreover, essentially unique (i.e., unique up to a numerical factor.) [W. Pauli, *Ann. Inst. Henri Poincaré*, **6:** 109 (1936). An exposition of Pauli's method is contained in R. H. Good, Jr., *Rev. Mod. Phys.*, **27:** 187 (1955). This article contains other pertinent references, including one to W. K. Clifford. For modern discussion on the interesting topic of Clifford numbers see, e.g., Weyl, *op. cit.* (Classical Groups), sec. 13; Boerner, *op. cit.*, chap. 8.]
(*b*) Show that these results can also be proved in an instructive way by considering the reduction of any arbitrary Dirac matrix set to the standard form (8-21) [we have only to take $\beta = \gamma_0$, $\alpha_k = i\gamma_k$ for the relations (8-25) to go over into (8-18)]. {By the relation $\alpha_\nu^2 = 1$ [taking now $\beta = \alpha_0$ and not $\alpha_0 = 1$ as in (8-24)] it follows that the eigenvalues of α_ν are ± 1, and since by (iii), the eigenvalues of α_ν = eigenvalues of $(-\alpha_\nu)$, it can be concluded that $N/2$ eigenvalues (N = order of the matrices) are $+1$ and the other $N/2$ eigenvalues are -1, and hence in particular N is even. $N = 2$ is excluded because it leads, as we know, to the Pauli matrices. We can in fact prove the following sharper result that will be needed: (1) Given any set of three 2×2 matrices satisfying (8A-41), there exists a similarity transformation, which is essentially unique, that brings this set into the standard form (8A-40). (We can, for instance, first diagonalize one of the matrices, so that we get the set $\begin{bmatrix} 1 & 0 \\ 0 & -1 \end{bmatrix}, \begin{bmatrix} 0 & \lambda \\ 1/\lambda & 0 \end{bmatrix}, \begin{bmatrix} 0 & \pm i\lambda \\ \mp i/\lambda & 0 \end{bmatrix}$, and then look for a matrix that transforms the first and the second matrices of this set into σ_1 and σ_3 respectively.) For $N = 4$, we begin by diagonalizing one of the matrices of the given Dirac set. The resulting Dirac set can then be shown by (8-18) to consist of the matrices

$$\alpha_0' = \begin{bmatrix} \sigma_0 & \\ & -\sigma_0 \end{bmatrix}, \qquad \alpha_k' = \begin{bmatrix} & a_k \\ a_k^{-1} & \end{bmatrix} \tag{iv}$$

where

$$a_k^{-1}a_r + a_r^{-1}a_k = 0, \qquad r \neq k \tag{v}$$

Transforming the set (iv) by the matrix $U = \begin{bmatrix} a_1 & \\ & u \end{bmatrix}$, where

$$u^2 = \sigma_0 \tag{vi}$$

leaves α_0' unchanged, while the transformed matrices

$$\alpha_k'' = \begin{bmatrix} & b_k \\ b_k^{-1} & \end{bmatrix} = U^{-1}\alpha_k' U$$

will satisfy the condition

$$b_k^2 = \sigma_0 \tag{vii}$$

provided

$$b_k = a_1^{-1}a_k u = u a_k^{-1} a_1 \tag{viii}$$

[using (vi)]. This is satisfied for $k = 1$, and for $k = 2, 3$ (viii) can be written

$$\{v_k,u\} = 0, \qquad v_k = a_1^{-1}a_k \qquad k = 2, 3 \tag{ix}$$

using (v), which gives $v_k^2 = -1$. Putting $w_k = iv_k$ ($k = 2, 3$), we have then, by (vi) and (ix)—and since $\{w_2,w_3\} = 0$ [as follows from (v)]—that the matrix set u, w_2, w_3 satisfies (8A-41). Hence by the above result (1), u can be determined essentially uniquely and the same is therefore true by (viii) of the b_k, which then satisfy (vii). Since the b_k also satisfy (v), the remainder of our proof is obvious.} (*c*) The matrices (8-21) were originally introduced by Dirac with the aid of the matrices (8-20). Show that the latter matrices (including ρ_2) are given by the Kronecker products $\rho_k = \sigma_k \times \iota$ [ι given in (8-20)] while the matrices (8-19) coincide with $\iota \times \sigma_k$; so that the commutativity of these two sets of matrices is in immediate evidence, and $\alpha_k = \sigma_1 \times \sigma_k$, $\beta = \sigma_3 \times \iota$, with the relations (8-18) an immediate consequence. [In addition to the rule (5-3), note that the distributive law with respect to addition is also satisfied by the Kronecker product.]

8-24 (*a*) Compare the Wigner and the Dirac-Fierz-Pauli-Bhabha approaches as far as concerns the relativistic definition of the spin of an elementary particle. Is there anything in the latter approach that corresponds to Wigner's "little groups"? What is the role if any of the group of space-time translations in the latter approach? (*b*) Is there a common idea underlying Eqs. (8C-29), (8-44) and (8-58)?

8-25 Show that the simplest connection between the matrices $U_{\mu\nu}$ and A_ν occurring in (8-60) is of the form

$$U_{\mu\nu} = CA_{[\mu}A_{\nu]} \tag{i}$$

and check that Eq. (i) holds in the case of the Dirac equation and the Duffin-Kemmer equations. In particular, verify that for the Dirac equation $C = -\frac{1}{2}$, and check that this agrees with the known result for this equation [see, e.g., Bjorken and Drell, *op. cit.* (on p. 546), sec. 2.2]. [Note that by (8-26) and (8-55), $A_\nu = i\gamma_\nu$ for the Dirac equation, and that in using Eq. (8B-2) we have to take the negative of the $U_{\mu\nu}$ occurring in this equation, in accordance with the convention introduced in Appendix 8C and followed in Sec. 8.3.]

8-26 Prove that for the Dirac equation (8-26) the matrix M of Eq. (8-72) can be identified with γ^0, the matrix S involved in (8-66) is proportional to γ^0, and Eqs. (8-75), (8-84), and (8-85) reduce to the corresponding familiar results for a Dirac (spin $\frac{1}{2}$) particle.

8-27 (*a*) Find an expression for the spin density of a Dirac (spin $\frac{1}{2}$) particle, using the general method presented in Sec. 8-3, and compare with the corresponding result considered in Sec. 8-1. (*b*) Find a symmetric form of the energy-momentum tensor for such a particle, by applying pertinent theory presented in Sec. 8-3. (One finds that if the canonical tensor is $T^{\mu\nu}$ then the symmetrical tensor is just $T^{(\mu\nu)}$.)

8-28 Find the simplest equations of the type discussed in Sec. 8-3 that apply to a massless particle of spin $\frac{1}{2}$. Show that we have two independent equations, and—using plane wave solutions and proper expressions for energy momentum and angular momentum—establish characteristic physical properties. Compare with current two-component neutrino theory. [Consider transformation properties of the wave function, and the projection of spin along the direction of the line of flight for positive or negative frequencies (helicity). See, e.g., Roman, *op. cit.* (on page 332), chap. 4, sec. 6.e. Elementary quantum field-theoretical considerations are required for a complete discussion of the last questions.]

8-29 Using pertinent results in Appendix 8C, show that the *helicity* (referred to in Prob. 8-28) of a massless free particle has one of the values (8C-21), and that it is given by the expression

$$j = -\frac{a_\nu S^\nu}{a_\nu P^\nu} = \frac{\mathbf{J} \cdot \mathbf{P}}{|\mathbf{P}|}, \qquad a \text{ arbitrary} \tag{i}$$

representing the projection of the particle's spin along the direction of its momentum.

Answers to Selected Problems

1-2 (*a*) The Lagrangian of this problem, given in (1-5), is $L = \sqrt{y_i y_i}$, $y_i \equiv x'_i$; the subsidiary condition is (1-5*a*), i.e.,

$$F \equiv y_i y_i = \text{const. along extremals} \tag{a}$$

Hence the Euler-Lagrange equations (1-6) give

$$0 = F^{-3/2}(F\,\delta_{ij} - y_i y_j)y'_j = F^{-1/2}y'_i \tag{b}$$

since $F' = 0$ along extremals, by (a), and Eqs. (1-7) follow.

If it is not assumed that the parameter u is chosen so that (a) is satisfied, we cannot conclude from the first part of (b) that $y'_i = 0$, because the determinant of $\|F\,\delta_{ij} - y_i y_j\| \equiv \|F_{ij}\|$ is zero, since $F_{ij}y_j = 0$. However, (b) and the latter equation imply the proportionality of y_i and y'_i: $y'_i = \alpha(u)y_i$. Thus, $y_i = C_i\beta(u)$, C_i constants, $\beta(u) > 0$; and we can introduce the new parameter $\bar{u} = \int\beta(u)\,du$ for which $\bar{x}_i(\bar{u}) \equiv x_i(u)$ satisfy:

$$\bar{y}_i \equiv d\bar{x}_i/d\bar{u} = y_i\,du/d\bar{u} = C_i\beta(u)/\beta(u) = C_i$$

moreover, since L is homogeneous of the first degree in the y_i (see footnote on page 101), $\int L(y)\,du = \int L(\bar{y})\,d\bar{u}$. The form of the general solution of our variational problem in the case of unrestricted parameter is now apparent.

To show that our extremi are minimal, we can proceed geometrically by invoking the triangle inequality (discussed in Sec. 1-2) and resorting to known pertinent limiting processes. Analytically, we can proceed, for instance, as follows. We choose coordinates so that the extremal under consideration is along, say, the x axis, and we take $u = x$, so that the equations of comparison curves have the form $y = f(x)$, $z = g(x)$. Our result follows then at once from the obvious inequality $\int \{1 + [f'(x)]^2 + [g'(x)]^2\}^{1/2}\,dx > \int dx$.

(*b*) With F as defined in (iii), the Euler-Lagrange equations corresponding to our Lagrangian $L = s' \equiv ds/du$ [see (i)], upon expansion, lead to Eqs. (ii). If the parameter u is chosen so that (iv) is satisfied, these equations reduce to $0 = z_a' = 2g_{ab}x_b''$ (as $\partial F/\partial x_a = 0$, the g_{ab} being constants). Since (i) is positive definite, it follows in particular that $\det \|g_{ab}\| \neq 0$ and hence $x_a'' = 0$. The geodesics have therefore a linear parametric representation similar to (1-7). By a reasoning similar to that given in Sec. 1-2 it can be concluded that the coordinate lines of our space are rectilinear and in general oblique, the terms having a significance analogous to that obtaining in ordinary space.

If condition (iv) does not hold, we observe that (ii) can be written as $(4Fg_{ab} - z_az_b)x_b'' = 0$, and that $(4Fg_{ab} - z_az_b)x_b' = 0$. It follows that we can proceed similarly to the corresponding treatment in (*a*). The proof of the minimum property of the geodesics can obviously also be carried out by analogy to the corresponding proof in (*a*).

(*c*) Since, $\partial F/\partial x_a \equiv F_{,a} = g_{bc,a}x_b'x_c'$, $z_a' = 2(g_{ab}\,x_b'' + g_{ab,c}x_b'x_c')$, we get from (ii) and (iv),

$$0 = g_{ab}x_b'' + (g_{ab,c} - \tfrac{1}{2}g_{bc,a})x_b'x_c' = g_{ab}x_b'' + \tfrac{1}{2}(g_{ab,c} + g_{ac,b} - g_{bc,a})x_b'x_c'$$

i.e., (v).

To show the consistency of (ii) and (iv), note that $2F = z_ax_a'$ and hence $2F' = z_ax_a'' + z_a'x_a'$, which, together with

$$F' = F_{,a}x_a' + \left(\frac{\partial F}{\partial x_a'}\right)x_a'' = F_{,a}x_a' + z_ax_a''$$

gives $F' = (z_a' - F_{,a})x_a'$.

1-5 (*a*) By (1-13), $(\widetilde{AB})(AB) = \tilde{B}(\tilde{A}A)B = \tilde{B}IB = \tilde{B}B = I$, and

$$(\tilde{A}^{-1})A^{-1} = (A\tilde{A})^{-1} = I^{-1} = I$$

since $(AB)^{-1} = B^{-1}A^{-1}$ and $(\tilde{A})^{-1} = (\widetilde{A^{-1}})$ [i.e., $(\tilde{A})^{-1} = \tilde{B}$ where $B = A^{-1}$]. The condition (1-14) defines a subgroup, for $\det(AB) = \det A \cdot \det B$. That this condition must be satisfied by matrices associated with displacements can be seen, for instance, by noting that a displacement can be obtained, starting with the identity transformation, by a continuous variation of the parameters of the transformation matrix, and that the determinant of a matrix is a continuous function of the matrix elements.

If A is a nonproper orthogonal matrix, and R is the matrix of the reflection transformation, $x_i' = -x_i$, then AR is a proper orthogonal matrix (by the formula for the determinant of a product of matrices, and since $\tilde{R} = R = R^{-1}$, $\det R = -1$), and the geometric significance of the transformation given by A is clear. If A' is another such matrix, $\det(AA') = +1$, and the group property is violated.

(*b*) Combining the transformations $x_i' = A_{ij}x_j$, $t' = t$ and $x_i'' = x_i' + a_i t'$, $t'' = t'$, we get $x_i'' = A_{ij}x_j + a_i t$, $t'' = t$ $(\tilde{A} = A^{-1})$, or, in terms of the associated matrices,

$$\begin{bmatrix} 1 & 0 & 0 & a_1 \\ 0 & 1 & 0 & a_2 \\ 0 & 0 & 1 & a_3 \\ 0 & 0 & 0 & 1 \end{bmatrix} \begin{bmatrix} A_{11} & A_{12} & A_{13} & 0 \\ A_{21} & A_{22} & A_{23} & 0 \\ A_{31} & A_{32} & A_{33} & 0 \\ 0 & 0 & 0 & 1 \end{bmatrix} \equiv \begin{bmatrix} I & a \\ 0 & 1 \end{bmatrix} \begin{bmatrix} A & 0 \\ 0 & 1 \end{bmatrix} = \begin{bmatrix} A & a \\ 0 & 1 \end{bmatrix} \tag{a}$$

The matrix of the special Lorentz transformation (2-6) has, in the present coordinates, the form

$$\begin{bmatrix} \gamma & 0 & 0 & -\gamma v \\ 0 & 1 & 0 & 0 \\ 0 & 0 & 1 & 0 \\ -\gamma c^{-2} v & 0 & 0 & \gamma \end{bmatrix} \tag{b}$$

If we take $A = I$ and $a_i = (-v, 0, 0)$ in (a), the resulting matrix agrees with (b) when v^2/c^2 can be neglected.

2-1 (*a*) If we use (i) directly, then the invariance in question is obvious; moreover, the form (ii) and (iii) of the Maxwell-Hertz equations follows at once by substituting into Maxwell's phenomenological electromagnetic equations (modified as stated) the explicit expression

$$\frac{D\mathbf{A}}{Dt} = \dot{\mathbf{A}} + \operatorname{curl}(\mathbf{A} \times \mathbf{v}) + \mathbf{v} \cdot \operatorname{div} \mathbf{A}$$

To prove this covariance of the Maxwell-Hertz equations explicitly under the stated assumptions, it is obviously sufficient to show that if we start with the 'stationary' coordinate frame S', relative to which these equations take the pure maxwellian form,

$$\nabla' \cdot \mathbf{D}' = 4\pi\rho', \qquad \nabla' \cdot \mathbf{B}' = 0$$
$$\nabla' \times \mathbf{E}' = -\frac{1}{c}\dot{\mathbf{B}}', \qquad \nabla' \times \mathbf{H}' = \frac{1}{c}(\dot{\mathbf{D}}' + 4\pi\mathbf{j}') \tag{a}$$

then equations of the type (ii) are obtained for any frame S having arbitrary rigid body motion relative to S':

$$x = A(t)x' + b(t), \qquad t = t'$$
$$\tilde{A}A = I \tag{b}$$

[using matrix notation as in Eq. (1-12)]. Since by assumption, $\rho' = \rho$, it follows from familiar vector-analysis relations that the first two equations in (a) remain form invariant under (b). Again, since

$$\frac{\partial x_i}{\partial t'} = \frac{\partial x_i}{\partial t}\bigg|_{x'=\text{const.}} = -v_i$$

where $\mathbf{v}$ is the velocity field of S relative to S', $\partial/\partial t' = \partial/\partial t - v_i\,\partial/\partial x_i$, and $(\nabla' \times \mathbf{E}')_i = \epsilon_{ijk}E'_{k,j} = \epsilon_{ijk}(A_{sk}E_s)_{,r}\,\partial x_r/\partial x'_j = \epsilon_{ijk}A_{sk}A_{rj}E_{s,r} = \epsilon_{prs}A_{pi}E_{s,r}$ [by (v)], one finds from the third of Eqs. (a):

$$0 = A_{pi}\left(\epsilon_{prs}E_{s,r} + \frac{\dot{B}_p - v_jB_{p,j}}{c}\right) + \frac{\dot{A}_{pi}B_p}{c}$$

When these are multiplied-summed by A_{ki} and use is made of the relation

$$A_{ki}\dot{A}_{pi} = -\dot{A}_{ki}A_{pi} = -(\dot{A}_{ki}x'_i)_{,p} = v_{k,p} \tag{c}$$

[as $A_{pi} = \partial x'_i/\partial x_p$ and noting that by (b), $-v_i = \dot{b}_i + \dot{A}_{ij}x'_j$], it follows that

$$\epsilon_{krs}E_{s,r} + \frac{1}{c}\,(\dot{B}_k - v_jB_{k,j} + v_{k,p}B_p) = 0 \tag{d}$$

The volume-preserving property of the transformations (b) implies the vanishing of $\nabla \cdot \mathbf{v}$ [see Prob. 6-3; also by (c), $v_{k,p} = -v_{p,k}$ and hence $v_{k,k} = 0$]. Hence, applying the identity (iv), the third of Eqs. (ii) follows from (d). The last of Eqs (ii) is obtained in a similar manner when attention is paid to Hertz' assumptions.

(*b*) The negative result of the Michelson-Morley experiment is consistent with Hertz' theory. On the other hand, since the unrestricted use of newtonian kinematics is incorporated in his theory, it follows that Fresnel's coefficient as given by this theory has the unacceptable value 1.

2-2 By (1-25) and (i), $\partial/\partial\mathbf{x} = \partial/\partial\mathbf{x}' + \beta\boldsymbol{\tau}\,\partial/\partial t'$, $\boldsymbol{\tau} \equiv \nabla T$, and

$$\frac{\partial}{\partial t} = \frac{\partial}{\partial t'} - \mathbf{v}\cdot\frac{\partial}{\partial \mathbf{x}'}$$

Hence, by (ii),

$$0 = \nabla \cdot \mathbf{B} = \nabla' \cdot \mathbf{B}' + \beta(\boldsymbol{\tau} \cdot \dot{\mathbf{B}}' - \nabla' \cdot \mathbf{B}_1) - \beta^2 \boldsymbol{\tau} \cdot \frac{\partial \mathbf{B}_1}{\partial t'}, \qquad \dot{f}' \equiv \frac{\partial f'}{\partial t'}$$

$$4\pi\rho = \nabla \cdot \mathbf{E} = \nabla' \cdot \mathbf{E}' + \beta(\boldsymbol{\tau} \cdot \dot{\mathbf{E}}' - \nabla' \cdot \mathbf{E}_1) - \beta^2 \boldsymbol{\tau} \cdot \frac{\partial \mathbf{E}_1}{\partial t'}$$

$$0 = \nabla \times \mathbf{E} + \frac{1}{c}\dot{\mathbf{B}} = \nabla' \times \mathbf{E}' + \beta(\boldsymbol{\tau} \times \dot{\mathbf{E}}' - \nabla' \times \mathbf{E}_1) - \beta^2 \boldsymbol{\tau} \times \frac{\partial \mathbf{E}_1}{\partial t'}$$

$$+ \frac{1}{c}\dot{\mathbf{B}}' - \beta\left(w_i \frac{\partial \mathbf{B}'}{\partial x_i'} + \frac{1}{c}\frac{\partial \mathbf{B}_1}{\partial t'}\right) + \beta^2 w_i \frac{\partial \mathbf{B}_1}{\partial x_i'}, \qquad \mathbf{w} \equiv \frac{\mathbf{v}}{v}$$

$$\nabla \times \mathbf{B} - \frac{1}{c}\dot{\mathbf{E}} = \cdots = \frac{4\pi\rho}{c}\mathbf{u} = \frac{4\pi\rho}{c}(\mathbf{u}' + \mathbf{v})$$

Neglecting terms in β^2, it is seen that Eqs. (2-1) and (2-2) retain their form in the primed quantities, provided

$$\begin{aligned} 0 &= \boldsymbol{\tau} \cdot \dot{\mathbf{B}}' - \nabla' \cdot \mathbf{B}_1 = \boldsymbol{\tau} \cdot \dot{\mathbf{E}}' - \nabla' \cdot \mathbf{E}_1 \\ &= \boldsymbol{\tau} \times \dot{\mathbf{E}}' - \nabla' \times \mathbf{E}_1 - w_i \frac{\partial \mathbf{B}'}{\partial x_i'} - \frac{1}{c}\frac{\partial \mathbf{B}_1}{\partial t'} \\ &= \boldsymbol{\tau} \times \dot{\mathbf{B}}' - \nabla' \times \mathbf{B}_1 - 4\pi\rho\mathbf{w} + w_i \frac{\partial \mathbf{E}'}{\partial x_i'} + \frac{1}{c}\frac{\partial \mathbf{E}_1}{\partial t'} \end{aligned} \tag{a}$$

If one applies the identity (iv) of Prob. 2-1, which, since $\mathbf{v}$ is here constant, is simply, $v_j A_{k,j} = [\nabla \times (\mathbf{A} \times \mathbf{v})]_k + v_k \nabla \cdot \mathbf{A}$, it is seen that the third of Eqs. (a) is satisfied provided (to first order):

$$\mathbf{E}_1 = \mathbf{w} \times \mathbf{B}' \approx \mathbf{w} \times \mathbf{B}, \qquad \mathbf{B}_1 = c\boldsymbol{\tau} \times \mathbf{E}' \approx c\boldsymbol{\tau} \times \mathbf{E} \tag{b}$$

and then one finds that the last of Eqs. (a) is satisfied provided $\boldsymbol{\tau} = -\mathbf{w}/c$, and

$$\nabla' \cdot \mathbf{E}' = 4\pi\rho \tag{c}$$

The first two of Eqs. (a) then follow using (b) and the Maxwell curl equations in the primed quantities just proven, thus also establishing Eq. (c)—all expressions of course being taken to first order, it being also assumed that $u \sim v$. Finally, the first-order form invariance of Eq. (2-3) is in immediate evidence:

$$\mathbf{E}' + \frac{1}{c}(\mathbf{u}' \times \mathbf{B}') = \mathbf{E} + \frac{1}{c}(\mathbf{v} \times \mathbf{B}) + \frac{1}{c}\left\{(\mathbf{u} - \mathbf{v}) \times \left[\mathbf{B} - \frac{1}{c}(\mathbf{v} \times \mathbf{E})\right]\right\}$$

$$= \mathbf{E} + \frac{1}{c}(\mathbf{u} \times \mathbf{B}) - \frac{1}{c^2}[\mathbf{u}' \times (\mathbf{v} \times \mathbf{E})]$$

2-4 (*a*) By Eqs. (iii), the condition of form invariance of Eq. (i), i.e.,

$$\frac{1}{c^2}\frac{\partial^2}{\partial t^2} - \nabla^2 = l\left(\frac{1}{c^2}\frac{\partial^2}{\partial t'^2} - \nabla'^2\right)$$

leads to the relations

$$\begin{aligned} \frac{1}{c^2} - q_i q_i &= \frac{l}{c^2} \\ \frac{1}{c^2}\, p_i - a_{ij} q_j &= 0 \\ \frac{1}{c^2}\, p_i p_j - a_{ik} a_{jk} &= -l\delta_{ij} \end{aligned} \tag{a}$$

In matrix notation, the first set of Eqs. (iii) reads $x' = Ax - pt$; and $dx' = 0$ gives $v = dx/dt = A^{-1}p$. Hence, by the second of Eqs. (a),

$$Aq = \frac{1}{c^2}\, p, \qquad q = \frac{1}{c^2}\, A^{-1}p = \frac{1}{c^2}\, v \tag{b}$$

The first and last of Eqs. (a) yield therefore Eq. (iv) (as $\tilde{A} = A$), which suggests putting

$$A = \mu I + \nu p\tilde{p} \tag{c}$$

One finds then that $A^2 = \mu^2 I + (2\mu\nu + \nu^2 \tilde{p}p)p\tilde{p}$, and comparison with (iv) shows that one can take $\mu = \lambda$. It now follows from (b) first that $(Aq)_i = \lambda q_i + \nu p_i p_j q_j = p_i/c^2$, i.e., that $p_i = \rho q_i$; next, that $Aq = \rho q/c^2$; and lastly by (iv) that $A^2 q = \rho^2 q/c^4 = (c^{-6}\rho^2 \mathbf{v}^2 + \lambda^2)q$ and hence, by the definition of λ in (ii), $\rho^2 = c^4$. Taking $\rho = c^2$, and remembering the second of Eqs. (b), it is then seen that $p = v$; hence Eq. (v) is verified. Finally, substituting (c) (with $\mu = \lambda$) in (v) one finds that $\nu = (1 - \lambda)/\mathbf{v}^2$, and Eqs. (ii) are obtained with $\alpha_i = v_i/v$.

(*b*) The form-invariance requirement yields the relations

$$\begin{aligned} \frac{\sigma^2}{c^2} - \tilde{q}q &= \frac{1}{c^2} \\ \frac{\sigma}{c^2}\, p - Aq &= 0 \\ \frac{1}{c^2}\, p\tilde{p} - A^2 &= -I \end{aligned} \tag{d}$$

In place of (b) one now has $q = \sigma v/c^2$ (as $A^{-1}p = v$), and hence by the first of Eqs. (d), it follows that

$$\sigma = \pm\gamma \tag{e}$$

By Eq. (c) and the last of Eqs. (d),

$$\mu = \pm 1 \tag{f}$$

As in part (a), one can conclude that $p = \rho q$; the combination of the last two of Eqs. (d) and Eq. (e) then gives $A^2 q = \gamma^2 \rho^2 q/c^4 = (c^{-6}\rho^2\gamma^2\mathbf{v}^2 + 1)q$, so that $\rho^2 = c^4$, and hence $p = \pm\gamma v$, $Av = \pm\gamma v$. If all signs are chosen as $+$, one finds from the last two equations and Eqs. (c) and (f) that $\nu = (\gamma - 1)/\gamma^2\mathbf{v}^2$, and Eqs. (vi) are thus established.

2-5 Poincaré's method of deriving the result (ii) for the transformation of volumes by considering the moving "sphere" (i) can be explained as follows. We are assuming that the shape of an (ideally rigid) body is represented in S by Eq. (i), and it has therefore in S the volume $V = 4\pi r^3/3$. In S' its volume can be obtained by applying (2-6) to Eq. (i) and finding the resulting shape of the body for fixed t'. For $t' = 0$ we find

$$a^2x'^2 + \left(y' - \frac{1}{c}\beta\gamma u_y x'\right)^2 + \left(z' - \frac{1}{c}\beta\gamma u_z x'\right)^2 = r^2, \qquad a = \gamma\left(1 - \frac{1}{c}\beta u_x\right)$$

This is the equation of an ellipsoid of volume $V' = V/a$, which establishes the relation (ii) in this particular case. By appropriate continuity considerations (relating to spatial integration) this result can be extended to bodies of arbitrary shape.

The relation (ii) follows also in more direct fashion from the relativistic contraction of lengths as given in Eq. (3-4). If V_0 is the volume of the body as measured in the frame in which it is instantaneously at rest, then by (3-4) its volume in S is $V = V_0/\gamma_u$, while in S' it is $V' = V_0/\gamma_{u'}$. Hence, $V'/V = \gamma_u/\gamma_{u'}$, and this ratio can be shown to equal $1/a$ [see Eq. (i) in Prob. 3-3].

3-8 After establishing the invariance of the phase function

$$\Psi = \frac{2\pi}{c}(\nu x_0 - \nu\mathbf{n}\cdot\mathbf{x}) = \frac{2\pi}{c}(\mathsf{n},\mathsf{x}), \qquad \mathsf{n} = (\nu,\nu\mathbf{n}) \tag{i}$$

one can conclude from the arbitrariness of the 4-vector x, that n is a 4-vector (see Prob. 5-2); and an application of (3-29a) then yields the transformation laws for ν and $\mathbf{n}$. The latter is of the same form as the transformation law for $\mathbf{u}/c$, since $\mathbf{u}/c = d\mathbf{x}/dx_0$ and $n_i = (\mathsf{n})_i/n_0$. The invariance of (i) follows for instance from the first of Eqs. (2-7) upon taking $\mathbf{E} = \mathbf{E}^{(0)}\sin\Psi$, so that $E'_x = E_x^{(0)}\sin\Psi'$, and hence $\Psi' = \Psi$.

3-15 (a) The lines of intersection of the locus (*) and the null cone through the origin are given by the u,v ratios satisfying the equation

$$0 = (\mathsf{x},\mathsf{x}) = Au^2 + 2Cuv + Bv^2; \qquad A = (\mathsf{a},\mathsf{a}),\ C = (\mathsf{a},\mathsf{b}),\ B = (\mathsf{b},\mathsf{b})$$

If $A \neq 0$, then

$$\frac{u}{v} = \frac{-C \pm \sqrt{C^2 - AB}}{A}$$

and the stated conclusion is evident; and if $B \neq 0$ one can reason similarly by solving for v/u; while if both $A = 0$ and $B = 0$, then the plane is obviously timelike, being determined by the lines through the origin directed along the null vectors a and b. [We cannot also have $C = 0$; two linearly independent null vectors in $\mathfrak{M}$ cannot be orthogonal: if $\mathbf{a}^2 = a_0{}^2$, $\mathbf{b}^2 = b_0{}^2$, and $\mathbf{a} \cdot \mathbf{b} = a_0 b_0$, then $(\mathbf{a} \cdot \mathbf{b})^2 = \mathbf{a}^2\mathbf{b}^2$ and hence $\mathbf{a} = \alpha\mathbf{b}$, $a_0 b_0 = \alpha b_0{}^2$, i.e., $a_0 = \alpha b_0$, or $\mathsf{a} = \alpha\mathsf{b}$—a contradiction.]

If $\mathsf{c} = p\mathsf{a} + q\mathsf{b}$, $\mathsf{d} = r\mathsf{a} + s\mathsf{b}$, and $\Delta = ps - qr \neq 0$, so that c, d are in the plane (i) (i.e., more precisely, so that c, d are in the vector space of $\mathfrak{M}$ spanned by a, b), and are linearly independent, one finds that

$$(\mathsf{c},\mathsf{d})^2 - (\mathsf{c},\mathsf{c})(\mathsf{d},\mathsf{d}) = \Delta^2[(\mathsf{a},\mathsf{b})^2 - (\mathsf{a},\mathsf{a})(\mathsf{b},\mathsf{b})]$$

(*b*) Both planes cannot be timelike because no two timelike vectors are mutually perpendicular, as follows from the result (1) on page 60;‡ nor can they be both spacelike, since one cannot have a *base* in $\mathfrak{M}$ that is purely spacelike.

(*c*) The vectors b are spacelike, since $a_0{}^2 = \mathbf{a}^2$ and

$$a_0 b_0 = \mathbf{a} \cdot \mathbf{b} = ab \cos \theta$$

imply $b_0{}^2 = b^2 \cos^2 \theta < b^2$ (we cannot have $\theta = 0$ or π because of nonexistence in $\mathfrak{M}$ of two perpendicular null vectors); they form together with a a 3-plane tangent to the light cone along a. In fact, with the normalization $b_0 = 1$, one can find a pair of solutions $\mathbf{b}$, $\mathbf{b}'$ of the equations $\mathbf{a} \cdot \mathbf{b} = a_0$, $\mathbf{b} \cdot \mathbf{b}' = 1$, and the 3-plane given by the parametric equation

$$\mathsf{x} = \mathsf{a}u + \mathsf{b}v + \mathsf{b}'w \tag{a}$$

has the stated property, since the equation $0 = (\mathsf{x},\mathsf{x}) = (\mathsf{b},\mathsf{b})v^2 + (\mathsf{c},\mathsf{c})w^2$ implies that $v = w = 0$.

3-17 (*a*) U is timelike, since $(\mathsf{U},\mathsf{U}) = (d\mathsf{x},d\mathsf{x})/d\tau^2 = c^2$; and hence, by (2) on page 60, A is spacelike.

(*b*) $A_0 = \gamma\, d(c\gamma)/dt = c\gamma u\, (du/dt)\gamma^3/c^2 = \gamma^4\mathbf{u} \cdot \mathbf{a}/c$,

$$\mathbf{A} = \gamma \frac{d(\gamma\mathbf{u})}{dt} = \gamma^2\mathbf{a} + \gamma^4 \frac{(\mathbf{u} \cdot \mathbf{a})\mathbf{u}}{c^2}$$

‡ If a, b are timelike and $a_0 b_0 < 0$, then applying (1) to a and $-\mathsf{b}$, it follows that $(\mathsf{a},\mathsf{b}) < 0$. More simply, if $(\mathsf{a},\mathsf{b}) = 0$ then $a_0{}^2 b_0{}^2 = (\mathbf{a} \cdot \mathbf{b})^2$ and hence we cannot have $a_0{}^2 > \mathbf{a}^2$ and $b_0{}^2 > \mathbf{b}^2$.

(*c*) By (3-29*a*)

$$\mathbf{A} = \mathbf{A}^* + \frac{\gamma - 1}{\beta^2}(\boldsymbol{\beta}\cdot\mathbf{A}^*)\boldsymbol{\beta} \qquad \boldsymbol{\beta} = \frac{\mathbf{u}}{c} \tag{a}$$
$$A_0 = \gamma\boldsymbol{\beta}\cdot\mathbf{A}^*$$

as $A_0^* = 0$ according to (ii). With the initial velocity and acceleration having the direction of the x_1 axis, the motion continues along the x_1 axis and one finds from (a): $A_1 = \gamma(\gamma\ddot{x}_1 + \dot{\gamma}\dot{x}_1) = A_1^* + \beta^2 A_1^*(\gamma - 1)/\beta^2 = \gamma A_1^*$, $A_0 = c\gamma\dot{\gamma} = \gamma\beta A_1^*$ $(\dot{x} \equiv dx/dt)$. Hence $\gamma\ddot{x}_1 + \beta^2 A_1^* = A_1^*$, i.e.,

$$\ddot{x}_1 = \frac{(1 - \beta^2)A_1^*}{\gamma}$$

Thus

$$\ddot{x} = \alpha\left(1 - \frac{\dot{x}^2}{c^2}\right)^{3/2} \qquad x \equiv x_1 \qquad \alpha \equiv A_1^* \tag{b}$$

A first immediate integration yields (since by our initial conditions the velocity does not reverse its direction)

$$\beta = \frac{\dot{x}}{c} = T(1 + T^2)^{-1/2} \qquad T = \frac{\alpha}{c}t + \gamma_0\beta_0 \qquad \beta_0 = \beta\Big|_{t=0} \tag{c}$$

and thence

$$X = \sqrt{1 + T^2} + C \qquad X = \frac{\alpha}{c^2}x \qquad C = \frac{\alpha}{c^2}x_0 - \gamma_0 \qquad x_0 = x\Big|_{t=0} \tag{d}$$

(as $\beta = dX/dT$).

When $T \ll 1$ (and $\beta_0 \ll 1$), (d) gives to terms of second order,

$$X = 1 + \frac{1}{2}\left(\frac{\alpha^2t^2}{c^2} + {\beta_0}^2 + \frac{2\beta_0\alpha t}{c}\right) + \frac{\alpha x_0}{c^2} - \left(1 + \frac{{\beta_0}^2}{2}\right) = \frac{\alpha^2t^2}{2c^2} + \frac{\beta_0\alpha t}{c} + \frac{\alpha x_0}{c^2}$$

i.e., $x = \alpha t^2/2 + u_0t + x_0$—the classical expression. If $T \gg 1$, (c) shows that $\beta = 1 - 1/2T^2 + \cdots$. Thus, $u \to c$ as $t \to \infty$.

When $x_0 = \beta_0 = 0$, then by (d)

$$X = \sqrt{1 + T^2} - 1 \qquad X = \frac{\alpha}{c^2}x \qquad T = \frac{\alpha}{c}t \tag{e}$$

and if we substitute in (e) $T + T'$ for T, it is seen that $x > ct$, that is, $X > T$, provided $1 + (T + T')^2 > (T + 1)^2$, which is certainly true for $T' = 1$, that is, $t' = c/\alpha$ sec. Thus, the fastest signals sent out from the origin will overtake the particle only if the delay is less than c/α sec.

3-19 (*a*) The differential system (3A-16) has, in this case, the form

$$\frac{\partial x'_A}{\partial a_1} \equiv \frac{dx'_A}{da} = f_A(x')g(a), \qquad x'_A(a^0) = x_A \tag{a}$$

Introducing the new parameter $\int_{a^0}^{a} g(a)\, da$, and calling it again a, the system (a) assumes the form

$$\frac{dx'_A}{da} = f_A(x'), \qquad x'_A(0) = x_A \tag{b}$$

Denoting the solution of this system by $F_A(a;x)$, the result $h(a,b) = a + b$ means that whenever $x'_A = F_A(a';x)$, $x''_A = F_A(a'';x')$, then

$$x''_A = F_A(a' + a''; x)$$

and this conclusion follows from the uniqueness of solutions of differential systems such as (b), since $dF_A(a' + a''; x)/da'' = f_A(x'')$ and

$$F_A(a' + a''; x)\Big|_{a''=0} = x'_A$$

In terms of the representation of the elements of a one-parameter group by infinite iteration, the present result is immediate:

$$\lim_{n\to\infty} \left(I + \frac{t}{n} Q\right)^n = e^{tQ}$$

$$e^{t_1 Q} \cdot e^{t_2 Q} = e^{(t_1+t_2)Q}$$

(*b*) If $T_k = I + \epsilon_k Q_k + \epsilon_k^2 Q_k^2/2$ ($k = 1, 2$; no summation), then to second order,

$$T_1 T_2 T_1^{-1} T_2^{-1} = I + 2\epsilon_1\epsilon_2 Q_1 Q_2 - \epsilon_1^2 Q_1^2 - \epsilon_2^2 Q_2^2 - \epsilon_1\epsilon_2(Q_1Q_2 + Q_2Q_1) + 2\frac{\epsilon_1^2 Q_1^2 + \epsilon_2^2 Q_2^2}{2} = I + \epsilon_1\epsilon_2(Q_1Q_2 - Q_2Q_1)$$

3-22 (*a*) The relations (1) and (2) are immediate consequences of Eqs. (3-53) and (iv), which imply that $(1 - \lambda'\lambda'')(\mathrm{u}',\mathrm{u}'') = 0$; while the truth of (3) can be seen by noting that

$$\det\,(T^{-1} - \lambda I) = \det\,[M(\tilde{T} - \lambda I)M] = \det\,(\tilde{T} - \lambda I) = \det\,(T - \lambda I)$$

where one uses (3-53) and the product law for determinants.

Under the alternative (1), if the eigenvector set is complete, the set of eigenvalues is either 1, 1, 1, 1, or -1, -1, 1, 1 (since the matrices are unimodular), and the resulting transformation is either the identity or a spatial rotation of 180° (as $\mathfrak{L}$ is orthochronous); if the set is not complete, then the eigenvalues are all 1, and one can conclude that there exists one and essentially only one null eigenvector. In fact, it follows from (iv) and the length-preserving property of T that the vector space normal to u is left invariant by T and that if u is not null, then that vector space and u span the complete vector space. Consequently, if no null eigenvector existed, then by this result one would arrive at the contradiction that $T = I$, while if two linearly independent null eigenvectors existed there would also exist a timelike eigenvector, and the same contradictory conclusion would be reached by a similar argument.

Having arrived at the existence of a unique null eigenvector u (unique of course only as to direction), one can show that there must also exist a unique spacelike eigenvector, v, necessarily normal to u, the resulting 2-plane being tangent to the light cone along u, with each vector in it remaining invariant under T; and that moreover the 3-plane tangent to the light cone along u (see Prob. 3-15*c*) is invariant under T as a whole.‡ The canonical form (iii) is obtained upon making the following choice of base in $\mathfrak{M}$. One starts with the above eigenvectors u, v, and adjoins another spacelike vector w that is orthogonal to them, and another null vector, u', linearly independent of u and orthogonal to v and w; the required base is then formed by taking $\mathsf{r} \propto \mathsf{u} + \mathsf{u}'$, $\mathsf{s} \propto \mathsf{u} - \mathsf{u}'$, w, and v, which, when normalized, are seen to form an orthonormal set of 4-vectors of which all but r are spacelike when u' is chosen, as is always possible, so that $(\mathsf{u},\mathsf{u}') > 0$. The transformation T (looked upon as a *motion* in $\mathfrak{M}$) is now represented by the relations

$$\begin{aligned} \mathsf{r} \to T\mathsf{r} &= \lambda\mathsf{r} + \mu\mathsf{s} + \nu\mathsf{w} \\ \mathsf{s} \to T\mathsf{s} &= \lambda'\mathsf{r} + \mu'\mathsf{s} + \nu'\mathsf{w} \\ \mathsf{w} \to T\mathsf{w} &= \lambda''\mathsf{r} + \mu''\mathsf{s} + \nu''\mathsf{w} \\ \mathsf{v} \to T\mathsf{v} &= \mathsf{v} \end{aligned}$$

Since $T\mathsf{u} = \mathsf{u}$ and hence $T(\mathsf{r} + \mathsf{s}) = \mathsf{r} + \mathsf{s}$, it follows that

$$\nu = -\nu', \qquad \lambda + \lambda' = \mu + \mu' = 1 \tag{a}$$

By the relations $(T\mathsf{r},T\mathsf{s}) = 0$, $(T\mathsf{r},T\mathsf{r}) = 1$ and (a) one has $\lambda - \mu = 1$, and hence $1 + \nu^2 = (\lambda + \mu)(\lambda - \mu) = \lambda + \mu$; so that $\lambda = 1 + \nu^2/2$, $\mu = \nu^2/2$. The quantities ν', λ', μ' are then determined in terms of ν by (a), and λ'', μ'', and ν'' are then obtained in terms of ν by solving the equations $(T\mathsf{r},T\mathsf{w}) = 0$, $(T\mathsf{s},T\mathsf{w}) = 0$, $(T\mathsf{w},T\mathsf{w}) = -1$, which give $\lambda'' = \nu$, $\mu'' = \nu$, $\nu'' = 1$, when one notices that for $\nu = 0$ one must get the identity. The resulting matrix with $\nu = \alpha$ is the transpose of (iii), the latter corresponding thus to the

‡ We are, of course, referring to the light cone through the origin, and the 'planes' represent, strictly speaking, the corresponding vector subspaces (see footnote, page 86). Similarly we now denote by $\mathfrak{M}$ the corresponding vector space.

motion T represented by the transformation of the components of an arbitrary vector a.

Under the alternative (2), one has the null eigenvalue pair u_λ, u_μ ($\mu = 1/\lambda$) [by relations (2) and (3)], and no other such pair, since $\mathfrak{M}$ cannot contain two orthogonal null vectors (see Prob. 3-15). Taking

$$\mathsf{v}_\pm = (2p)^{-1/2}(\mathsf{u}_\lambda \pm \mathsf{u}_\mu)$$

with $p = (\mathsf{u}_\lambda, \mathsf{u}_\mu) > 0$, it is seen that v_+, v_- form an orthonormal pair with v_+ timelike and v_- spacelike; and that $T\mathsf{v}_\pm = (2p)^{-1/2}(\lambda \mathsf{u}_\lambda \pm \mu \mathsf{u}_\mu)$, that is, $T\mathsf{v}_\pm = \alpha_\pm \mathsf{v}_+ + \alpha_\mp \mathsf{v}_-$, $\alpha_\pm = (\lambda \pm \mu)/2$. Since $\lambda > 0$ (as $\mathfrak{L}$ is orthochronous), one can write $\lambda = e^\psi$, ψ real, and the stated result follows.

The alternative (3) leads to the lower submatrix in (ii), since $\lambda + i\mu = e^{i\phi}$, ϕ real [as $|\lambda + i\mu| \neq 1$ would imply that $(\mathsf{u},\mathsf{u}) = (\mathsf{v},\mathsf{v}) = 0$, which, in view of (v), is impossible in $\mathfrak{M}$]; and when this is substituted in (iv) the lower submatrix in (ii) is obtained: $T\mathsf{u} = \cos\phi\,\mathsf{u} - \sin\phi\,\mathsf{v}$, $T\mathsf{v} = \sin\phi\,\mathsf{u} + \cos\phi\,\mathsf{v}$. Only one such eigenvalue pair is possible because either by the first or by the second relation in (v), u and v are spacelike, and hence by the latter relation and (1) the existence of such a pair would mean that there exist four mutually orthogonal spacelike vectors in $\mathfrak{M}$.

(*b*) Both results follow directly by carrying out the required matrix multiplications.

(*c*) When (iii) is interpreted as representing a change of axes, $S \to S'$, then, by reference to (3-31) and the accompanying text, one verifies (vi) and (vii); while (viii) follows from (3-31):

$$\begin{bmatrix} S_{11} & S_{12} \\ S_{21} & S_{22} \end{bmatrix} = \begin{bmatrix} \cos\theta & \sin\theta \\ -\sin\theta & \cos\theta \end{bmatrix} = \begin{bmatrix} 1 - \dfrac{\alpha^2}{2} & \alpha \\ -\alpha & 1 \end{bmatrix} + \frac{\gamma - 1}{\beta^2\gamma^2} \begin{bmatrix} \dfrac{\alpha^4}{4} & -\dfrac{\alpha^3}{2} \\ \dfrac{\alpha^3}{2} & -\alpha^2 \end{bmatrix}$$

and $(\gamma - 1)/\beta^2\gamma^2 = 1/(\gamma + 1) = 2/(4 + \alpha^2)$, by (vi). As a check one confirms (3-32).

(*d*) The expression (xii) can be derived, for instance, by using the formula, $\det \|A_{\lambda\mu}\| = \epsilon_{\alpha\beta\gamma\delta} A_{\alpha 0} A_{\beta 1} A_{\gamma 2} A_{\delta 3}$, where $\epsilon_{\alpha\beta\gamma\delta}$ is antisymmetric in its indices and $\epsilon_{0123} = 1$. An examination of the two alternatives $b \neq 0$, $b = 0$ in (xiii), making use of the relations (1), (2), (3), and of properties of the vector space $\mathfrak{M}$ that were employed in the proof of (*a*) leads to the canonical forms (ix) and (x) respectively. To verify the limits (xiv) one needs only note that $P^2 = \begin{bmatrix} 1 & 0 \\ 0 & 1 \end{bmatrix}$, $Q^2 = \begin{bmatrix} -1 & 0 \\ 0 & -1 \end{bmatrix}$, and that $U^2 = \begin{bmatrix} 1 & -1 & 0 & 0 \\ 1 & -1 & 0 & 0 \\ 0 & 0 & 0 & 0 \\ 0 & 0 & 0 & 0 \end{bmatrix}$, $U^3 =$ zero matrix.

[For further details see H. M. Schwartz, *Am. J. Phys.*: **31**: 864 (1963); **33**: 376 (1965).]

(*e*) Using the result in (*d*), the proof proceeds similarly to the corresponding proof for $\mathfrak{R}$ given in Appendix 3A.

4-10 (*a*) By our assumption and Eqs. (4-4) and (4-7), the equation of motion of the particle in S is as follows,

$$\frac{d\mathbf{P}}{dt} \equiv \dot{\mathbf{P}} = \frac{d}{dt}(m(u)\mathbf{u}) = -\nabla V(r)$$

from which the second of the relations (i) follows directly as in the classical case. The first relation (i) follows at once from Eq. (4-11), since $\mathbf{f}\cdot\mathbf{u} = -\nabla V\cdot\dot{\mathbf{x}} = -\dot{V}$. The fact that the motion takes place in a plane is established precisely as in the classical case.

Equation (ii) is obtained from (i), the angular-momentum relation having in polar coordinates the form

$$m(u)r^2\dot{\phi} = J, \qquad J = \text{component of } \mathbf{J} \text{ in plane of motion}$$

which gives $\dot{r} = -s'J/m(u)$ [the symbols as defined in (ii)]. When the last relation is substituted in $1 - (m/m(u))^2 = u^2/c^2 = (\dot{r}^2 + r^2\dot{\phi}^2)$ and the resulting equation is combined with the energy equation (i), one obtains the trajectory equation (ii).

When $E \approx mc^2$ and $|V| \ll E$, then by (i) one has the nonrelativistic condition $m(u) \approx m$. Thus, the second conservation equation (i) reduces to its classical approximation, while if we rewrite the first equation as

$$[m(u) - m]c^2 + V = \frac{m}{2}u^2 + \cdots + V = E - mc^2 = W \qquad \text{(a)}$$

we recognize the newtonian conservation-of-energy relation as its limiting case. Again, by dividing Eq. (ii) by $2mc^2$ we find that

$$\frac{J^2(s'^2 + s^2)}{2m} = W - U$$

$U = E - [(E - V)^2 + (\mathrm{mc}^2)^2]/2mc^2 \approx V$; that is, in the classical limit, Eq. (ii) reduces to the corresponding well-known trajectory equation.

When the potential-energy function is as given in (iii), and $J \neq 0$, differentiation of (ii) yields the equation

$$s'' + a^2(s - \eta) = 0 \qquad \text{(b)}$$

the symbols being defined in (iv) and (v). Hence when $a \neq 0$, one has the general solution (v). Equation (vi) for A is obtained by combining (ii), (iii), and (v), which lead to the equation $m^2c^4 - E^2 + c^2J^2A^2a^2 - E^2\alpha^2/a^2 = 0$ [α defined in (iv)], when it is observed that $c^2J^2a^2\eta - 2EC\eta = -E^2\alpha^2/a^2$.

That, in relativistic mechanics just as well as in classical mechanics, it is necessary for the force to be attractive for bound orbits to exist is almost self-evident, and can be formally proved in many ways, e.g., by taking the scalar product with $\mathbf{x}$ of both sides of the equation of motion

$$\frac{d}{dt}\left(m(u)\frac{d\mathbf{x}}{dt}\right) = \mathbf{f} = f(r)\mathbf{x}$$

obtaining,

$$\frac{1}{2}\frac{d}{dt}\left(m(u)\frac{d}{dt}\mathbf{x}^2\right) = f(r)\mathbf{x}^2 + m(u)\left(\frac{d\mathbf{x}}{dt}\right)^2$$

If $f(r) > 0$, the right-hand side of this equation is positive and, as $m(u)$ is an increasing function of u, it is readily concluded that $\mathbf{x}^2$ cannot remain bounded. Thus, in the case (iii) it is necessary for the boundedness of the solutions that $C > 0$. The second inequality in (vii) is dictated by the form (v) of these solutions, since one must have $A^2 < \eta^2$ for s to be bounded away from zero, and this inequality reduces to the former inequality, while the first inequality in (vii) is required by the reality of s as given in (v).

If $a = 0$, Eq. (b) reduces to $s'' = \lambda \equiv EC/c^2J^2$, with the general solution

$$s = \frac{\lambda}{2}\phi^2 + A\phi + B \tag{c}$$

and the constants A, B satisfying by (ii) the relation

$$C^2A^2 - 2ECB + m^2c^4 - E^2 = 0 \tag{d}$$

Hence the orbits spiral into the origin, and they are bounded only if (c) does not have real zeros, i.e., only if $A^2 - 2\lambda B = A^2 - 2EB/C < 0$, or by (d), only if the second of the inequalities (vii) is satisfied.

When $a^2 < 0$ one can either use the results (iv) and (v) with a^2 replaced by $-|a|^2$, or else start with the general solution $s = Ae^{|a|\phi} + Be^{-|a|\phi} + \eta$, and apply Eq. (ii) with the result $AB = (m^2c^4|a|^2 + E^2)/4c^2J^2|a|^4$. Both the unboundedness and the spiraling into the origin obviously follow from this relation.

The limiting conditions for the classical elliptic and hyperbolic orbits in the case of $C > 0$ are obtained at once by recalling the previous result concerning the classical limit and observing that the second inequality (vii) can also be written [see Eq. (a)] $W < 0$ (the positiveness of E is assured by the limiting condition $E \approx mc^2$).

(*b*) The advance of the perihelion per revolution is by Eqs. (v) and (iv), $\Delta\phi = 2\pi[(1 - \alpha^2)^{-1/2} - 1] = \pi\alpha^2 + \cdots$, and hence its value for the orbit of the planet Mercury comes out close to $\frac{1}{6}$ the quoted experimental value. [The result given by Einstein's general theory is in fact $6\pi\alpha^2$. See, e.g., G. C. McVittie, "General Relativity and Cosmology," p. 89, Chapman and Hall, Ltd., London, 1956, which contains a table of the needed astronomical data. Note that according to the pertinent classical results, $a(1 - e^2) = J^2/mC$.]

4-12 The proof of the first part of the question follows immediately when we observe that according to our definition,

$$P_\alpha^{(w')} = \frac{\partial(\mathfrak{L}\, dw/dw')}{\partial(dx_\alpha/dw')}$$

In proving the second part of the question, one can consider an arbitrary variation of $\mathfrak{L}$, $\delta\mathfrak{L} = \delta x_\alpha\, \partial\mathfrak{L}/\partial x_\alpha + \delta\dot{x}_\alpha\, \partial\mathfrak{L}/\partial\dot{x}_\alpha$ ($\dot{x} \equiv dx/d\tau$). Since $\delta\mathfrak{L}$ is a scalar and δx_α, $\delta\dot{x}_\alpha$, and $\partial\mathfrak{L}/\partial x_\alpha$ are vectors in $\mathfrak{M}$ by the corresponding rules in ordinary vector analysis, it follows that $P_\alpha\, \delta\dot{x}_\alpha$ is a 4-scalar; and since $\delta\dot{x}_\alpha$ can be taken as an arbitrary 4-vector, it follows, again by appeal to a corresponding result in ordinary vector analysis, that also P_α is a 4-vector. (The general extension of the result in question is given in Prob. 5-2.)

The 4-vector character of $(p_k, iH/c)$ follows from (4-46), recalling the steps that led to these relations, and since—with the time variable $x_4 = ict$ and with $dw = d\tau$—we have now to take in place of π_0 the time component $P_4 = \pi_4 = \partial\mathfrak{L}/\partial(dx_4/d\tau) = -(i/c)\,\partial\mathfrak{L}/\partial(dt/d\tau) = iH/c$, by (4-49).

4-18 (*a*) If m_1, m_2 are the rest masses of the decay products, and M is the rest mass of the decaying particle, we have (taking $c = 1$)

$$m_i^2 = (\mathsf{P}_i)^2 = (\mathsf{P} - \mathsf{P}_j)^2 = M^2 + m_j^2 - 2(\mathsf{P},\mathsf{P}_j) \quad (i, j = 1, 2)$$

But in the center-of-mass frame S^* (i.e., the frame where the decaying particle is stationary), $(\mathsf{P},\mathsf{P}_j) = ME_j^*$. Hence,

$$E_j^* = \frac{1}{2M}(M^2 + m_j^2 - m_i^2)$$

and $K_j^* = E_j^* - m_j = [(M - m_j)^2 - m_i^2]/2M = \Delta M(\Delta M + 2m_i)/2M$, where, $\Delta M = M - m_1 - m_2$; or,

$$K_i^* = \frac{\Delta M}{2M}[\Delta M + 2(M - \Delta M - m_i)] = \Delta M\left(1 - \frac{\Delta M}{2M} - \frac{m_i}{M}\right)$$

(*b*) We prove first the inequality (ii). Since

$$(\Sigma\mathsf{P}_i)^2 = \Sigma m_i^2 + \sum_{i\neq j}\sum m_i m_j \gamma_i\gamma_j(1 - \mathbf{u}_i\cdot\mathbf{u}_j)$$

it suffices to show that the quantities $\gamma_i\gamma_j(1 - \mathbf{u}_i\cdot\mathbf{u}_j) \equiv \Gamma_{ij}$ are all $\geqq 1$; but this follows at once from formula (i) of Prob. 3-3 for the general case, according to which $\Gamma_{ij} = \gamma_{u_i'}$—considering, say, $\mathbf{u}_j$ as the relative velocity of the coordinate frames and $\mathbf{u}_i$ as the particle velocity. The minimum is attained for $u_i' = 0$ or, by Eq. (ii) of Prob. 3-3, when $\mathbf{u}_i = \mathbf{u}_j$. This is as it should be, since when all $\mathbf{u}_i$ are equal, we find by evaluating $(\Sigma\mathsf{P}_i)^2$ in the center-of-mass frame S^* the value $(\Sigma P_{0i}^*)^2 = (\Sigma m_i)^2$.

Using (ii), we have:

$$(\mathsf{P} - \mathsf{P}_i)^2 = M^2 + m_i^2 - 2ME_i{}^* = \Big(\sum_{j\neq i} \mathsf{P}_j\Big)^2 \geq \Big(\sum_{j\neq i} m_j\Big)^2 \equiv N^2$$

Hence, $E_i^* \leq (M^2 + m_i^2 - N^2)/2M$, and

$$K_i{}^* \leq \frac{[(M - m_i)^2 - N^2]}{2M} = \frac{[(\Delta M + N)^2 - N^2]}{2M}$$

The result (i) follows by replacing N by $M - m_i - \Delta M$.

In muon decay, taking the electron mass as unit, we have by (i), $K_e{}^{\max} = (M-1)^2/2M \approx M/2$, and $K_\nu{}^{\max} = (M^2-1)/2M \approx M/2$.

4-19 (*a*) Since for each particle, $u\gamma_u/c = \sinh\psi$, $E = m\gamma_u c^2 = mc^2\cosh\psi$ as follows from the identities, $\sinh\psi = \tanh\psi(1 - \tanh^2\psi)^{-1/2}$ and $\cosh\psi = (1-\tanh^2\psi)^{-1/2}$, the conservation laws give immediately the equation

$$\frac{\cosh\psi_1 - \cosh\bar{\psi}_1}{\sinh\psi_1 - \sinh\bar{\psi}_1} = \frac{\cosh\psi_2 - \cosh\bar{\psi}_2}{\sinh\psi_2 - \sinh\bar{\psi}_2}$$

The result (i) then follows by using the indicated identity, and the nonrelativistic limit results from the relation $\operatorname{arctanh}\beta = \beta + O(\beta^3)$.

(*b*) If the 4-momenta of the particles before and after the collision are P_1, P_2 and $\bar{\mathsf{P}}_1$, $\bar{\mathsf{P}}_2$, then, by our assumption, $\mathsf{P}_k{}^2 = \bar{\mathsf{P}}_k{}^2$ $(k = 1, 2)$ and $\mathsf{P}_1 + \mathsf{P}_2 = \bar{\mathsf{P}}_1 + \bar{\mathsf{P}}_2$, and hence $(\mathsf{P}_1,\mathsf{P}_2) = (\bar{\mathsf{P}}_1,\bar{\mathsf{P}}_2)$. It follows that if we start with a Lorentz transformation T that sends P_1 into $\bar{\mathsf{P}}_1$, then if P_2 goes into $\mathsf{Q} \neq \bar{\mathsf{P}}_2$, we can find another Lorentz transformation T' that leaves $\bar{\mathsf{P}}_1$ invariant and sends Q into $\bar{\mathsf{P}}_2$; the product $T'T$ will then be the required transformation.

5-1 (*a*) Denote $u_{(ab)}$ by v_{ab} and write

$$v_{ab} = v'_{ab} + v''_{ab}, \qquad v'_{ab} = \frac{1}{p}\, v_{cc}\,\delta_{ab} \tag{a}$$

where p is the order of the matrix $\|v_{ab}\|$. Since both p and v_{aa} $(= u_{aa})$ are invariants and δ_{ab} is an unchanging tensor, it follows that if, under a given transformation of $\mathfrak{G}$, the matrix v is transformed into $\bar{v}$, then, in the notation of (a), $\bar{v}' = \overline{v'}$ and $\bar{v}'' = \overline{v''}$; the resulting decomposition of the representation submatrices $Q_{(s)}$ is thus apparent. Note that the matrices v'' are *traceless* $(v''_{aa} = 0)$.

(*b*) We always have (i) with

$$A_{\alpha\beta}{}^{(\pm)} = \tfrac{1}{2}(A_{\alpha\beta} \pm A^*_{\alpha\beta}) \tag{b}$$

since $(A^*)^* = A$, as follows at once from the readily verifiable identity, $\epsilon_{\alpha\beta\gamma\delta}\epsilon_{\gamma\delta\lambda\mu} = 2(\delta_{\alpha\lambda}\delta_{\beta\mu} - \delta_{\alpha\mu}\delta_{\beta\lambda})$ [see (5-60)]. The covariance of the decomposition in question means in the notation employed above that $\bar{A}^{(\pm)} = \overline{A^{(\pm)}}$, and by (b) these relations will hold provided $\bar{A}^* = \overline{A^*}$, i.e., provided, $(T_{\alpha\lambda}T_{\beta\mu}A_{\lambda\mu})^* = T_{\alpha\lambda}T_{\beta\mu}A^*_{\lambda\mu}$, if the T is the transformation under consideration. The latter relations written more explicitly are:

$$\epsilon_{\alpha\beta\gamma\delta}T_{\gamma\lambda}T_{\delta\mu}A_{\lambda\mu} = T_{\alpha\gamma}T_{\beta\delta}\epsilon_{\gamma\delta\lambda\mu}A_{\lambda\mu}$$

These will be satisfied if $\epsilon_{\alpha\beta\gamma\delta}T_{\gamma\lambda}T_{\delta\mu} = \epsilon_{\gamma\delta\lambda\mu}T_{\alpha\gamma}T_{\beta\delta}$, or [multiplying-summing with $T_{\alpha\iota}T_{\beta\kappa}$ and using (5-9)], if $\epsilon_{\alpha\beta\gamma\delta}T_{\alpha\iota}T_{\beta\kappa}T_{\gamma\lambda}T_{\delta\mu} = \epsilon_{\iota\kappa\lambda\mu}$, and this is merely an expression of the unimodularity of the transformation [see the similar result (5-16)].

5-3 Take $Q^{a\ c}_{\ b}$ as an example. We are assuming the transformation equations for scalars and vectors. Hence the assumption that $Q^{a\ c}_{\ b}A_aB^bC_c$ is a scalar when A, B, C are vectors, implies that

$$Q^{a\ c}_{\ b}A_aB^bC_c = Q'^{d\ f}_{\ e}A'_dB'^eC'_f = Q'^{d\ f}_{\ e}M^a_{\ d}A_aN^e_{\ b}B^bM^c_{\ f}C_c$$

that is,

$$(Q^{a\ c}_{\ b} - Q'^{d\ f}_{\ e}M^a_{\ d}N^e_{\ b}M^c_{\ f})A_aB^bC_c = 0$$

The identical vanishing of this sum for *arbitrary* A, B, C implies the vanishing of the expression within the parentheses, i.e., the validity of the transformation law (5-37) (when inverted). The converse is obvious.

5-6 By Eqs. (5-28) and (5-26), $\mathbf{e}^a \cdot \mathbf{e}^b = g^{ac}g^{bd}\mathbf{e}_c \cdot \mathbf{e}_d = g^{ac}g^{bd}g_{cd} = g^{ac}\delta^b_c = g^{ab}$, and, by (5-35), $g'^{ab} = \mathbf{e}'^a \cdot \mathbf{e}'^b = N^a_{\ c}N^b_{\ d}\mathbf{e}^c \cdot \mathbf{e}^d = N^a_{\ c}N^b_{\ d}g^{cd}$.

5-7 In the case of euclidean spaces, the geometrical significance of reciprocal bases and of covariant and contravariant components of a vector can be adequately illustrated by a consideration of the two-dimensional case. The generalization to higher-dimensional spaces is obvious. In the euclidean plane, an arbitrary base is given by any set of two vectors $\mathbf{e}_1$, $\mathbf{e}_2$ that are not collinear. The associated metric tensor components are

$$g_{11} = \mathbf{e}_1^2 \equiv a^2$$

$$g_{12} = g_{21} = \mathbf{e}_1 \cdot \mathbf{e}_2$$

$$g_{22} = \mathbf{e}_2^{\ 2} \equiv b^2$$

and by (5-26),

$$\begin{bmatrix} g^{11} & g^{12} \\ g^{21} & g^{22} \end{bmatrix} = \begin{bmatrix} g_{11} & g_{12} \\ g_{21} & g_{22} \end{bmatrix}^{-1} = \frac{1}{\Delta}\begin{bmatrix} g_{22} & -g_{12} \\ -g_{21} & g_{11} \end{bmatrix}$$

where $\Delta = a^2b^2 \sin^2 \theta$ is the determinant of the matrix g, θ being the angle between the base vectors. Hence, by (5-28),

$$\mathbf{e}^1 = \frac{1}{\Delta}(b^2\mathbf{e}_1 - ab \cos \theta \mathbf{e}_2) = \frac{1}{a^2 \sin^2 \theta}\left(\mathbf{e}_1 - \frac{a}{b}\cos \theta \mathbf{e}_2\right)$$

$$\mathbf{e}^2 = \frac{1}{\Delta}(-ab \cos \theta \mathbf{e}_1 + a^2\mathbf{e}_2) = \frac{1}{b^2 \sin^2 \theta}\left(-\frac{b}{a}\cos \theta \mathbf{e}_1 + \mathbf{e}_2\right)$$

Formula (5-30) is immediately verified and can serve as a check. If A^1, A^2 are the contravariant components of a vector **A**, one finds by (5-20), that is, $\mathbf{A} = A^1\mathbf{e}_1 + A^2\mathbf{e}_2$, and a graphical construction of A^1, A^2, that these components represent the projections of **A** parallel to the directions $\mathbf{e}_1$, $\mathbf{e}_2$, with due regard to the magnitudes a, b of these vectors. The geometric significance of the covariant components is apparent when we combine Eqs. (5-29) and (5-30): $A_1 = \mathbf{e}_1 \cdot \mathbf{A}$, $A_2 = \mathbf{e}_2 \cdot \mathbf{A}$.

In the case of $\mathfrak{M}$, we need only observe that of the vectors $\mathbf{e}_0$, $\mathbf{e}_1$, $\mathbf{e}_2$, $\mathbf{e}_3$ of any given base, one must be timelike and the others spacelike, the latter forming a spatial base (i.e., satisfying the condition: det $\|g_{ij}\| \neq 0$). It follows that all the results for euclidean spaces concerning reciprocal bases retain their validity for $\mathfrak{M}$, since any vector perpendicular (in the $\mathfrak{M}$ metric) to all the spatial base vectors is necessarily timelike, while any vector perpendicular to a 3-flat spanned by two spacelike and one timelike vector is necessarily spacelike according to the result (2) on page 60.

5-8 Since $\mathbf{e}_a(x) = \mathsf{u}_b\, \partial y^b/\partial x^a$, we have—using (5-30) and denoting by X_b^a the b component of $\mathbf{e}^a(x)$ relative to the base $\{\mathsf{u}^a\}$—

$$\delta_b^a = \mathbf{e}_b(x) \cdot \mathbf{e}^a(x) = \frac{\partial y^c}{\partial x^b}\, \mathsf{u}_c \cdot X_d^a \mathsf{u}^d = \frac{\partial y^c}{\partial x^b}\, \delta_c^d X_d^a = X_c^a \frac{\partial y^c}{\partial x^b}$$

and hence $X_c^a = \partial x^a/\partial y^c$ (as $\|\partial y^a/\partial x^b\|^{-1} = \|\partial x^a/\partial y^b\|$). Consistency with (5-36) can be seen as follows, using Eqs. (5-79):

$$A'_a \mathbf{e}'^a = A'_a \mathsf{u}^b \frac{\partial x'^a}{\partial y^b} = A_a \mathbf{e}^a = A_c \mathsf{u}^b \frac{\partial x^c}{\partial y^b}$$

$$A'_a \frac{\partial x'^a}{\partial y^b} = A_c \frac{\partial x^c}{\partial y^b}$$

$$A'_d = A_c \frac{\partial x^c}{\partial y^b} \frac{\partial y^b}{\partial x'^d} = A_c \frac{\partial x^c}{\partial x'^d} = A_c M_d^c$$

5-11 By the definition of B_r we have $\mathsf{B}_r = \sum_{l=0}^{r-1} \alpha_l \mathsf{A}_l$. Hence, if we denote the quantity $\mathsf{A}_r - \mathsf{B}_r$ by N_r, and write (a,b) for $\mathsf{A}_a \cdot \mathsf{A}_b$, we have

$$0 = \mathsf{N}_r \cdot \mathsf{A}_m = (r,m) - \sum_{l=1}^{r-1} \alpha_l(l,m), \qquad m = 1, \ldots, r-1$$

$$d_r^2 \equiv \mathsf{N}_r^2 = \mathsf{N}_r \cdot \mathsf{A}_r = (r,r) - \Sigma\alpha_l(l,r)$$

and consequently,

$$0 = \begin{vmatrix} (1,1) & \cdots & (r-1,1) & -(r,1) \\ \cdots & \cdots & \cdots & \cdots \\ (1,r-1) & \cdots & (r-1,r-1) & -(r,r-1) \\ (1,r) & \cdots & (r-1,r) & -(r,r)+d_r^2 \end{vmatrix}$$

$$= d_r^2 D_{r-1} - D_r$$

Thus, $V_r^{\ 2} = d_r^{\ 2} V_{r-1}^{\ \ 2} = d_r^{\ 2} \cdots d_2^{\ 2} V_1^{\ 2} = (D_r/D_1)D_1 = D_r$. To see that (ii) agrees with (i), we make use of the permutation properties of the δ symbols:

$$\begin{aligned} D_r &= \delta^{a_1 \cdots a_r}_{b_1 \cdots b_r} A^{b_1}_{(1)} A_{(1)a_1} \cdots A^{b_r}_{(r)} A_{(r)a_r} \\ &= \frac{1}{r!} \delta^{c_1 \cdots c_r}_{b_1 \cdots b_r} A^{b_1}_{(1)} \cdots A^{b_r}_{(r)} \delta^{a_1 \cdots a_r}_{c_1 \cdots c_r} A_{(1)a_1} \cdots A_{(r)a_r} \\ &= \frac{1}{r!} T^{c_1 \cdots c_r} T_{c_1 \cdots c_r} \end{aligned}$$

In $\mathfrak{M}$ we see in the case of $r = 2$, by referring to the result (a) in Prob. 3-15, that we have to deal with three types of bivectors determined by the sign or vanishing of D_2. This can also be seen by considering the equivalent bivector (i.e., one determining the same geometric structure) consisting of perpendicular 4-vectors. For example, in the case of a 'timelike bivector,' one of these vectors must be timelike and the other must be spacelike, and hence D_2 is negative. For $r = 3$ we have similar results. Thus, the expression (5-76) in the case of a 'spacelike 3-vector' can be seen to be negative by taking three perpendicular spacelike vectors determining the same geometric structure as given by the original vectors A, B, C. Again, the 3-vector determined by the vectors a, b, b' considered in the solution to part (c) of Prob. 3-15, is seen to have zero 'magnitude.'

5-12 (b) The first part follows at once when in the tensor transformation equations

$$T'^{\mu\nu} = L^\mu{}_\sigma L^\nu{}_\tau T^{\sigma\tau} \tag{a}$$

we substitute the values giving a pure spatial rotation: $L^0{}_\sigma = \delta^0_\sigma$, $L^i{}_0 = 0$, $L^i{}_j = R^i{}_j$. The first two equations in (iv) are obtained when we substitute in (a) the values of $L^\mu{}_\sigma$ given in (3-29), and invoke the antisymmetry of T:

$$\begin{aligned} U'^i_\parallel &= \frac{\beta^i\beta^k}{\beta^2} T'^{0k} = \frac{\beta^i\beta^k}{\beta^2} \gamma(\delta^0_\lambda - \beta^j\delta^j_\lambda)\left(-\gamma\beta^k\delta^0_\mu + \delta^k_\mu + \frac{\gamma-1}{\beta^2}\beta^k\beta^s\delta^s_\mu\right) T^{\lambda\mu} \\ &= \frac{\beta^i}{\beta}\beta^k T^{0k}\left(\frac{\gamma}{\beta} + \frac{\gamma(\gamma-1)}{\beta} - \beta\gamma^2\right) = \frac{\beta^i\beta^k}{\beta^2} T^{0k} = U^i_\parallel \end{aligned}$$

$$\begin{aligned} U'^i_\perp &= T'^{0i} - \frac{\beta^i\beta^k}{\beta^2} T'^{0k} \\ &= \gamma(\delta^0_\lambda - \beta^j\delta^j_\lambda)\left(-\gamma\beta^i\delta^0_\mu + \delta^i_\mu + \frac{\gamma-1}{\beta^2}\beta^i\beta^k\delta^k_\mu\right) T^{\lambda\mu} - \cdots \\ &= \gamma\left[T^{0i} - \beta^j T^{ji} + \beta^i\beta^k T^{0k}\left(\frac{\gamma-1}{\beta^2} - \gamma - \frac{1}{\gamma\beta^2}\right)\right] \\ &= \gamma\left(T^{0i} - \frac{\beta^i\beta^s}{\beta^2} T^{0s} + \beta^j V^k - \beta^k V^j\right) \end{aligned}$$

where i, j, k are a cyclic permutation of 1. 2, 3. We can deduce the second pair in (iv) from the first, when we note that by (i) and (ii),

$$\mathbf{U}^* \equiv (T^{*01}, T^{*02}, T^{*02}) = -(T^*{}_{01,\ldots}) = -\mathbf{V}$$
$$\mathbf{V}^* \equiv (T^{*23}, T^{*31}, T^{*12}) = (T^*{}_{23,\ldots}) = \mathbf{U}$$

as $\sqrt{-g} = 1$ in rectangular coordinates.

5-13 Applying the appropriate formulas, one has:

$$\begin{aligned} \mathsf{A}_{,a} \cdot \mathbf{e}_b &= (A^c\mathbf{e}_c)_{,a} \cdot \mathbf{e}_b = A^c\mathbf{e}_{c,a} \cdot \mathbf{e}_b + A^c{}_{,a}\mathbf{e}_c \cdot \mathbf{e}_b = A^c[ca,b] + A^c{}_{,a}g_{cb} \\ &= g_{cb}(g^{cd}A_d)_{,a} + A^c[ca,b] = \delta^d_b A_{d,a} + g_{cb}g^{cd}{}_{,a}A_d + A_d g^{cd} g_{be}\Gamma^e{}_{ca} \\ &= A_{b,a} + g_{be}A_d(g^{ed}{}_{,a} + g^{cd}\Gamma^e{}_{ca}) \end{aligned}$$

and since $g^{ed}{}_{;a} = 0$, this expression $= A_{b,a} + g_{be}A_d(-g^{ec}\Gamma^d{}_{ca}) = A_{b,a} - \Gamma^d{}_{ba}A_d$ $= A_{b;a}$.

5-14

$$\begin{aligned} (\text{Rot Rot } T)_{a_1\cdots a_{n+2}} &\propto \delta^{b_1\cdots b_{n+2}}_{a_1\cdots a_{n+2}}(\text{Rot } T)_{b_1\cdots b_{n+1},b_{n+2}} \\ &\propto \cdots \delta^{c_1\cdots c_{n+1}}_{b_1\cdots b_{n+1}} T_{c_1\cdots c_n,c_{n+1}b_{n+2}} \propto \delta^{c_1\cdots c_{n+1}b_{n+2}}_{a_1\cdots a_{n+1}a_{n+2}} T_{c_1\cdots c_n,c_{n+1}b_{n+2}} \\ &\propto T_{\ldots,[a_{n+1}a_{n+2}]} = 0 \end{aligned}$$

If T is a scalar, we can take the expression in (5-105) when $n = 0$ to stand for Grad T by taking $T_{\ldots}$ as T and $a_1 = a$, $b_1 = b$: $(\text{Grad } T)_a = T_{,a}$. Of course, the proof of the identity is now in any case immediate, using (5-104): $T_{,ba} - T_{,ab} = 0$.

5-15 The identity (i) is an immediate consequence of the identities (5-102) and (5-101) and the definition of E [an extension of (5-56)]. When T is an alternating tensor of order n, we find by (5-69) and (5-105), assuming that $n < p$, where p is the dimensionality of our space, and taking $r = n + 1$,

$$\begin{aligned} (\text{Rot } T)^{*a_{r+1}\cdots a_p} &= \frac{1}{r!} E^{a_1\cdots a_p}(\text{Rot } T)_{a_1\cdots a_r} \\ &= \cdots \frac{(-1)^{r-1}}{(r-1)!} \delta^{b_1\cdots b_r}_{a_1\cdots a_r} T_{b_1\cdots b_{r-1};b_r} \\ &= \frac{(-1)^n}{n!} (E^{b_1\cdots b_n b a_{r+1}\cdots a_p} T_{b_1\cdots b_n})_{;b} \\ &= (-1)^{p-1} T^{*a_{r+1}\cdots a_p b}{}_{;b} \end{aligned}$$

When $n = p - 1$, (Rot T)* is a pseudoscalar and the indices in the above expressions must be modified accordingly.

5-17 (*a*) Recall the definition (5-17) and the relations (5-46), as well as the integral calculus rule,

$$dx'^1 \cdots dx'^p = \frac{\partial(x'^1, \ldots, x'^p)}{\partial(x^1, \ldots, x^p)} dx^1 \cdots dx^p \tag{a}$$

(*b*) Since

$$\frac{\partial(x^{i_1}, \ldots, \partial x^{i_n})}{\partial(u^1, \ldots, u^n)} = \delta^{i_1 \cdots i_n}_{j_1 \cdots j_n} \frac{\partial x^{j_1}}{\partial u^1} \cdots \frac{\partial x^{j_n}}{\partial u^n} \tag{b}$$

and for every u^k, $\partial x^i/\partial u^k$ are the contravariant components of a vector, therefore by the properties of the $\delta^{\cdots}_{\cdots}$, the quantities (b) are the contravariant components of an alternating tensor. Because of this total antisymmetry property of the quantities (b), there is no loss of generality in supposing that the $A \cdots$ are alternating, and because (b) forms a tensor and $du^1 \cdots du^n$ a scalar under transformations on the x, the integral (i) is invariant under these transformations if A is a tensor. The invariance in general of this integral under changes of the u follows at once from the rule (a) as applied to the integration parameters.

6-1 Taking $\Delta a_i \equiv \xi_i$ and d_i as infinitesimal, we expand $\Delta x_i = \Delta(a_i + d_i)$ (see Fig. 6-2) in powers of ξ_i, retaining only the leading terms

$$\Delta x_i = \xi_i + d_{i,j}\xi_j = \xi_i + d_{(i,j)}\xi_j + d_{[i,j]}\xi_j \equiv \xi_i + e_{ij}\xi_j + \omega_{ij}\xi_j$$

Generally, $\Delta x_i\, \Delta x_i = \xi_i\xi_i + 2e_{ij}\xi_i\xi_j$ as far as the leading terms are concerned, it being assumed that the $d_{i,j}$ are also infinitesimals of the first order. Remembering that $\xi_i \equiv \Delta a_i$, this leads directly to (6-14); while if $e_{ij} = 0$, we see that lengths are preserved, and the motion $\mathbf{a} \to \mathbf{x}$ in the infinitesimal vicinity of the point under consideration represents a rigid body rotation of the medium. Moreover, in the latter case,

$$\Delta\mathbf{x} = \boldsymbol{\xi} + (\mathbf{C} \times \boldsymbol{\xi}), \qquad \mathbf{C} = \tfrac{1}{2} \text{ rot } \mathbf{d} \tag{a}$$

since [referring to Eqs. (5-53) and (5-60), but not distinguishing pseudovectors notationally], $\omega_{ij}\xi_j = \frac{1}{2}\delta^{kr}_{ij}\omega_{kr}\xi_j = \frac{1}{2}\epsilon_{sij}\epsilon_{skr}\omega_{kr}\xi_j = \epsilon_{isj}C_s\xi_j$, where $C_s = \frac{1}{2}\epsilon_{skr}\omega_{rk}$, and $\omega_{rk} = (d_{r,k} - d_{k,r})/2$. With $\mathbf{v} = \lim_{\Delta t \to 0} \mathbf{d}/\Delta t$, it follows from Eq.(a) that $(\Delta\mathbf{x} - \boldsymbol{\xi})/\Delta t = (\mathbf{C}/\Delta t) \times \boldsymbol{\xi} \to \boldsymbol{\Omega} \times \boldsymbol{\xi}$ (as $\Delta t \to 0$), where $2\boldsymbol{\Omega} = \lim_{\Delta t \to 0} \text{rot } (\mathbf{d}/\Delta t) = \text{rot } \mathbf{v}$.

The result (a) corresponds to Eq. (3A-8), the symbols dx_i, x_j, ω_k in the latter equation corresponding to the present $\Delta x_i - \xi_i$, ξ_j, and $-C_k$.

By changing derivatives into covariant derivatives, replacing the ϵ symbols by the corresponding E symbols, and paying attention to the placement of indices, the above results go over into the corresponding results in general coordinates.

6-4 Using rectangular coordinates (and hence employing only lower indices), we find from conservation of angular momentum, by Eqs. (6-7) and (6-8), the integrals being taken over a *moving* volume filled with the medium

$$\int [(\mathbf{x} \times \mathbf{f})_i + \tfrac{1}{2}\epsilon_{ijk}Q_{jk}]\, dV + \epsilon_{ijk} \int x_j T_{kr} n_r \, dS = \frac{d}{dt} \int \rho[\mathbf{s} + (\mathbf{x} \times \mathbf{v})]_i \, dV$$

$$= \int \left[\rho \frac{ds_i}{dt} + \left(\mathbf{x} \times \frac{d\mathbf{v}}{dt} \right)_i \right] dV = \int \left[\rho \frac{ds_i}{dt} + (\mathbf{x} \times \mathbf{f})_i + \epsilon_{ijk} x_j T_{kr,r} \right] dV$$

$$= \int \{ \cdots + \epsilon_{ijk}[(x_j T_{kr})_{,r} - T_{kj}]\} \, dV = \int [\cdots + \epsilon_{ijk} T_{jk}] \, dV + \epsilon_{ijk} \int x_j T_{kr} n_r \, dS$$

Here the surface integral in the first line arises from the torque due to the stress acting across the surface bounding the volume of integration. Since this volume can be chosen arbitrarily within the moving medium, it follows that

$$\rho \frac{ds_i}{dt} + \epsilon_{ijk} T_{jk} = \tfrac{1}{2}\epsilon_{ijk} Q_{jk}$$

When $\mathbf{s} = 0$, as is commonly the case, this reduces to (i).

6-8 (*a*) Since ρ is the amount of rest mass per unit volume at the event $\mathbf{x}$ under consideration as measured in our frame S, the ratio of ρ to the corresponding rest mass density ρ^*, as measured in the local rest frame S^* at $\mathbf{x}$, is inversely proportional to the corresponding ratio of the volume elements at $\mathbf{x}$; and by (3-4), the latter ratio is γ_u, where u is the velocity in S of the element of the medium at $\mathbf{x}$. Thus, $\rho^* = \rho/\gamma_u$, and ρ^* is a 4-scalar by its operational definition.

The left-hand side of (i) can be written, with $\gamma \equiv \gamma_u$ and $u^\nu = dx^\nu/dt$,

$$(\gamma\rho^* u^\nu)_{,\nu} = (\rho u^\nu)_{,\nu} = \frac{\partial\rho}{\partial t} + \nabla \cdot (\rho\mathbf{u}) \tag{a}$$

To check Eq. (ii) we need only note that $U^\nu{}_{,\nu} = U^{*\nu}{}_{,\nu} = \nabla^* \cdot \mathbf{u}$ (as $\gamma^*{}_{,i} = 0$), and apply the result of Prob. 6-3.

Integration of (i) over a 4-region leads to the vanishing of $\int \rho^* U^\nu \, dS_\nu$ over the bounding 3-surface, and taking the 4-region as a 4-tube with the two sections $t = t_1$ and $t = t_2$ $(t_1 < t_2)$, we have that

$$\int_{t=t_2} \rho^* U^0 \, d^3x - \int_{t=t_1} \rho^* U^0 \, d^3x + \int_{\text{lateral boundary}} \rho^* U^\nu \, dS_\nu = 0$$

Substituting $t_1 = t$, $t_2 = t + T$, dividing by T, and letting $T \to 0$, we find the familiar expression $(d/dt)\int \rho \, d^3x = -\int \rho\mathbf{u} \cdot d\mathbf{S}$, which is commonly derived from (a) by application of the classical Gauss identity.

(*b*) When employing general coordinates we need formally only change ordinary to covariant partials, and we can also apply the general form of

Gauss' theorem. In applying the results, we must keep in mind the relativistic limitations on the magnitude of the velocities, and the relevance of principle C of Sec. 3-5.

6-9 Corresponding to the infinitesimal transformation $\mathbf{x} \to \mathbf{x}'$ of matrix $I + Q$ (Q infinitesimal), we have

$$0 = P'^{[i0]} = (\delta_{i\mu} + Q_{i\mu})(\delta_{0\nu} + Q_{0\nu})P^{[\mu\nu]} \approx P^{[i0]} + Q_{0\nu}P^{[i\nu]} + Q_{i\mu}P^{[\mu 0]} = Q_{0j}P^{[ij]}$$

by our assumption (6-33). Since $Q_{0j} = \epsilon q_j$, q_j *arbitrary*, it follows that $P^{[ij]} = 0$.

6-13 (*a*) Since

$$S^{\lambda\mu} = \int P^{\lambda\mu} \frac{1}{\gamma}\, d^3x^* = \frac{1}{\gamma} \int P^{\lambda\mu}\, d^3x^* \tag{a}$$

the vector $\mathbf{u}$ being constant by our assumption (1), it follows that Eqs. (i) can be deduced directly, using Eqs. (6-40) that connect the systems S and S^* to transform P, and noting that by assumption (2) we can then take

$$\int_{t=\text{const.}} = \int_{t^*=\text{const.}}$$

while the time independence of G^λ follows as well from (2). If the mechanical system is also bounded and closed, then by the last result and by (6-26) as well as assumption (1)

$$0 = \frac{d}{dt^*} \int g^{*i}\, d^3x^* = -\int P^{*ij}{}_{,j}\, d^3x^*$$

and the result $S^{*ij} = 0$ follows by further integration and applying the assumption of boundedness. For a perfect fluid the result (iv) is obtained when we note that now since $P^{*ij} = -T^{*ij} = p^*\delta^{ij}$, we have $S^{*ij} = \delta^{ij}P^*$, and $\sigma = P^*\beta^2$; Eqs. (v) then follow by (6-65) and since $\gamma\beta^2 + \gamma^{-1} = \gamma$.

(*b*) Under our assumptions, the special form (6-36) applies effectively (upon integration) to our continuous system, with $\rho^* = h^*/c^2$, since by the result under (*a*) we can take effectively $T^{*ij} = 0$ in (6-37). Moreover, since the system is 'static', $d(\rho^*\,\delta V^*)/d\tau = 0$, and hence [see (ii) in Prob. 6-8] $(\rho^* U^\lambda)_{,\lambda} = 0$. Thus, $f^\lambda = (\rho^* U^\lambda U^\mu)_{,\mu} = \rho^* U^\lambda{}_{,\mu} U^\mu = \rho^*\, dU^\lambda/d\tau$. Hence, by our additional assumption,

$$F^\lambda = \int \rho^* \frac{dU^\lambda}{d\tau}\, dV = \int \rho^* \frac{dU^\lambda}{dt}\, dV^* = \frac{dU^\lambda}{dt} \int \rho^*\, dV^* = M^* \frac{dU^\lambda}{dt}$$

However, as observed by v. Laue, the assumption of the constancy of $dU^\lambda/d\tau$ throughout the integration region V^* when its extent is nonvanishing would generally come into conflict with Lorentz contraction (see Prob. 6-6*c*).

6-18 (*a*)

$$g^i u^i = P^{0i}\beta^i = (P_0{}^{0i} + C^{0i})\beta^i = h_0 - h^* - C^{0\nu}\beta_\nu + C^{00}$$
$$= h_0 + C^{00} - h^* - \frac{C^0}{c\gamma} = h - h^* - \frac{w}{c\gamma}$$

where use is made of the third set in (6-94), and of Eqs. (6-31) and (i) in Prob. 6-7 that give [recalling also Eq. (6-46)]

$$P_0{}^{0i}\beta^i = -T_0{}^{ij}\beta^j\beta^i + h_0\beta^2 = \frac{g}{\gamma^2} + h_0\beta^2 = g(\gamma^{-2} + \beta^2) + \beta^2\gamma^2 h^*$$
$$= g + (1 + \beta^2\gamma^2)h^* - h^* = g + \gamma^2 h^* - h^* = h_0 - h^*$$

(*b*) Equation (6-100) follows by applying the first set in (6-94). Then

$$\gamma\left(T^{ij}u^i{}_{,j} - G^{0i}\frac{d\beta^i}{dt}\right) = \gamma\left(T_0{}^{ij}u^i{}_{,j} - G^{0i}\frac{d\beta^i}{dt}\right) + \frac{\gamma}{c}u^i{}_{,j}W^i(w\beta^j - C^j)$$
$$= G^{\mu\nu}U_{\mu,\nu} + \frac{1}{\gamma}\gamma_{,j}(w\beta^j - C^j)$$

by Eqs. (6-89) and (6-97). Since

$$-\gamma C^{0i}\frac{d\beta^i}{dt} = -\frac{\gamma^2}{c}\frac{d\beta^i}{dt}(C^i + w\beta^i) = \frac{\gamma^2}{c}C^\mu\frac{d\beta_\mu}{dt} - \frac{w}{\gamma c}\frac{d\gamma}{dt} = \frac{1}{c^2}C^\mu\frac{dU_\mu}{d\tau} - \frac{w}{\gamma c}\frac{d\gamma}{dt}$$

using the second equation in (6-94), and

$$-\gamma\left[\left(\frac{C^i}{\gamma}\right)_{,i} + \frac{\partial}{\partial t}\frac{w}{c\gamma}\right] = -\gamma\left(\frac{C^\mu}{\gamma}\right)_{,\mu}$$

one finds (6-101) by combining terms and making a few obvious substitutions.

7-1 (*a*) Suppose that the equation of charge conservation holds in every inertial reference system, i.e., suppose that $s^\nu{}_{,\nu} = 0$, with s^ν given in (7-5), is a covariant equation. Then if the s^ν obey the law of transformation $s^\nu \rightarrow s'^\nu = T^\nu{}_\mu s^\mu$, the matrix T must be independent of $\mathbf{x}$ by the homogeneity of Minkowski space-time, and hence, by our assumption,

$$0 = \frac{\partial s'^\nu}{\partial x'^\nu} = T^\nu{}_\mu s^\mu{}_{,\sigma}L_\nu{}^\sigma = s^\mu{}_{,\mu}$$

where $x \rightarrow x' = Lx$. It follows that $T^\nu{}_\mu L_\nu{}^\sigma = l\delta^\sigma_\mu$, and by the group properties satisfied by the set of matrices T we can conclude that $l = 1$. The s^ν are therefore the components of a 4-vector, and hence $\rho(u)\,d^3x$ [in the notation of (7-5)] is a 4-scalar. Conversely, if the invariance of charge is assumed, then $c\rho(u)\,d^3x/d^4x = \rho(u)/dt \equiv k$ is a 4-scalar and hence

$$k\,dx^\nu = \rho(u)u^\nu$$

is a 4-vector.

The proper charge density $\rho = \rho(u)/\gamma_u$ is similar to the proper rest-mass density ρ^* in Prob. 6-8, and correspondingly, Eq. (7-14) is similar to Eq. (i), Prob. 6-8.

(*b*) The conditions are those assumed in the lemma in Sec. 6-3 (page 188), and the integral multiplied by $1/c$ equals $\int s^0\,d^3x/c = \int \rho(u)\,d^3x =$ total charge.

(*c*) Under a gauge transformation $\mathsf{A} \to \mathsf{A} + \text{Div}\ \chi$ the integral $\int s^\mu A_\mu d^4x$ goes over upon integration by parts, and under conditions normally assumed, into the expression $\int (s^\mu A_\mu - \chi\ \text{Div}\ \mathsf{s})\,d^4x$.

7-4 Equation (i) follows directly from (5-106) and Eq. (ii) in Prob. 5-15. The expression (ii) for (7-17) can be obtained by applying the general identity

$$\tfrac{1}{2}A_{\lambda\mu}B^{\lambda\mu}\delta^\alpha_\beta = A^{*\alpha\mu}B^*_{\mu\beta} - A^{\alpha\mu}B_{\mu\beta} \qquad \begin{aligned} A_{\lambda\mu} &= -A_{\mu\lambda} \\ B_{\lambda\mu} &= -B_{\mu\lambda} \end{aligned}$$

This identity is established using (5-69), (5-74), and (5-75) when we evaluate $A^{*\alpha\mu}B^*{}_{\mu\beta}$, recalling the definition of the generalized Kronecker deltas.

7-5 The result (i) follows by (iii) of Prob. 5-18, since

$$A^\beta{}_{;\alpha\beta} - A^\beta{}_{;\beta\alpha} = R^\beta{}_{\sigma\alpha\beta}A^\sigma = -R^\beta{}_{\sigma\beta\alpha}A^\sigma = -R_{\sigma\alpha}A^\sigma$$

Equation (7-14) in general riemannian space-time manifolds results from (7-4) by virtue of the identity $B^{\alpha\beta}{}_{;[\beta\alpha]} = 0$, which implies that

$$4\pi s^\alpha{}_{;\alpha}/c = B^{\alpha\beta}{}_{;\beta\alpha} = B^{\alpha\beta}{}_{;\alpha\beta} = -B^{\beta\alpha}{}_{;\alpha\beta} \equiv -B^{\alpha\beta}{}_{;\beta\alpha} = 0$$

The identity follows from the general formula $2B^{\lambda\mu}{}_{;[\beta\alpha]} = R^\lambda{}_{\sigma\beta\alpha}B^{\sigma\mu} + R^\mu{}_{\sigma\beta\alpha}B^{\lambda\sigma}$ when we set $\lambda = \alpha$, $\mu = \beta$, obtaining $B^{\alpha\beta}{}_{;[\beta\alpha]} = R_{\sigma\alpha}B^{\alpha\sigma} = 0$ owing to the symmetry properties of the tensor R.

7-9 (*a*) Equations (v) and (vi) follow directly from Eq. (iv), Prob. 5-12.

The conditions (1), (2) are relativistically covariant, since they are given by the covariant equations $J = 0$, $K = 0$. When these hold and if $\mathbf{v}$ has the same direction as $\mathbf{S}$, then, by (v) and (vi),

$$\mathbf{E}' = \gamma(\mathbf{E} - \beta\mathbf{E}) = \left(\frac{1-\beta}{1+\beta}\right)^{1/2}\mathbf{E}, \quad \mathbf{B}' = \gamma(\mathbf{B} - \beta\mathbf{B}) = \left(\frac{1-\beta}{1+\beta}\right)^{1/2}\mathbf{B}$$

while for $\mathbf{v}$ in the opposite direction to $\mathbf{S}$ we find similar results with $[(1-\beta)/(1+\beta)]^{1/2}$ replaced by its reciprocal. The possibility of obtaining all values of $|\mathbf{E}'|$ between 0 and ∞ is thus established.

The conditions (1) and (3) or (4) are also relativistically covariant by virtue of (ii), for as we proceed to show, these conditions correspond to

(1) and $J < 0$ or $J > 0$, respectively. In fact, by the second equation in (v), if there exists a frame S' such that $\mathbf{B}' = 0$, then by (vi),

$$\mathbf{B} = \boldsymbol{\beta} \times \mathbf{E} \tag{a}$$

and hence $\boldsymbol{\beta}$ is restricted only by being normal to $\mathbf{B}$ and having an angle θ with $\mathbf{E}$ given by $|\sin\theta| = B/\beta E$, which is consistent with the requirements $|\sin\theta| \leq 1$ and $\beta < 1$ if and only if $J < 0$. Similar reasoning, involving a reversal of $\mathbf{E}$ and $\mathbf{B}$, applies to the case (1), (4). In both cases, using (ii), we find the respective unique values

$$E'^2 = -\frac{J}{2}, \qquad B'^2 = \frac{J}{2} \tag{b}$$

If $K \neq 0$ and $\mathbf{E} \times \mathbf{B} \neq 0$, and there exists a frame S' such that

$$\mathbf{B}' = \alpha\mathbf{E}' \tag{c}$$

(since α cannot $= 0$, this is fully equivalent to the condition $\mathbf{E}' \times \mathbf{B}' = 0$), then by (v) and (vi),

$$\mathbf{B} - \alpha\mathbf{E} = \boldsymbol{\beta} \times (\mathbf{E} + \alpha\mathbf{B}) \tag{d}$$

From the perpendicularity of the vectors $\mathbf{B} - \alpha\mathbf{E}$ and $\mathbf{E} + \alpha\mathbf{B}$ it then follows, using (ii), that $\alpha^2 - 2J\alpha/K - 1 = 0$, or $\alpha = (J \pm Q)/K$, where Q is defined in (i). Since by (c) and (ii),

$$\mathbf{E}' \cdot \mathbf{B}' = \frac{K}{4} = \alpha\mathbf{E}'^2 \tag{e}$$

so that $\alpha K > 0$, we have thus the unique value

$$\alpha = \frac{Q + J}{K} \tag{f}$$

and hence also the unique values $E'^2 = K/4\alpha$, $B'^2 = \alpha K/4$, which by (f) reduce to (i) in view of the identity $(Q + J)(Q - J) = K^2$.

When $K \to 0$, then $Q \to |J|$ and hence Eqs. (i) go over into Eqs. (b) when $J \neq 0$; at the same time, if we consider for instance the case $J < 0$, we find by (e), since $E' \neq 0$, that $\alpha = 0$ and hence $B' = 0$, while (d) reduces to (a).

Equation (iii) can be deduced by noting that according to (d), $\mathbf{v}$ must lie in the 2-space formed by $\mathbf{S}$ and $\mathbf{E} + \alpha\mathbf{B}$:

$$\mathbf{v} = a\mathbf{S} + b(\mathbf{E} + \alpha\mathbf{B}) \tag{g}$$

By multiplying Eq. (d) by $\alpha\mathbf{B}$ and $-\mathbf{E}$ and adding, and then using the identity $(1 + \alpha^2)K/4\alpha = (1 + \alpha^2)E'^2 = E'^2 + B'^2 = 8\pi h'$ that follows from (e), we find

$$\mathbf{S}^2 a = \mathbf{v} \cdot \mathbf{S} = c^2(h - h') \tag{h}$$

Multiplication of Eq. (g) by **E** and use of (ii) and (f), giving

$$E^2 + \alpha \mathbf{B} \cdot \mathbf{E} = E^2 + \frac{Q + J}{4} = 4\pi h + \frac{Q}{4}$$

yields

$$b = \frac{4\mathbf{v} \cdot \mathbf{E}}{16\pi h + Q}$$

Our result now follows using the identity

$$\mathbf{S}^2 = c^2 \left[h^2 - \left(\frac{Q}{16\pi} \right)^2 \right] \tag{k}$$

that is equivalent to the identity $Q^2 = 4(E^2 + B^2)^2 - 16(\mathbf{E} \times \mathbf{B})^2$, and the relation

$$Q = 16\pi h' \tag{l}$$

following from the last identity (as $\mathbf{S}' = 0$).

Equation (iv) is obtained when $b = 0$ in (g), by using (h), (k), and (l): $\beta^2 = a^2\mathbf{S}^2/c^2 = c^2(h - h')^2/c^2(h^2 - h'^2) = (h - h')/(h + h')$. It is apparent that $\beta < 1$. In the general case we have the same result for $\beta^2 \sin^2 \theta = (\boldsymbol{\beta} \cdot \mathbf{S})/\mathbf{S}^2$, where θ is the angle between $\mathbf{v}$ and $\mathbf{E} + \alpha \mathbf{B}$ (in direct generalization of the result found in the special case $K = 0$).

(*b*) The result (vii) is obtained immediately from (xii), Prob. 3-22 by proper identification of quantities. Equations (viii) follow using Eqs. (i). To obtain (viii) directly we observe that as a result of the antisymmetry of B, we can conclude that the eigenvector associated with a nonvanishing real eigenvalue is null; that for an eigenvector $\mathsf{u} + i\mathsf{v}$ associated with the imaginary eigenvalue $i|\lambda|$, we have

$$B_{\alpha\beta}u^\beta = -|\lambda|v_\alpha, \qquad B_{\alpha\beta}v^\beta = |\lambda|u_\alpha \tag{m}$$

and that $\mathsf{u} \cdot \mathsf{v} = 0$, $\mathsf{u}^2 = \mathsf{v}^2$; and that if λ_1, λ_2 are eigenvalues such that $\lambda_1 + \lambda_2 \neq 0$, then the associated eigenvectors are mutually orthogonal in $\mathfrak{M}$. These results show that when $K \neq 0$ we can form a base in $\mathfrak{M}$ with the vectors proportional to $\mathsf{u}_{+(+)} + \mathsf{u}_{-(+)}$, $\mathsf{u}_{+(+)} - \mathsf{u}_{-(+)}$, $\mathsf{u}_{+(-)} + \mathsf{u}_{-(-)}$, $i\ (\mathsf{u}_{+(-)} - \mathsf{u}_{-(-)})$, the notation for the eigenvectors u corresponding to that for the associated eigenvalues as represented in (vii). The result (viii) is obtained when the frame S' corresponds to this base, in a few simple steps involving Eqs. (m).

7-10 The vanishing of the trace of the tensor (7-17) is an immediate consequence of the antisymmetry of B, and the positiveness of the trace of the tensor (6-36) is also evident. The result (i) follows from (vii), Prob. 7-9, since by (7-17), if $B_{\alpha\beta}u^\beta = \lambda u_\alpha$, then $4\pi T_{\alpha\beta}u^\beta = (\lambda^2 + \frac{1}{4}J)u_\alpha$, so that u is also an eigenvector of T with eigenvalue $\mu = (4\lambda^2 + J)/16\pi$. The statement concerning (ii) follows immediately from the fact that

$$\frac{u}{c} = \frac{2|(\mathbf{E} \times \mathbf{B})|}{E^2 + B^2} \leq \frac{2EB}{E^2 + B^2} < 1$$

except when $E = B$ and $\mathbf{E} \cdot \mathbf{B} = 0$. However, unlike what is true normally for material continuous media, we cannot define local rest frames for electromagnetic fields. As shown in Prob. 7-9, if we have $u = 0$ in a given inertial frame S, there exist other such frames with a nonvanishing velocity relative to S.

7-17 (*a*) The second of Eqs. (7-81) follows directly from (7-80). The first equation can be deduced by integrating by parts with respect to ξ^0 in the integral representing the quantity $\overline{\{\rho x^0 U^i\}}_{\text{pol}}$, taking account of the fact that by the statistical considerations involved in our definitions of expectation values, the density ρ can be treated as a constant in this integration.

(*b*) Taking the elementary current in the comoving frame S' as a circular loop of radius a' and cross-sectional area σ', and choosing our spatial axes so that $\mathbf{m}'$ is in the z direction and $u_x = 0$, we find from (7-55) (with $\rho' = 0$) and (3-21*a*) (ϕ denoting the angle in S' between $\mathbf{x}'$ and the x' axis):

$$p_x = \int x\rho\, dV = \frac{\gamma\beta_y}{c} \int x'i'_y \frac{dV'}{\gamma} = \beta_y \frac{i'\sigma'a'^2}{c} \int_0^{2\pi} \cos^2\phi\, d\phi$$

$$= \beta_y \frac{I'\pi a'^2}{c} = \beta_y m'_z = (\boldsymbol{\beta} \times \mathbf{m}')_x$$

That $dV = dV'/\gamma$ as a result of Lorentz contraction, is apparent geometrically; it also follows easily from (3-29):

$$\left.\frac{\partial(x'_1, x'_2, x'_3)}{\partial(x_1, x_2, x_3)}\right|_{x_0=\text{const.}} = \det \left\| \delta_{ij} + \frac{\gamma - 1}{\beta^2} \beta_i\beta_j \right\| = 1 + \frac{\gamma - 1}{\beta^2} \beta_i\beta_i = \gamma$$

On the other hand, by symmetry considerations, or also by direct evaluation as for p_x, we find that $p_y = p_z = 0$, and Eq. (7-83) is proved.

7-18 By Murnaghan's integral identity referred to in Prob. 5-17, we find from (7-1) that

$$\int_\Sigma B_{\alpha\beta}\, d\Sigma^{\alpha\beta} = 0$$

where Σ is an arbitrary closed 2-surface in $\mathfrak{M}$ and $d\Sigma^{\alpha\beta}$ is a surface-element tensor. Similarly from (7-4), and using (ii), Prob. 5-15,

$$\int_\Sigma B^*_{\alpha\beta}\, d\Sigma^{\alpha\beta} = \frac{4\pi}{3c} \int_\Omega s^*_{\alpha\beta\gamma}\, d\Sigma^{\alpha\beta\gamma}$$

where Ω is the 3-region enclosed by Σ, and the stars indicate duals. By the nature of the integrals (i), Prob. 5-17, it is seen that the above equations hold in general coordinates. They embody, in an elegant compact form, all the equations of the usual integral formulation of the Maxwell-Lorentz theory.

7-20 (*a*) Equation (v) with ϕ defined in (iv) is a special case of the following result that is verified directly: $g^{ab}\phi_{,ab} \equiv \phi_{,a}{}^{a} = 0$ is satisfied in $\mathfrak{F}_p$ by $\phi = R^{2u}$ for $R^2 = x_a x^a \neq 0$, provided $u = (2 - p)/2$. In obtaining Eq. (vi) from (iii), the 3-sphere whose radius $\to \infty$ gives a contribution that $\to 0$; while the contribution from the other 3-sphere is $\psi(x) \lim_{\epsilon \to 0} \int (\partial R^{-2}/\partial y^{\alpha})\, dS_{\alpha} = 4\pi^2 \psi(x)$, since the positive direction of the normal points into the interior of the hypersphere, and since the 'area' of the three-dimensional surface of a hypersphere of radius r is $2\pi^2 r^3$ (in a euclidean space of p dimensions, the corresponding area is $S_p(r) = 2\pi^{p/2} r^{p-1}/\Gamma(p/2)$, as is found, e.g., by considering $\int e^{-x_a x_a}\, d^p x = S_p(1) \int_0^{\infty} e^{-r^2} r^{p-1}\, dr$). Equation (vi) follows then from (iii), since by (i), $\psi_{,\alpha\alpha} = -4\pi s$. The subsequent derivation of (viii) as indicated in the problem, is straightforward.

7-23 Since the energy density of the field is always positive, its total energy momentum cannot be a spacelike 4-vector; it is, in particular, a null vector for a null (i.e., plane wave) electromagnetic field, as is verified directly.

8-5 Denoting by J_k and J_k' the generators (8A-17) and (8A-15) respectively, one can find a unitary matrix S such that $J_3 S = S J_3'$. This leaves two real parameters open, which are fixed by evaluating $J_1 S = S J_1'$, with the result

$$S = \begin{bmatrix} 1/\sqrt{2} & 0 & -1/\sqrt{2} \\ i/\sqrt{2} & 0 & i/\sqrt{2} \\ 0 & -1 & 0 \end{bmatrix}$$

As a check one finds that $J_2 S = S J_2'$.

8-26 By the result (i) of Prob. 8-25,

$$U_{\mu\nu} = \tfrac{1}{2}\gamma_{[\mu}\gamma_{\nu]} \tag{a}$$

Equation (8-74), that is, $A_{\nu}^{\dagger} M = -M A_{\nu}$, is here [remembering (8-24) and (8-33)]

$$\gamma_0 M = M \gamma_0, \qquad \gamma_k M = -M \gamma_k \tag{b}$$

Then (8-73) is satisfied for the representations T of $\mathfrak{L}$, since the equation is equivalent (with $T = I + \epsilon^{\mu\nu} U_{\mu\nu}/2$) to $U_{\mu\nu}^{\dagger} M = -M U_{\mu\nu}$, or, by (a), to

$\gamma_\nu^\dagger\gamma_\mu^\dagger M = -M\gamma_\mu\gamma_\nu$ $(\mu \neq \nu)$. The solution M of (b) is $\propto \gamma_0$. This can be seen by writing $M = \begin{bmatrix} a & b \\ c & d \end{bmatrix}$, finding from the first of relations (b) that $b = c = 0$, and then that $(a + d)\sigma_k + \sigma_k(a + d) = 0$, $a = -d$, $a\sigma_k = \sigma_k a$, $a \propto \sigma_0 \equiv \begin{bmatrix} 1 & 0 \\ 0 & 1 \end{bmatrix}$. We can therefore take $M = \gamma_0$.

That S is also $\propto \gamma_0$ can be seen from (8-58) with $T = S$ and $L_\mu{}^\nu = g_{\mu\nu}$, showing that S satisfies the same Eqs. (b) as are satisfied by M. From the two-valuedness of the representation (as $P^2 = I$), the proportionality constants are ± 1, $\pm i$.

With the aid of (8-74), i.e.,

$$\gamma_0\gamma_\nu^\dagger\gamma_0 = \gamma_\nu \tag{c}$$

(8-75) and (8-84) reduce in the present case, using (8-102), to

$$\mathcal{L} = \frac{i}{2}\left(\bar\psi\gamma^\nu \frac{\partial\psi}{\partial x^\nu} - \frac{\partial\bar\psi}{\partial x^\nu}\gamma^\nu\psi\right) + \frac{mc}{\hbar}\bar\psi\psi$$

and

$$T^{\lambda\mu} = \frac{i}{2}\left(\bar\psi\gamma^\mu \frac{\partial\psi}{\partial x_\lambda} - \frac{\partial\bar\psi}{\partial x_\lambda}\gamma^\mu\psi\right) \tag{d}$$

If we take $q = -ec$ in (8-85), we obtain the Dirac 4-current density $ec\bar\psi\gamma^\nu\psi$ that is proportional to the probability 4-current (8-34).

8-27 (a) By its definition as given in (8-80), $\Pi^\nu = \psi^\dagger M A^\nu/2$ generally; hence in the present case $\Pi^\nu = i\bar\psi\gamma^\nu/2$, $2\Pi^{\nu\dagger} = -i\gamma^{\nu\dagger}\gamma^0\psi = -i\gamma^0\gamma^\nu\psi$, using (c), Prob. 8-26. We therefore find for the spin part of the tensor R given in (8-80), that is, $R_{sp}^{\lambda\mu\nu} \equiv S^{\lambda\mu\nu} = \Pi^\nu U^{\lambda\mu}\psi + \psi^\dagger(U^{\lambda\mu})^\dagger\Pi^{\nu\dagger}$ [remembering the observation in the text following Eq. (8-81)], using (a), Prob. 8-26, and the commutativity properties of the γ matrices, the expression

$$S^{\lambda\mu\nu} = \frac{i}{2}\bar\psi(\gamma^\nu U^{\lambda\mu} + U^{\lambda\mu}\gamma^\nu)\psi \tag{a}$$

In particular, by (8-25),

$$S^{kr0} = \frac{i}{2}\psi^\dagger\gamma^{[k}\gamma^{r]}\psi$$

With the obvious extension to the present situation of the pertinent results in Sec. 6-3, remembering (8-28), and taking into account the physical dimensions of our quantities, we can see the agreement of this result with the corresponding result considered in Sec. 8-1.

(*b*) By (8-81) and (a), with $U^{\lambda\mu}$ given in (a), Prob. 8-26, and using (8-25),

$$\Omega^{\lambda\mu\nu} = \frac{i}{4}\bar{\psi}(\gamma^\nu U^{\mu\lambda} + U^{\mu\lambda}\gamma^\nu)\psi \qquad \begin{array}{l}\nu \neq \lambda,\mu \\ \lambda \neq \mu\end{array}$$

$$= \frac{i}{2}\bar{\psi}(\gamma^\lambda U^{\mu\lambda} + U^{\mu\lambda}\gamma^\lambda)\psi \qquad \text{no summation, } \nu = \lambda \neq \mu$$

$$= \frac{i}{2}\bar{\psi}(\gamma^\lambda U^{\lambda\nu} + U^{\lambda\nu}\gamma^\lambda)\psi \qquad \text{no summation, } \lambda = \mu \neq \nu$$

$$= 0 \qquad \text{otherwise}$$

In computing $\Omega^{\lambda\mu\nu}{}_{,\nu}$, we find the contribution of $\sum_{\nu\neq\lambda,\mu}$ (with $\lambda \neq \mu$) by noting that by (8-26) and the associated adjoint equation $-\hbar i\bar{\psi}_{,\mu}\gamma^\mu + mc\bar{\psi} = 0$, the corresponding complete sum $\sum_\nu$ vanishes. Noting also that $(\gamma^\lambda)^2 = g^{\lambda\lambda}$ (no summation), we find after a few obvious steps that

$$\Omega^{\lambda\mu\nu}{}_{,\nu} = \frac{i}{4}\left(\frac{\partial\bar{\psi}}{\partial x_\lambda}\gamma^\mu\psi - \frac{\partial\bar{\psi}}{\partial x_\mu}\gamma^\lambda\psi + \bar{\psi}\gamma^\lambda\frac{\partial\psi}{\partial x_\mu} - \bar{\psi}\gamma^\mu\frac{\partial\psi}{\partial x_\lambda}\right)$$

When this is added to the tensor $T^{\lambda\mu}$ given in (d), Prob. 8-26, according to (7-29) and the equation following it, we find that the result is simply $T^{(\lambda\mu)}$.

8-28 Referring to (8-98), we see that for $\lambda = \mu = 0$, we have two independent equations, each invariant under $\mathfrak{L}$ but not under $\mathfrak{L}^\uparrow$, since they are interchanged by P. We can write both equations as

$$(p^0 \pm \sigma_k p^k)\psi_\pm \equiv \sigma_\nu^\pm p^\nu\psi_\pm = 0$$
$$\sigma_\nu^+ \equiv \sigma_\nu, \qquad \sigma_\nu^- \equiv \bar{\sigma}_\nu, \qquad \sigma_0^\pm = \begin{bmatrix}1 & 0\\ 0 & 1\end{bmatrix} \tag{a}$$

Since $\sigma_\nu^\dagger = \sigma_\nu$, we find by (8-74) that $M = \sigma_0$, and with $A_\nu = i\sigma_\nu^\pm$, the expressions for the Lagrangian, the energy-momentum tensor and the 4-current density are immediately written down. The former expression is, for instance,

$$\mathfrak{L}_\pm = \frac{i}{2}\left(\psi_\pm^\dagger\sigma_\nu^\pm\frac{\partial\psi}{\partial x_\nu} - \frac{\partial\psi_\pm^\dagger}{\partial x_\nu}\sigma_\nu^\pm\right) \tag{b}$$

One way of finding our $U_{\mu\nu}$ is to note that by (8A-39) and (8-31), we can take $U_{ks} = \sigma_{[s}\sigma_{k]}/2$, which suggests trying

$$U_{k0} = \frac{\sigma_0\sigma_k}{2} = \frac{\sigma_k}{2}, \qquad U_{0k} = -\frac{\sigma_k}{2}$$

This choice is found to satisfy (8B-2) (with the changed sign). An independent check is provided by the fact that our group of transformations of ψ must coincide with C_2 (the complex binary unimodular group), as we know from the pertinent considerations in Secs. 8-3, 8-2, and Appendix 8B. With $U_{\mu\nu}$ as found, for which we introduce the notation $\{\sigma_\nu\sigma_\mu\}/2$, and the momenta Π computed from (b), we get (in the notation used in the preceding answer, and dropping the $\pm$ indices)

$$S_{\lambda\mu\nu} = \frac{i}{4}\psi^\dagger(\sigma_\nu\{\sigma_\mu\sigma_\lambda\} - \{\sigma_\lambda\sigma_\mu\}\sigma_\nu)\psi$$

Thus,

$$S_{kr0} = \frac{i}{2}\psi^\dagger\sigma_s\sigma_k\psi = \tfrac{1}{2}\epsilon_{krs}\psi^\dagger\sigma_s\psi$$

confirming our spin assignment and obtaining another required density, again in agreement with the spinor character of our ψ.

By considering plane-wave solutions of (a) and applying our expressions for energy, etc., as well as by determining the transformation properties under T (time reversal) and particle-antiparticle conjugation, we can establish the basic physical properties associated with the Weyl equations (a) (including what is now termed "helicity"). However, these considerations take us outside the scope of the present text. They are discussed extensively in the literature on elementary particle physics, to which a few references have been given in Secs. 8-3 and 8-4.

8-29 By (8C-23) and the choice of p_* given on page 395 (i.e., with a suitable choice of reference frame), we find the following operator relations

$$\begin{aligned} S^1 &= -W_2,\ S^2 = W_1,\ S^3 = -J \\ S^0 &= J^k P_k = -\mathbf{J}\cdot\mathbf{P} \end{aligned} \tag{a}$$

where W_1, W_2, and J are defined on page 395 [with the agreement between (8C-16) and (8C-33) serving as a check]. For the case (1) listed on page 396 it then follows by use of (8C-31) that S is proportional to P, and hence in view of (8C-19) that $S = -\mathrm{j}P$. Equation (i) follows by taking $a = (1,0,0,0)$ and using the last of Eqs. (a).

Bibliography

The following books are referred to in the text by enclosing the corresponding numbers in brackets.

1 Eddington, A. S.: "The Mathematical Theory of Relativity," 2d ed., Cambridge University Press, London, 1924.

2 Einstein, A., H. A. Lorentz, H. Minkowski, and H. Weyl: "The Principle of Relativity," Dover Publications, Inc., New York, (reprint of original papers translated by W. Perrett and G. B. Jeffery).

3 Einstein, A.: "The Meaning of Relativity," Princeton University Press, Princeton, N.J., 1945 (and later editions).

4 Fock, V.: "The Theory of Space Time and Gravitation," Pergamon Press, New York, 1959, (translated from the Russian by N. Kemmer).

5 v. Laue, M.: "Die Relativitätstheorie," vol. 1, Friedr. Vieweg & Sohn, Braunschweig, 1955.

6 Møller, C.: "The Theory of Relativity," Clarendon Press, Oxford, 1952.

7 Pauli, W.: "Theory of Relativity," Pergamon Press, 1958, (translated from the article Relativitätstheorie in "Encyklopädie der mathematischen Wissenschaften," vol. 19, 1921, by G. Field, with supplementary notes by the author).

8 Synge, J. L.: "Relativity: The Special Theory," North-Holland Publishing Company, Amsterdam, 1958.

9 Tolman, R. C.: "Relativity Thermodynamics and Cosmology," Clarendon Press, Oxford, 1934.

10 Weyl, H.: "Space-Time-Matter," Dover Publications, Inc., New York, (translated by H. L. Brose, from the 4th German edition).

This list is adequate for any thorough study of the classical part of STR; it includes primary sources, recognized classics, and different important expositional points of view. The literature on the subject is, however, so rich that many other scholarly texts could no doubt have been included. We list here a few in the English language:

Aharoni, J.: "The Special Theory of Relativity," Clarendon Press, Oxford, 1959.

Bergmann, P. G.: "Introduction to the Theory of Relativity," Prentice-Hall, Inc., Englewood Cliffs, N.J., 1942.

Bergmann, P. G.: The Special Theory of Relativity, in S. Flügge (ed.), "Encyclopedia of Physics," vol. 4, Springer-Verlag, Berlin, 1962.

Landau, L. and E. Lifshitz: "The Classical Theory of Fields," Addison-Wesley Press, Inc., Cambridge, Mass., 1951 (translated from the Russian by M. Hamermesh).

Rindler, W.: "Special Relativity," Oliver & Boyd, Ltd., Edinburgh & London, 1960.

Rosser, W. G. V.: "An Introduction to the Theory of Relativity," Butterworth & Co., Ltd., London, 1964.

Of these references, the second and fourth have been well-known textbooks on the subject for many years, and include both the special and general theories of relativity. The others are more recent additions to the literature on special relativity.

In addition to extensive bibliographies found in the above references, especially in [5], [7], [8], and [10], a useful list of references on special relativity is contained in Resource Letter on STR, *Am. J. Phys.*, **30:** 462 (1962).

Name Index

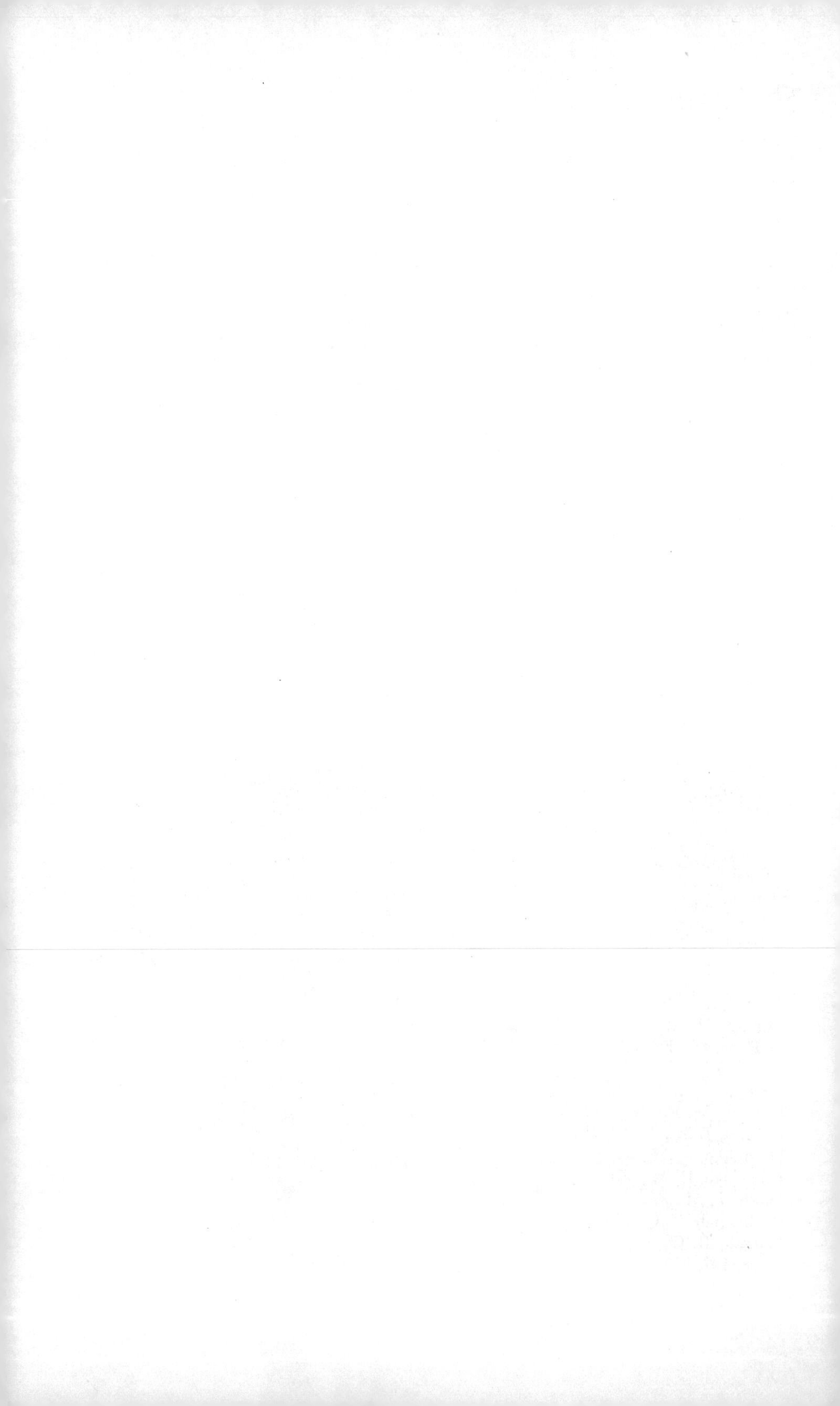

Subject Index

Special symbols and terms are listed under the headings "Notation" and "Terminology," respectively.